# PATEL'S ATLAS
## *of*
# TRANSRADIAL INTERVENTION:
## The Basics

**Tejas Patel, MD, DM, F.A.C.C., F.E.S.C., F.S.C.A.I.**
Director and Chief Interventional Cardiologist
Department of Cardiovascular Sciences
Total Cardiovascular Solutions
(TCVS Pvt. Ltd.)
Ahmedabad, India

*with*

**Sanjay Shah, MD, DM**
Senior Interventional Cardiologist
Department of Cardiovascular Sciences
Total Cardiovascular Solutions
(TCVS Pvt. Ltd.)
Ahmedabad, India

**Alok Ranjan, MD, DNB, MRCP, DM**
Interventional Cardiologist
Department of Cardiovascular Sciences
Total Cardiovascular Solutions
(TCVS Pvt. Ltd.)
Ahmedabad, India

*Editor*
Carol Garzona, MAEd

*Illustrator*
Gopal Limbad, MFA

*Photographers*
Kirit Engineer
Cyrus Mobadji

ISBN: 0-9785436-3-7

Library of Congress Control No.: 2006934695

First Printing January 2007

As the transradial procedure evolves, we can look forward to changes in technique, hardware, and drugs.
The authors and publisher have taken extreme care to ensure that this Atlas conveys the most accurate,
evidence-based information available at the time of publication.
Readers are advised to keep abreast of the latest developments in this elegant, patient-friendly procedure.

For additional information, contact:

Transradial Intervention Course
www.trico.in

SEA SCRIPT COMPANY
www.seascriptcompany.com
206.748.0345

## TRICO

The transradial approach should be the approach of choice for the vast majority of coronary angiographies and interventions.

Teaching hospitals worldwide must focus on transradial intervention so that interventional cardiologists can begin taking the learning curve in stride.

We understand that these changes in understanding and practice will not occur overnight. TRICO was designed to serve as a forum where the future can be visualized and planned.

The mission of TRICO is to help its students become competent and confident radialists so that patients worldwide can benefit from the safety, convenience, and comfort of transradial intervention. ■

(Transradial Intervention Course)
www.trico.in

**Shigeru Saito, MD, F.A.C.C., F.S.C.A.I., F.J.C.C.**
Director of Catheterization Laboratories & Cardiology
Shonan Kamakura General Hospital
Kamakura, Japan

*"Anyone can make things bigger, more complex, and more violent.*
*It takes a touch of genius—and a lot of courage—to move in the opposite direction."*

— E. F. Schumacher

This Atlas is dedicated to Dr. Shigeru Saito, my mentor and very close friend, who helped us establish a program which has become the largest transradial program in India and one of the most prestigious transradial programs in the world. ∎

# CONTENTS

FOREWORD
    Yves Louvard ............................................................................ XI
    Jeffrey Popma............................................................................ XIII

PREFACE.................................................................................... XVII

ACKNOWLEDGEMENTS.................................................................... XIX

INTRODUCTION ............................................................................ XXIX

ABBREVIATIONS............................................................................. XXIII

## CHAPTER 1: PATIENT SELECTION & EXCLUSION — 1

    ■ The Ideal Patient for New Radialists ........................................... 1
    ■ Exclusion Criteria in Our Cath Lab............................................. 1
    ■ Modified Allen's Test ............................................................. 2
    ■ Interpretation of the Modified Allen's Test.................................... 3
    ■ Inverse Allen's Test ............................................................... 3
    ■ Alternative Tests.................................................................. 4
    ■ Recommended Reading............................................................ 6

## CHAPTER 2: CATH LAB SET UP & PATIENT PREPARATION — 7

    ■ Equipment & Hardware.......................................................... 8
    ■ Preparation of the Forearm ..................................................... 9
    ■ Recommended Reading............................................................ 10

## CHAPTER 3: PUNCTURE TECHNIQUE — 11

    ■ The Ideal Site for Puncture...................................................... 12
    ■ Local Anesthesia.................................................................. 13
    ■ Radial Puncture.................................................................. 14
    ■ Guidewire Insertion ............................................................. 15
    ■ Sheath Insertion ................................................................. 16
    ■ Heparin & Spasmolytic Cocktail Administration.............................. 17
    ■ High Puncture of the Radial Artery ............................................ 18
    ■ Remember......................................................................... 19
    ■ Recommended Reading........................................................... 20

## CHAPTER 4: POST-PROCEDURE MANAGEMENT — 21

- Sheath Removal & Hemostasis — 22
  - After Diagnostic Procedures — 22
  - After Interventional Procedures — 24
- Patient Care & Discharge Instructions — 26
- Remember — 26
- Recommended Reading — 27

## CHAPTER 5: COMPLICATIONS — 29

- Major Local Complications — 30
- Minor Local Complications — 30
- Remember — 34
- Recommended Reading — 35

## CHAPTER 6: RADIAL REGION: UNDERSTANDING THE ISSUES — 39

- Normal Anatomy of the Radial Artery — 40
- Abnormal Caliber of the Radial Artery — 41
  - Spasm — 41
  - Hypoplasia — 42
  - Atherosclerosis — 44
  - Calcification — 45
- Abnormal Course of the Radial Artery — 46
  - Tortuosity — 46
  - High Origin — 49
  - Loops & Curvatures — 57
- Perforation of the Radial Artery — 59
- Recommended Reading — 60

## CHAPTER 7: RADIAL REGION: ADDRESSING THE ISSUES — 61

- Abnormal Caliber of the Radial Artery — 62
  - Spasm — 62
  - Hypoplasia — 63
  - Atherosclerosis & Calcification — 63
- Abnormal Course of the Radial Artery — 64
  - Tortuosity — 64
  - High Origin — 68
  - Loops & Curvatures — 68
    - "Easy" — 68
    - "More Challenging" — 75
    - "Most Challenging" — 83
- Perforations of the Radial Artery — 96
- Remember — 101
- Recommended Reading — 102

## CHAPTER 8: PATEL'S ALGORITHM FOR ADDRESSING LOOPS & CURVATURES© — 103

## CHAPTER 9:   BRACHIAL TO SUBCLAVIAN REGION: UNDERSTANDING THE ISSUES — 127

- Normal Anatomy of the Brachial to Subclavian Region .................................................. 128
- Abnormal Caliber of the Brachial to Subclavian Region ................................................. 131
  - Occlusion .................................................................................................................... 131
- Abnormal Course of the Brachial to Subclavian Region ................................................ 133
  - Tortuosity ................................................................................................................... 133
- Recommended Reading .................................................................................................. 136

## CHAPTER 10:   BRACHIAL TO SUBCLAVIAN REGION: ADDRESSING THE ISSUES — 137

- Entering the Ascending Aorta ......................................................................................... 138
  - Right Radial Artery Approach ..................................................................................... 138
  - Left Radial Artery Approach ....................................................................................... 140
- Tortuosity ....................................................................................................................... 142
- Remember ....................................................................................................................... 143
- Recommended Reading .................................................................................................. 144

## CHAPTER 11:   INNOMINATE-ARCH JUNCTION: UNDERSTANDING & ADDRESSING THE ISSUES — 145

- Normal Anatomy of the Innominate-Arch Junction ....................................................... 146
- Abnormal Angle of the Innominate-Arch Junction ........................................................ 147
  - Loops & Curvatures .................................................................................................... 147
- Arteria Lusoria: The Right Transradial Approach ........................................................... 151
- Remember ....................................................................................................................... 153
- Recommended Reading .................................................................................................. 154

## CHAPTER 12:   CANNULATION OF THE CORONARY OSTIA — 155

- Understanding the Catheter's Course: Radial vs. Femoral .............................................. 156
- Diagnostic Catheters ...................................................................................................... 157
- Guiding Catheters ........................................................................................................... 171
- Remember ....................................................................................................................... 174
- Recommended Reading .................................................................................................. 175

## CHAPTER 13:   RIGHT OR LEFT RADIAL ARTERY: DOES IT MATTER? — 177

- Discussion ....................................................................................................................... 178
- Recommended Reading .................................................................................................. 180

## CHAPTER 14:   HOW & WHY I STARTED MY TRANSRADIAL PROGRAM — 181

- John Coppola .................................................................................................................. 181
- Samir Pancholy ............................................................................................................... 184

## CHAPTER 15:   TRANSRADIAL INTERVENTION: TODAY AND TOMORROW — 187

APPENDIX
- Frequently Asked Questions ........................................................................................... 191
- Commonly Used Equipment & Hardware ....................................................................... 197

# FOREWORD
## YVES LOUVARD

THE STENT REVOLUTION, THE EVOLUTION OF STENT DESIGN, AND ASSOCIATED BIOTECHNOLOGY have significantly improved the results of coronary angioplasty. Angioplasty is being used in more and more situations once reserved for open surgery.

Questions about the skills of interventional cardiologists are at the forefront as the number and complexity of coronary interventions increase.

The well-known vascular complications associated with the transfemoral approach remain a significant concern. Today's patients expect procedures to be safe, simple, and preferably ambulatory; hospitals expect high success rates, low costs, less demanding post-procedure care, and efficient patient turnover.

The transradial approach virtually eliminates major vascular complications while increasing the numerous benefits that operators, their staffs, hospitals, and patients demand.

While the radial approach does have a learning curve, it is surmountable. The purpose of this Atlas is to help operators in this regard.

Authored by Tejas Patel, the charismatic leader of one of the very best interventional centers in India, the Atlas is a treasure trove of experience. You will find detailed explanations about how to overcome the challenges of the transradial approach, including those produced by congenital and acquired anatomic variations, frequent and rare. Classic and new solutions to every basic challenge are outlined.

The most important advice Dr. Patel offers is to select your first cases carefully, to be patient, to persevere, to be gentle, and to use angiography to identify all problems.

*Patel's Atlas of Transradial Intervention: The Basics* contains over 55 close-up photos, over 160 helpful (and beautiful) drawings, and over 275 angiograms that have been hand-selected from over 20,000 diagnostic and interventional cases. It is an essential book for those who wish to begin or to improve a transradial program. ∎

**Yves Louvard, MD**
Department of Interventional Cardiology,
Institut Hospitalier Jacques Cartier—ICPS
Massy, France

I LEARNED TRANSRADIAL CATHETERIZATION BY NECESSITY. My former partners at the Brigham and Women's Hospital, Dan Simon and Campbell Rogers, brought the transradial technique to us several years ago, and it was soon clear that to be a "respected" interventional cardiologist at the Brigham, one needed to master this approach.

Cases were selectively referred to those of us who "did radials." By trial and error we learned the basics of transradial catheterization and together experienced the challenges and complications of the transradial approach in complex cases.

We often asked for each other's help (or, at least, I did) and we sought advice from our national and international friends and colleagues who were experts in transradial access and intervention. Further, we learned from the lectures and experience of the radial pioneers Ferdinand Kiemeneij, Shigeru Saito, and Gerald Barbeau.

What was not available to us before now was this Atlas. I am sure this Atlas would have shortened our learning curve significantly. Even with five years of transradial experience behind me, I have found many pearls, tips, and tricks here that will help me with my next radial cases.

The thorough and thoughtful approach to the major issues of transradial catheterization addressed by this Atlas have culminated in the definitive teaching source for our Fellows on the transradial approach. The Atlas's side-by-side angiograms and illustrations are unique to interventional textbooks. They provide the visual reinforcement that will help interventionalists truly understand the anatomy and find solutions for challenging cases.

Why is this Atlas so valuable and unique? The reasons begin with Tejas Patel's exquisite attention to the basics of transradial catheterization. He is an international expert in the field and has trained scores of interventionalists around the world. The Atlas also has detailed discussions of the complex anatomy that is sometimes faced when negotiating the radial, brachial, subclavian, and aortic vasculature. As a result, this Atlas has all of the components of a single-source teaching tool for radial access and catheterization. After studying this text, all that is needed for a successful transradial program is an engaged physician, a motivated support staff, and willing patients who are excited about having a safer, less complicated, and more convenient coronary procedure.

Let me review some specifics in this Atlas that I found most useful. A fundamental first step is selecting the right patient for learning the transradial technique. A clear delineation of the basic criteria for radial catheterization is found in Chapter 1 (Patient Selection & Exclusion) and its understanding is essential for surmounting the early learning curve. Initial procedures that focus on the "basics" with low-risk patients are the surest way to gain confidence with this technique. Mastering the fundamental maneuvers in straightforward cases renders the more complex cases less problematic.

Our nurses and technologists are the most enthusiastic supporters of the transradial technique. Chapter 2 (Cath Lab Set Up & Patient Preparation), Chapter 3 (Puncture Technique), and Chapter 4 (Post-Procedure Management) are critical chapters for the catheterization laboratory staff. We have often found that it is their enthusiasm that determines the success of the radial program. The photos and the illustrations in this Atlas will support the catheterization laboratory team.

Even if an operator is highly skilled, minor procedural complications sometimes occur and Chapter 5 (Complications) is likely the most important chapter in this Atlas. When the radial procedure goes well, it is a real joy to perform. When it does not go well, the procedure can be challenging and lengthy. Success is based on whether complications can be avoided or managed appropriately. Clearly those most stimulating meetings are those in which we discuss the management of our complications. My favorite adage, attributable to a number of skilled interventionalists, including David Holmes, is: "Good judgment comes from experience, and experience comes from bad judgment." This Atlas goes a long way in helping us make good judgments, without having to pass through the bad judgments first.

Patience is key in performing the transradial approach. Chapters 6 and 7 (Radial Region) discuss the anatomic variations and complexities of the radial artery, and Chapter 8 (Patel's Algorithm) and Chapters 9 and 10 (Brachial to Subclavian Region and Innominate-Arch

Junction) provide valuable information relating to common challenges to attaining access to the ascending aorta. Knowing how to proceed when the guidewire does not pass easily into the central circulation is one of the keys to success with the transradial approach.

I have been amazed at how similar the radial approach can be to the femoral approach once a few techniques are mastered, particularly from the left radial artery. Chapter 12 (Cannulation of the Coronary Ostia) and Chapter 13 (Right or Left Radial Artery) address the issues of size and shape of the diagnostic and guiding catheters from the right and left radial approaches. Deep-seating techniques, particularly with smaller-diameter guiding catheters during coronary intervention, are invaluable in getting stents and balloons to the distal vessels through tortuous proximal anatomy.

It takes courage to start a radial program, especially when other physicians are very comfortable in their transfemoral ways. Two US interventionalists give their reasons for taking on the transradial approach in Chapter 14 (How & Why I Started My Transradial Program). In Chapter 15 (Transradial Intervention: Today and Tomorrow), Tejas Patel gives us his perspective about "What's Next" for transradial intervention.

*Patel's Atlas of Transradial Intervention: The Basics* is a "must have" for all interventional cardiologists. It will be on my shelf for ready access and we will use it as our teaching guide for our interventional Fellows.

Whether you are a beginner who is considering becoming a radialist or an experienced radialist who wishes to fine-tune your skills, you will find this Atlas an important part of your interventional library. ■

**Jeffrey J. Popma, MD**
Director, Interventional Cardiology
Brigham and Women's Hospital;
Associate Professor of Medicine
Harvard Medical School
Boston, Massachusetts, USA

# PREFACE

IN 1989, LUCIEN CAMPEAU OF CANADA PUBLISHED HIS EXPERIENCES after performing 100 coronary angiographies through the transradial route. In 1992, Ferdinand Kiemeneij of the Netherlands performed the world's first coronary angioplasty through the transradial route. Since then, the transradial approach has become increasingly popular with leading coronary interventionalists worldwide.

Our own coronary catheterization team made a total switch from the femoral to the radial approach in late 2000 after we lost two patients due to major vascular complications of the femoral approach. When I learned that Shigeru Saito had performed several thousand transradial procedures in Japan—a land where patients have relatively small radial arteries—I was inspired to start a radial program in our hospital after having performed tens of thousands of femoral procedures.

Studies from around the world that have compared the transradial approach to the transfemoral approach have shown, beyond a doubt, that major local vascular complications with the transradial approach are virtually nonexistent even when high-dose anticoagulation is used.

Still, many interventionalists have shied away from the transradial approach. This is in spite of the fact that even minor complications are extremely rare, and that hospital staffs and patients overwhelmingly prefer the safety, comfort, and convenience of having interventions performed through the wrist.

This reluctance to switch to the radial approach is no doubt due to the new learning curve which, admittedly, is relatively long and sometimes frustrating. The good news is that if our Cath Lab can achieve so much success, yours can, too. We have now performed over 20,000 diagnostic and interventional procedures through the radial route and have encountered, documented, and overcome 99% of the challenges.

The purpose of this Atlas is to inspire interventional cardiologists worldwide to learn as much as possible about this elegant, staff-and-patient-friendly procedure. We hope that those who are performing 50%, 60%, or 70% of their work through the transradial approach will be able to increase this number to 95%. And that those who are performing fewer radial cases will become eager to perform more.

Working with beginning and intermediate radialists from many countries, we have discovered the best way to teach transradial intervention and have simplified every step. In this Atlas, you will find detailed discussions and examples of the procedure's basics—from the initial puncture to the cannulation of the coronary ostia.

We have not attempted to address complex intervention subsets here. These include unprotected left main stenosis, bypass graft lesions, peripheral interventions, bifurcation lesions, and acute myocardial infarction. We will save these for a more advanced Atlas.

If, after reading this text, you still have doubts about transradial intervention, ask any of the patients who has experienced both the femoral and the radial approach which approach *they* preferred.

There is your answer. ■

**Tejas Patel**

# ACKNOWLEDGEMENTS

OUR DEEPEST APPRECIATION GOES TO OUR INTERVENTIONAL CARDIOLOGY TEAM COLLEAGUES, Sanjay Gupta, Amol Agarwal, Jayesh Rawal, Shrenik Shah, and Rajesh Pandya. We especially thank Hemant Malhotra for shouldering our workload while the Atlas was being shaped. Special thanks go to Narendra S. Tanwar. We thank our intensivists, Rajnikant Radadiya and Leena Shah who helped us with our challenging cases and shared their thoughtful comments.

We thank our cardiac surgeon colleagues, Sukumar Mehta and Utpal Shah. Special thanks go to Malay Patel who advised us and uplifted our spirits. Thank-yous go to our Cath Lab nurses, technicians, and attendants for doing all of the things that help make the transradial procedure so easy. We thank Mamta Patel, Prathmesh Patel, and Rushang Shah for recording and organizing the cases for this Atlas. Sincere thanks go to Keith Fonseca, Kintur Sanghvi, Shanthi Sarvagyam, Urmish Vaishnav, and Dhiren Chudasama. Heartfelt thanks go to our editor, our illustrator, our photographers, and our publisher without whom this project would have remained a dream.

We offer our deepest appreciation to our patients who have taught us that the fastest and best way to a man's (and a woman's) heart is through the wrist.

We offer apologies and gratitude to our wives, Sonali, Komal, and Pooja who put up with our moods as we put together a first-of-its-kind book.

And, finally, we offer our most profound appreciation to our critics—a constant source of inspiration and motivation. If any have read this far, we hope they continue reading. ■

# INTRODUCTION

THIS ATLAS IS DIVIDED INTO FIFTEEN CHAPTERS, from patient selection and exclusion criteria to the future of transradial intervention. In each chapter, we have attempted to cover every detail.

There are many technical issues involved in the radial puncture, the passage through the radial, brachial, and subclavian regions and the innominate-arch junction; and the cannulation of the coronary ostia. Experienced operators may approach these issues slightly differently, but after performing over 20,000 procedures, we are making a humble attempt to share our knowledge and experiences with the international cardiology world.

This Atlas can be used by beginning interventionalists who wish to become radialists, and by experienced femoral operators who wish to switch to the radial approach. We hope that even hard-core radialists will be able to find new ideas and self-confidence.

After cannulation of the coronary ostia for interventional procedures, simple cases remain simple and difficult cases remain difficult, except for rare exceptions which we will present in a future Atlas. This particular Atlas addresses basic issues for the interventionalist who hopes to become an expert radialist.

We are now reaching a plateau as far as the technical aspects of this procedure are concerned. But when technological advances are made and special hardware is designed for the transradial approach, we can be sure there will be exciting new things to learn and discover. ∎

# ABBREVIATIONS

## ABBREVIATIONS USED IN THIS TEXT

| | |
|---|---|
| cc | Cubic centimeter |
| cm | Centimeter |
| ml | Milliliter |
| mm | Millimeter |

| | |
|---|---|
| AA | Axillary artery |
| AAo | Ascending aorta |
| BA | Brachial artery |
| CCA | Common carotid artery |
| DAo | Descending aorta |
| IA | Interosseous artery |
| InA | Innominate artery |
| LCCA | Left common carotid artery |
| LIMA | Left internal mammary artery |
| LSA | Left subclavian artery |
| RA | Radial artery |
| RCCA | Right common carotid artery |
| RSA | Right subclavian artery |
| SA | Subclavian artery |
| UA | Ulnar artery |

| | |
|---|---|
| C | Catheter |
| C&W | Catheter over wire (guidewire) |
| F | French |
| G | Gauge |
| GC | Guiding catheter |
| W | Wire (guidewire) |

| | |
|---|---|
| CABG | Coronary artery bypass graft |
| LAO | Left anterior oblique |
| PCI | Percutaneous coronary intervention |
| PTCA | Percutaneous transluminal coronary angioplasty |

# Patel's Atlas of Transradial Intervention: The Basics

# PATIENT SELECTION & EXCLUSION

An experienced radialist can complete virtually every coronary angiography and intervention through the radial route. However, when an interventionalist is first establishing a radial program, it is important that he selects his first 200 cases carefully. Being selective in the beginning will give him the insight and confidence he needs to convert himself into a hard-core radialist.

In this chapter, we have listed the criteria for patient selection and exclusion for the beginning radialist. These are the criteria our team used when we started our transradial program.

The Modified Allen's Test, the Inverse Allen's Test, and alternative tests are discussed in detail. Although a number of radial-approach experts do not perform these tests, we strongly recommend that the beginning radialist do so. ■

---

### THE IDEAL PATIENT FOR NEW RADIALISTS

- Hemodynamically stable
- Well-palpable radial pulse
- Avoid acute coronary syndrome, bypass-graft lesions, unprotected left main stenosis, chronic total occlusions, and peripheral vascular lesions.
- Avoid elderly (70+) hypertensive patients. (They often have dilation and/or distortion of the aortic arch which makes entry into the ascending aorta difficult.)

---

### EXCLUSION CRITERIA IN OUR CATH LAB

- Absence of radial artery pulse
- Absence of functional collaterals between the radial and the ulnar arteries, as judged by the Modified Allen's Test or alternative tests (described on following pages)
- Arteriovenous shunt for renal dialysis on the procedure forearm
- Raynaud's phenomenon
- Any procedure that requires more than an 8F catheter

# MODIFIED ALLEN'S TEST

The Modified Allen's Test is a test of functional collaterals between the radial and the ulnar arteries through the deep and superficial palmer arches. It should be performed on both forearms prior to the procedure.

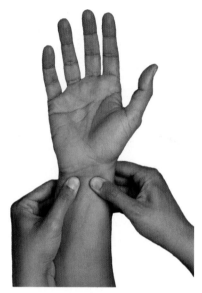

**1** Palpate the radial and the ulnar arteries. Obliterate both pulses with the thumbs and fingers of both hands.

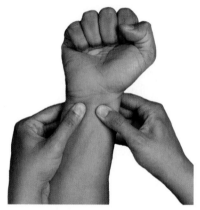

**2** Ask the patient to clench his fist repeatedly until his palm blanches white.

**3** Ask the patient to open his palm.

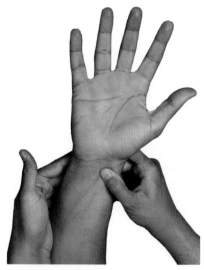

**4** Release only the ulnar pulse and watch for the time of reappearance of normal palm color.

## INTERPRETATION OF THE MODIFIED ALLEN'S TEST

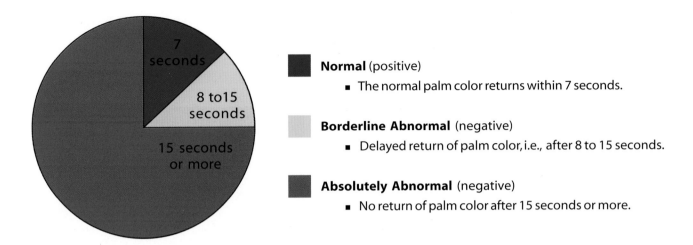

**Normal** (positive)
- The normal palm color returns within 7 seconds.

**Borderline Abnormal** (negative)
- Delayed return of palm color, i.e., after 8 to 15 seconds.

**Absolutely Abnormal** (negative)
- No return of palm color after 15 seconds or more.

## INVERSE ALLEN'S TEST

This test is performed to determine the patency of the radial artery. It is useful in repeat procedures with the same radial artery. The steps in this test are similar to those in the Modified Allen's Test, except that the radial pulse is released instead of the ulnar pulse. (See Step 4 on the previous page.) The interpretation is the same as in the Modified Allen's test.

If the Inverse Allen's Test is negative, then the radial artery is not suitable for a repeat procedure. Therefore, both the Modified Allen's Test and the Inverse Allen's Test should be positive before the patient is selected for a repeat transradial procedure through the same forearm.

## ALTERNATIVE TESTS

Perform alternative tests if the Modified Allen's Test is abnormal (negative). These tests require finger plethysmography and pulse oximetry readings for interpretation.

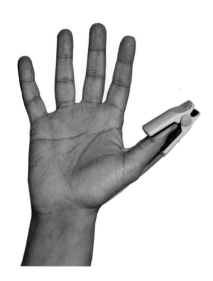

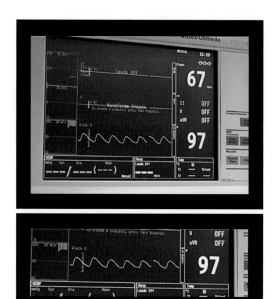

**1** Clip the sensor onto the thumb of the patient and obtain a normal (sharp) tracing and SpO2 (pulse oximeter) reading.

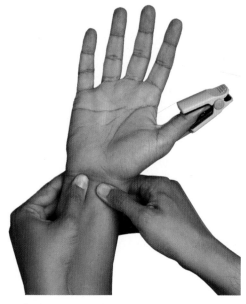

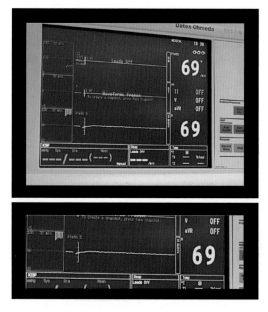

**2** Compress the radial and the ulnar arteries as described in the Modified Allen's Test. The tracing will flatten and there will be a drop in the SpO2 reading.

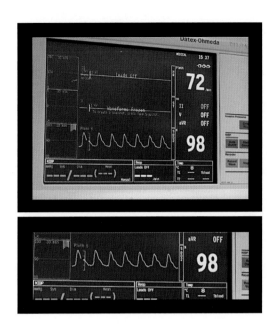

**3** Release the pressure over the ulnar artery and watch for the tracing and SpO2 reading. Immediate return of a normal tracing and the normal SpO2 reading suggest a normal (positive) test, indicating the presence of collaterals.

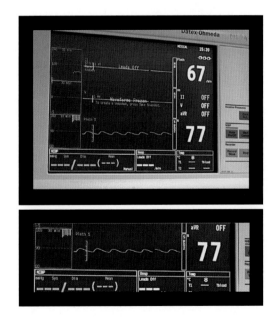

**4** If the tracing and the SpO2 reading do not return immediately, wait an extra minute. If a normal tracing and the SpO2 reading return slowly, there are recruiting collaterals. A repeat test on the same forearm will show a rapid return of the normal tracing and the SpO2 reading, which means the collaterals are functional. In this case, the radial artery can be used for the procedure.

If there is persistent flattening of the tracing and the SpO2 reading does not improve, there are no collaterals between the radial and the ulnar arteries. In this case, the radial artery is not suitable for the procedure.

## RECOMMENDED READING

Allen EV. Thromboangiitis obliterans: methods of diagnosis of chronic occlusive arterial disease distal to the wrist with illustrative cases. Am J of Med Sci. 1929;178:237-44.

Husum B, Berthelsen P. Allen's test and systolic pressure in the thumb. Br J Anaesth. 1981 Jun;53(6):635-7.

Williams T, Schenken JR. Radial artery puncture and the Allen test. Ann Intern Med. 1987 Jan;106(1):164-5.

O'Mara K, Sullivan B. A simple bedside test to identify ulnar collateral flow. Ann Intern Med. 1995 Oct 15;123(8):637.

Benit E, Vranckx P, Jaspers L, et al. Frequency of a positive modified Allen's test in 1,000 consecutive patients undergoing cardiac catheterization. Cathet Cardiovasc Diagn. 1996 Aug;38(4):352–4.

McConnell EA. Performing Allen's test. Nursing. 1997 Nov;27(11):26.

Caputo RP, Simons A, Giambartolomei A. Transradial cardiac catheterization in elderly patients. Catheter Cardiovasc Interv. 2000 Nov;51(3):287-90.

Yokoyama N, Takeshita S, Ochiai M, et al. Direct assessment of palmar circulation before transradial coronary intervention by color Doppler ultrasonography. Am J Cardiol. 2000 Jul 15;86(2):218–21.

Barbeau GR, Arsenault F, Dugas L, et al. Evaluation of the ulnopalmar arterial arches with pulse oximetry and plethysmography. Am Heart J. 2004 Mar;147(3):489-93.

Hildick-Smith DJ, Walsh JT, Lowe MD, et al. Transradial coronary angiography in patients with contraindications to the femoral approach: an analysis of 500 cases. Catheter Cardiovasc Interv. 2004 Jan;61(1):60-6.

# CATH LAB SET UP
# & PATIENT PREPARATION

With a few minor modifications, the same Cath Lab set up and patient preparation that are used for the femoral approach can be used for the radial approach.

An arm board is a must. We have described the arm board that we use, but radial operators use various arm-supporting devices.

We do not generally sedate our patients, feeling this defeats the "Walk In, Walk Out" benefit of the radial approach. We have found that showing patients a short educational video prior to the procedure removes their anxiety.

Beginning radialists may prep the groin area for their first 200 procedures just in case they decide to switch to the femoral approach. Patients can be told there is a remote chance their doctor may decide to use the femoral artery for the procedure.

We have described our use of hardware, heparin, and spasmolytic cocktails based on over 20,000 cases. Depending upon the operator and the Cath Lab, there may be slight variations in these.

Please see the Appendix for a list of commonly used transradial intervention equipment and hardware. ■

# EQUIPMENT & HARDWARE

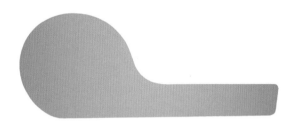

The patient rests his procedure arm on this. It is 3'9" long, and 18" at its widest width and 6" at its narrowest width.

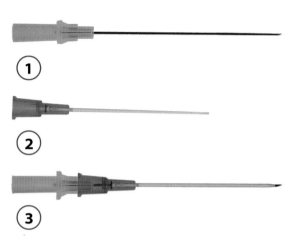

1. Needle
2. Plastic cannula
3. Jelco (Johnson and Johnson). 45 mm. Size 20G (Instead of a Jelco needle, a 20G, one-piece metal needle can be used.)

Terumo Glidewire
Straight tip, Hydrophilic, Size 0.025"

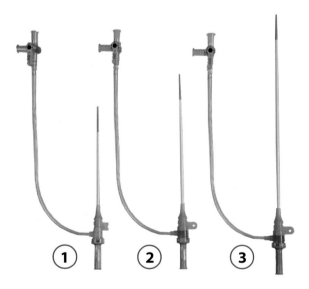

5F for diagnostic; 6F for interventions
1. Short: 70 mm
2. Medium: 100 mm
3. Long: 160 mm
If necessary, the diagnostic sheath can be downsized to 4F. For interventions, 5F to 8F can be used.

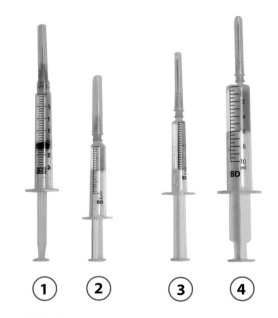

1. 2% Xylocaine
2. Intra-arterial heparin: 5000 IU for diagnostic study; 100 IU/kg for interventions (If Abxicimab is planned, use 70 IU/kg.)
3. Intra-arterial spasmolytic cocktail: injectable nitroglycerine (NTG) 200 mcg
4. Intra-arterial spasmolytic cocktail: injectable verapamil 2.5 mg or injectable diltiazem 5 mg

# PREPARATION OF THE FOREARM

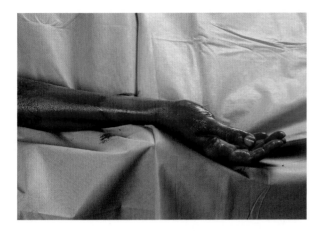

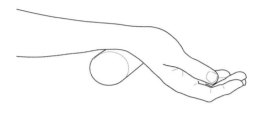

Shave the forearm up to the mid-part. Paint and drape both the flexor and extensor surfaces. The forearm should be supinated and hyperextended at the wrist joint for puncture. Position the arm parallel to the table.

The hyperextention at the wrist joint can be achieved by putting a saline pint or some other soft, rounded object under the wrist.

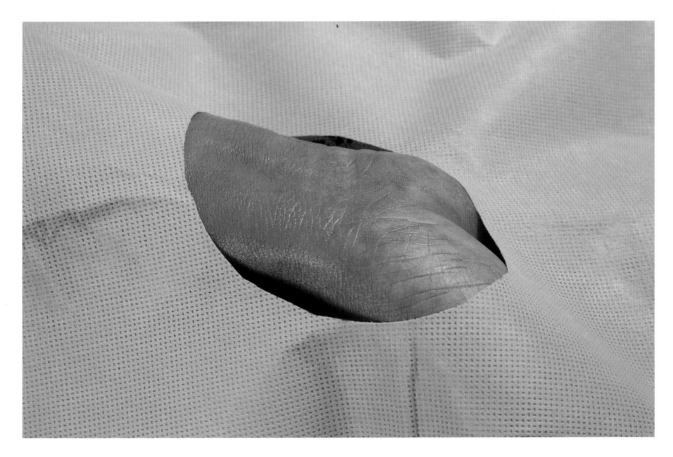

The forearm is ready for puncture.

## RECOMMENDED READING

Almany, S.L., & O'Neill, W.W. (1999). Radial artery access for diagnostic and interventional procedures (pp. 1-17). Ann Arbor, MI: Accumed Systems.

Hamon, M., & McFadden, E. (2003). Trans-radial approach for cardiovascular interventions. France: Europa Stethoscope Media.

# PUNCTURE TECHNIQUE

"Well begun is half done."

Taking a little extra care at the time of puncture will pay off later. The radial puncture is a critical part of the transradial procedure and it takes some time to master, even for experienced interventionalists.

In this chapter, we have described how we perform the puncture. There are several different puncture techniques, but we have found that our simplified approach is very helpful for the beginning radialist who may eventually develop his own method.

We have explained how to find the standard puncture site as well as a site for high puncture, which is useful in rare situations. ■

# THE IDEAL SITE FOR PUNCTURE

The ideal site for puncture is 2 to 3 cm proximal to the flexor crease of the wrist.

If the puncture is too distal, there can be an inadvertent puncture of the superficial branches of the radial artery. This puncture is also not advised because the radial artery lies deep and lateral. A too-distal puncture may also lead to perforation of the reticular ligament of the wrist.

If the puncture is too proximal, it is difficult to palpate the radial artery beneath the forearm muscles. Then after the procedure is completed, the radial artery is difficult to compress and there is an increased chance of hematoma. Finally, the proximal segments of the radial artery should be preserved for re-puncture or repeat procedures at a later date.

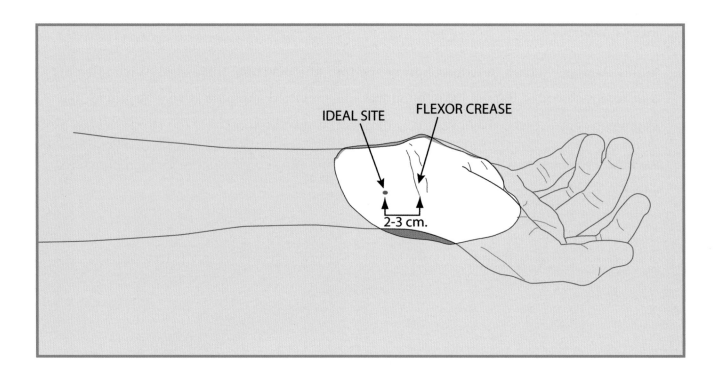

# LOCAL ANESTHESIA

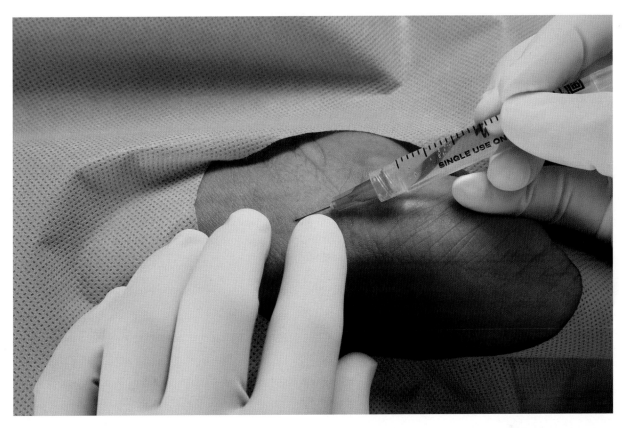

**1** Inject a small (1 ml) amount of 2% Xylocaine at the planned site of puncture. A large amount will obliterate the pulse and may cause difficulty in the puncture.

# RADIAL PUNCTURE

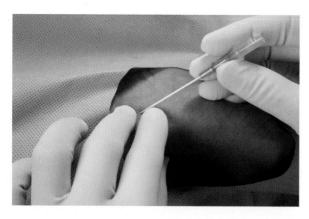

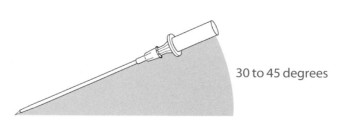

30 to 45 degrees

**1** Fix the radial artery with the index and middle finger of your left hand. Puncture the radial artery with a Jelco with the bevel pointing upward. The angle between the Jelco and the forearm should be 30 to 45 degrees.

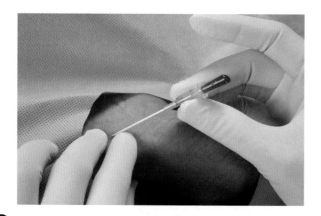

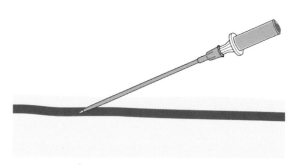

**2** Push the Jelco along the line of the arterial pulsations and watch for the backflow of blood in the hub of the needle. Backflow indicates a successful puncture of the radial artery.

**3** Push the Jelco forward to counter puncture the radial artery. We counter puncture the artery because it is difficult to do an anterior puncture with a Jelco. (However, it is possible with a metal needle.)

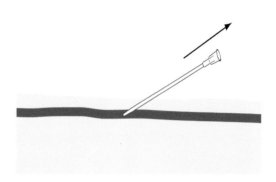

**4** Remove the needle of the Jelco and leave behind the plastic cannula. Slowly pull back the plastic cannula and watch for a free backflow of blood. Free flow of blood indicates intraluminal position of the plastic cannula.

## GUIDEWIRE INSERTION

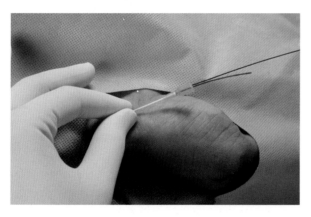

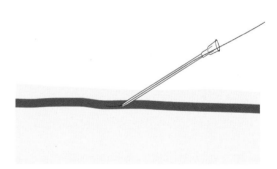

**1** Insert the 0.025" Terumo Glidewire into the radial artery through the plastic cannula.

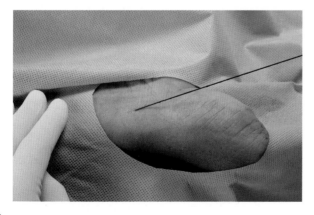

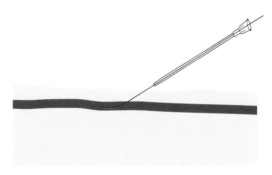

**2** Once the 0.025" Terumo Glidewire is well inside the artery, remove the plastic cannula and leave behind the Terumo Glidewire.

## SHEATH INSERTION

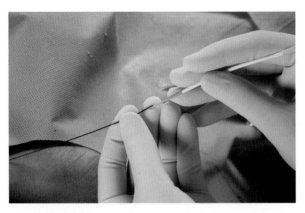

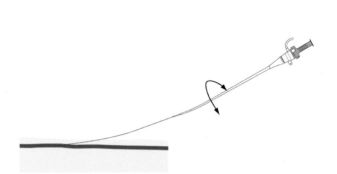

**1** Insert the sheath over the 0.025" Terumo Glidewire. In case of difficulty, the skin can be nicked with a No. 11 scalpel to facilitate insertion. If there is some resistance, insert the sheath using a corkscrew motion.

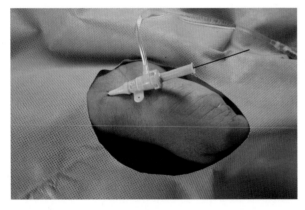

**2** Remove the sheath's dilator and the 0.025" Terumo Glidewire.

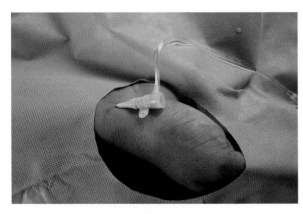

**3** The sheath is in place.

# HEPARIN & SPASMOLYTIC COCKTAIL ADMINISTRATION

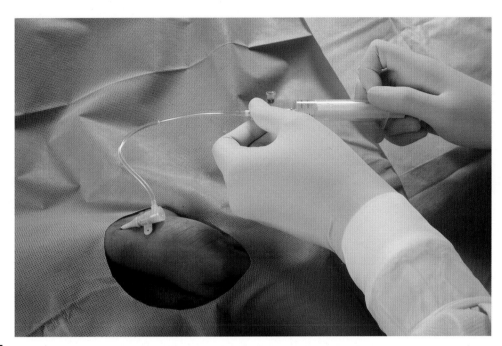

**1** Warn the patient that there will be a slight burning sensation. Aspirate blood into the syringe before injecting the heparin and the spasmolytic cocktail through the sidearm of the sheath. (The blood mixed with the spasmolytic cocktail brings the pH of the mixture close to that of blood, which minimizes the burning sensation.)

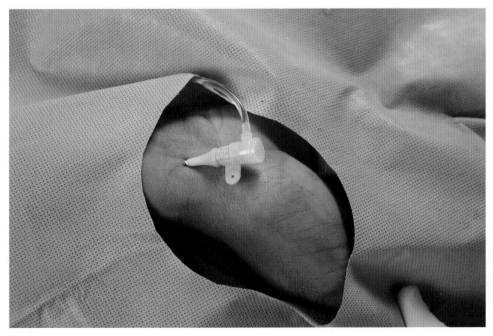

**2** The puncture is complete and the patient is ready for the procedure.

# HIGH PUNCTURE OF THE RADIAL ARTERY

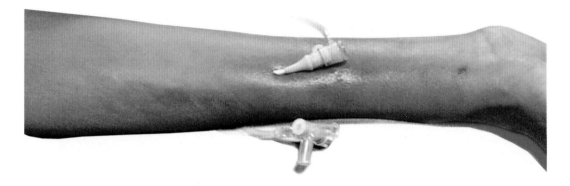

Although the ideal site for puncture is 2 to 3 cm proximal to the flexor crease of the wrist, the radial artery can be punctured right up to the mid-forearm as long as the pulsations of the radial artery can still be felt.

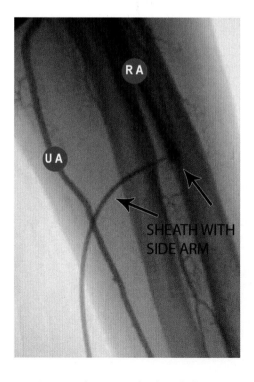

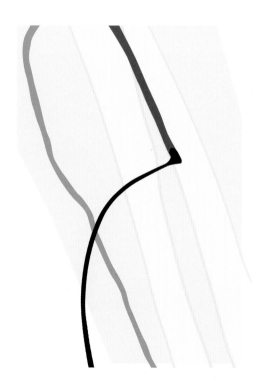

Angiogram showing a high radial puncture.

# REMEMBER

■ Take enough time to locate and fix the radial artery before the puncture.

■ The first stick is usually the best stick because repeated sticks can induce spasm.

■ Do not worry about having to counter puncture the radial artery; it is not a problem. The radial artery lies superficially and because of bone support beneath, it is easily compressible so there is little chance of hematoma.

■ Do not hesitate to perform a high puncture when necessary. High puncture is used for infradiaphragmatic lesions and sometimes for repeat transradial procedures.

# RECOMMENDED READING

Saito S, Ikei H, Hosokawa G, et al. Influence of the ratio between radial artery inner diameter and sheath outer diameter on radial artery flow after transradial coronary intervention. Catheter Cardiovasc Interv. 1999 Feb;46(2):173-8.

Gilchrist IC. Transradial technical tips. Catheter Cardiovasc Interv. 2000 Mar;49(3):353-4.

Campeau L. Entry sites for coronary angiography and therapeutic interventions: from the proximal to the distal radial artery. Can J Cardiol. 2001 Mar;17(3):319-25.

Caputo RP, Simons A, Giambartolomei A, et al. Safety and efficacy of repeat transradial access for cardiac catheterization procedures. Catheter Cardiovasc Interv. 2001 Oct;54(2):188-90.

Dery JP, Simard S, Barbeau GR. Reduction of discomfort at sheath removal during transradial coronary procedures with the use of a hydrophilic-coated sheath. Catheter Cardiovasc Interv. 2001 Nov;54(3):289-94.

Saito S, Tanaka S, Hiroe Y, et al. Usefulness of hydrophilic coating on arterial sheath introducer in transradial coronary intervention. Catheter Cardiovasc Interv. 2002 Jul;56(3):328-32.

Kiemeneij F, Fraser D, Slagboom T, et al. Hydrophilic coating aids radial sheath withdrawal and reduces patient discomfort following transradial coronary intervention: a randomized double-blind comparison of coated and uncoated sheaths. Catheter Cardiovasc Interv. 2003 Jun;59(2):161-4.

Kiemeneij F, Vajifdar BU, Eccleshall SC, et al. Evaluation of a spasmolytic cocktail to prevent radial artery spasm during coronary procedures. Catheter Cardiovasc Interv. 2003 Mar;58(3):281-4.

Coppola J, Patel T, Kwan T, et al. Nitroglycerin, nitroprusside, or both, in preventing radial artery spasm during transradial artery catheterization. J Invasive Cardiol. 2006 Apr;18(4):155-8.

Kiemeneij F. Prevention and management of radial artery spasm. J Invasive Cardiol. 2006 Apr;18(4):159-60.

# POST-PROCEDURE MANAGEMENT

Over time, we have observed that our nurses, technicians, and attendants have become very relaxed about patient care because transradial post-procedure management is stress-free.

With femoral patients, our staff spent long hours attending to patients—adjusting their beds, making sure they did not move or cross their legs, and helping them with bedpans. And there was the constant worry about bleeding and groin complications.

With radial patients, there is very little for the staff to do or to worry about.

In this chapter, we have described manual compression, and hemostasis with the closure device we like best. ■

## SHEATH REMOVAL & HEMOSTASIS

Remove the sheath immediately after the procedure. But before doing so, warn the patient that he may feel slight discomfort in his forearm when the sheath is removed. If necessary, inject an additional dose of spasmolytic cocktail.

## SHEATH REMOVAL & HEMOSTASIS AFTER DIAGNOSTIC PROCEDURES

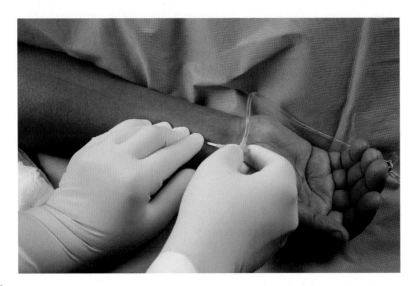

**1** Before removing the sheath, use your left hand to apply pressure on the radial artery, proximal to the puncture site. This prevents traction on the radial artery.

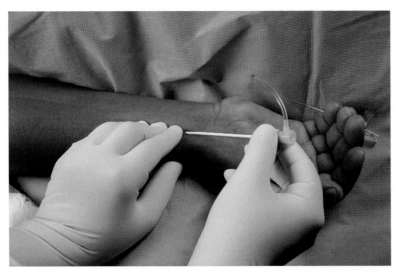

**2** Remove the sheath quickly. Slow removal causes more discomfort.

**3** Allow a slight back bleed from the puncture site and then compress the radial artery.

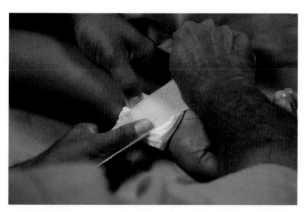 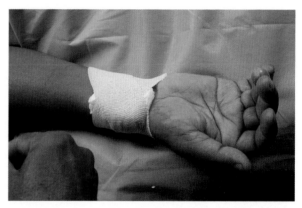

**4** Once hemostasis has been achieved, apply a small bunch of gauze over the puncture site. Place Dynaplast or a similar adhesive tape in a crisscross fashion over the gauze. Allow compression of the radial artery, but not the ulnar artery. To prevent venous stasis, do not completely encircle the wrist with the bandage. The bandage should be kept in place for four to six hours.

# SHEATH REMOVAL & HEMOSTASIS AFTER INTERVENTIONAL PROCEDURES

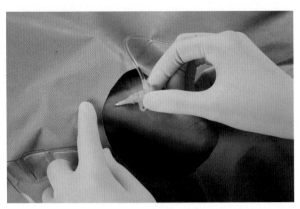 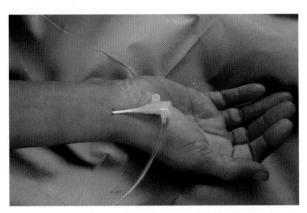

**1** Pull back the sheath 2 to 3 cm and clean the puncture site.

 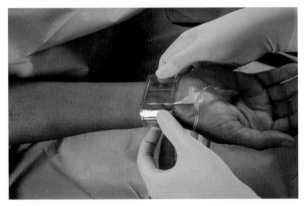

**2** Apply a TR Band (Terumo) over the wrist. Be sure the green mark lies over the site where the radial artery was most likely punctured. (Note that the skin puncture site and the radial artery puncture site are two different points.)

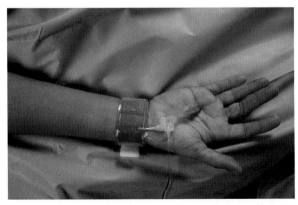

**3** Wrap the TR Band tightly around the wrist.

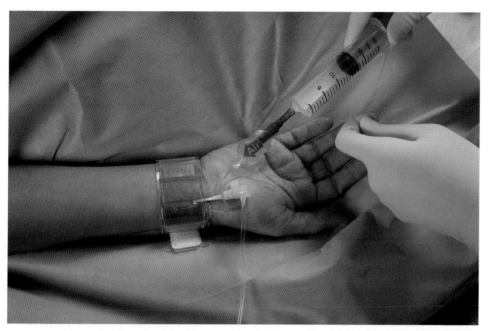

**4** With the syringe provided in the TR Band set, inflate the air-injection port of the TR Band with 13 to 17 ml of air.

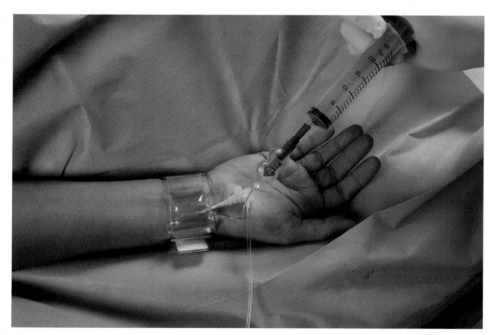

**5** Pull the sheath out. The patient may now leave the Cath Lab. The TR Band should be kept in place for six to eight hours. If the patient experiences discomfort at the puncture site, gradually remove 2 cc or more of air. After the alloted time, the TR band can be replaced with a simple bandage, as explained above. (See Appendix for other commonly used closure devices.)

# PATIENT CARE & DISCHARGE INSTRUCTIONS

Advise the patient not to put weight on the procedure hand for 24 hours. The patient may remove his bandage the next day before bathing.

Have the patient return for a follow-up appointment in one month. Check for the radial pulse and perform the Modified Allen's Test. If the radial pulse is absent, perform a Doppler ultrasound test on the radial artery. Look for any minor complication at the puncture site.

## REMEMBER

- Choose one closure device and stay with it so it becomes very familiar.

- Always use manual compression when your puncture is higher than the standard site. (A closure device is not recommended in this situation. As the puncture goes higher, the artery goes deeper and there is a greater risk of hematoma.)

- If you notice that a hematoma has developed after you have placed a closure device on the patient's wrist, remove the device and evacuate the hematoma to the extent possible. Then manually compress the site.

# RECOMMENDED READING

Kiemeneij F, Laarman GJ, de Melker E. Transradial artery coronary angioplasty. Am Heart J. 1995 Jan;129(1):1-7.

Lotan C, Hasin Y, Mosseri M, et al. Transradial approach for coronary angiography and angioplasty. Am J Cardiol. 1995 Jul 15;76(3):164-7.

Arnold A. Hemostasis after radial artery cardiac catheterization. J Invasive Cardiol. 1996; 8 Suppl D:26D-29D.

Edwards AC. Hemostatic technique summarized: Royal North Shore Hospital Device. In Kiemeneij F (ed): "Proceedings of the Second Course on Transradial Coronary Angioplasty, February 8-9, 1996." ADIC–OLGV, Amsterdam, 1996, p 201.

Kiemeneij F. Hemostatic technique summarized: Double Tourniquet. In Kiemeneij F (ed): "Proceedings of the Second Course on Transradial Coronary Angioplasty, February 8-9, 1996." ADIC-OLGV, Amsterdam, 1996, p 195.

Chatelain P, Arceo A, Rombaut E, et al. New device for compression of the radial artery after diagnostic and interventional cardiac procedures. Catheter Cardiovasc Diagn. 1997 Mar;40(3):297-300.

Saito S, Ikei H, Hosokawa G, etc. Influence of the ratio between radial artery inner diameter and sheath outer diameter on radial artery flow after transradial coronary intervention. Catheter Cardiovasc Interv.1999 Feb;46(2):173-8.

Ochial M, Sakai H, Takeshita S, et al. Efficacy of a new hemostatic device, Adapty, after transradial coronary angiography and intervention. J Invasive Cardiol. 2000 Dec;12(12):618-22.

Dery JP, Simard S, Barbeau GR. Reduction of discomfort at sheath removal during transradial coronary procedures with the use of a hydrophilic-coated sheath. Catheter Cardiovasc Interv. 2001 Nov;54(3):289-94.

Saito S, Tanaka S, Hiroe Y, et al. Usefulness of hydrophilic coating on arterial sheath introducer in transradial coronary intervention. Catheter Cardiovasc Interv. 2002 Jul;56(3):328-32.

Kiemeneij F, Fraser D, Slagboom T, et al. Hydrophilic coating aids radial sheath withdrawal and reduces patient discomfort following transradial coronary intervention: a randomized double-blind comparison of coated and uncoated sheaths. Catheter Cardiovasc Interv. 2003 Jun;59(2):161-4.

Sakatani T, Kawasaki T, Hadase M, et al. Novel application of the hemostatic device TOMETA KUN. Circ J. 2003 Oct;67(10):895-7.

Choi EY, Ko YG, Kim JB, et al. Hemostatic efficacy of hydrophilic wound dressing after transradial catheterization. J Invasive Cardiol. 2005 Sept;17(9):459-62.

# COMPLICATIONS

The data from several randomized studies comparing the transfemoral approach to the transradial approach have shown major vascular complication rates of between 1.5% and 6.5% for the femoral approach and near zero for the radial approach. (See Recommended Reading at the end of this chapter.)

No medical procedure is totally free of complications, however. Following are examples of the rare, minor local complications that we have seen after performing over 20,000 cases. ∎

## MAJOR LOCAL COMPLICATIONS:
## ☑ NONE

## MINOR LOCAL COMPLICATIONS

**1** Radial artery spasm and pain. Present in only 6.2% and 5.8% of patients (respectively) out of over 20,000 procedures.

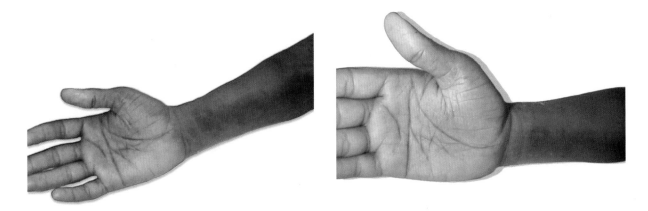

**2** Small hematoma involving the hand and forearm. Present in only 3% of over 20,000 procedures.

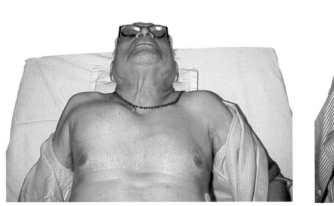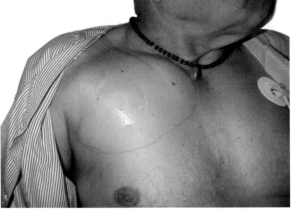

**3** Infraclavicular hematoma due to perforation of a small branch of the axillary artery. Present in only 1 out of over 20,000 procedures.

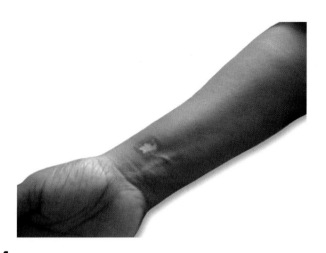
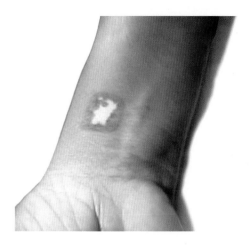

**4** Depigmented scar at the puncture site due to undue compression by the hemostatic device. This complication is less common with the TR Band. Present in only 4 out of over 20,000 procedures.

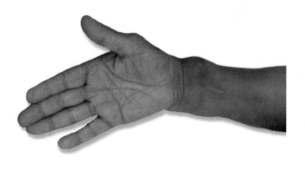
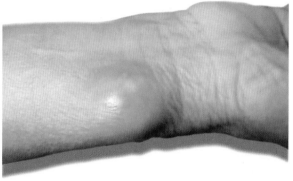

**5** Small pseudoaneurysm at the radial artery puncture site. If manual compression fails, this may require minor surgery. Present in only 6 out of over 20,000 procedures.

## MINOR LOCAL COMPLICATIONS

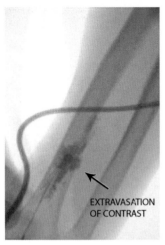

EXTRAVASATION
OF CONTRAST

**6** Perforation in the course of the radial-brachial regions. Present in only 6 out of over 20,000 procedures.

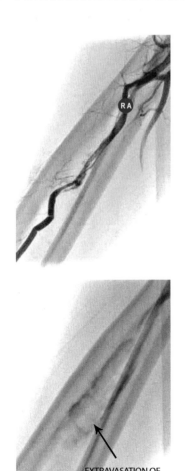

R A

EXTRAVASATION OF
CONTRAST

**7** Radial artery perforation leading to extravasation of contrast material into the surrounding tissue.

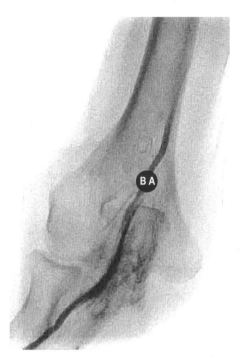

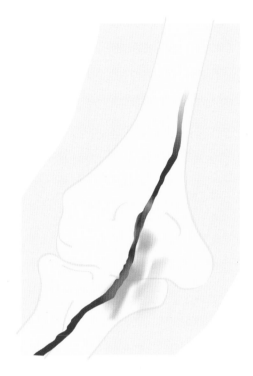

**8** Brachial artery perforation just before the bifurcation.

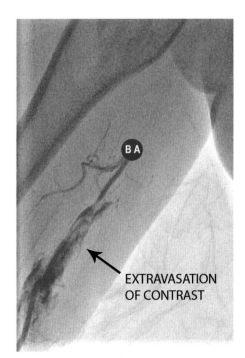

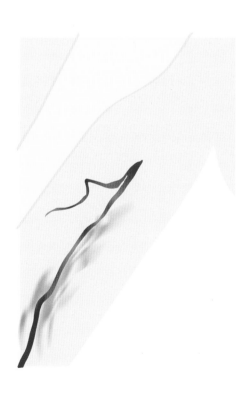

EXTRAVASATION
OF CONTRAST

**9** Brachial artery perforation in mid-arm.

## RARE MINOR COMPLICATIONS INCLUDE:

- Asymptomatic radial-artery occlusion (3.5% of cases in our series)
- Forearm discomfort that usually disappears within several days (0.2% of cases in our series)

The following minor complications are mentioned in the literature, but we have not seen any of these after performing over 20,000 transradial procedures:

- Nerve injury leading to causalgia
- Arteriovenous fistula
- Radial artery eversion during sheath removal
- Hand ischemia

## REMEMBER

- Identify and evacuate a hematoma as soon as possible to prevent the possibility of compartment compression syndrome.

- A depigmented scar occurs when the skin is injured because the radial artery closure device has been too tight.

- Perforations of the radial artery or the brachial artery are rare. To work past them, refer to Chapter 7.

# RECOMMENDED READING

## TRANSRADIAL APPROACH

Hildick-Smith DJR, Lowe MD, Walsh JT, et al. Coronary angiography from the radial artery—experience, complications and limitations. Int J Cardiol. 1998 May 15;64(3): 231-9.

Fagih B, Beaudry Y. Pseudoaneurysm: a late complication of the transradial approach after coronary angiography. J Invasive Cardiol. 2000 Apr;12(4):216-7.

Merin O, Shapira N, Silberman S, et al. Transradial catheterization: a word of caution. J Invasive Cardiol. 2000 Mar;12(3):142-3.

Dery JP, Simard S, Barbeau GR. Reduction of discomfort at sheath removal during transradial coronary procedures with the use of a hydrophilic-coated sheath. Catheter Cardiovasc Interv. 2001 Nov;54(3):289-94.

Papadimos TJ, Hofmann JP. Radial artery thrombosis, palmar arch systolic blood velocities, and chronic regional pain syndrome following transradial cardiac catheterization. Catheter Cardiovasc Interv. 2002 Dec; 57(4): 537-40.

Saito S, Tanaka S, Hiroe Y, et al. Usefulness of hydrophilic coating on arterial sheath introducer in transradial coronary intervention. Catheter Cardiovasc Interv. 2002 Jul;56(3):328-32.

Hildick-Smith DJ, Walsh JT, Lowe MD, et al. Coronary angiography in the fully anticoagulated patient: The transradial route is successful and safe. Catheter Cardiovasc Interv. 2003 Jan;58(1):8-10.

Kozak M, Adams DR, Ioffreda MD, et al. Sterile inflammation associated with transradial catheterization and hydrophilic sheaths. Catheter Cardiovasc Interv. 2003 Jun;59(2):207-13.

Wakeyama T, Ogawa H, Iida H, et al. Intima-media thickening of the radial artery after transradial intervention. An intravascular ultrasound study. J Am Coll Cardiol. 2003 Apr 2; 41(7):1109-14.

Calvino-Santos RA, Vazquez-Rodriquez JM, Salgado-Fernandez J, et al. Management of iatrogenic radial artery perforation. Catheter Cardiovasc Interv. 2004 Jan;61(1):74-8.

Sanmartin M, Cuevas D, Goicolea J, et al. Vascular complications associated with radial artery access for cardiac catheterization. Rev Esp Cardiol. 2004 Jun;57(6):581-4.

Bazemore E, Mann JT 3rd. Problems and complications of the transradial approach for coronary interventions: a review. J Invasive Cardiol. 2005 Mar;17(3):156-9.

Cantor WJ, Puley G, Natarajan MK, et al. Radial versus femoral access for emergent percutaneous coronary intervention with adjunct glycoprotein IIb/IIIa inhibition in acute myocardial infarction—the RADIAL-AMI pilot randomized trial. Am Heart J. 2005 Sep;150(3):543-9.

Edmundson A, Mann T. Nonocclusive radial artery injury resulting from transradial coronary interventions: radial artery IVUS. J Invasive Cardiol. 2005 Oct;17(10):528-31.

## TRANSRADIAL APPROACH VS. TRANSFEMORAL APPROACH

Kiemeneij F, Laarman GJ, Odekerken D, et al. A randomized comparison of percutaneous transluminal coronary angioplasty by the radial, brachial and femoral approaches: the access study. J Am Coll Cardiol. 1997 May;29(6):1269-75.

Mann T, Cubeddu G, Bowen J, et al. Stenting in acute coronary syndromes: a comparison of radial versus femoral access sites. J Am Coll Cardiol.1998 Sept;32(3):572-6.

Cooper CJ, El-Shiekh RA, Cohen DJ, et al. Effect of transradial access on quality of life and cost of cardiac catheterization: a randomized comparison. Am Heart J. 1999 Sep;138(3 Pt 1):430-6.

Mann T, Cowper PA, Peterson ED, et al. Transradial coronary stenting: comparison with femoral access closed with an arterial suture device. Catheter Cardiovasc Interv. 2000 Feb;49(2):157-9.

Morice MC, Dumas P, Lefèvre T, et al. Systematic use of transradial approach or suture of the femoral artery after angioplasty: attempt at achieving zero access site complications. Catheter Cardiovasc Interv. 2000 Dec;51(4):417-21.10

Louvard Y, Lefèvre T, Allain A, et al. Coronary angiography through the radial or the femoral approach: The CARAFE study. Catheter Cardiovasc Interv.2001 Feb;52(2):181-7.

Saito S, Tanaka S, Hiroe Y, et al. Comparative study on transradial approach vs. transfemoral approach in primary stent implantation for patients with acute myocardial infarction: results of the test for myocardial infarction by prospective unicenter randomization for access sites (TEMPURA) trial. Catheter Cardiovasc Interv. 2003 May;59(1):26-33.

Ziakas A, Klinke P, Mildenbergar R, et al. Comparison of the radial and the femoral approaches in percutaneous coronary intervention for acute myocardial infarction. Am J Cardiol. 2003 Mar1; 91(5):598-600.

Agostoni P, Biondi-Zoccai GG, de Benedictis ML, et al. Radial versus femoral approach for percutaneous coronary diagnostic and interventional procedures; Systematic overview and meta-analysis of randomized trials. J Am Coll Cardiol. 2004 Jul 21;44(2):349-56.

Cox N, Resnic FS, Popma JJ, et al. Comparison of the risk of vascular complications associated with femoral and radial access coronary catheterization procedures in obese versus nonobese patients. Am J Cardiol. 2004 Nov 1;94(9):1174-7.

Louvard Y, Benamer H, Garot P, et al. Comparison of transradial and transfemoral approaches for coronary angiography and angioplasty in octogenarians (the OCTOPLUS study). Am J Cardiol. 2004 Nov 1;94(9):1177-80.

Philippe F, Larrazet F, Meziane T, et al. Comparison of transradial vs. transfemoral approach in the treatment of acute myocardial infarction with primary angioplasty and abciximab. Catheter Cardiovasc Interv. 2004 Jan;61(1):67-73.

# RADIAL REGION: UNDERSTANDING THE ISSUES

In this chapter, we have discussed the normal and relevant abnormal anatomy of the radial artery.

We have shown clear examples of abnormal caliber with spasm, hypoplasia, atherosclerosis, and calcification.

There are examples of abnormal course with tortuosity and high origin, and loops and curvatures. And there is an example of a perforation. ■

# NORMAL ANATOMY OF THE RADIAL ARTERY

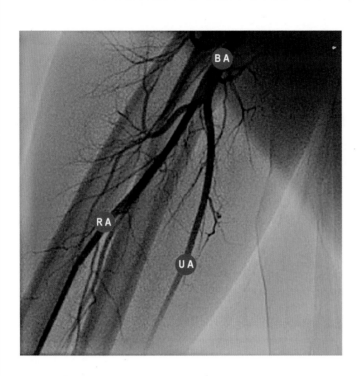 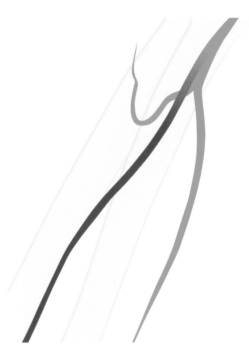

- **Origin**

  The radial artery commences at the bifurcation of the brachial artery, just below the bend of the elbow, and passes along the radial side of the forearm to the wrist.

- **Course**

  The radial artery extends from the neck of the radius to the front part of the styloid process. The upper part lies on the medial side of radius and the lower part lies on the bone. The upper part is deep and lies below the muscle (brachioradialis). The lower part is superficial, covered by skin and superficial and deep fascia.

- **Caliber**

  The radial artery is slightly smaller in caliber than the ulnar artery.

# ABNORMAL CALIBER OF THE RADIAL ARTERY

- **Spasm**
  - Focal
  - Diffuse
- **Hypoplasia**
  - Congenital
  - Acquired
- **Atherosclerosis & Calcification**

## SPASM (FOCAL)

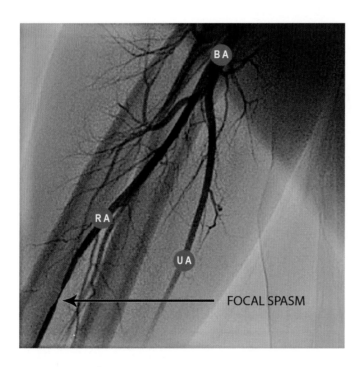
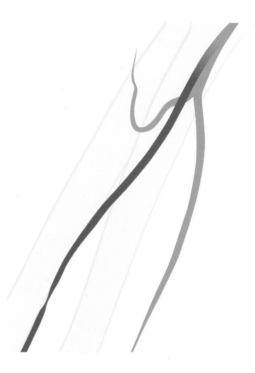

Focal spasm of the radial artery.

## SPASM (DIFFUSE)

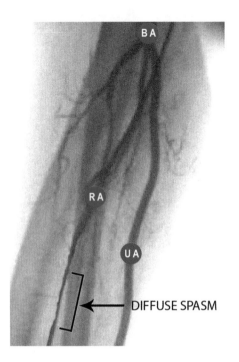

Diffuse spasm involving a segment length of 20 mm or more.

## HYPOPLASIA (CONGENITAL)

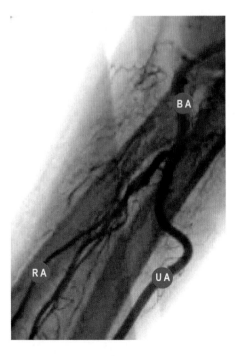

Congenital hypoplasia. The radial artery was hypoplastic. In this case, the difference in the caliber of the radial artery and the ulnar artery was marked and it remained this way even after an additional dose of spasmolytic cocktail was given, proving that this was true hypoplasia and not spasm.

## HYPOPLASIA (ACQUIRED)

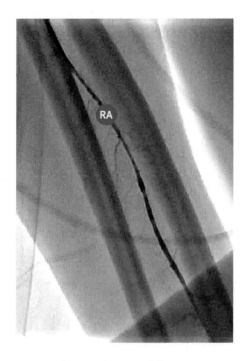

Acquired hypoplasia. Left forearm. A rare example in a pentazocine addict. Repeated intra-arterial injections led to fibrous obliteration of the radial, ulnar, and brachial arteries. Numerous collateral channels were observed.

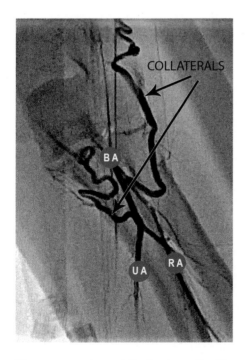

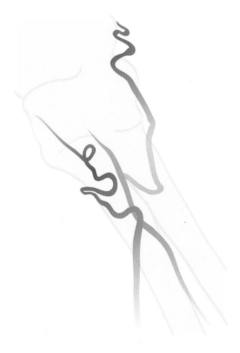

The pentazocine addict had small caliber radial, ulnar, and brachial arteries with prominent collateral channels.

## ATHEROSCLEROSIS

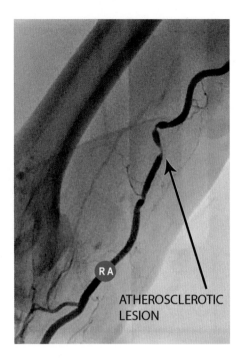

Focal narrowing in the radial artery (high origin).

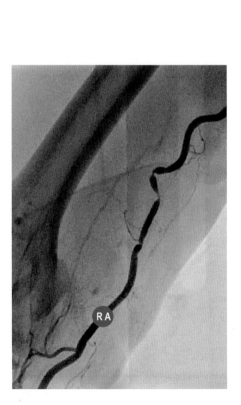

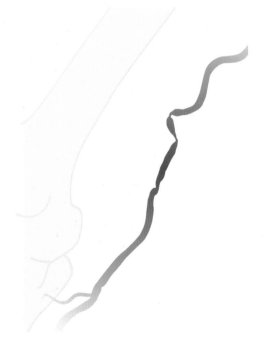

There was no change in the caliber of the radial artery after an additional dose of spasmolytic cocktail, proving that this was true atherosclerosis and not spasm.

## CALCIFICATION

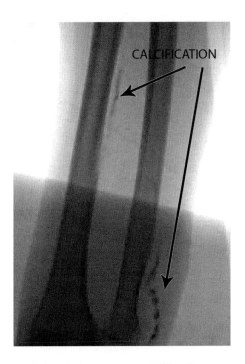

Radial and ulnar artery calcification seen on fluroscopy.

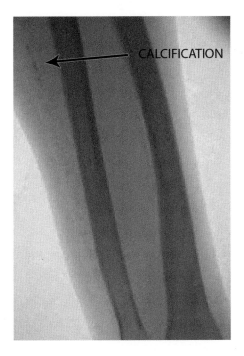

This is another example of radial and ulnar artery calcification seen on fluroscopy.

## ABNORMAL COURSE OF THE RADIAL ARTERY

- Tortuosity
  - With atherosclerosis
  - With superadded spasm
- High Origin
  - Brachial artery
  - Axillary artery
- Loops & Curvatures

## TORTUOSITY

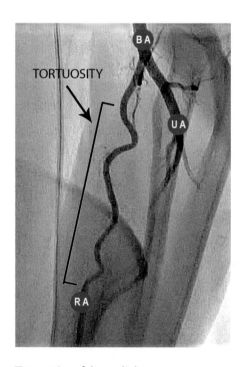

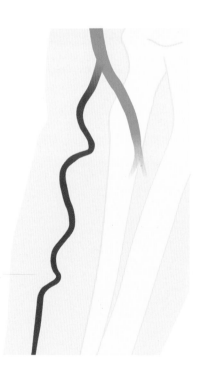

Tortuosity of the radial artery.

## TORTUOSITY (WITH ATHEROSCLEROSIS)

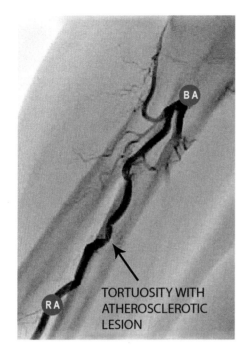

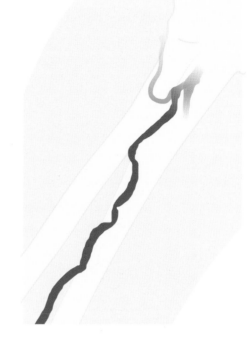

Tortuosity of the radial artery with minor atherosclerotic lesions.

## TORTUOSITY (WITH FOCAL SPASM)

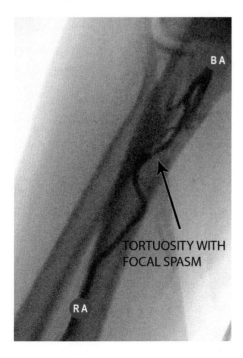

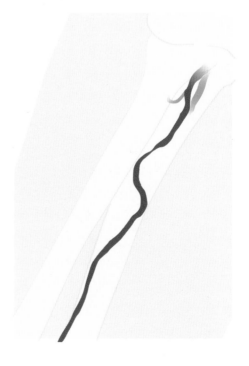

Tortuosity of the radial artery with focal spasm.

# TORTUOSITY (WITH FOCAL SPASM)

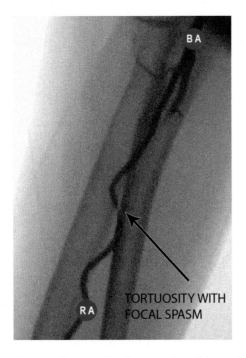

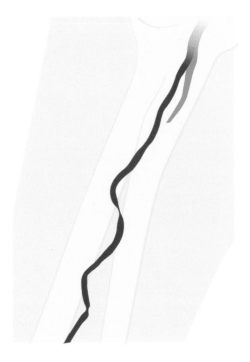

A second example of tortuosity of the radial artery with focal spasm.

# TORTUOSITY (WITH DIFFUSE SPASM)

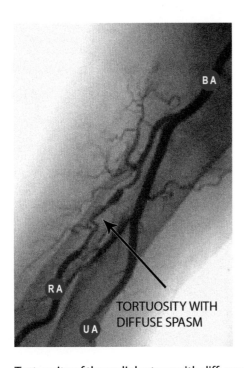

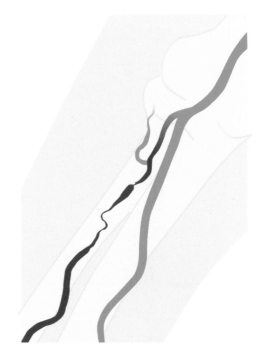

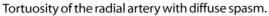

Tortuosity of the radial artery with diffuse spasm.

# HIGH ORIGIN OF THE RADIAL ARTERY

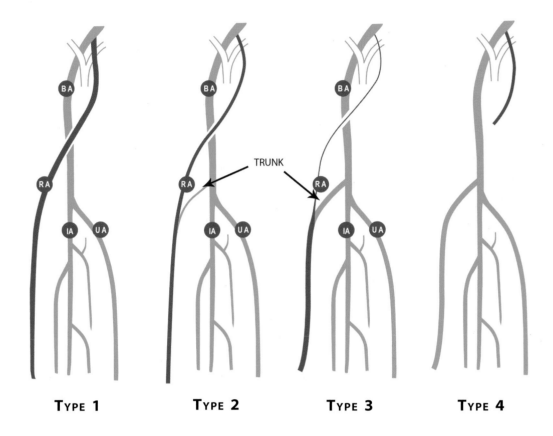

TYPE 1    TYPE 2    TYPE 3    TYPE 4

Here are four types of high origin of the radial artery. They are differentiated by site of origin, caliber, and contribution from the radiocubital trunk. Only the first three types are relevant to the transradial procedure.

In almost one out of eight cases, the origin of the radial artery is from the proximal part of the brachial artery (more often than from the distal part) or from from the axillary artery.

# HIGH ORIGIN FROM THE BRACHIAL ARTERY

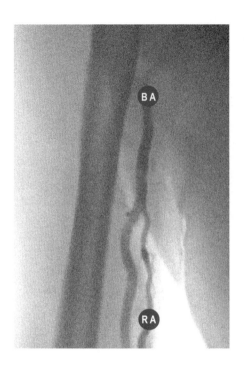

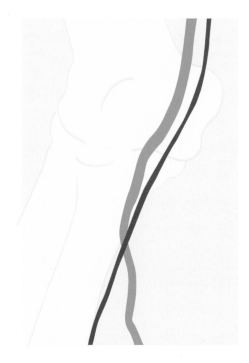

Radial artery arising from the proximal part of the brachial artery.

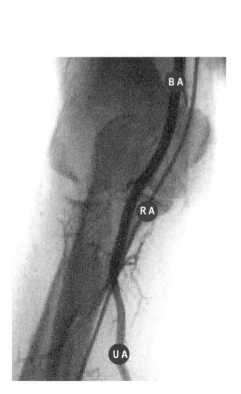

The course of the radial artery in the same patient. Note that there is no radiocubital trunk.

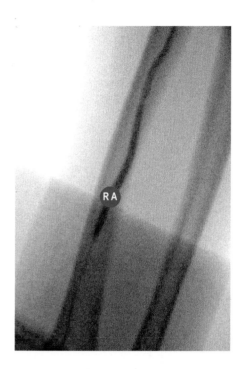 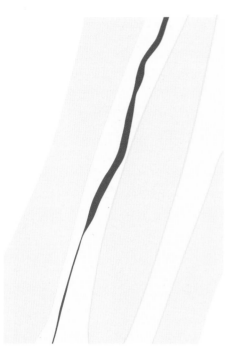

Angiogram showing the distal part of the radial artery in the same patient.

## TYPE 1: HIGH ORIGIN FROM THE BRACHIAL ARTERY

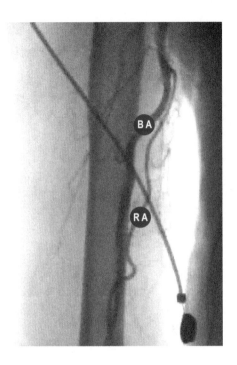

Type 1 high origin of the radial artery from the brachial artery.

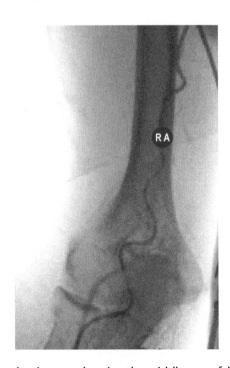

Angiogram showing the middle part of the radial artery in the same patient. Note that there is no radiocubital trunk.

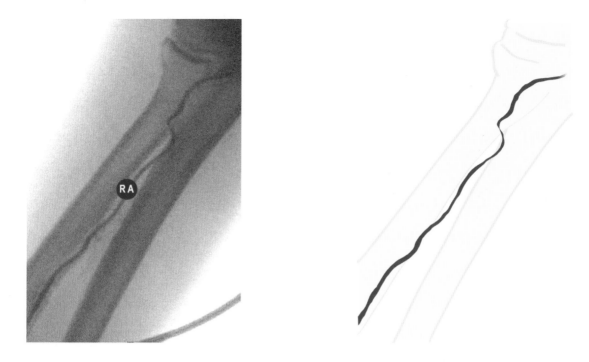

Angiogram showing the distal part of the radial artery in the same patient.

# TYPE 2: HIGH ORIGIN FROM THE BRACHIAL ARTERY

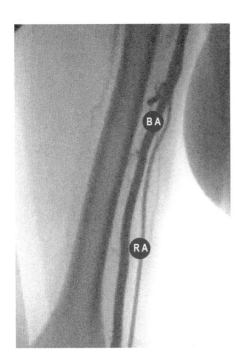

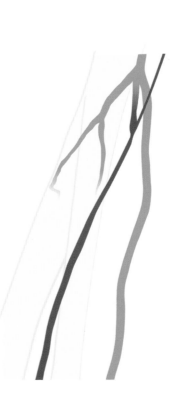

Type 2 high origin of the radial artery from the brachial artery.

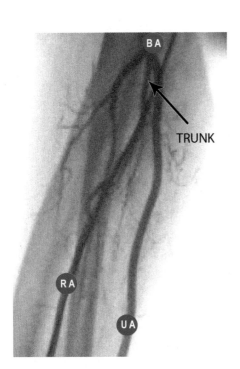

Angiogram showing the radiocubital trunk in the same patient.

## TYPE 3: HIGH ORIGIN OF THE RADIAL ARTERY

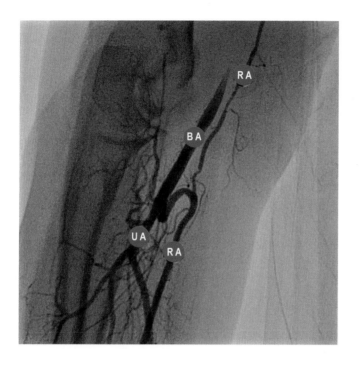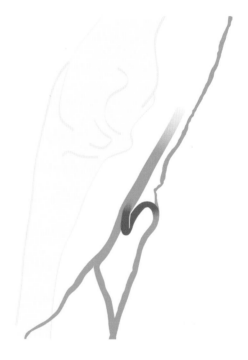

Type 3 high origin of the radial artery. Note the large caliber of the radiocubital trunk and the small caliber of the proximal part of the radial artery.

## HIGH ORIGIN FROM THE AXILLARY ARTERY

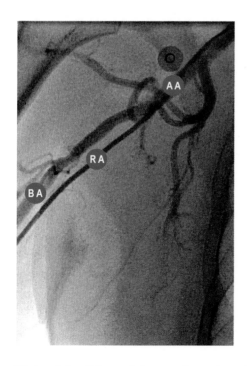

High origin of the radial artery from the axillary artery.

## HIGH ORIGIN FROM THE AXILLARY ARTERY

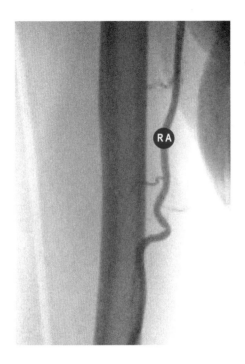

Angiogram of the same patient showing the course of the radial artery in the arm.

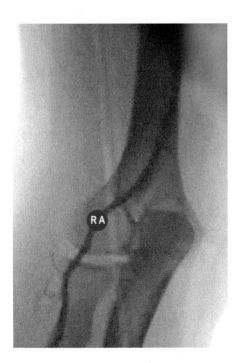

Angiogram showing the course of the distal part of the radial artery in the same patient.

# Loops & Curvatures
## Radiocubital Trunk

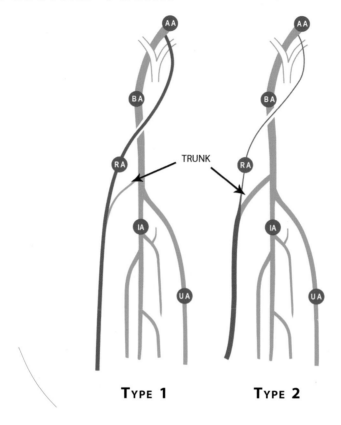

**TRUNK**

**TYPE 1**     **TYPE 2**

Two types of radiocubital trunk. In Type 1, the caliber of the radiocubital trunk is small and the caliber of the proximal radial artery is large. In Type 2, it is just the opposite.

# Examples of the Radiocubital Trunk

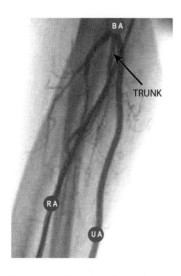

Type 1 radiocubital trunk.

# EXAMPLES OF THE RADIOCUBITAL TRUNK

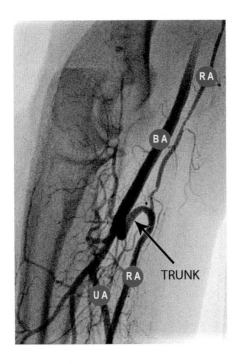
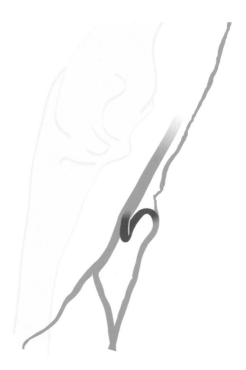

Type 2 radiocubital trunk.

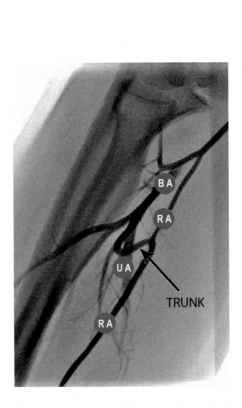

Another example of Type 2 radiocubital trunk.

## EXAMPLE OF A LOOP

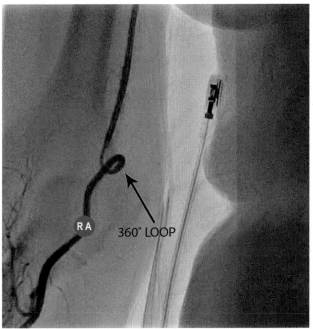

A 360-degree loop in the radial artery (high origin).

## PERFORATION OF THE RADIAL ARTERY

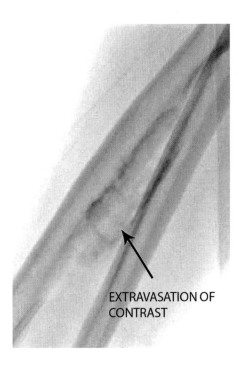

Radial artery perforation leading to extravasation of contrast material into surrounding tissue.

## RECOMMENDED READING

Tountas , CH. P. & Bergman, R.A. (1993). Anatomic variations of the upper extremity. (pp. 196-210). New York, NY. Churchill Livingstone.

Gilchrist IC. Transradial technical tips. Catheter Cardiovasc Interv. 2000 Mar;49(3):353-4.

Louvard Y, Lefèvre T. Loops and transradial approach in coronary diagnosis and intervention. Catheter Cardiovasc Interv. 2000 Oct;51(2):250-2.

Yokoyama N, Takeshita S, Ochiai M, et al. Anatomic variations of the radial artery in patients undergoing transradial coronary intervention. Catheter Cardiovasc Interv. 2000 Apr; 49(4):357-62.

Celik HH, Gormus G, Aldur MM, et al. Origin of the radial and ulnar arteries: variations in 81 arteriograms. Morphologie. 2001 Jun;85(269):25-7.10

Kiemeneij F, Vajifdar BU, Eccleshall SC, et al. Measurement of radial artery spasm using an automatic pullback device. Catheter Cardiovasc Interv. 2001 Dec;54(4):437-41.

Sakai H, Ikeda S, Harada T, et al. Limitations of successive transradial approach in the same arm: the Japanese experience. Catheter Cardiovasc Interv. 2001 Oct;54(2):204-8.

Patnaik VVG, Kalsey G, Singla RK. Branching pattern of brachial artery: a morphological study. J Anatomical Society of India. 2002 Dec;51(2):176-186.

Barbeau GR. Radial loop and extreme vessel tortuosity in the transradial approach: advantage of hydrophilic-coated guidewires and catheters. Catheter Cardiovasc Interv. 2003 Aug; 59(4):442-50.

Gray, H. (2004). Gray's anatomy: the anatomical basis of clinical practice (39th ed.). New York, NY. Churchill Livingstone.

Edmundson A, Mann T. Nonocclusive radial artery injury resulting from transradial coronary interventions: radial artery IVUS. J Invasive Cardiol. 2005 Oct;17(10):528-31.

Yoo BS, Yoon J, Ko JY, et al. Anatomical consideration of the radial artery for transradial coronary procedures: arterial diameter, branching anomaly and vessel tortuosity. Int J Cardiol. 2005 Jun 8;101(3):421-7.

# RADIAL REGION:
# ADDRESSING THE ISSUES

Each of the issues mentioned in the previous chapter has been addressed thoroughly in this chapter.

Radial artery spasm must be well identified and understood. Radialists handle radial artery spasm differently, but we have outlined a protocol for spasm that has worked for us in over 20,000 cases.

We have described how to address the different subsets of tortuosity and high origin of the radial artery.

Loops and curvatures have been divided into three categories—"easy," "more challenging," and "most challenging"—and examples of each have been discussed in great detail.

There is no need to panic when going through this chapter. Examples of challenging situations have been given only to prove that 99% of complex cases can be worked through. The "most challenging" loops and curvatures are rare and beginning radialists should not attempt them. But as their experience grows, they can begin dealing with loops very creatively—just as we did.

Experienced radialists will love this chapter because it will give them solutions they might not have thought of. We believe that once radial-dedicated hardware is developed, most loops will be very easy to handle, even for beginning radialists.

Finally, we have shown several examples of how we have dealt very effectively with perforations of the radial artery. ■

## ABNORMAL CALIBER OF THE RADIAL ARTERY

**SPASM**

- ■ **Focal or Diffuse**

  **Solution**

  - Confirm spasm on radial angiogram.
  - Give an additional dose of spasmolytic cocktail.
  - Cross with thin, hydrophilic guidewires (e.g., 0.014" PTCA guidewires or Terumo Glidewires).

  **Rationale**

  - It is easy to cross with thinner wires.
  - Hydrophilic wires are likely to aggravate spasm.

  **Note**

  - At times, these guidewires may provide poor support to catheters.

## SPASM

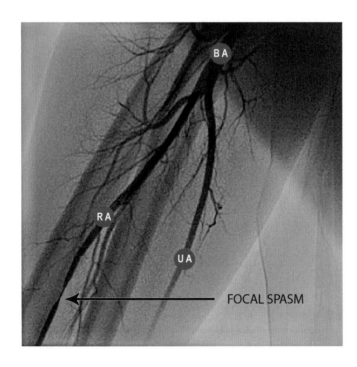

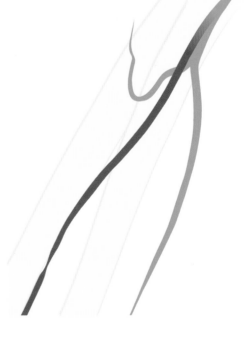

Focal spasm in the radial artery.

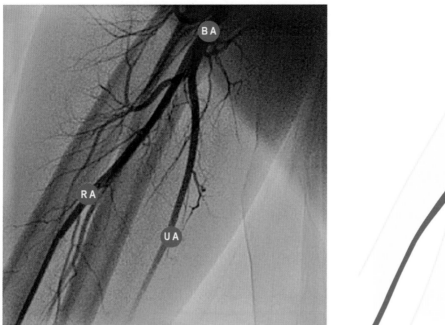

Angiogram in the same patient after an additional dose of spasmolytic cocktail. The spasm was relieved and the procedure was completed in the usual fashion.

# HYPOPLASIA

If the radial artery is mildly hypoplastic, the transradial procedure can be performed in the usual fashion. Give an additional dose of spasmolytic cocktail to facilitate the negotiation of the artery. However, if the artery is severely hypoplastic, the procedure can cause severe spasm and pain and it is better to switch to the contralateral radial route or to the femoral route.

# ATHEROSCLEROSIS & CALCIFICATION

Transradial intervention can be performed through insignificant atherosclerotic lesions. When the lesions are severely stenotic, they can be dilated with angioplasty balloons and the procedure can be completed in the usual fashion. As above, give an additional dose of spasmolytic cocktail to facilitate the procedure. In some cases, it is necessary to switch to the contralateral radial route or to the femoral route.

# ABNORMAL COURSE OF THE RADIAL ARTERY

## TORTUOSITY

### Solution

- Confirm tortuosity on the radial angiogram.
- Give an additional dose of spasmolytic cocktail. It will resolve any superadded spasm.
- Use a thin, hydrophilic, and flexible wire to cross the tortuosity; e.g., 0.014″ PTCA guidewire or Terumo Glidewire.
- The guidewire should be parked as proximal as possible to provide good support to the catheter.
- If required, catheters can be downsized to complete the procedure.

### Rationale

- Flexible wires can negotiate the curve easily without provoking spasm.

### Note

- At times, these guidewires may provide poor support for catheters.

# TORTUOSITY (LONG SEGMENT)

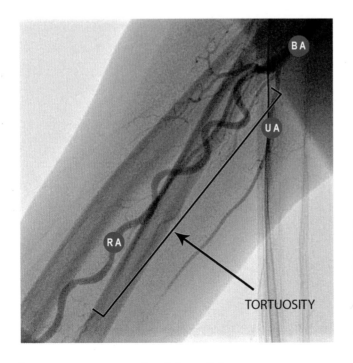
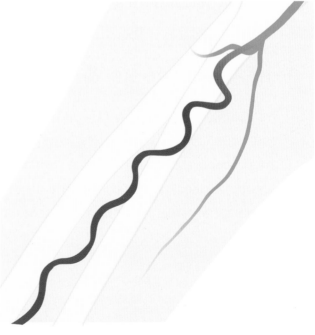

Long segment tortuosity of the radial artery.

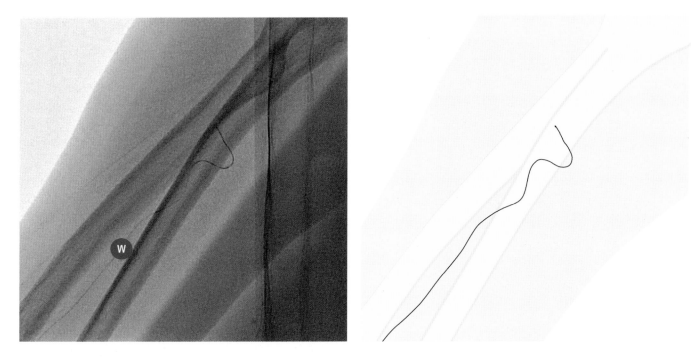

The 0.035" standard guidewire was unable to cross the tortuosity. We switched to a 0.014" PTCA guidewire.

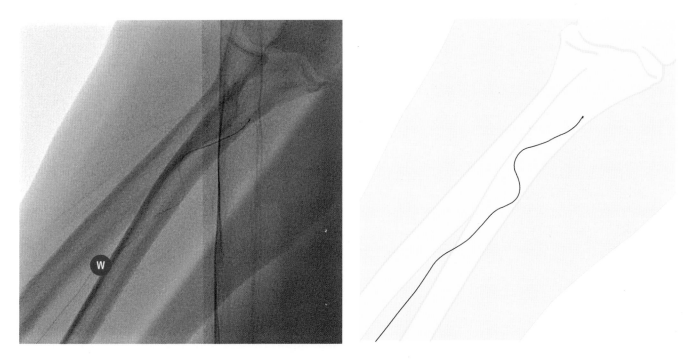

The 0.014" PTCA guidewire was parked proximally in the subclavian artery. The procedure was completed in the usual fashion.

# TORTUOSITY (WITH FOCAL SPASM)

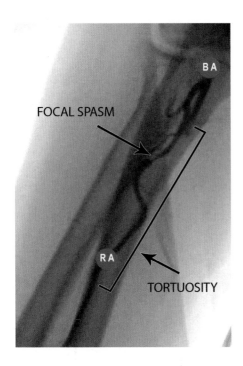
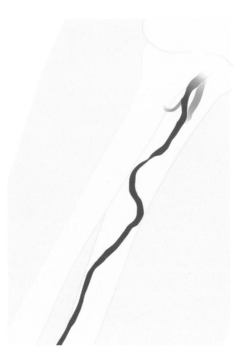

Tortuosity of the radial artery with focal spasm in mid-segment.

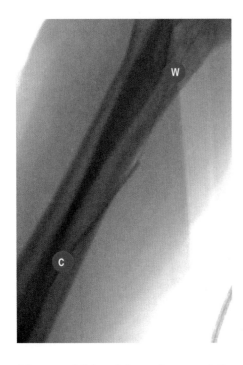
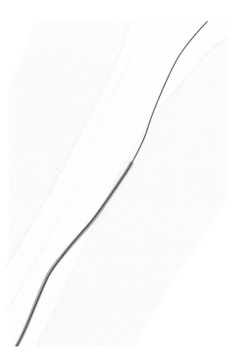

After an additional dose of spasmolytic cocktail, a 4F catheter and a 0.014" PTCA guidewire were used to cross the tortuosity and to complete the procedure in the usual fashion.

## Tortuosity (with Diffuse Spasm)

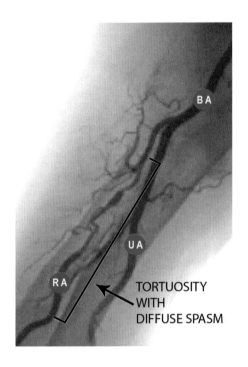

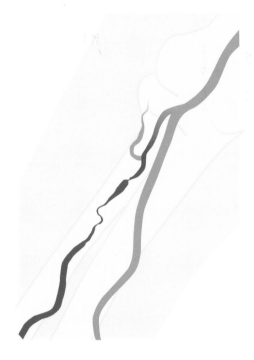

Tortuosity of the radial artery with diffuse spasm.

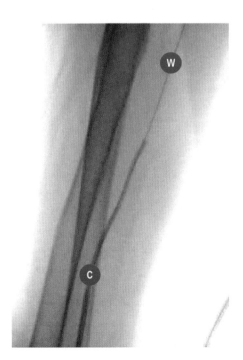

As in the previous case, a 4F catheter and a 0.014" guidewire were used to cross the tortuosity and to complete the procedure in the usual fashion.

## HIGH ORIGIN

- High origin of the radial artery is more prone to spasm and can make the procedure challenging at times.

- For Type 1 (without the radiocubital trunk), the procedure can be completed by downsizing the catheters. In case of severe spasm, it is better to switch to the contralateral radial route or to the femoral route.

- For Type 2 and Type 3 (with the radiocubital trunk), the procedure is described in detail in "Loops & Curvatures" below.

# LOOPS & CURVATURES

### "EASY"

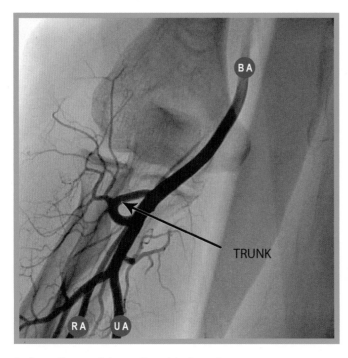

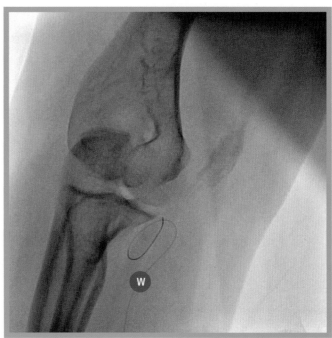

An "easy" loop of the radiocubital trunk.

A 0.014" PTCA guidewire was used to negotiate the loop.

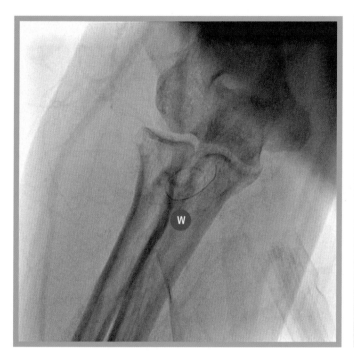

The 0.014" PTCA guidewire crossed the loop easily.

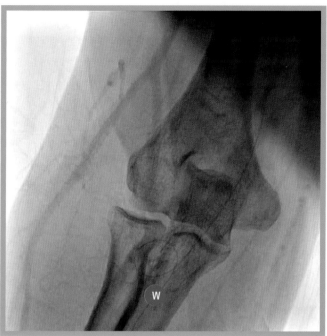

The guidewire was advanced as proximal as possible.

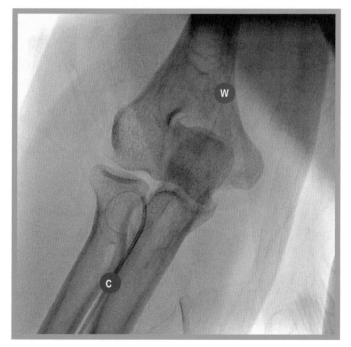

A 5F diagnostic catheter was advanced over the 0.014" PTCA guidewire.

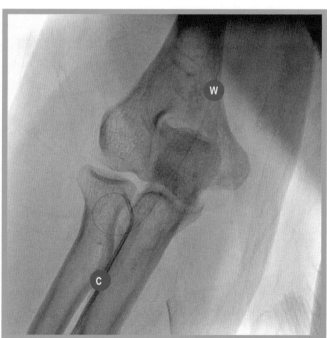

The catheter was ready to enter the loop.

# LOOPS & CURVATURES

## "EASY"

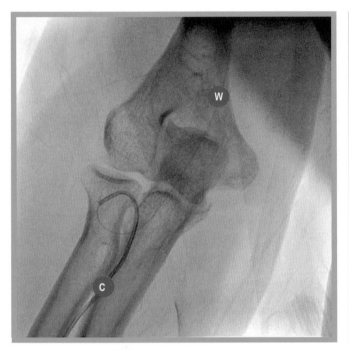

The catheter was advanced half way into the loop.

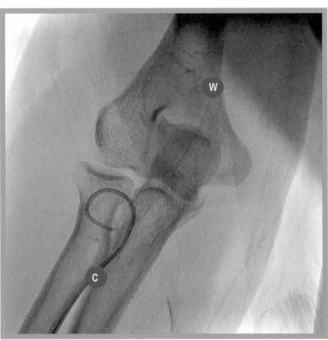

The catheter completely traversed the loop.

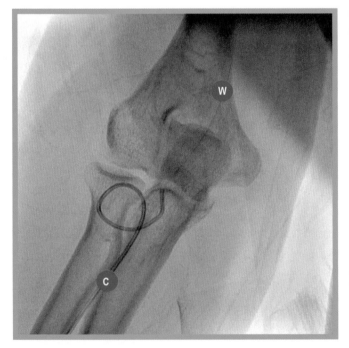

The catheter was advanced beyond the loop.

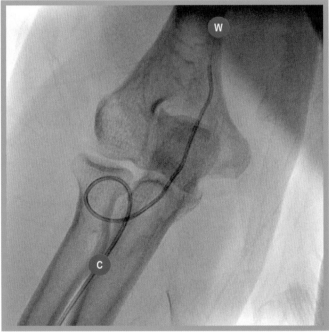

The catheter was advanced farther in the brachial artery.

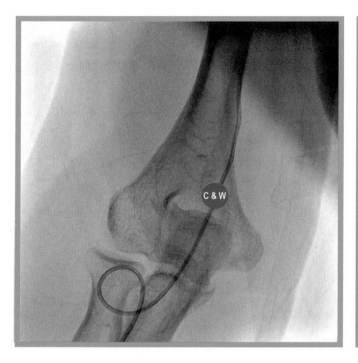

It was difficult to advance the catheter farther on the 0.014″ PTCA guidewire.

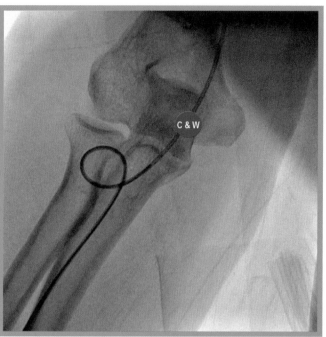

The 0.014″ PTCA guidewire was exchanged with a standard 0.035″ guidewire.

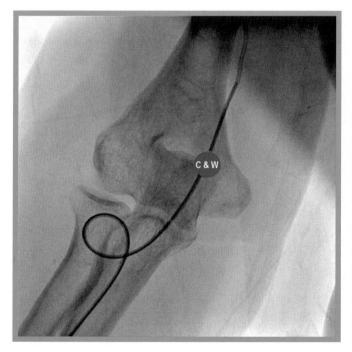

An effort was made to advance the catheter farther, but it refused to budge.

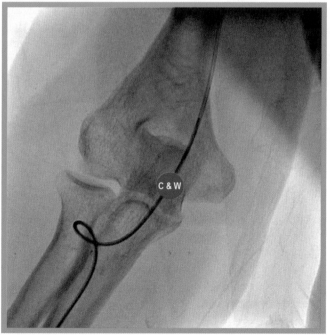

The loop was straightened by a gentle pull back of the entire assembly and the procedure was completed in the usual fashion.

# LOOPS & CURVATURES

## "EASY"

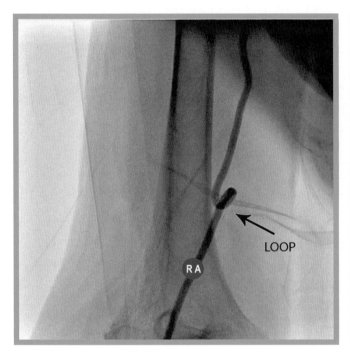

This is another example of an "easy" loop of the radial artery (high origin).

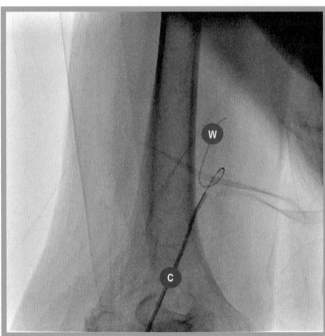

A 0.014" PTCA guidewire negotiated the loop.

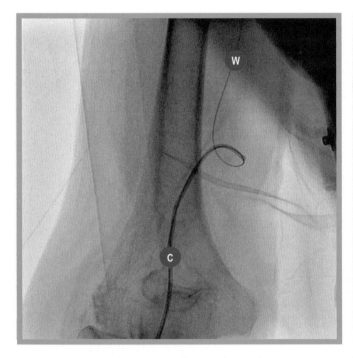

A 4F diagnostic catheter was advanced over the 0.014" PTCA guidewire.

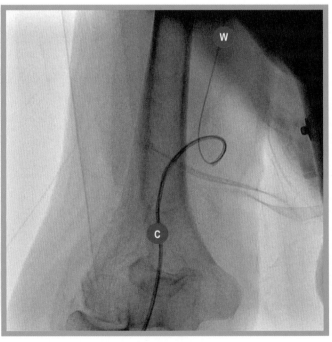

The catheter was advanced farther into the loop.

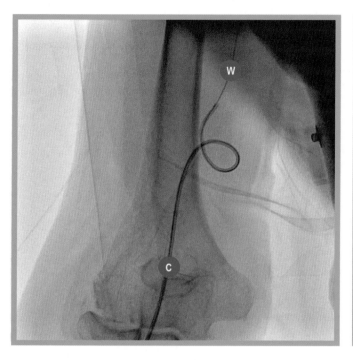

The catheter crossed the loop.

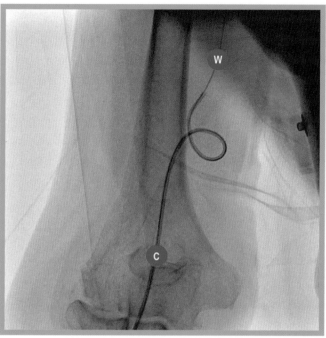

The catheter was advanced farther into the radial artery.

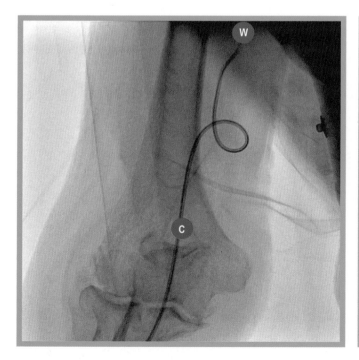

The catheter refused to advance.

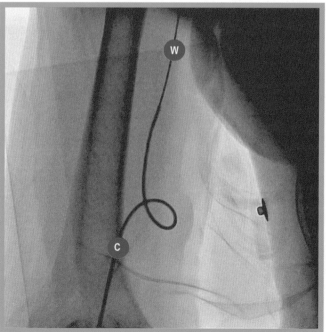

At this point, the 0.014" PTCA guidewire was exchanged with a standard 0.035" guidewire.

## LOOPS & CURVATURES

### "EASY"

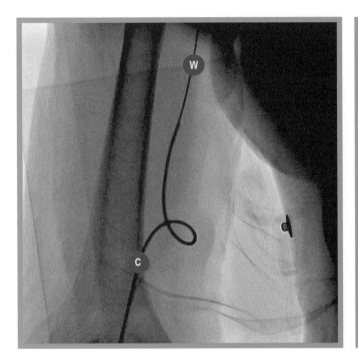

We decided to straighten the loop.

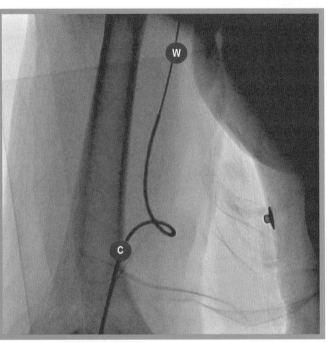

The entire assembly was pulled back.

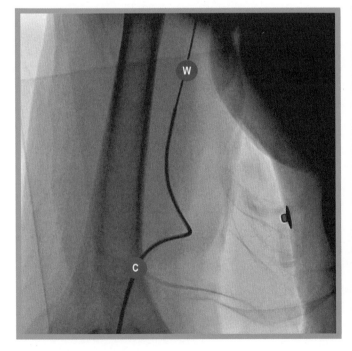

The loop was starting to straighten.

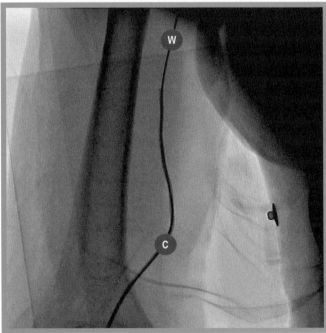

The loop was successfully straightened.

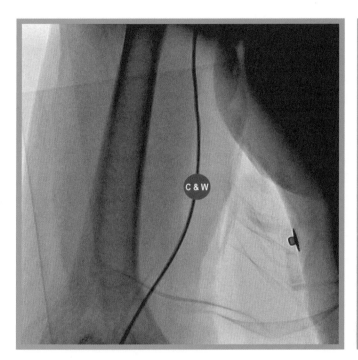

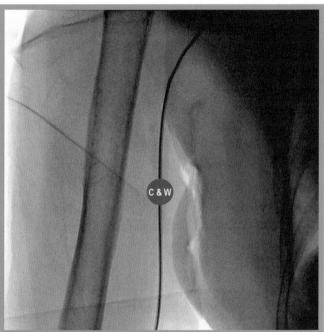

The catheter could now be advanced easily over the guidewire.

The procedure was completed in the usual fashion.

## "MORE CHALLENGING"

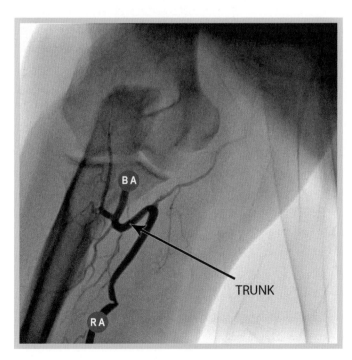

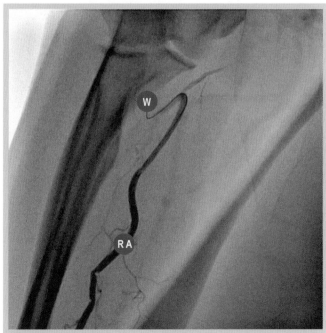

This is an example of a "more challenging" loop.

A 0.014" PTCA guidewire was used to cross the loop.

## LOOPS & CURVATURES

### "MORE CHALLENGING"

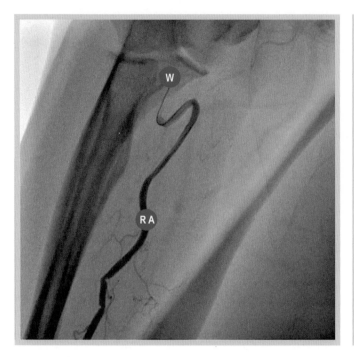

The 0.014" PTCA guidewire crossed the loop.

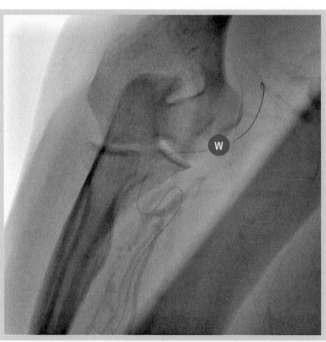

The 0.014" PTCA guidewire was parked in the brachial artery.

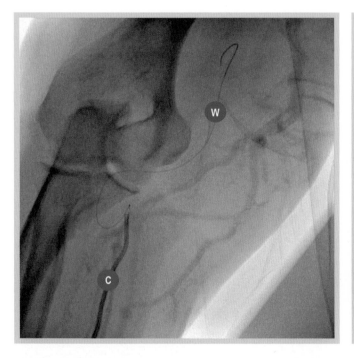

An attempt was made to advance a 4F diagnostic catheter over the 0.014" PTCA guidewire.

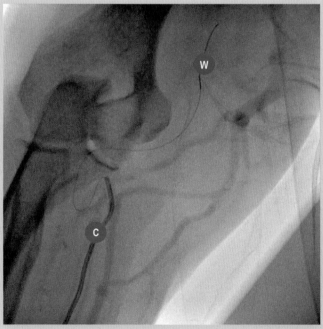

The catheter was in the inital part of the loop, but it refused to budge farther.

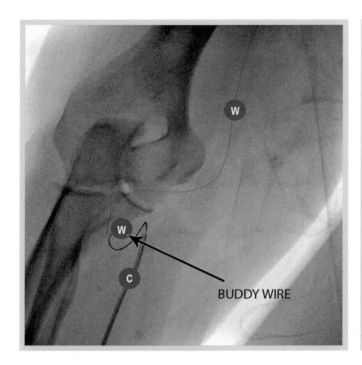

Another 0.014" PTCA guidewire (buddy wire) was used to provide additional support.

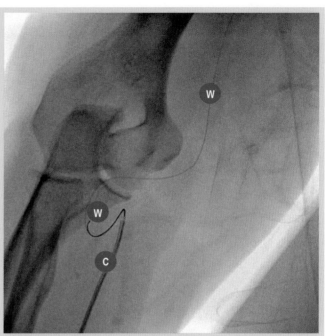

The buddy wire was advanced farther into the loop.

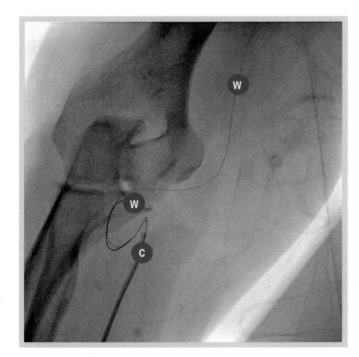

The buddy wire crossed the loop.

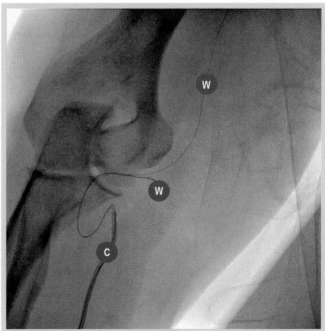

The buddy wire was parked in the brachial artery.

# LOOPS & CURVATURES

## "MORE CHALLENGING"

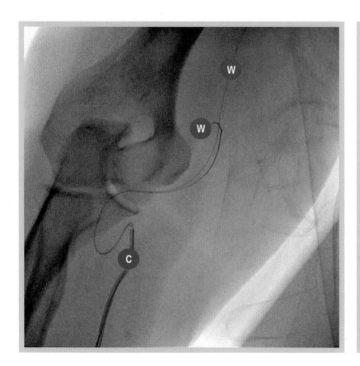

The buddy wire was advanced farther.

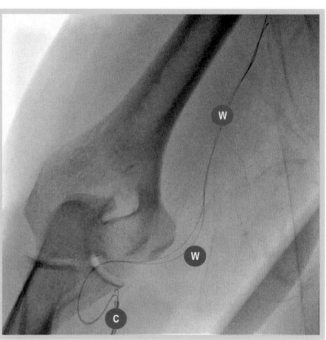

The buddy wire was advanced still farther.

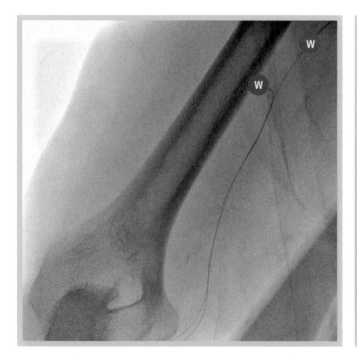

Now an attempt was made to advance the catheter. (The catheter is not seen in this angiogram.)

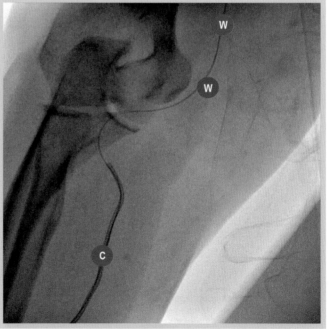

The catheter advanced into the initial part of the loop.

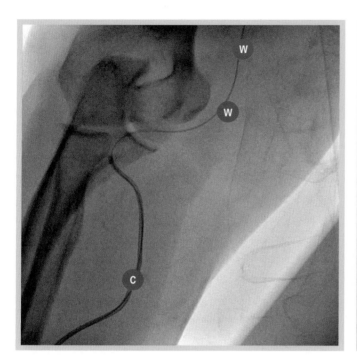

The catheter was advanced still farther into the loop.

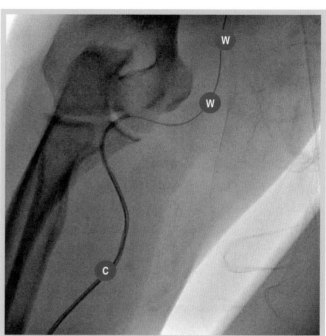

The catheter crossed the loop.

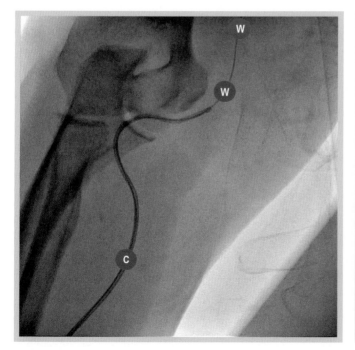

The catheter was advanced beyond the loop into the brachial artery.

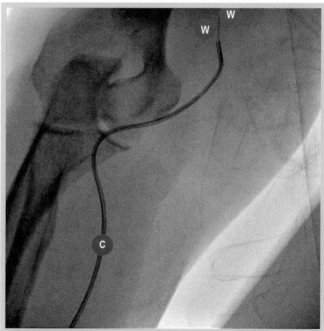

The procedure was completed in the usual fashion.

# LOOPS & CURVATURES

## "MORE CHALLENGING"

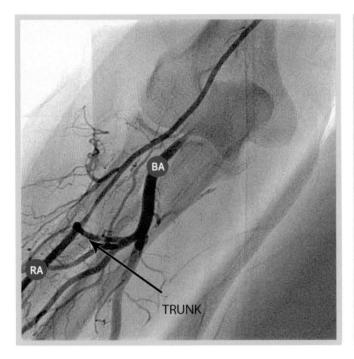

This is another example of a "more challenging" loop.

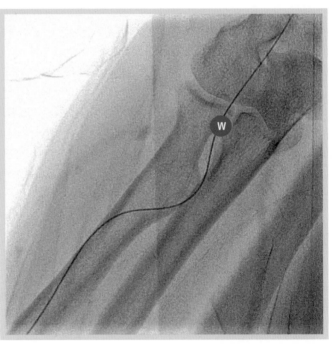

A 0.014" PTCA guidewire was used to negotiate the loop.

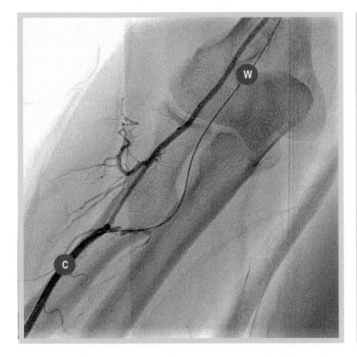

An angiogram confirmed the position of the 0.014" PTCA guidewire in the distal part of the brachial artery across the loop.

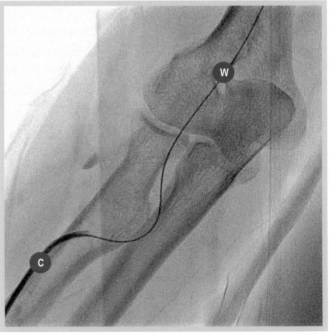

An attempt was made to advance a 5F diagnostic catheter over the 0.014" PTCA guidewire.

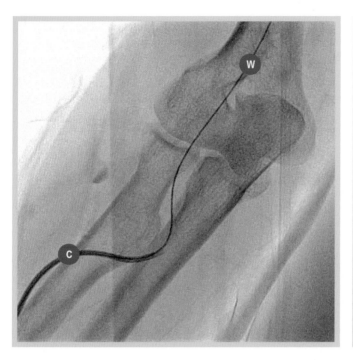

The catheter refused to budge beyond the mid-part of the loop.

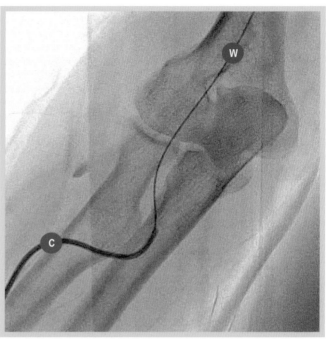

At this point, a second 0.014" PTCA guidewire (buddy wire) was used to provide adequate support.

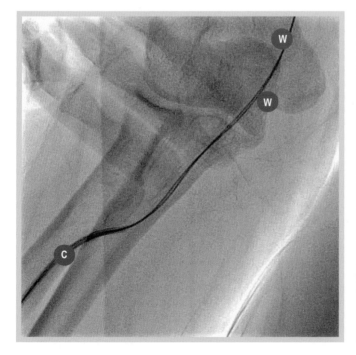

An attempt was made to advance the catheter over the two 0.014" PTCA guidewires.

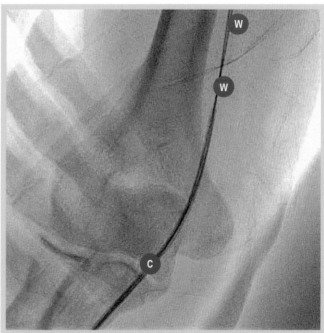

We successfully crossed the loop this time.

# LOOPS & CURVATURES

## "MORE CHALLENGING"

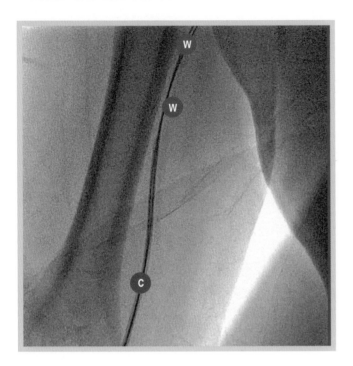

The catheter was advanced farther.

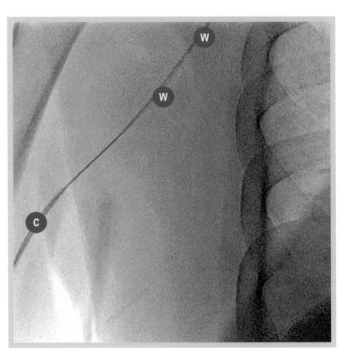

The catheter crossed the brachial artery.

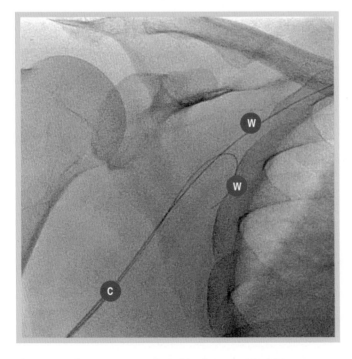

The procedure was completed in the usual fashion.

# LOOPS & CURVATURES

## "MOST CHALLENGING"

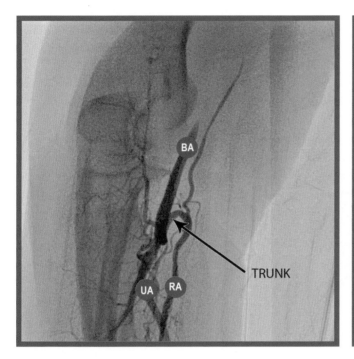

An example of a "most challenging" loop.

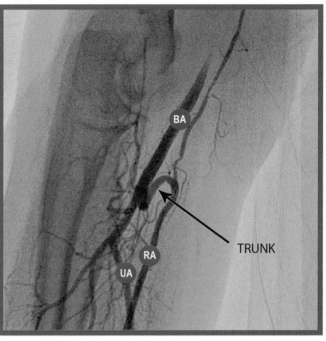

Another angiogram was taken from a different angle to better define the loop.

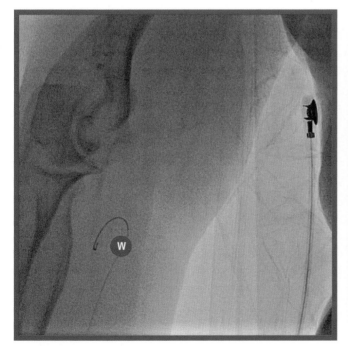

A 0.014" PTCA guidewire was used to cross the loop.

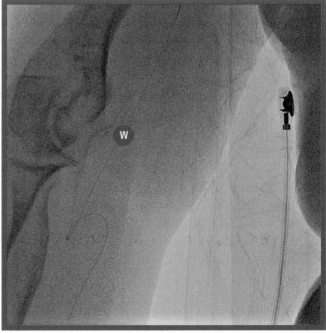

The 0.014" PTCA guidewire was parked in the brachial artery.

# Loops & Curvatures

## "MOST CHALLENGING"

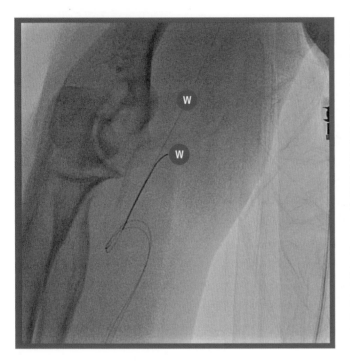

In anticipation that the catheter would require additional support, we used another 0.014" PTCA guidewire (buddy wire).

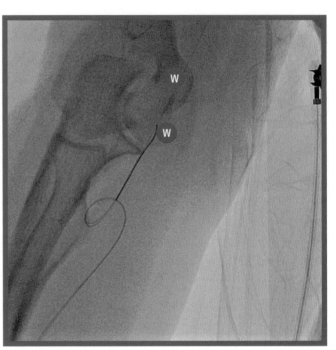

The buddy wire crossed the loop and was parked in the brachial artery.

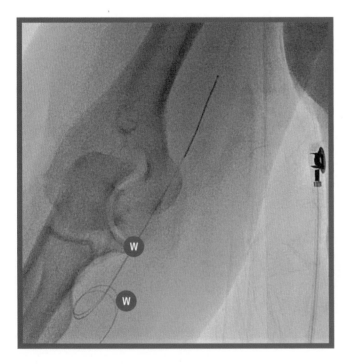

The buddy wire was advanced still farther into the brachial artery.

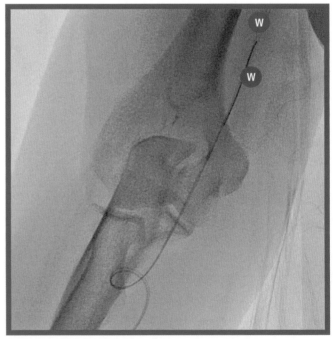

A catheter (not seen on the fluroscopy) was advanced over the two 0.014" PTCA guidewires.

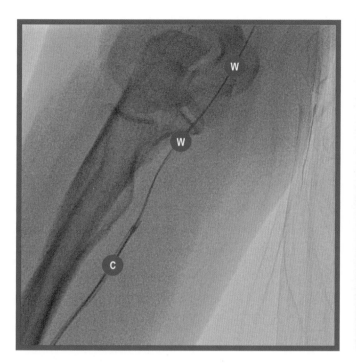

The entire assembly was pulled back slightly to straighten the loop.

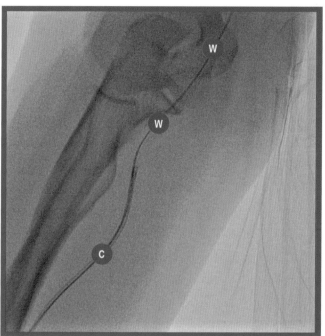

The catheter was advanced farther.

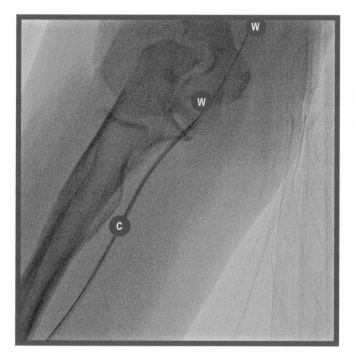

The catheter easily crossed the loop.

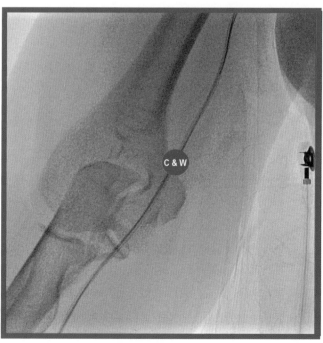

The procedure was completed in the usual fashion.

# LOOPS & CURVATURES

## "MOST CHALLENGING"

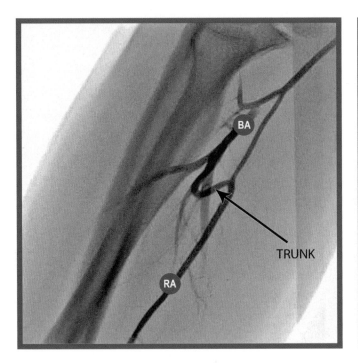

This is another example of a "most challenging" loop.

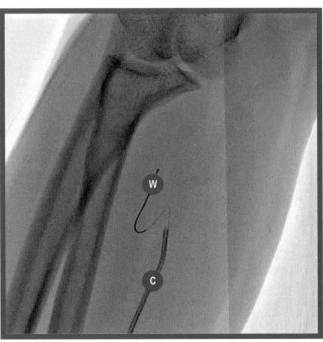

A 0.014" PTCA guidewire was used to negotiate the loop.

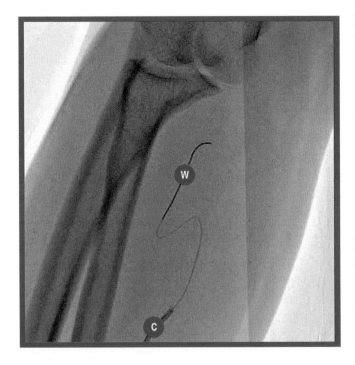

The 0.014" PTCA guidewire was advanced farther.

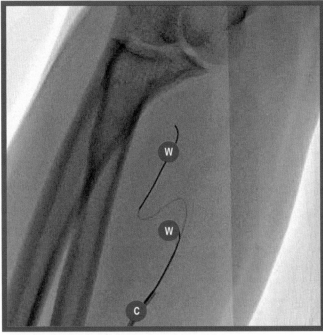

Another 0.014" PTCA guidewire (buddy wire) was used to provide additional support.

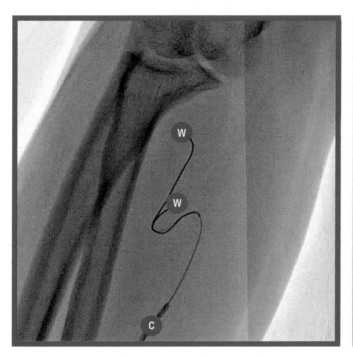

The buddy wire crossed the loop.

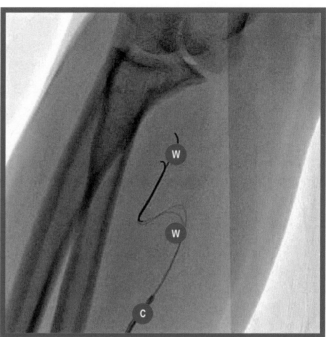

The buddy wire was placed in the distal part of the brachial artery.

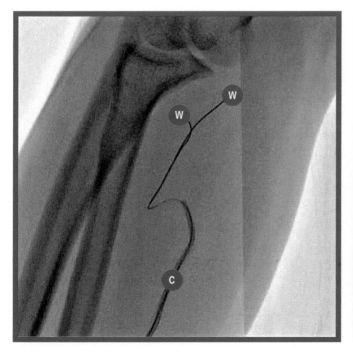

A 4F diagnostic catheter was advanced over these two guidewires.

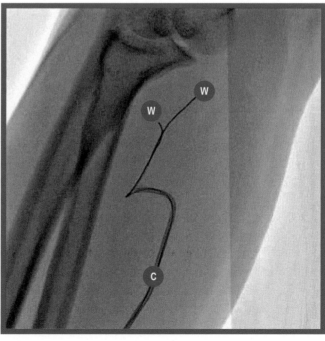

The catheter crossed the first hairpin turn successfully.

# LOOPS & CURVATURES

## "MOST CHALLENGING"

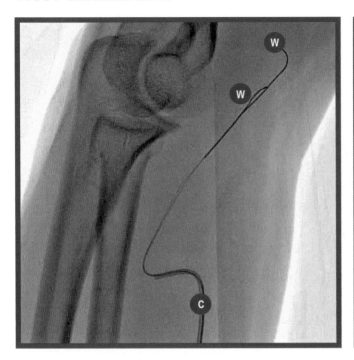

The catheter could not negotiate the entire loop.

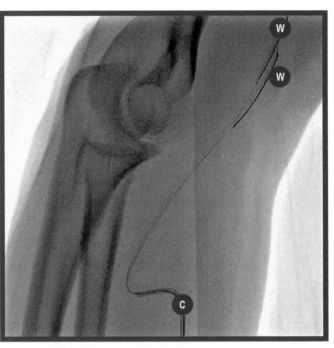

With the support of the diagnostic catheter, the two 0.014" PTCA guidewires were advanced still farther into the brachial artery.

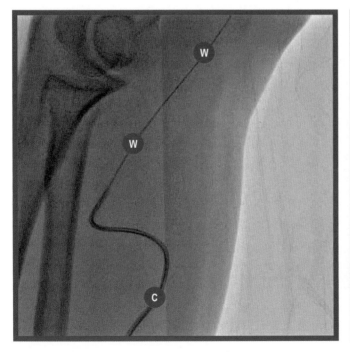

The new position of the 0.014" PTCA guidewires provided additional support for the catheter.

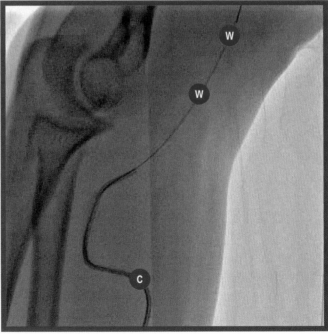

The catheter easily crossed the loop.

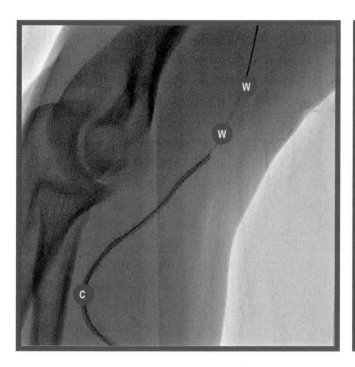

The catheter was advanced farther.

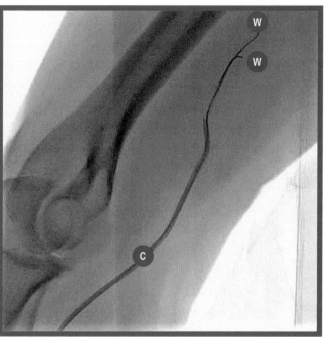

The loop was straightened while advancing the catheter over the guidewires.

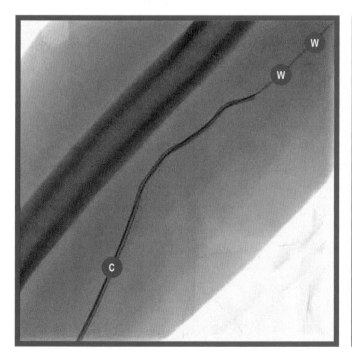

The catheter advanced farther without effort.

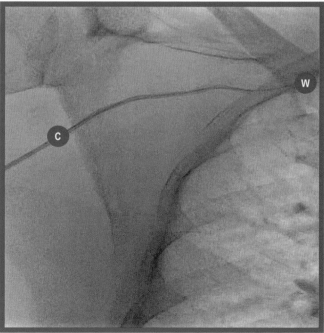

The procedure was completed in the usual fashion.

# LOOPS & CURVATURES

## "MOST CHALLENGING"

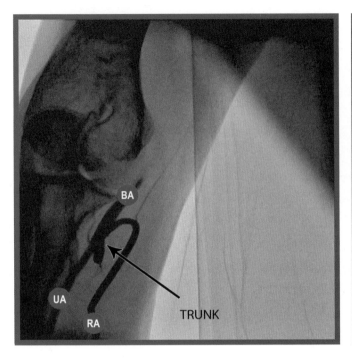

This is the third example of a "most challenging" loop.

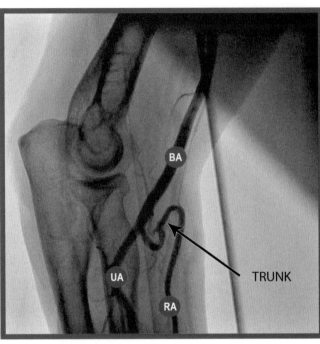

An angiogram was taken from a different angle to better define the loop.

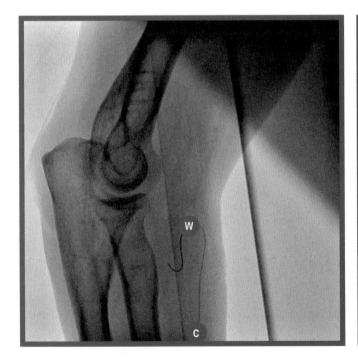

A 0.014" PTCA guidewire was used to negotiate the loop.

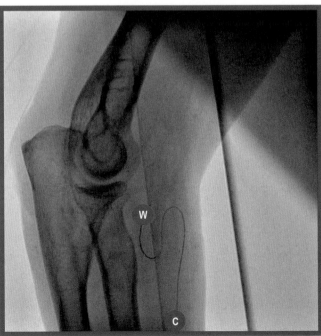

The 0.014" PTCA guidewire nearly crossed the loop.

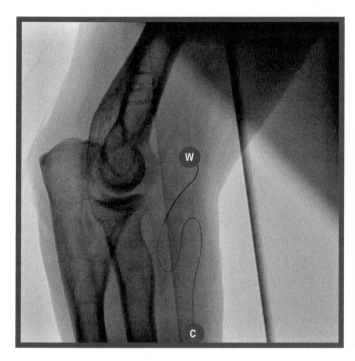

The 0.014" PTCA guidewire was advanced into the distal part of the brachial artery.

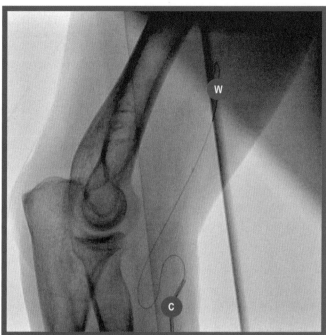

The 0.014" PTCA guidewire was advanced farther into the brachial artery. A 4F diagnostic catheter was used in an attempt to cross the loop.

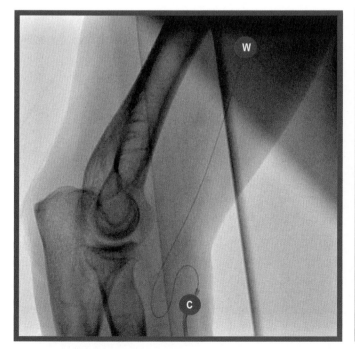

The 4F diagnostic catheter was advanced into the initial part of the loop.

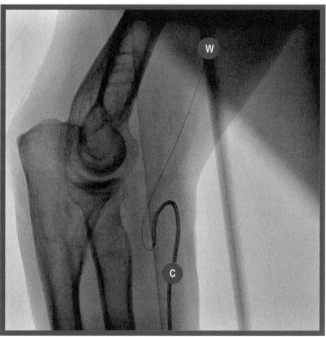

The 4F diagnostic catheter negotiated the first hairpin turn of the loop, but refused to budge any farther.

# LOOPS & CURVATURES

## "MOST CHALLENGING"

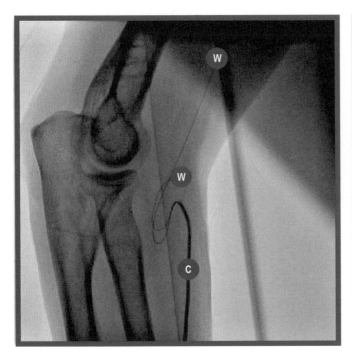

Another 0.014" PTCA guidewire (buddy wire) was used.

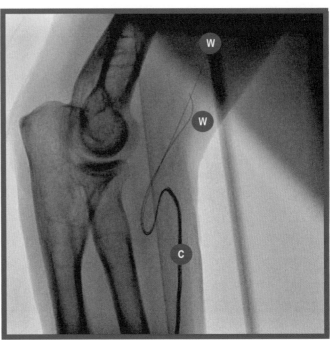

The buddy wire advanced into the distal part of the brachial artery.

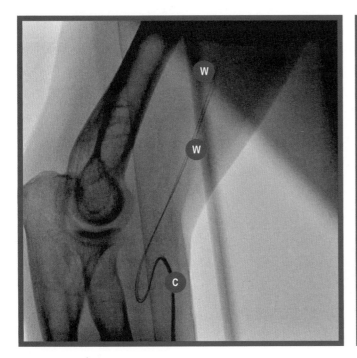

The buddy wire was advanced farther.

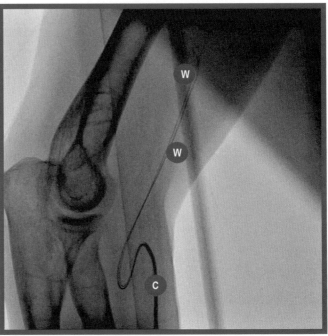

The catheter was advanced over the two 0.014" PTCA guidewires.

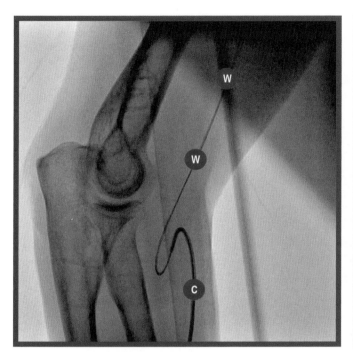

The catheter negotiated the first hairpin turn.

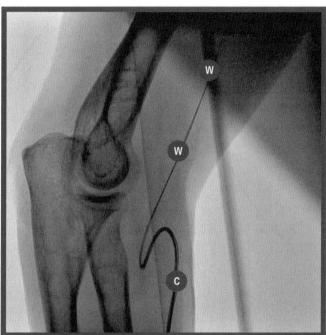

The catheter was advanced farther.

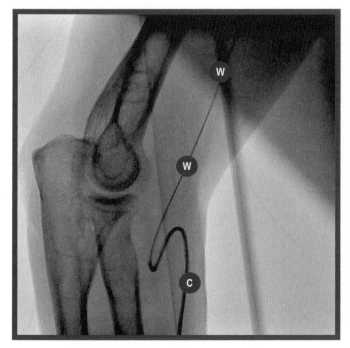

The catheter entered the second hairpin turn.

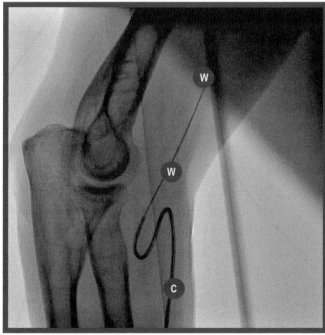

The catheter crossed the second hairpin turn.

# LOOPS & CURVATURES

## "MOST CHALLENGING"

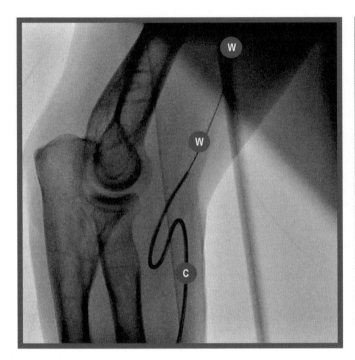

The catheter was advanced into the brachial artery.

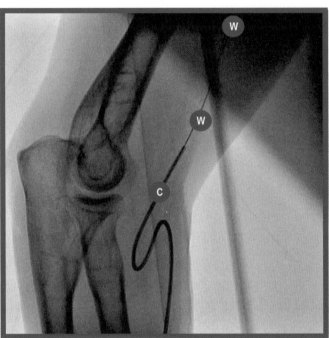

The catheter was advanced still farther.

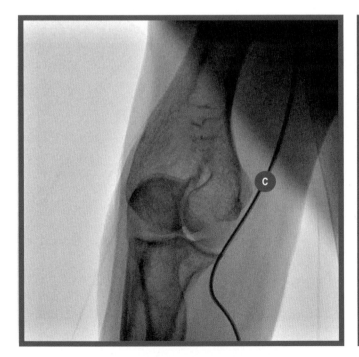

A gentle pull back of the entire assembly straightened the loop and eased the further advancement of the catheter.

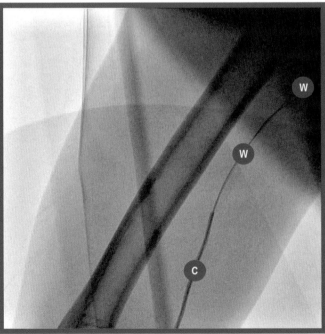

The catheter was advanced farther without effort.

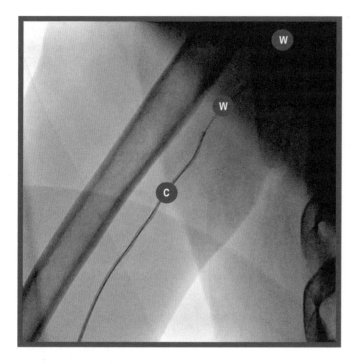

The procedure was completed in the usual fashion.

# PERFORATIONS OF THE RADIAL ARTERY

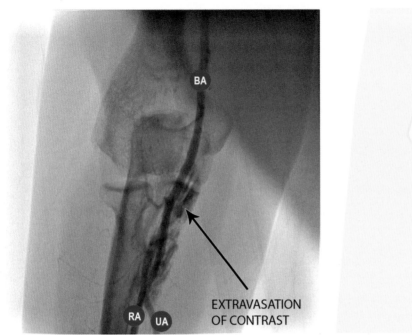
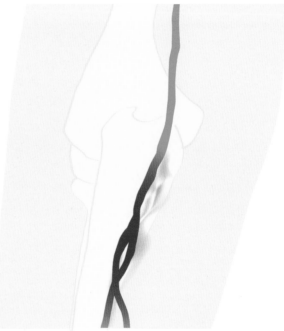

EXTRAVASATION
OF CONTRAST

Here we see extravasation of contrast in the forearm due to perforation of a small branch of the radial artery. The distal section of the brachial artery was seen well on the angiogram. In view of this, we planned to complete the procedure using the same radial approach.

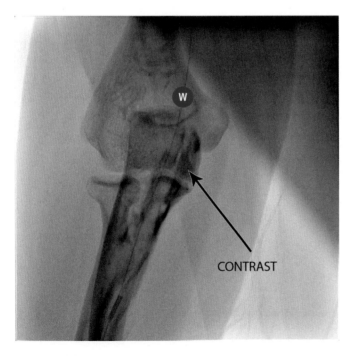
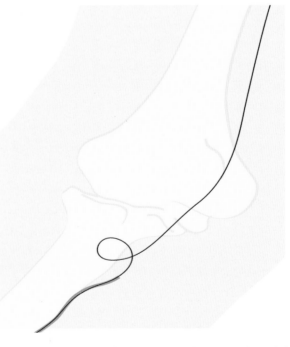

CONTRAST

A 0.014" PTCA guidewire was used and was parked in the brachial artery. The use of a thinner guidewire reduced the chance of further injury to the arterial bed.

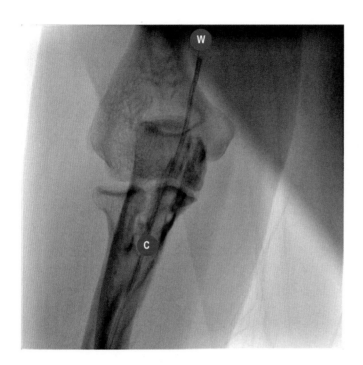

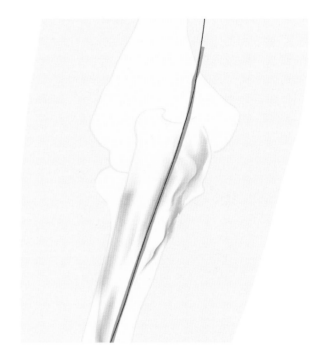

A 5F diagnostic catheter was advanced over the 0.014" PTCA guidewire.

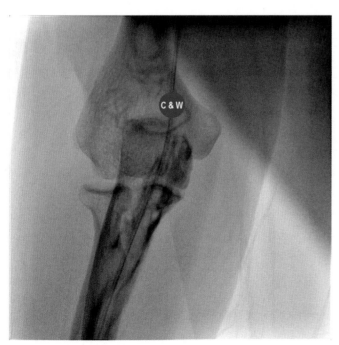

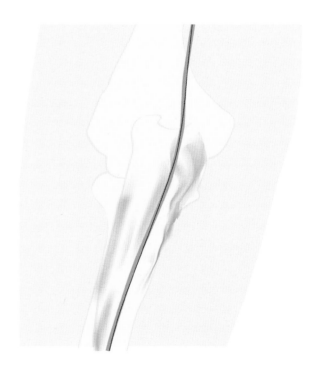

The procedure was completed in the usual fashion.

## PERFORATIONS OF THE RADIAL ARTERY

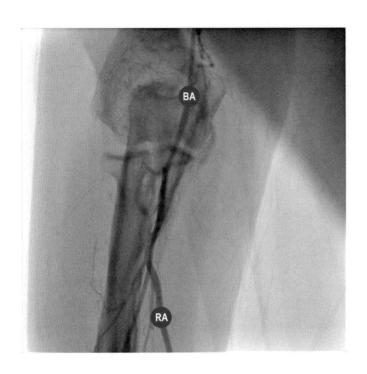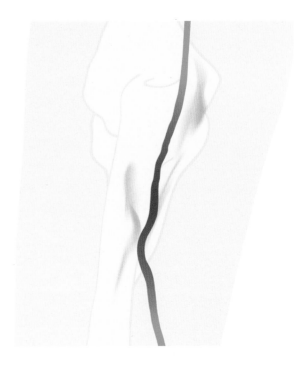

A post-procedure radial angiogram taken while pulling back the diagnostic catheter revealed that the perforation had sealed.

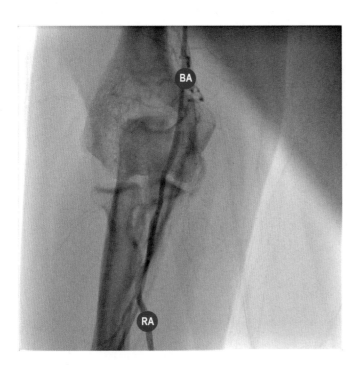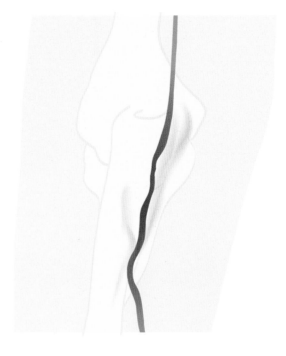

There was no further extravasation of contrast.

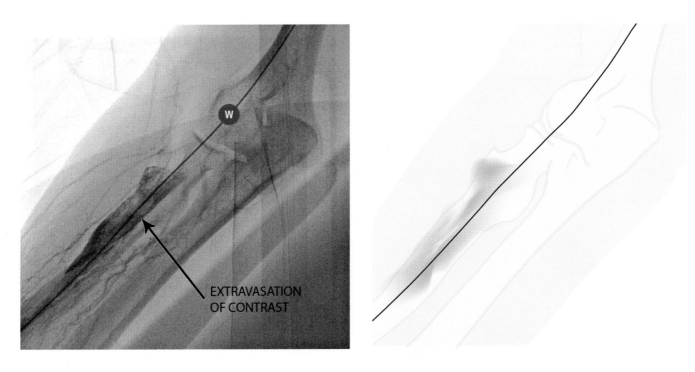

This is another example of a perforation of a small branch of the radial artery.

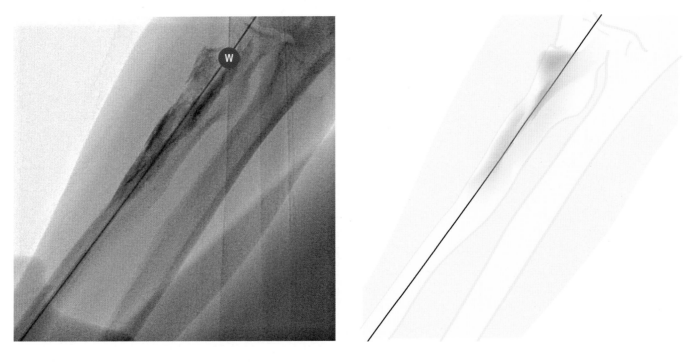

The procedure was successfully executed from the same radial approach using a 0.014" PTCA guidewire and a 5F diagnostic catheter.

## PERFORATIONS OF THE RADIAL ARTERY

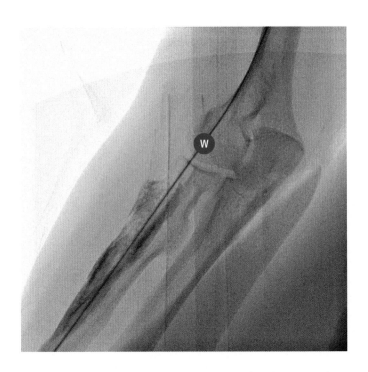

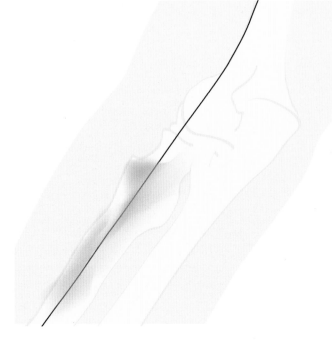

Extravasation of contrast was seen even after the procedure.

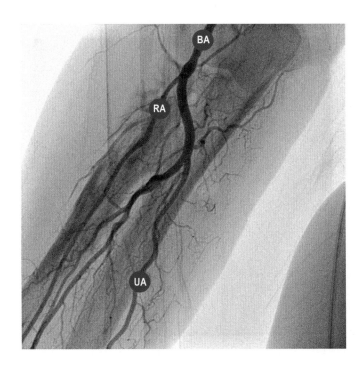

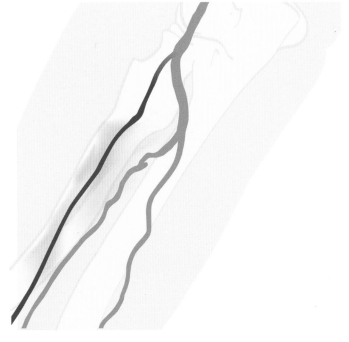

The post-procedure angiogram of the radial artery revealed that the perforation had sealed completely and there was no further extravasation of contrast.

# REMEMBER

- Normally there is no resistance in advancing guidewires and catheters up to the ascending aorta. However, if a patient complains of pain or there is resistance in the maneuvering of guidewires and catheters, it indicates problems of passage.

- Resistance of a wire or catheter in this region is most commonly interpreted as spasm. In our experience, many times what we think is spasm is actually an anatomical variation that is caused by tortuosity, loops and curvatures or, rarely, stenosis of the artery. In these situations, we strongly recommend performing an angiogram of the radial artery to define the anatomy. The vast majority of challenges can be worked through.

- Keep a very low threshold for radial angiogram and a very high threshold for crossover.

- Terumo hydrophilic Glidewires and 0.014" PTCA guidewires are true friends in challenging situations.

- Beginning radialists should avoid working through challenging loops.

- With increasing experience, you can move past a perforation using a 0.014" PTCA guidewire and a diagnostic or guiding catheter.

# RECOMMENDED READING

Gilchrist IC. Transradial technical tips. Catheter Cardiovasc Interv. 2000 Mar;49(3):353-4.

Louvard Y, Lefevre T: Loops and transradial approach in coronary diagnosis and intervention. Catheter Cardiovasc Interv. 2000 Oct; 51:250-2.

Yokoyama N, Takeshita S, Ochiai M. Anatomic variations of the radial artery in patients undergoing transradial coronary intervention. Catheter Cardiovasc Interv. 2000 Apr;49(4);357-62.

Kiemeneij F, Vajifdar BU, Eccleshall SC, et al. Measurement of radial artery spasm using an automatic pullback device. Catheter Cardiovasc Interv. 2001 Dec;54(4):437-41.

Sakai H, Ikeda S, Harada T, et al. Limitations of successive transradial approach in the same arm: the Japanese experience. Catheter Cardiovasc Interv. 2001 Oct;54(2): 204-8.

Esente P, Giambartolomei A, Simons AJ, et al. Overcoming vascular anatomic challenges to cardiac catheterization by the radial artery approach: specific techniques to improve success. Catheter Cardiovasc Interv 2002 Jun; 56(2): 207-11.

Barbeau GR. Radial loop and extreme vessel tortuosity in the transradial approach: advantage of hydrophilic-coated guidewires and catheters. Catheter Cardiovasc Interv. 2003 Aug;59(4):442-50.

Kiemeneij F, Vajifdar BU, Eccleshall SC, et al. Evaluation of a spasmolytic cocktail to prevent radial artery spasm during coronary procedures. Catheter Cardiovasc Interv. 2003 Mar;58(3):281-4.

Calvino-Santos RA, Vazquez-Rodriguez JM, Salgado-Fernandez J. Management of iatrogenic radial artery perforation. Catheter Cardiovasc Interv. 2004 Jan;61(1):74-8.

Edmundson A, Mann T. Nonocclusive radial artery injury resulting from transradial coronary interventions: radial artery IVUS. J Invasive Cardiol. 2005 Oct;17(10):528-31.

Coppola J, Patel T, Kwan T, et al. Nitroglycerin, nitroprusside, or both, in preventing radial artery spasm during transradial artery catheterization. J Invasive Cardiol. 2006 Apr;18(4):155-8.

Kiemeneij F. Prevention and management of radial artery spasm. J Invasive Cardiol. 2006 Apr;18(4):159-60.

Valsecchi O, Vassileva A, Musumeci G, et al. Failure of transradial approach during coronary interventions: anatomic considerations. Catheter Cardiovasc Interv. 2006 Jun; 67(6):870-8.

# PATEL'S ALGORITHM FOR ADDRESSING LOOPS & CURVATURES©

When a challenge is approached one step at a time, it can be surmounted.

After performing over 20,000 transradial procedures, we created an algorithm to describe our methodical approach to dealing with loops and curvatures.

This algorithm will help the beginning radialist convert himself into a hard-core operator and will give the hard-core operator additional confidence. ■

# PATEL'S ALGORITHM
## ADDRESSING LOOPS & CURVATURES©

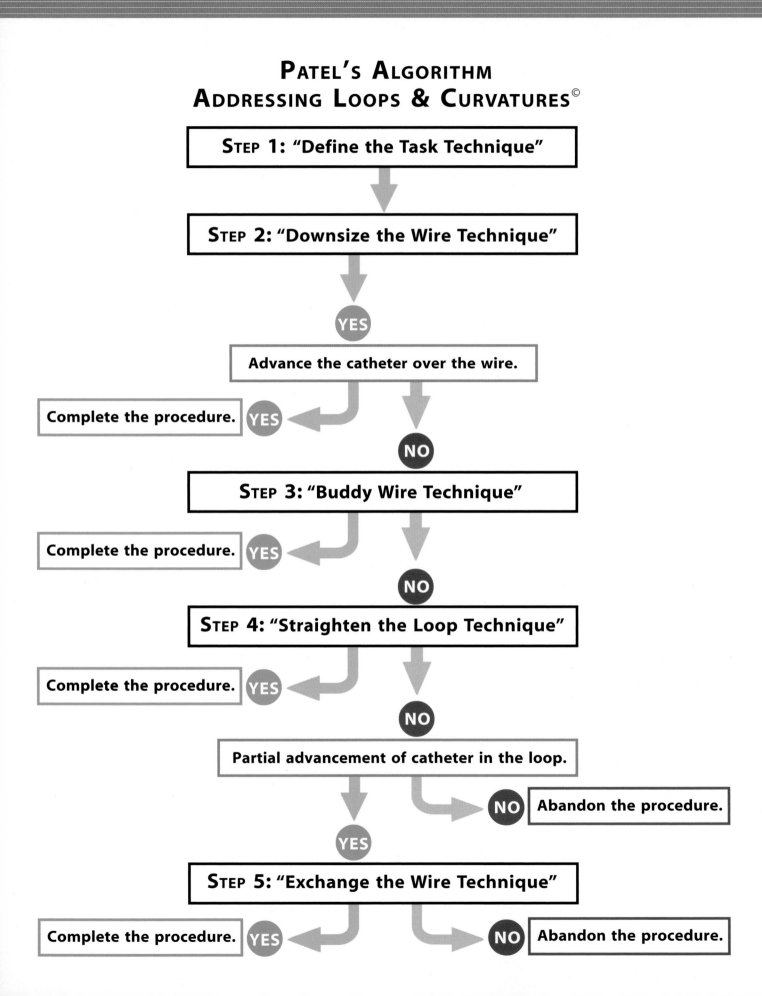

**STEP 1: "Define the Task Technique"**

**STEP 2: "Downsize the Wire Technique"**

YES

Advance the catheter over the wire.

YES — Complete the procedure.

NO

**STEP 3: "Buddy Wire Technique"**

YES — Complete the procedure.

NO

**STEP 4: "Straighten the Loop Technique"**

YES — Complete the procedure.

NO

Partial advancement of catheter in the loop.

NO — Abandon the procedure.

YES

**STEP 5: "Exchange the Wire Technique"**

YES — Complete the procedure.

NO — Abandon the procedure.

# STEP 1: "DEFINE THE TASK TECHNIQUE"

The first step is to obtain a view of the loop that best defines the loop. The view that is chosen can then be used as a "road map" for further maneuvers. In this set, View 3 best defined the loop.

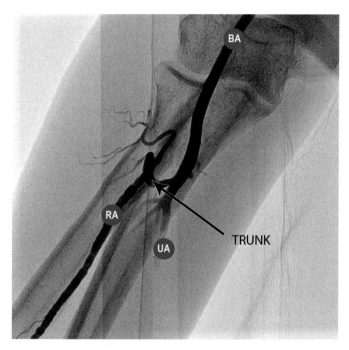

**VIEW 1**

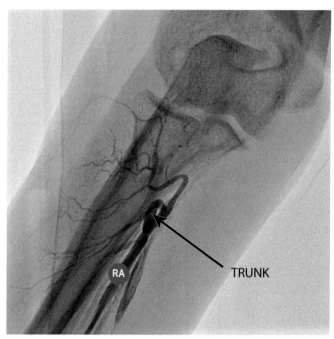

**VIEW 2**

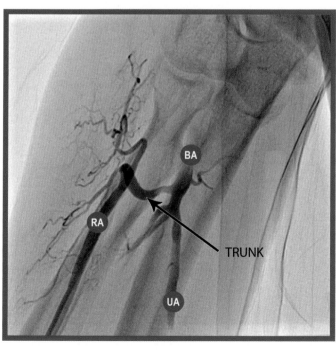

**VIEW 3**

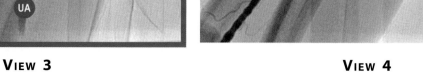

**VIEW 4**

# STEP 1: "DEFINE THE TASK TECHNIQUE"

Here is another example of a loop. In this set, View 4 best defined the loop and was used as a "road map" for further maneuvers.

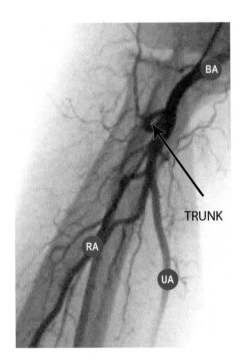

**VIEW 1**

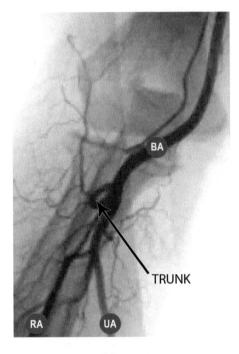

**VIEW 2**

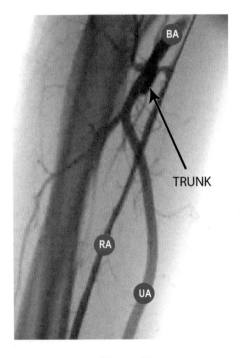

**VIEW 3**

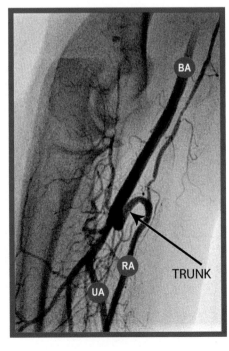

**VIEW 4**

# STEP 2: "DOWNSIZE THE WIRE TECHNIQUE"

Thin, flexible, and hydrophilic guidewires (0.014" PTCA guidewires or Terumo Glidewires) should be used in place of standard guidewires to cross the loop. The terminal end of the wire (especially of 0.014" PTCA guidewires) can be shaped to the angle of the loop to facilitate crossing. When these guidewires cross the loop and are parked as proximal as possible, catheters can be advanced over them. The disadvantage of these guidewires is that they provide poor support for the catheters. If the guidewire does not cross the loop, abandon the procedure.

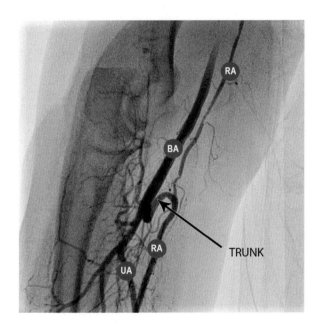

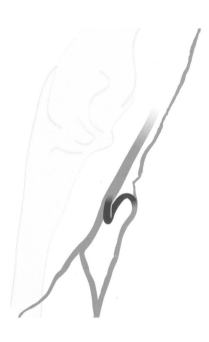

Loop due to the radiocubital trunk.

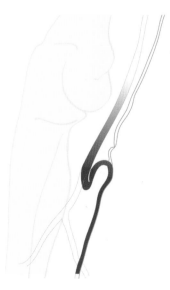

This was the preferred route for completing the procedure.

# STEP 2: "DOWNSIZE THE WIRE TECHNIQUE"

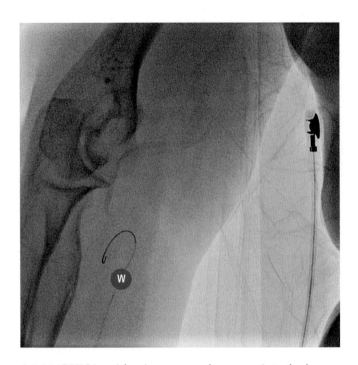

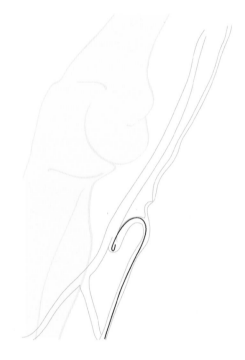

A 0.014" PTCA guidewire was used to negotiate the loop.

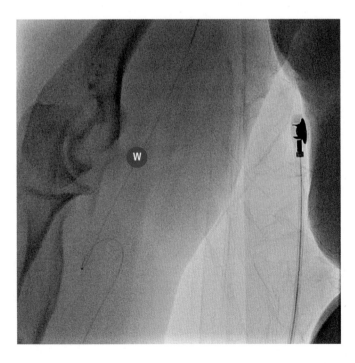

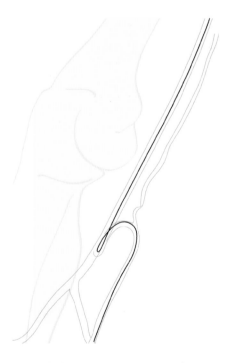

A 0.014" PTCA guidewire was advanced into the brachial artery after successfully crossing the loop. Then the catheter was advanced and the procedure was completed in the usual fashion. In case the catheter fails to advance on a single 0.014" PTCA guidewire, proceed to the next step.

# STEP 3: "BUDDY WIRE TECHNIQUE"

This is used if a single 0.014″ PTCA guidewire fails to help the catheter cross the loop. Additional 0.014″ PTCA guidewires (up to three) can be used in such cases to complete the procedure. These guidewires should be parked as proximal as possible after crossing the loop. The catheter can then be advanced over these wires.

The rationale is that the buddy wire(s) provides additional support and helps the catheter advance farther into the arterial system.

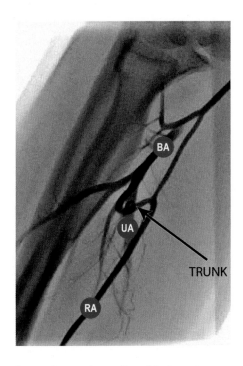
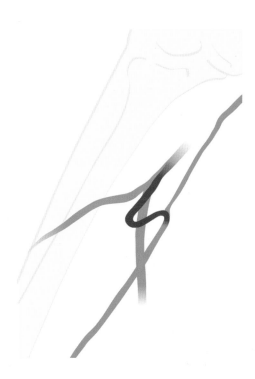

Loop due to the radiocubital trunk.

# STEP 3: "BUDDY WIRE TECHNIQUE"

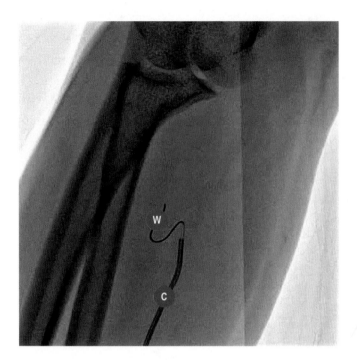

A 0.014" PTCA guidewire was advanced into the loop.

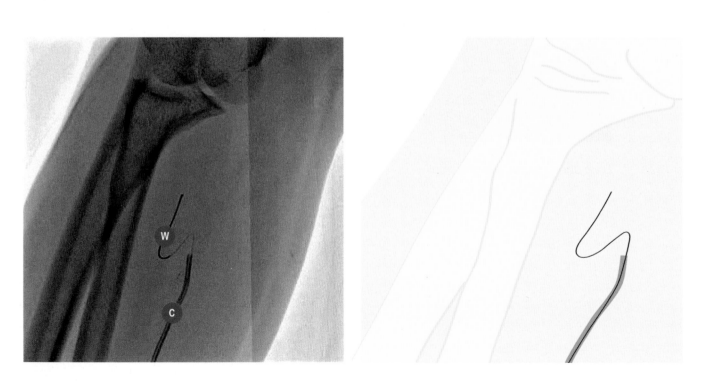

The single 0.014" PTCA guidewire was parked in the brachial artery, but the catheter failed to advance over the guidewire.

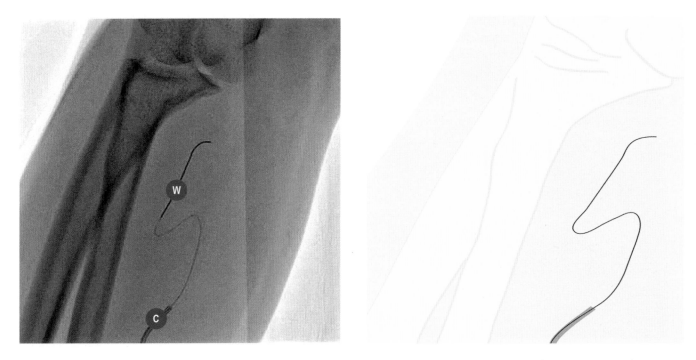

Another 0.014" PTCA guidewire (buddy wire) was used and was parked in the brachial artery after crossing the loop.

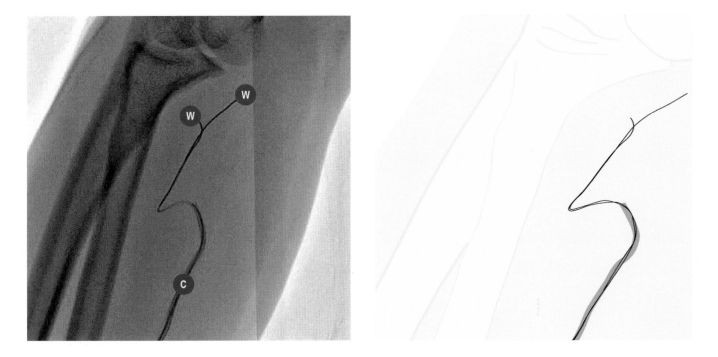

The catheter was then able to advance over these two 0.014" PTCA guidewires.

# STEP 3: "BUDDY WIRE TECHNIQUE"

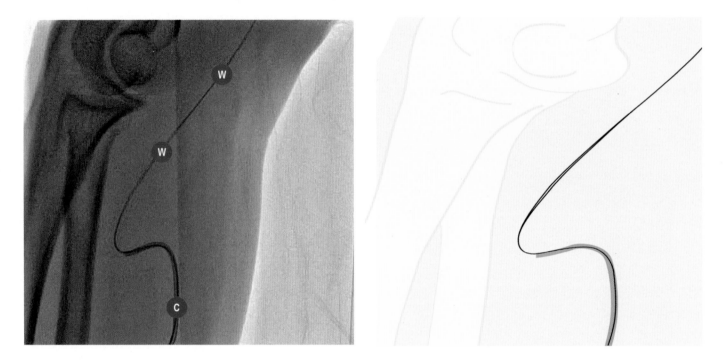

The procedure was completed in the usual fashion. If required, additional 0.014" PTCA guidewires can be used if two guidewires do not provide adequate support. If this technique fails, proceed to the next step.

# STEP 4: "STRAIGHTEN THE LOOP TECHNIQUE"

### Steps

- Push the catheter as far as possible into the loop.
- Pull back the entire assembly (catheter and guidewire(s)) slightly to straighten the loop.
- Advance the catheter on the relatively straight course of the loop.

### Rationale

It is easier to advance a catheter on the straight course of an artery's loop. The guidewire and the catheter in the loop grip the artery, allowing it to be straightened.

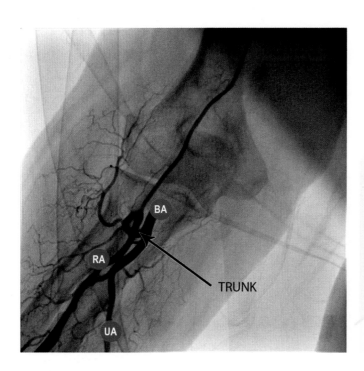
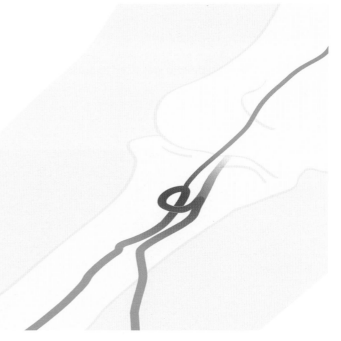

A complex loop of the the radiocubital trunk.

# STEP 4: "STRAIGHTEN THE LOOP TECHNIQUE"

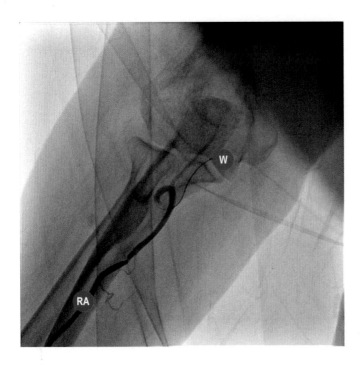

A 0.014" PTCA guidewire was used to cross the loop and was then parked in the brachial artery.

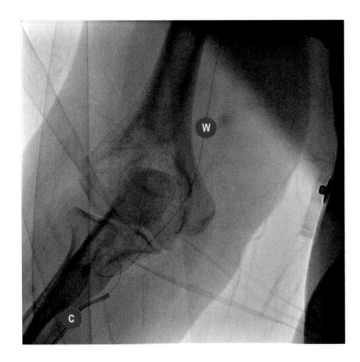

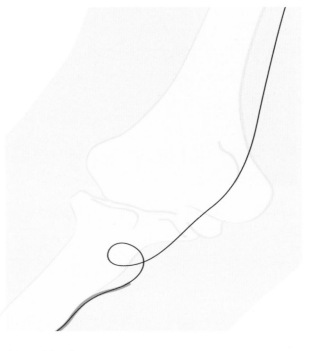

An attempt was made to advance a 4F diagnostic catheter over this guidewire.

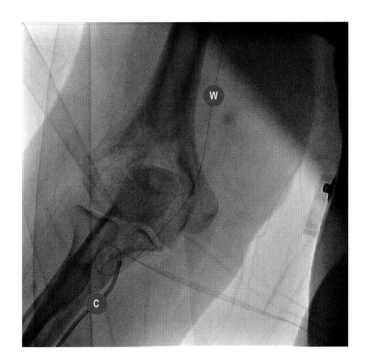

The catheter could negotiate only the initial part of the loop.

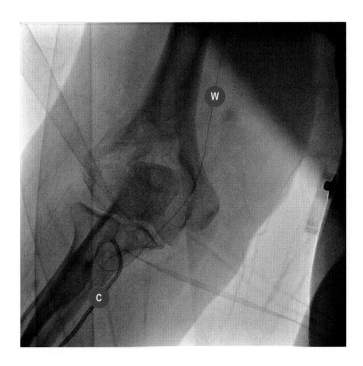

The catheter would not budge farther.

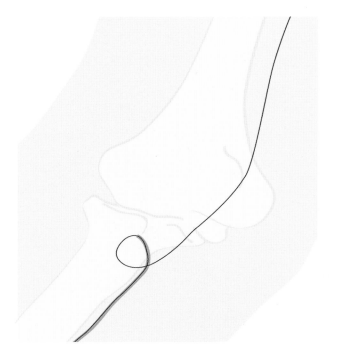

# STEP 4: "STRAIGHTEN THE LOOP TECHNIQUE"

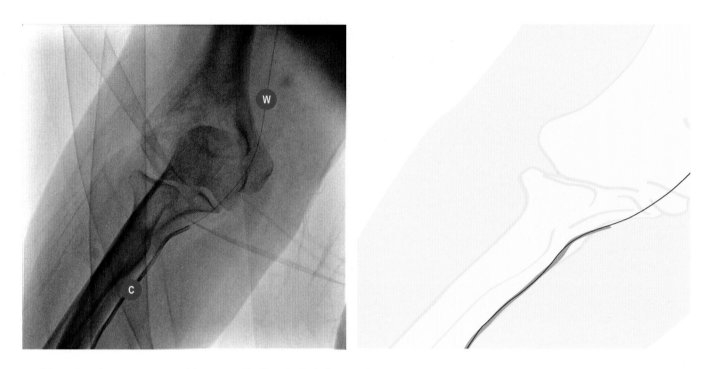

At this point, the entire assembly was pulled back slightly and the loop was straightened.

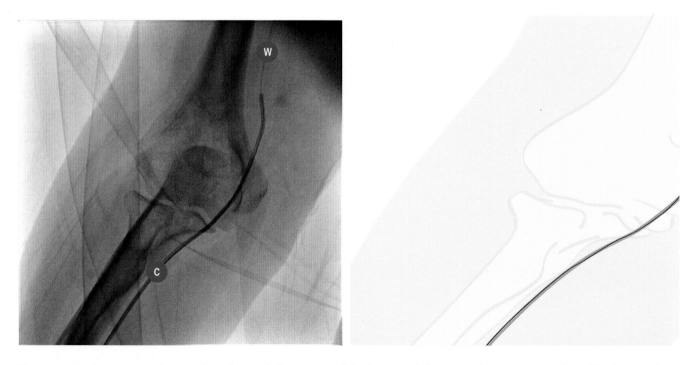

The same catheter was advanced on the straight course of the loop and the procedure was completed in the usual fashion.

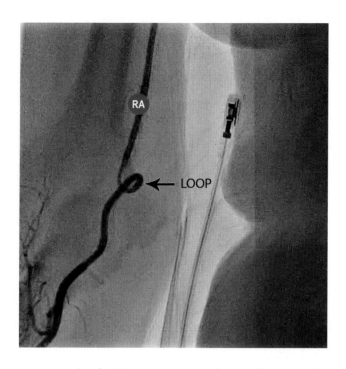

An example of a 360-degree loop of the radial artery (high origin).

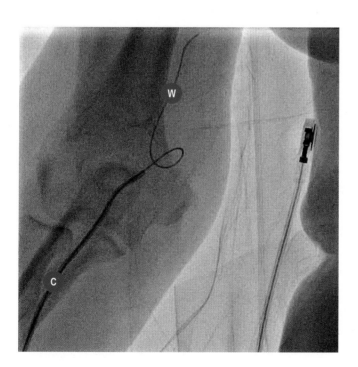
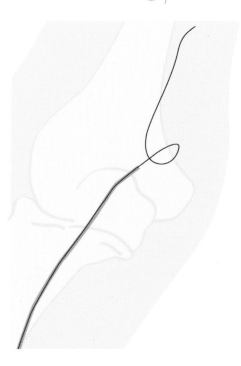

A 0.014" PTCA guidewire was parked in the proximal part of the radial artery after crossing the loop.

# STEP 4: "STRAIGHTEN THE LOOP TECHNIQUE"

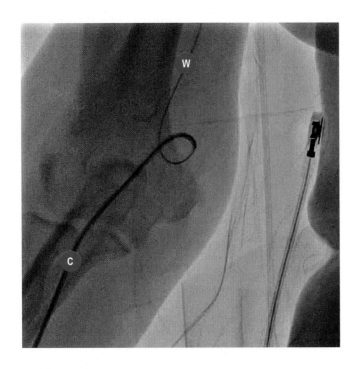

An attempt was made to advance a 5F diagnostic catheter over the 0.014" PTCA guidewire.

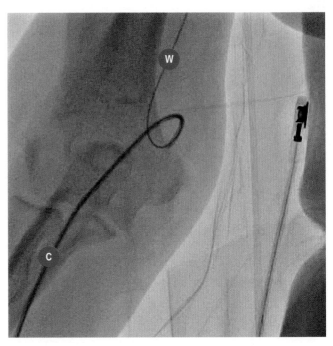

The catheter refused to budge.

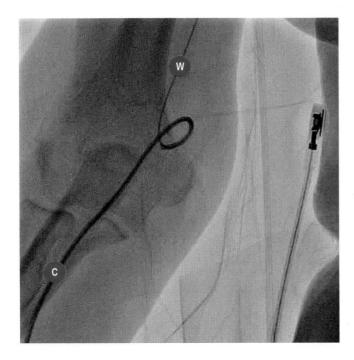

At this point, we tried the "Straighten the Loop Technique."

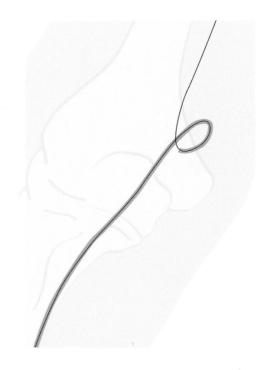

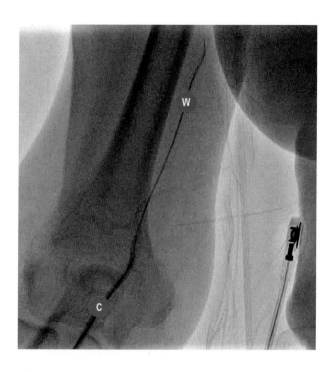
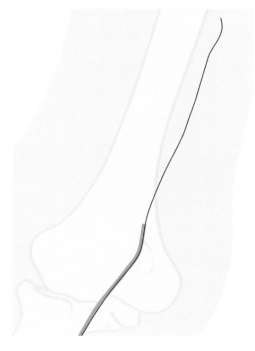

The entire assembly was pulled back and the loop was straightened.

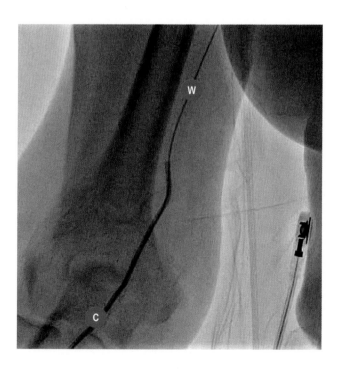
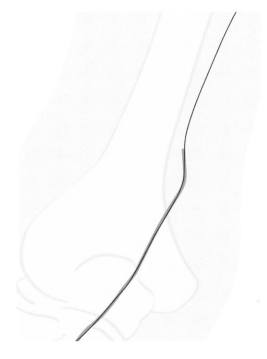

The catheter was advanced easily over the 0.014" PTCA guidewire this time.

## STEP 4: "STRAIGHTEN THE LOOP TECHNIQUE"

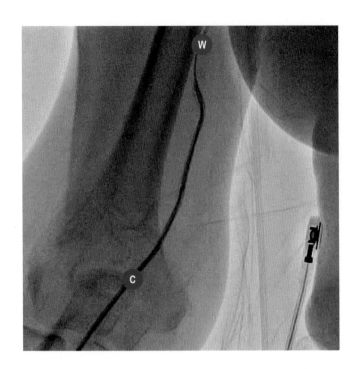

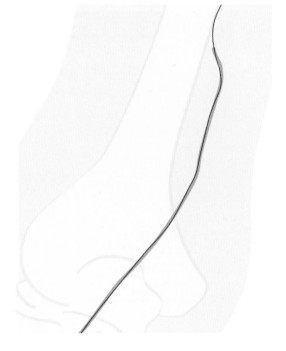

The procedure was completed in the usual fashion.

# STEP 5: "EXCHANGE THE WIRE TECHNIQUE"

This technique is used if the catheter is partly inside the loop, but has not crossed the entire loop and it is difficult to advance it any farther.

## Steps

- Advance the catheter into the loop as far as possible.
- Exchange the thinner guidewire with another guidewire to provide extra support. A 0.014" PTCA guidewire can be exchanged with a Terumo Glidewire, and a Terumo Glidewire can be exchanged with a standard 0.035" guidewire, if necessary.
- Advance the catheter on the new guidewire.
- Avoid using a super-stiff guidewire unless you have crossed the loop and the catheter is well into the proximal arterial segment.

## Rationale

Once inside the loop, the catheter fails to advance because of the poor support of thin guidewires. Moreover, because the catheter is partly inside the loop, a standard 0.035" guidewire has a better chance of negotiating the loop.

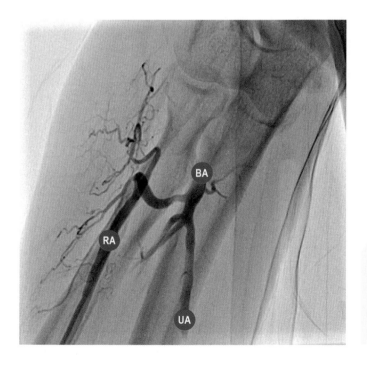
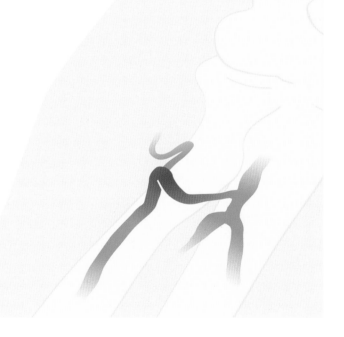

Radiocubital trunk with two right-angle turns.

# STEP 5: "EXCHANGE THE WIRE TECHNIQUE"

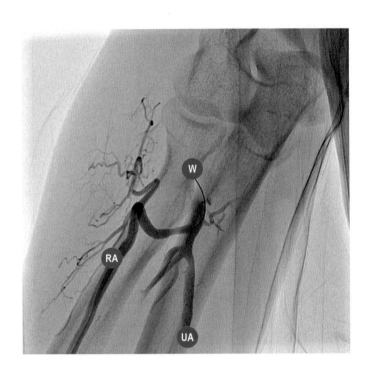

A 0.014" PTCA guidewire crossed the loop easily and was parked in the brachial artery.

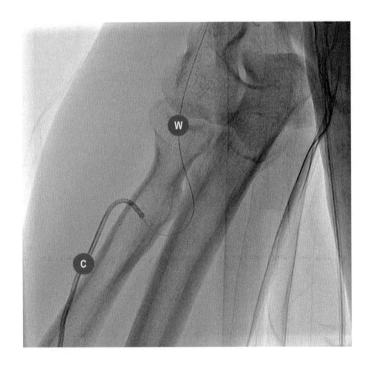
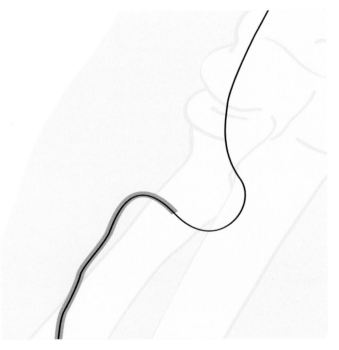

A 5F diagnostic catheter was advanced over the 0.014" PTCA guidewire and it refused to budge.

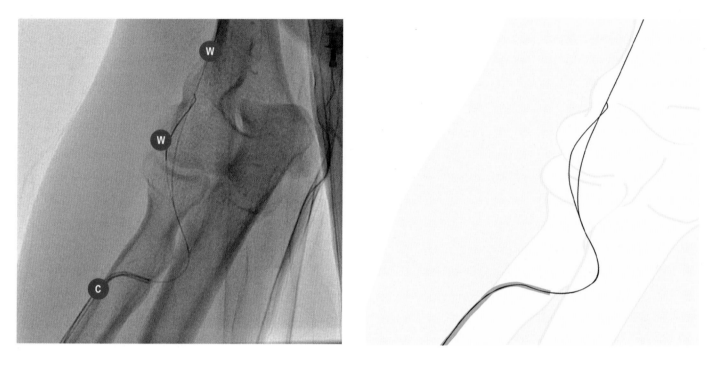

Even a buddy 0.014" PTCA guidewire failed to provide enough support for the catheter to cross the loop.

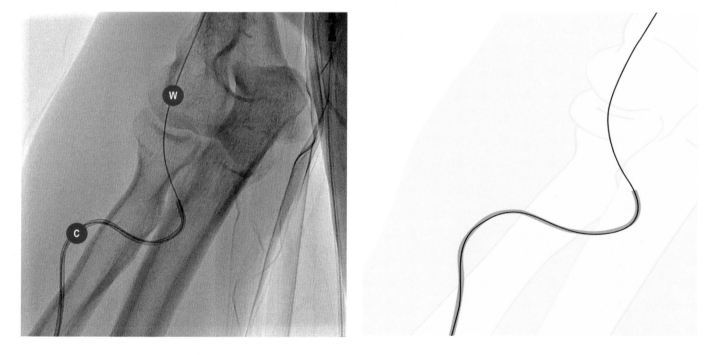

Because the catheter was partly inside the loop, the 0.014" PTCA guidewire was exchanged with a Terumo Glidewire to provide extra support for the catheter.

## STEP 5: "EXCHANGE THE WIRE TECHNIQUE"

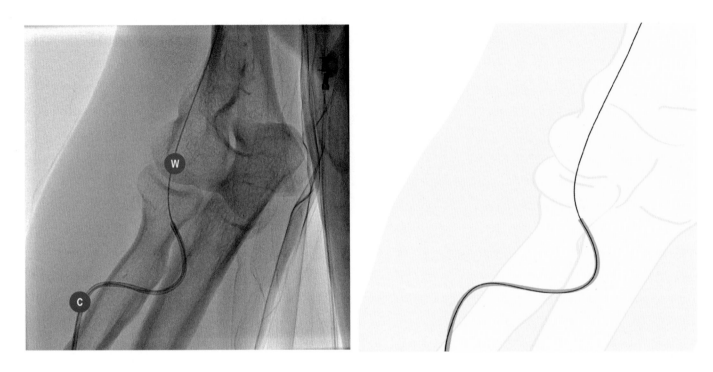

The catheter was advanced a little farther, but refused to budge beyond the distal part of the brachial artery.

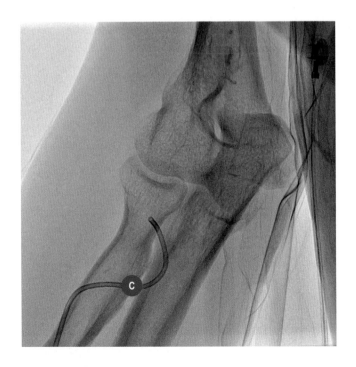
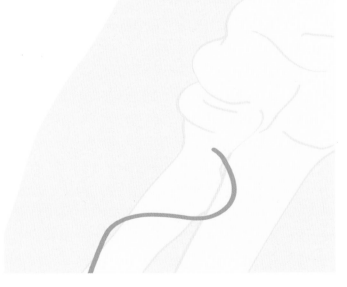

The Terumo Glidewire was removed.

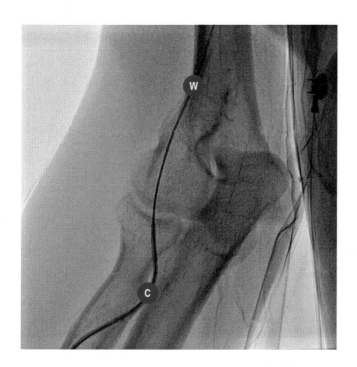

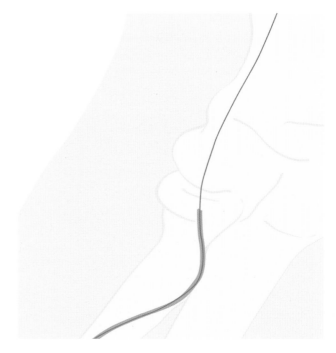

A standard 0.035" guidewire was inserted into the catheter and was parked in the proximal part of the brachial artery.

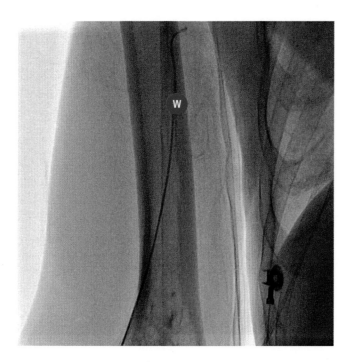

The standard guidewire in situ.

# STEP 5: "EXCHANGE THE WIRE TECHNIQUE"

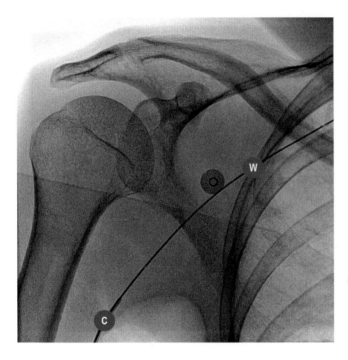

The procedure was completed in the usual fashion.

# BRACHIAL TO SUBCLAVIAN REGION: UNDERSTANDING THE ISSUES

In this chapter, we have discussed the normal and relevant abnormal anatomy of the right and left subclavian regions. You will find clear examples of total occlusions of the subclavian and innominate arteries, and subclavian tortuosities and stenosis. This chapter lays the foundation for the following chapter. If you understand this anatomy, you can address the issues confidently. ■

## NORMAL ANATOMY OF THE BRACHIAL TO SUBCLAVIAN REGION

The artery that supplies the upper limb continues as a single trunk from its origin down to the elbow. But different parts of the artery have different names, depending on the regions through which they pass. The part of the artery that extends from its origin to the lateral border of the first rib is the subclavian artery. Beyond this point, to the lower border of axilla, is the axillary artery. From that point, to the bend of the elbow, is the brachial artery.

The anatomy differs on the right and left sides as far as the subclavian artery is concerned. The anatomy of the other two arteries is the same on each side.

On the right side, the subclavian artery arises from the innominate artery. On the left side, it arises from the arch of the aorta. Therefore, they differ in length, direction, and their relationship to neighboring structures in their proximal parts.

## Normal Brachial Artery Anatomy

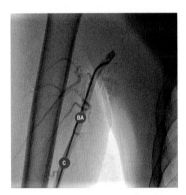

Normal brachial artery anatomy.

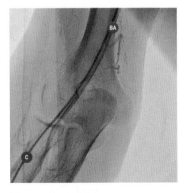

Normal brachial artery anatomy.

## Normal Axillary & Subclavian Anatomy

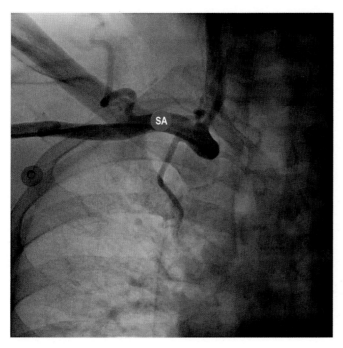

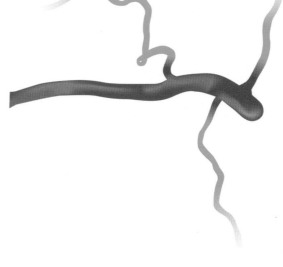

Normal right axillary and subclavian arteries.

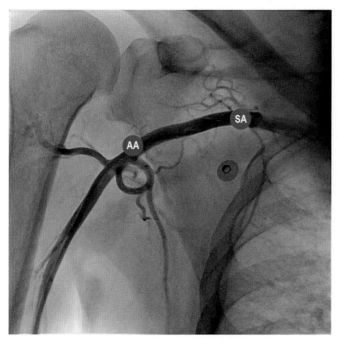

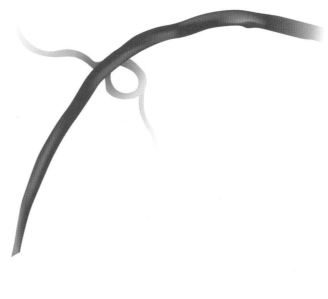

Normal right axillary and subclavian arteries.

## Normal Axillary & Subclavian Anatomy

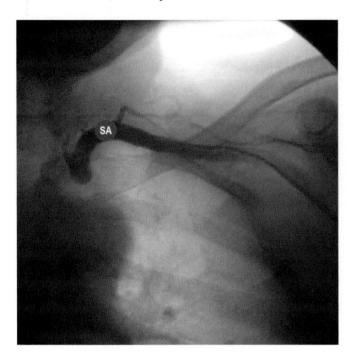

Normal left axillary and subclavian arteries.

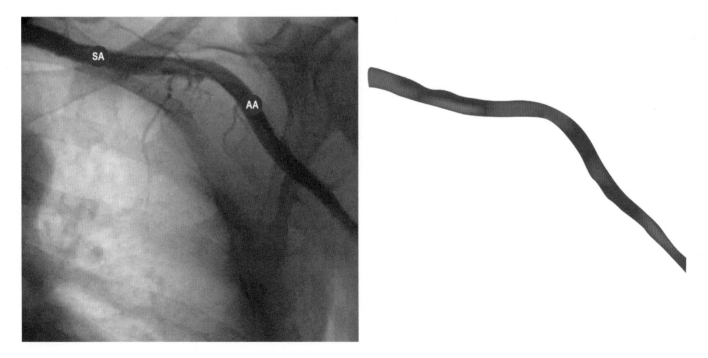

Normal left axillary and subclavian arteries.

# ABNORMAL CALIBER
## Occlusion

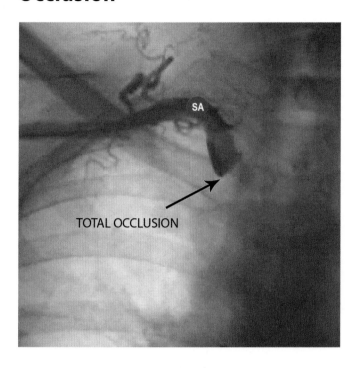

Total occlusion of right subclavian artery. (Note: This patient had a normal Modified Allen's Test.)

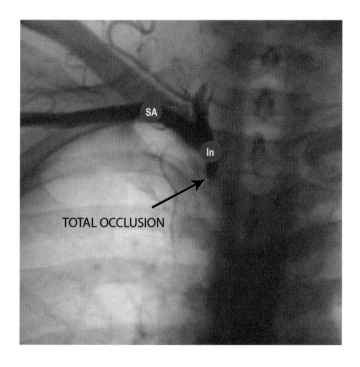

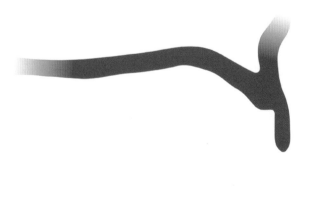

Total occlusion of the distal part of the right innominate artery.

## Occlusion

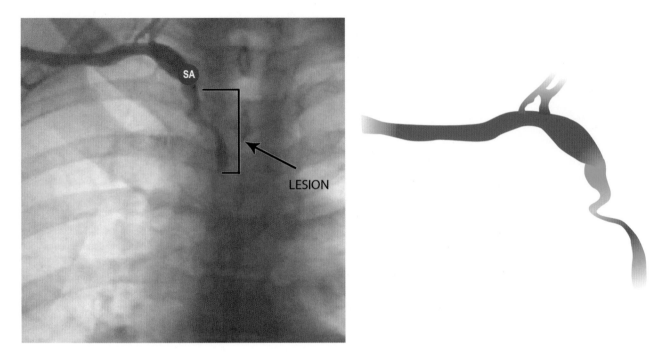

Long-segment stenosis in the proximal part of the right subclavian artery.

# ABNORMAL COURSE
## Tortuosity

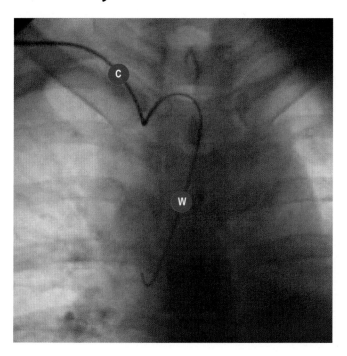

An example of simple tortuosity of the right subclavian artery.

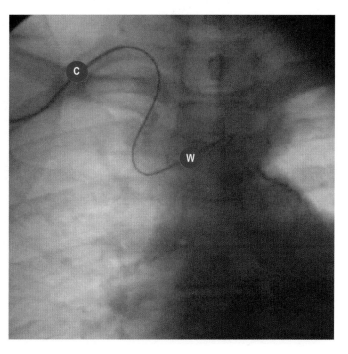

An example of complex tortuosity of the right subclavian artery.

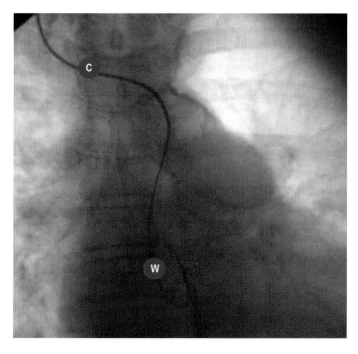

Fluroscopy of the same patient showing tortuosity extending into the innominate artery.

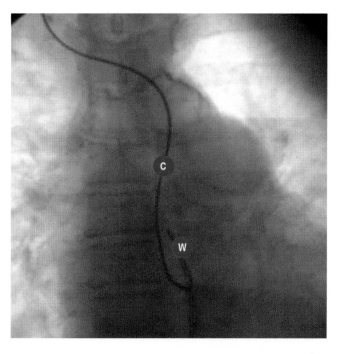

Fluroscopy of the same patient with the catheter positioned in the ascending aorta.

## Tortuosity

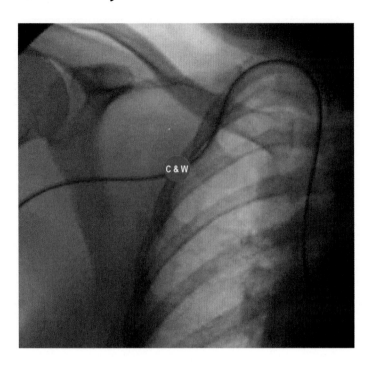

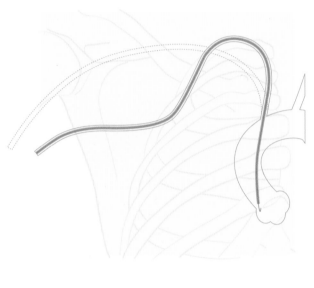

Tortuosity involving the right axillary artery and the right subclavian artery.

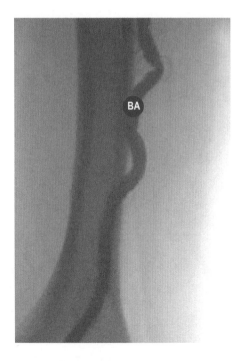

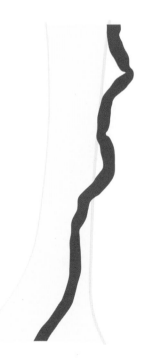

Tortuosity of the right brachial artery.

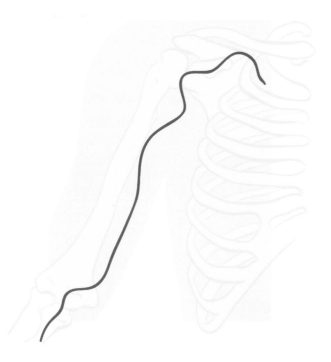

A rare case of tortuosity extending from the radial artery to the subclavian artery. We call this the "Anaconda Loop."

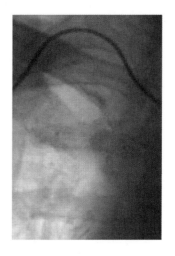

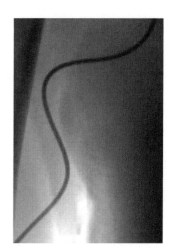

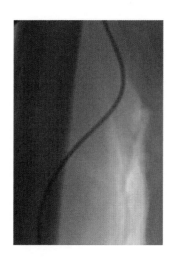

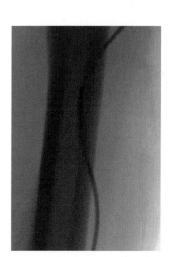

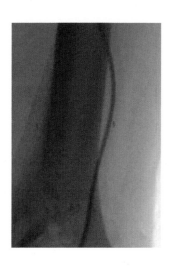

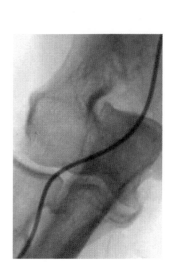

## RECOMMENDED READING

Mewissen MW, Zavitz WR, Lipchik EO. Brachiocephalic vessels in the elderly: technique for catheterization. Radiology. 1989 Mar;170(3 Pt 1):887.

Gilchrist IC. Transradial technical tips. Catheter Cardiovasc Interv. 2000 Mar;49(3):353-4.

Cha KS, Kim MH, Kim HJ. Prevalence and clinical predictors of severe tortuosity of right subclavian artery in patients undergoing transradial coronary angiography. Am J Cardiol. 2003 Nov.15;92(10):1220-2.

# BRACHIAL TO SUBCLAVIAN REGION: ADDRESSING THE ISSUES

In this chapter we have outlined how to best enter the ascending aorta from the right and left radial approach. We have also dealt with subclavian tortuosities and have shown the best ways to approach them by giving appropriate examples.

We always traverse this region under fluorscopic guidance to avoid accidental entry into the vertebral artery, the internal mammary artery, the common carotid artery, or other branches.

Compared to the radial region, the brachial to subclavian region does not pose many challenges to the radialist. The most common situation is the tendency of the guidewire to go into the descending rather than the ascending aorta.

The tortuosity of this region can easily be negotiated using Terumo Glidewires or, rarely, 0.014" PTCA guidewires.

In cases where there is total occlusion of the subclavian artery, we prefer to use the contralateral radial artery or the femoral route for completion of the procedure. ■

# ENTERING THE ASCENDING AORTA

In the majority of cases, the diagnostic catheter and the guidewire enter the ascending aorta effortlessly. However, sometimes they selectively enter the descending aorta. Here we have shown angiograms and schematic drawings to demonstrate how to enter the ascending aorta in such cases.

## Right Radial Artery Approach

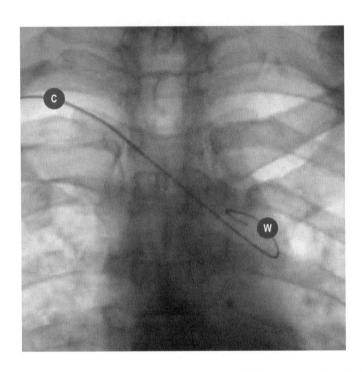 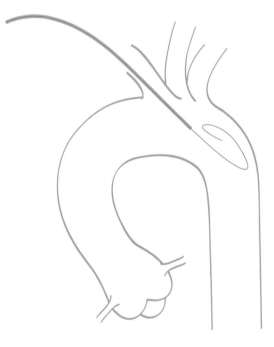

A diagnostic catheter and a standard 0.035" guidewire inside the descending aorta.

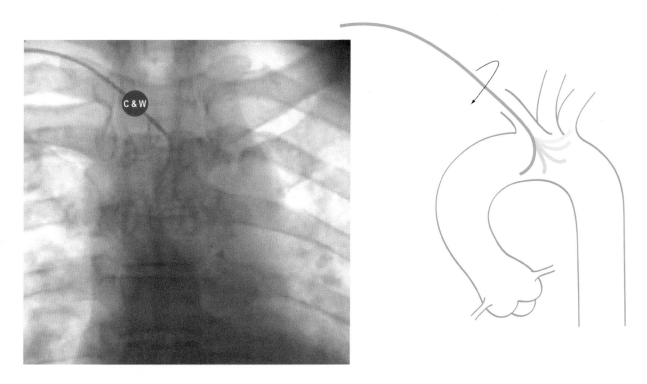

We pulled the guidewire inside the catheter, and then the entire assembly into the aortic arch. We asked the patient to take a deep breath. We rotated the tip of the catheter toward the ascending aorta.

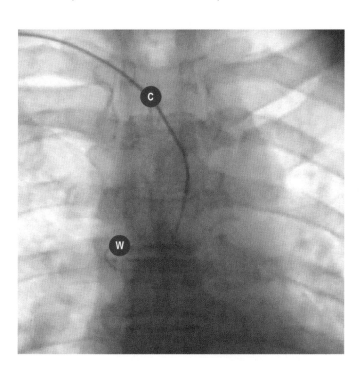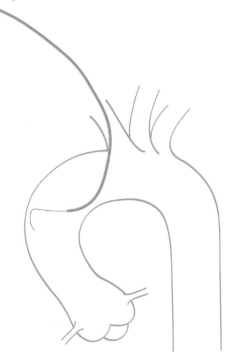

We gently pushed the guidewire into the ascending aorta and advanced the catheter over the guidewire. (In case of difficulty, a LAO 40-degree view helps to enter the ascending aorta.)

## Left Radial Artery Approach

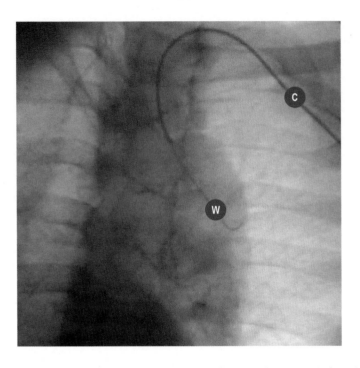

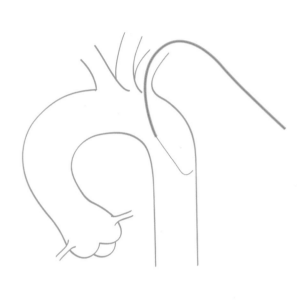

In this case, the procedure was performed from the left radial route. The catheter and the guidewire entered the descending aorta.

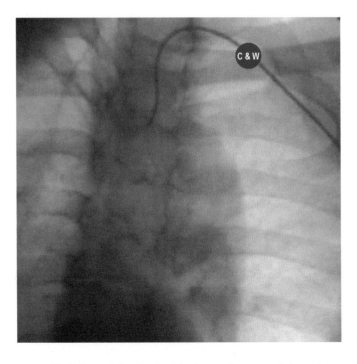

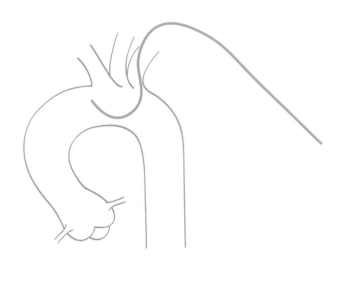

We pulled the guidewire inside the catheter, and then the entire assembly into the aortic arch. We asked the patient to take a deep breath. We rotated the tip of the catheter toward the ascending aorta.

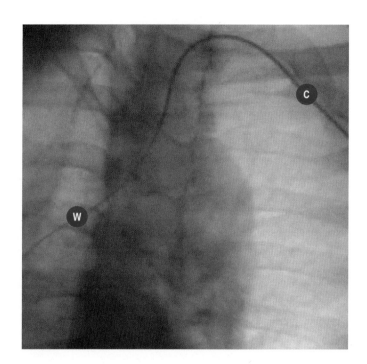
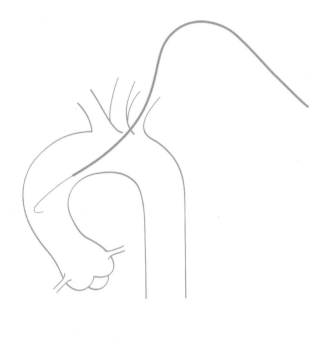

We gently pushed the guidewire into the ascending aorta and advanced the catheter over the guidewire. (In case of difficulty, a LAO 40-degree view helps to enter the ascending aorta.)

# TORTUOSITY

Subclavian tortuosity is easy to negotiate even with standard 0.035" guidewires because the caliber of the artery is large. In challenging cases, switch to a Terumo Glidewire or, rarely, to 0.014" PTCA guidewire. Once the guidewire has reached the ascending aorta, the catheter can be advanced over the guidewire in the usual fashion. In very challenging cases, pull the entire assembly back slightly to straighten the guidewire and then advance the catheter.

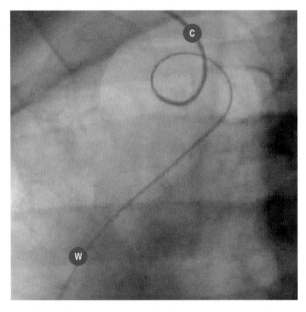

A case of tortuosity of the subclavian artery. A standard 0.035" guidewire was used to cross the tortuosity.

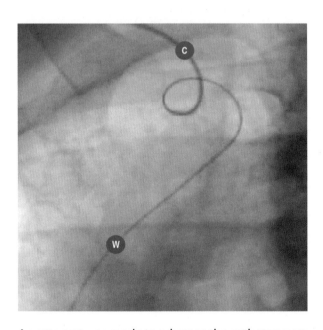

An attempt was made to advance the catheter over the guidewire, but it refused to budge.

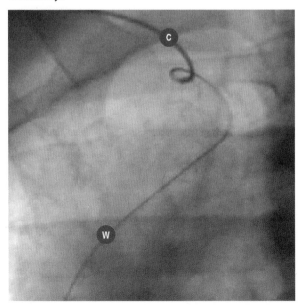

We pulled back the entire assembly to straighten the guidewire.

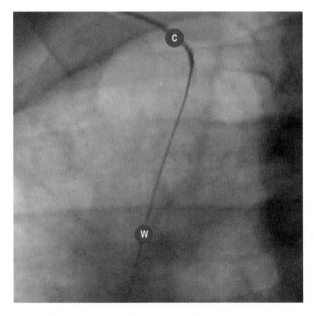

The catheter was easily advanced over the guidewire and the procedure was completed in the usual fashion.

# REMEMBER

- Always use fluroscopic guidance to enter the ascending aorta from the axillary artery. It prevents entry into other important branches.

- Handle tortuosities very gently. Avoid pushing maneuvers or the artery can dissect.

- If a standard 0.035" guidewire fails to negotiate the tortuosity, switch to a Terumo hydrophilic wire. If that fails, a 0.014" PTCA guidewire with the support of a Judkins right diagnostic catheter can do the job.

- Sometimes the standard 0.035" guidewire enters the ascending aorta, but even a gentle push of the catheter does not help it enter completely. Here, a gentle pullback of the assembly (the guidewire and the catheter) can usually straighten the tortuosity to allow easy passage of the catheter into the ascending aorta.

- Asking the patient to take a deep breath partially straightens the subclavian tortuosity and makes for easy entry into the ascending aorta.

- Avoid using super-stiff guidewires unless the catheter tip is inside the ascending or the descending aorta to prevent dissection in the subclavian region.

## RECOMMENDED READING

Caputo RP, Simons A, Giambartolomei A, et al. Transradial cardiac catheterization in elderly patients. Catheter Cardiovasc Interv. 2000 Nov;51(3):287-90.

Gilchrist IC. Transradial technical tips. Catheter Cardiovasc Interv. 2000 Mar;49(3):353-4.

Cha KS, Kim MH, Kim HJ. Prevalence and clinical predictors of severe tortuosity of right subclavian artery in patients undergoing transradial coronary angiography. Am J Cardiol. 2003 Nov.15;92(10):1220-2.

# INNOMINATE-ARCH JUNCTION: UNDERSTANDING & ADDRESSING THE ISSUES

In this chapter, we have discussed the normal anatomy of the region and we have shown clear examples of different loops. These loops are actually the abnormal curves that occur as the result of dilation and distortion of the innominate-arch junction.

In very rare situations, you may also come across a congenital loop where the retro-esophageal right subclavian artery arises from the descending aorta.

The drawings in this chapter are schematic representations of the relevant anatomy. ∎

# NORMAL ANATOMY OF THE INNOMINATE-ARCH JUNCTION

The innominant-arch junction is unique to transradial procedures. Here the catheters and guidewires must take an obtuse-angle turn to enter into the ascending aorta.

In cases of normal anatomy, the turn is smooth and does not pose challenges in performing diagnostic or interventional procedures. In cases of abnormal anatomy due to dilation and/or distortion of the aorta, the procedure requires judicious use of guidewires (Terumo Glidewires, standard 0.035" guidewires, and super-stiff guidewires) and catheters (unusual curves, if necessary) to complete the procedure.

## Normal Innominate-Arch Junction Anatomy

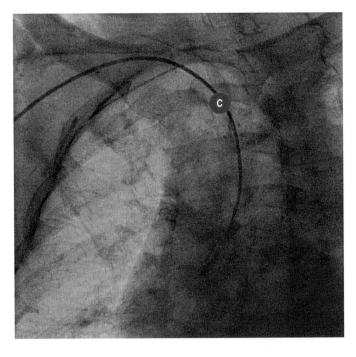
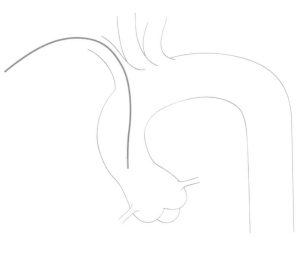

Normal anatomy of the innominate-arch junction. Note the smooth curve at the junction.

# ABNORMAL ANGLE OF THE INNOMINATE-ARCH JUNCTION
## Loops & Curvatures

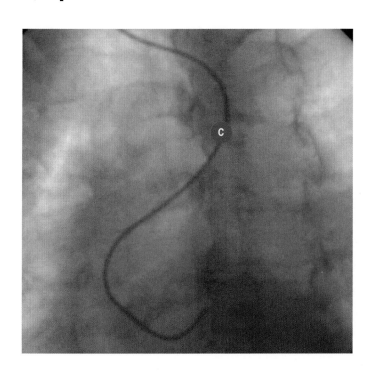

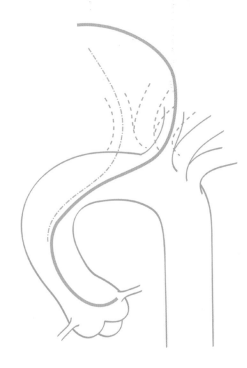

A "Z Loop" of the catheter due to dilation and distortion at the innominate-arch junction. Dotted lines show the normal anatomy.

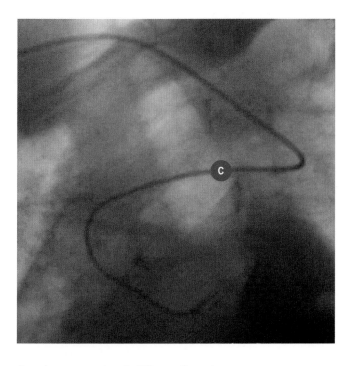

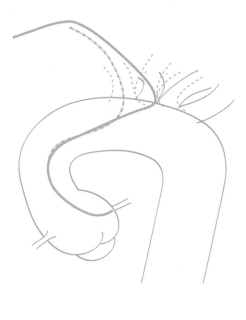

Another example of a "Z Loop."

## Loops & Curvatures

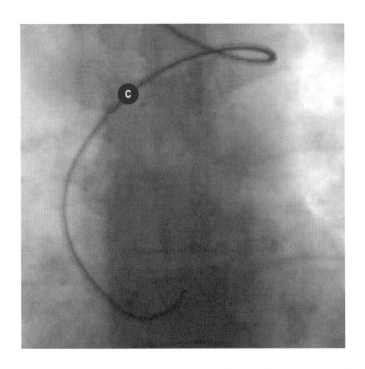

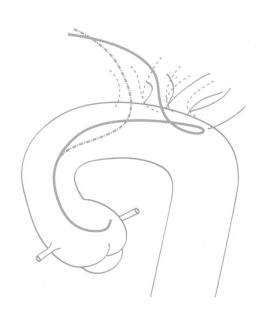

A "Roller-Coaster Loop" due to more advanced dilation and distortion at the innominate-arch junction.

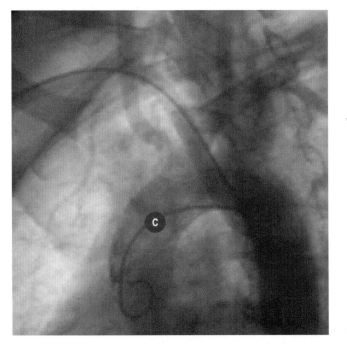

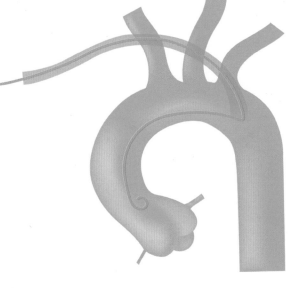

A "Cobra Loop" due to arteria lusoria. The schematic drawing shows the aortogram in the LAO 40-degree view.

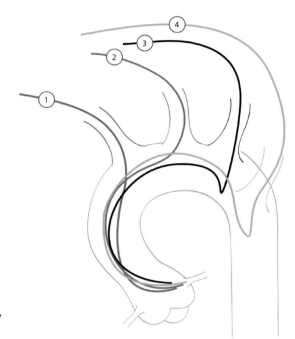

1. Normal anatomy
2. Z Loop
3. Roller-Coaster Loop
4. Cobra Loop

A schematic drawing showing the different loops that are formed when the normal innominate-arch junction is distorted.

## Loops & Curvatures

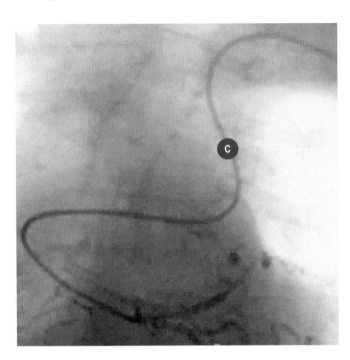

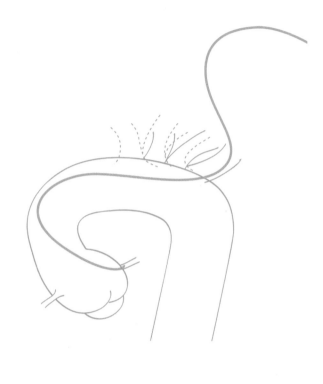

A "Sigma Loop" on the left-radial artery approach due to abnormal anatomy.

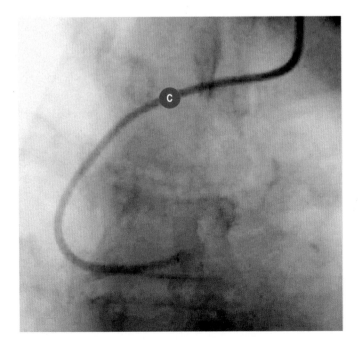

Magnified view of the distal part of the catheter in the same patient.

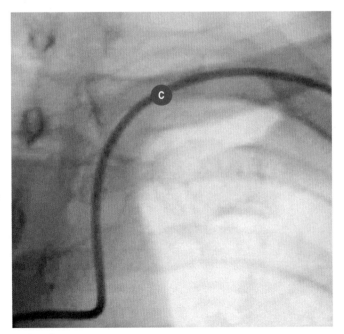

Magnified view of the proximal part of the catheter in the same patient.

# ARTERIA LUSORIA: THE RIGHT TRANSRADIAL APPROACH

In over 20,000 transradial cases, we have come across arteria lusoria only twenty-one times, so it is very rare. But we have developed a protocol to work through this situation. It is divided into two parts: 1) entering the ascending aorta through arteria lusoria and, 2) the cannulation of the coronary arteries.

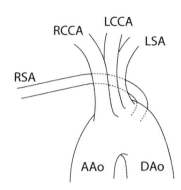

## 1 ENTERING THE ASCENDING AORTA

### Step 1

The catheter and guidewire have a tendency to enter the descending aorta. If this happens, withdraw the catheter and the guidewire together as an assembly.

After asking the patient to take deep breath, gently push the 0.035" standard guidewire. If the guidewire enters the ascending aorta effortlessly, you can then push the catheter over the guidewire.

### Step 2

If Step 1 is not successful, keep the guidewire in the descending aorta. Remove the Judkins right or left catheter, or the first catheter you tried. Take a LIMA diagnostic catheter, put it into the descending aorta over the guidewire, and try the same maneuver. In many cases, you will be successful in entering the ascending aorta.

### Step 3

If the LIMA catheter fails, then a SIM catheter can be used to enter the ascending aorta.

### Step 4

If the 0.035" standard guidewire has a tendency to slip into the descending aorta, the second choice is a 0.032" or a 0.025" hydrophilic Terumo Glidewire. The slippery Terumo wire facilitates relatively easy entry into the ascending aorta in challenging situations.

### Note:

- Always work in the 40-degree LAO view.
- Do not use super-stiff guidewires unless you have entered the ascending aorta.

# ARTERIA LUSORIA: THE RIGHT TRANSRADIAL APPROACH

## 2 CANNULATION OF THE CORONARY ARTERIES

Once the guidewire and the catheter are in the ascending aorta, cannulate the left or right coronaries in the usual fashion.

It is relatively easy to cannulate the coronaries. If there is a challenge, follow these steps:

### Step 1

Remove the standard 0.035" guidewire or the Terumo Glidewire, whichever you used first.

### Step 2

Using a 0.035" super-stiff guidewire, make a loop of wire in the ascending aorta, and slowly slide the catheter over it so that you can make a loop of the assembly (catheter and guidewire).

### Step 3

Slowly pull the guidewire slightly inside the mouth of the catheter and pull the assembly back. This usually cannulates the left coronary artery.

For cannulation of the right coronary artery, slowly and gently rotate the assembly clockwise.

For diagnostic procedures, use a Judkins left, Optitorque TIG, or an Amplatz left catheter to cannulate the left coronary ostium. Use a Judkins right or an Amplatz left catheter to cannulate the right coronary ostium.

For intervention in the left coronary arteries, choose any extra back-up guiding catheter as your first choice. If this is not successful, use a Judkins left or an Amplatz left guiding catheter.

For intervention in the right coronary arteries, Amplatz right is the first choice. If this does not succeeed, a Judkins right or an Amplatz left catheter can be used.

### Note:

- At any stage during cannulation of the coronary ostium, do not push too much or the assembly may flip into the descending aorta.

## Summary

These steps may seem complicated, but arteria lusoria is very rare, and patience and perseverance can help you complete the procedure in the usual fashion. If the first few attempts to enter the ascending aorta are unsuccessful, gracefully switch to the left radial or to the femoral route. Do not get discouraged. One day you will beat the learning curve and address this situation effortlessly. ∎

---

### Remember

- The loops occurring in this region are usually acquired loops due to dilation and/or distortion of the aorta—except for arteria lusoria, which is a congenital condition.

- In most cases, loops are easy to tackle if the operator has patience and perseverance.

- Beginning radialists should avoid working through arteria lusoria.

## RECOMMENDED READING

Caputo RP, Simons A, Giambartolomei A, et al. Transradial cardiac catheterization in elderly patients. Catheter Cardiovasc Interv. 2000 Nov;51(3):287-90.

Gilchrist IC. Transradial technical tips. Catheter Cardiovasc Interv. 2000 Mar;49(3):353-4.

Abhaichand RK, Louvard Y, Gobeil JF, et al. The problem of arteria lusoria in the right transradial coronary angiography and angioplasty. Catheter Cardiovasc Interv. 2001 Oct;54(2):196-201.

Grollman JH Jr. The many faces of the anomalous left aortic arch. Catheter Cardiovasc Interv. 2001 Oct;54(2):202-3.

# CANNULATION OF THE CORONARY OSTIA

The device industry has designed the perfect hardware to cannulate the coronary ostia through the femoral route. Unfortunately, this is not yet true for the radial route, although a number of experienced radialists have designed diagnostic and guiding catheters with differently shaped curves.

In this chapter we have shown coronary cannulation using the OPTITORQUE TIG (Terumo) catheter, traditional Judkins diagnostic catheters, and extra back-up guiding catheters. ■

# UNDERSTANDING THE CATHETER'S COURSE: RADIAL VS. FEMORAL

With transfemoral intervention, it does not matter whether the right or the left femoral artery is used for coronary cannulation. But with transradial intervention, there are subtle differences between the right and the left approaches which the following schematic drawings show.

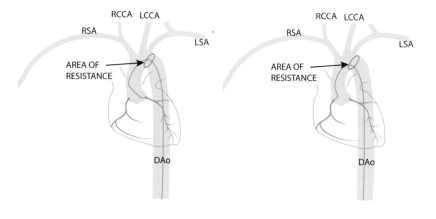

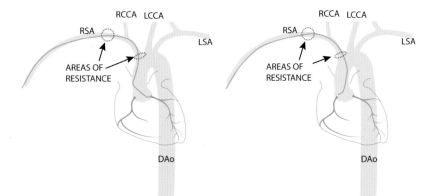

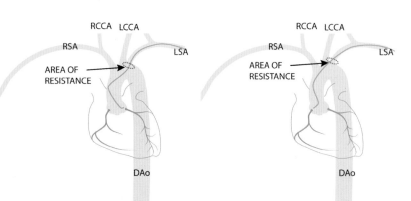

These six, self-explanatory drawings depict the course of the catheter via the transfemoral and the transradial (right and left) approaches. You can see the sites of resistance in the passage of catheters and guidewires through these approaches. These sites of resistance explain the different maneuvers needed to cannulate the coronary arteries. These maneuvers result in the torqueability and steerability of catheters and guidewires through the different configurations of the arterial system.

## Eye-Hand Coordination

For the femoral and the left-radial approach, there is only one level of resistance that affects the torqueability of the catheter. For the right-radial approach, there are two levels of resistance.

In routine cases where there are no significant tortuosities of the subclavian artery and no dilation and/or distortion of the arch, torque may not be a major issue and you can cannulate the coronary ostia without much effort. However, if there is a significant tortuosity at the subclavian level, dilation and/or distortion leading to loops at the arch level, or arteria lusoria, eye-hand coordination is your friend.

This means that rather than being fussy about whether you are performing a clockwise or a counterclockwise rotation, simply keep your eyes on the screen and direct the catheter's tip toward the coronary ostia.

We actually advise operators to play video games regularly to improve their eye-hand coordination!

# DIAGNOSTIC CATHETERS

Various diagnostic catheters are used by operators to cannulate coronary arteries. The 5F OPTITORQUE TIG (Terumo) catheter is our first choice for coronary cannulation. This catheter cannulates both the left and right coronary arteries; a left ventriculogram is also possible with this catheter because it has an additional side hole.

The Judkins catheter is popular for diagnostic studies and it is successful in most cases. However, it requires two different catheters, left and right, to cannulate the left and right coronary arteries, respectively. These catheters must be exchanged over a double-length, standard 0.035" guidewire. In rare cases, we use different catheters for abnormal anatomy (e.g., Amplatz, Multi-Purpose).

## EXAMPLES OF DIAGNOSTIC CATHETERS

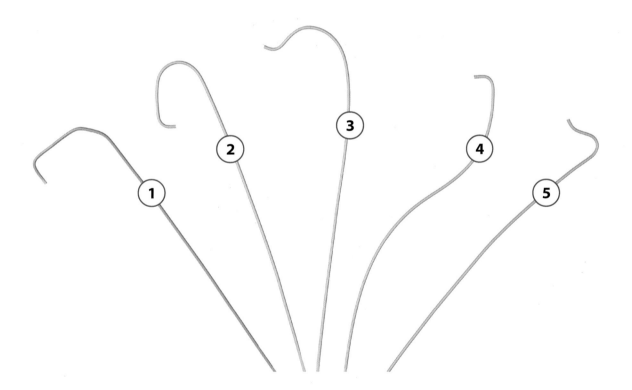

1. OPTITORQUE TIG (Terumo)
2. Judkins Left
3. Amplatz Left
4. Judkins Right
5. Amplatz Right

## CANNULATION WITH DIAGNOSTIC CATHETERS

**OPTITORQUE TIG (TERUMO)**

**Left Coronary Cannulation**

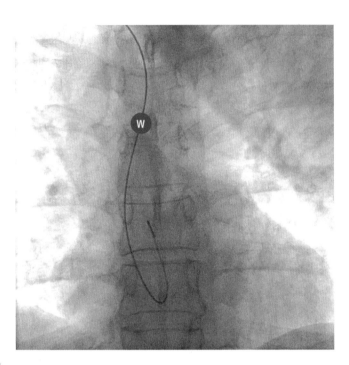

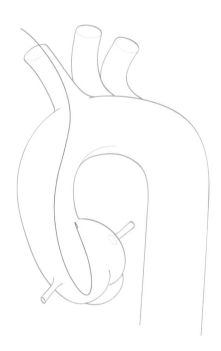

**1** We made a loop of the standard 0.035" guidewire in the aortic root.

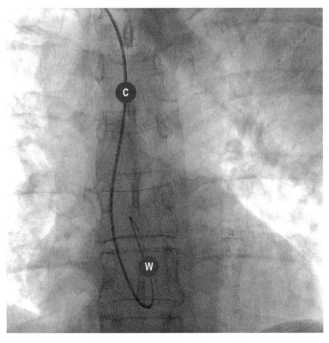

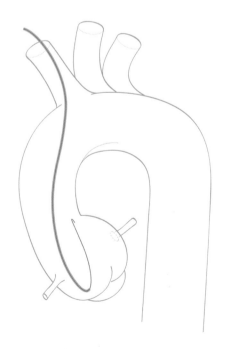

**2** The catheter was advanced over the guidewire.

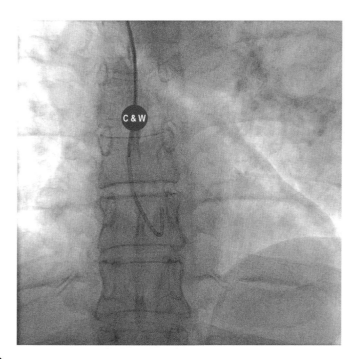
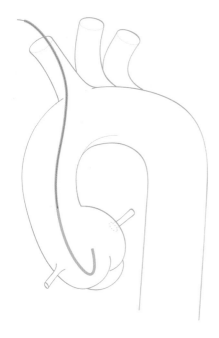

**3** The guidewire was removed.

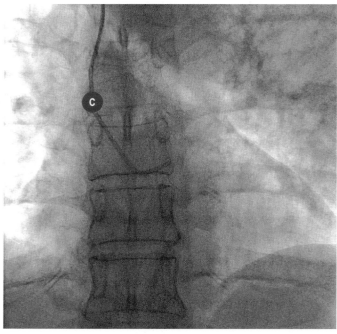
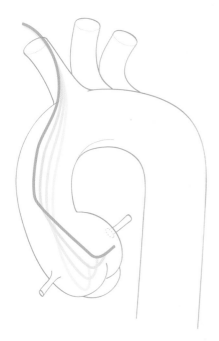

**4** The catheter was pulled back gently and rotated clockwise.

# CANNULATION WITH DIAGNOSTIC CATHETERS

## OPTITORQUE TIG (TERUMO)

### Left Coronary Cannulation

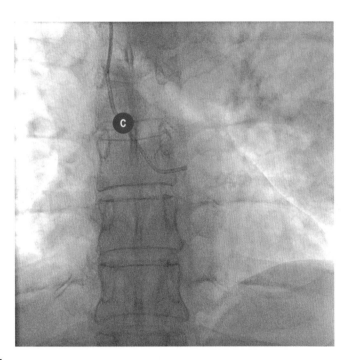

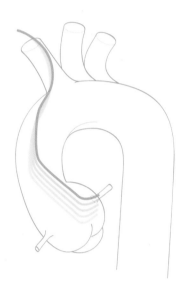

**5** We continued the same movement.

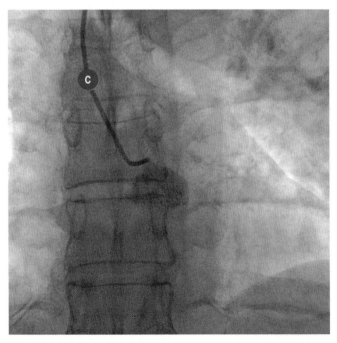

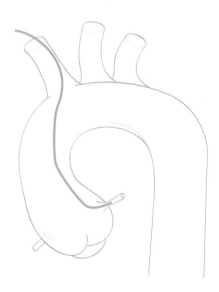

**6** The catheter moved closer to the coronary ostia.

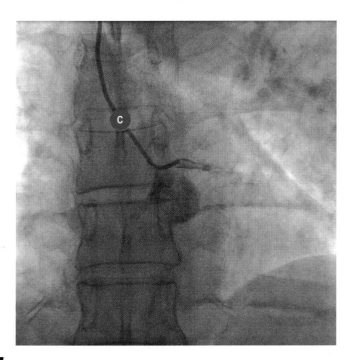
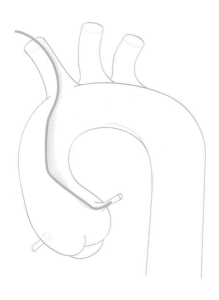

**7** The catheter tip entered the left coronary artery.

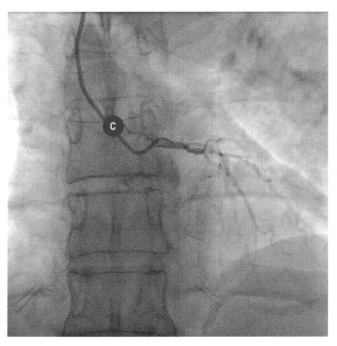
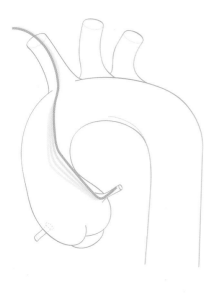

**8** The left coronary artery was cannulated.

# CANNULATION WITH DIAGNOSTIC CATHETERS

## OPTITORQUE TIG (TERUMO)

### Right Coronary Cannulation

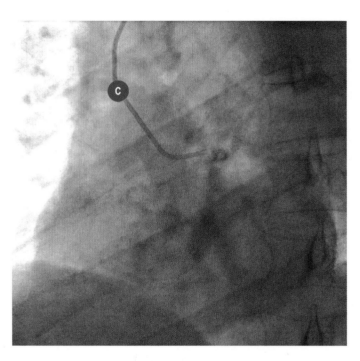
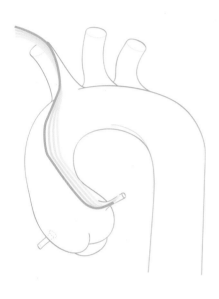

**1** We started disengaging the catheter from the left coronary artery.

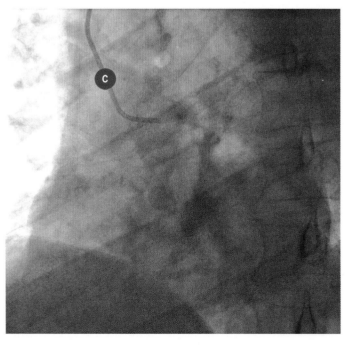
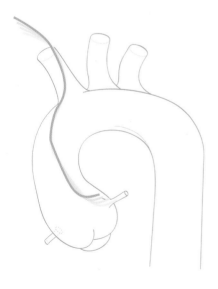

**2** The catheter was disengaged from the left coronary artery.

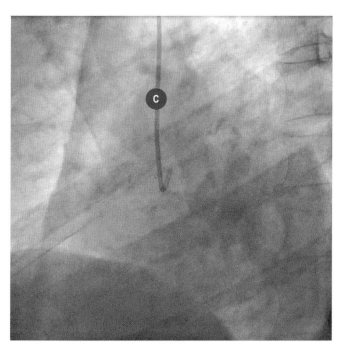
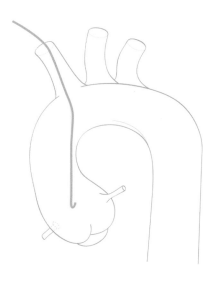

**3** We rotated the catheter clockwise.

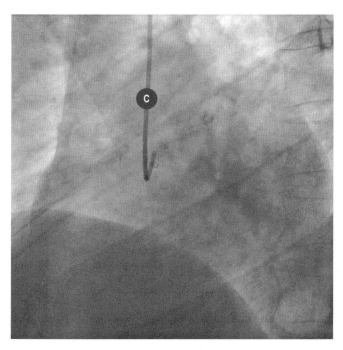
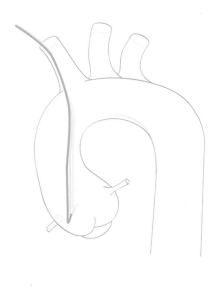

**4** We gently pushed the catheter downward toward the aortic valve.

## CANNULATION WITH DIAGNOSTIC CATHETERS

### OPTITORQUE TIG (TERUMO)

#### Right Coronary Cannulation

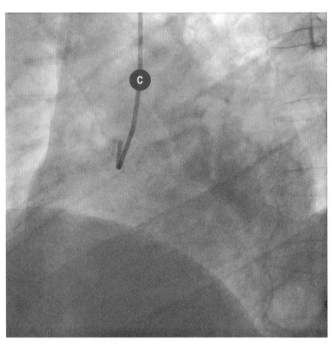
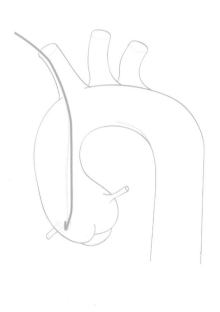

**5** The catheter was pulled back gently and rotated clockwise to cannulate the right coronary artery ostium.

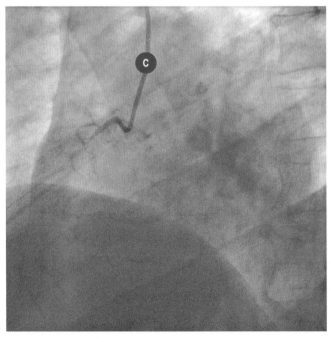
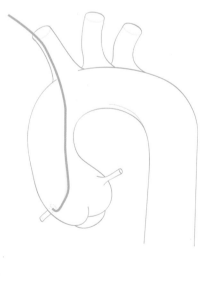

**6** Simultaneous clockwise rotation and gentle pullback resulted in cannulation of the right coronary artery.

**JUDKINS**

### Left Coronary Cannulation

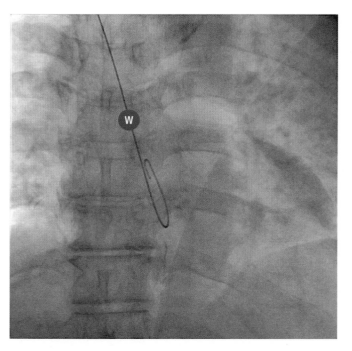
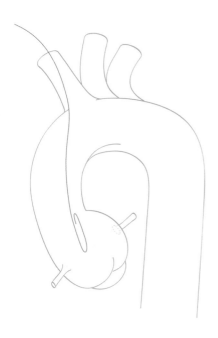

**1** We made a loop of standard 0.035" guidewire in the aortic root.

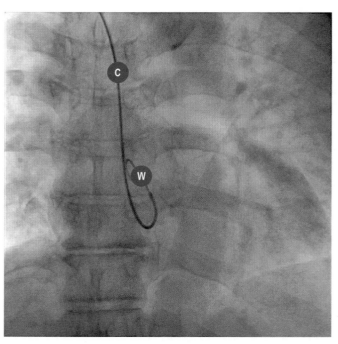
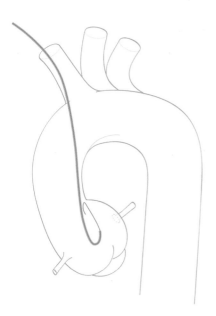

**2** The catheter was advanced over the guidewire.

# CANNULATION WITH DIAGNOSTIC CATHETERS

### JUDKINS

#### Left Coronary Cannulation

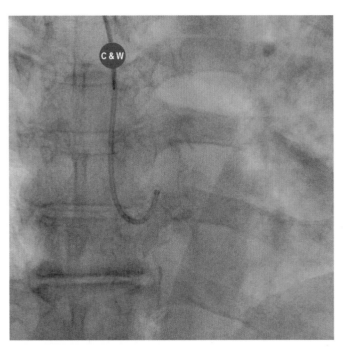

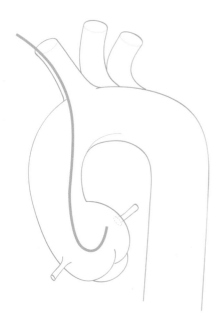

**3** The guidewire was removed.

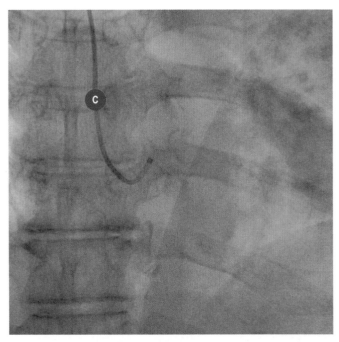

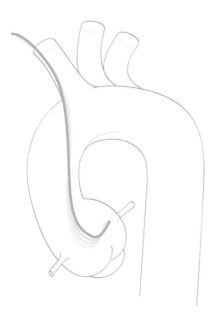

**4** The catheter was pulled back gently and rotated clockwise.

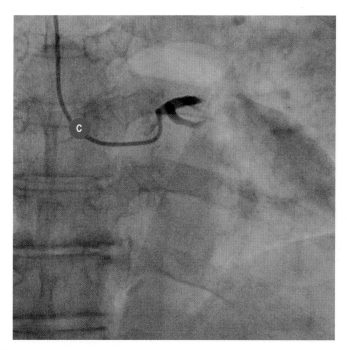 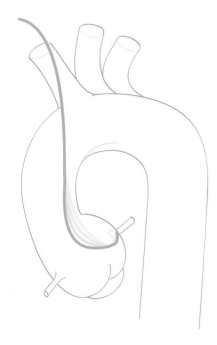

**5** The left coronary artery was cannulated.

# CANNULATION WITH DIAGNOSTIC CATHETERS

### JUDKINS

#### Right Coronary Cannulation

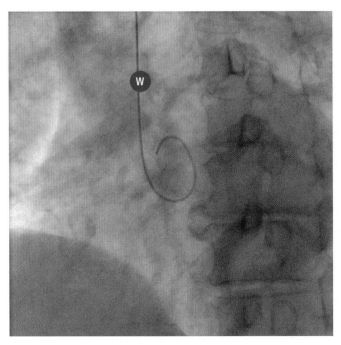 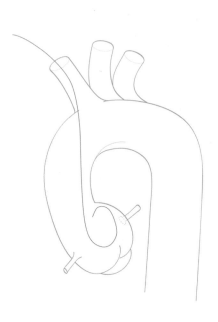

**1** We made a loop of standard 0.035" guidewire in the aortic root.

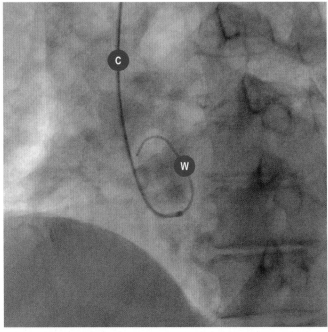 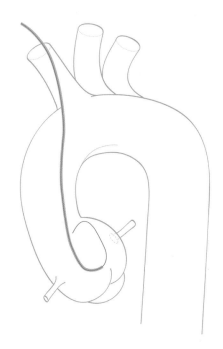

**2** The catheter was advanced over the guidewire.

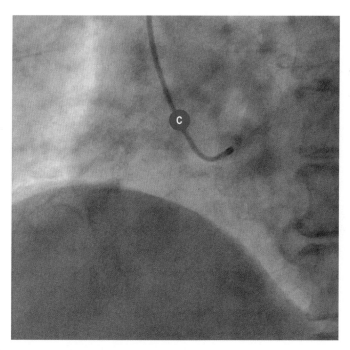

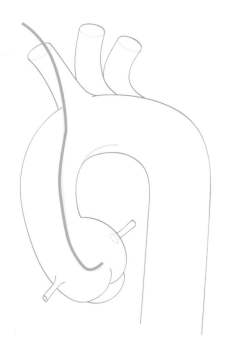

**3** The guidewire was removed.

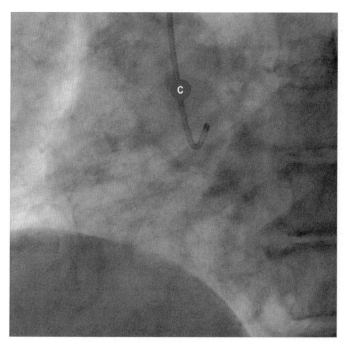

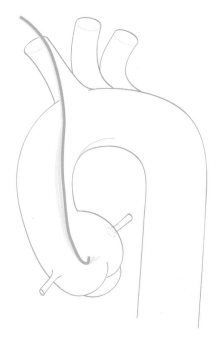

**4** The catheter was pulled back gently and rotated clockwise.

## CANNULATION WITH DIAGNOSTIC CATHETERS

### JUDKINS

#### Right Coronary Cannulation

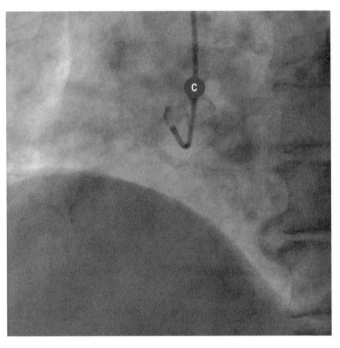 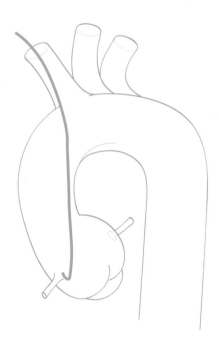

**5** The catheter was facing toward the right coronary cusp.

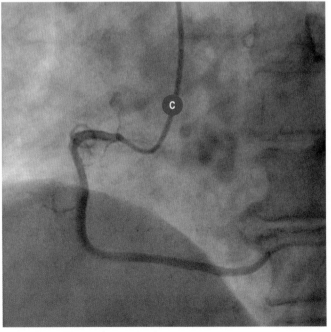 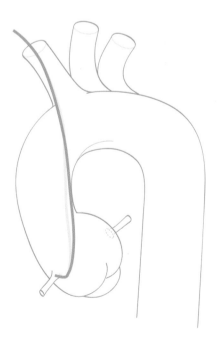

**6** The right coronary artery was cannulated.

# GUIDING CATHETERS

Various guiding catheters are used by operators to cannulate coronary arteries. The EBU, XB, and VODA catheters are our first choices for left coronary cannulation.

A second choice for left cononary cannulation is a Judkins left guiding catheter.

For right coronary artery cannulation, a Judkins right or a Patel right catheter are the preferred curves. In selected situations, Amplatz right, Multipurpose, or Amplatz left can be used.

## EXAMPLES OF GUIDING CATHETERS

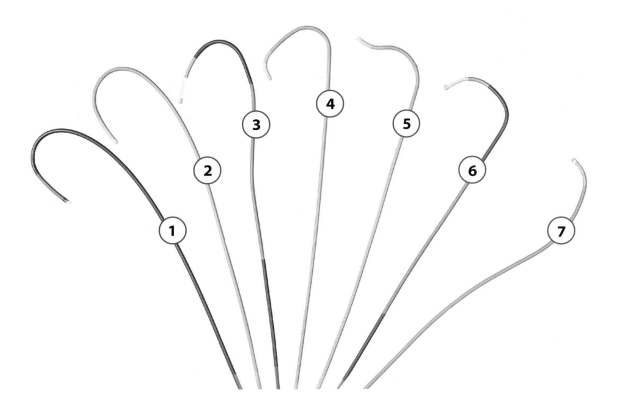

1. EBU
2. XB
3. VODA
4. Judkins Left
5. Amplatz Left
6. Patel Right
7. Judkins Right

# CANNULATION WITH GUIDING CATHETERS

### EXTRA BACK-UP CATHETERS

#### Left Coronary Cannulation

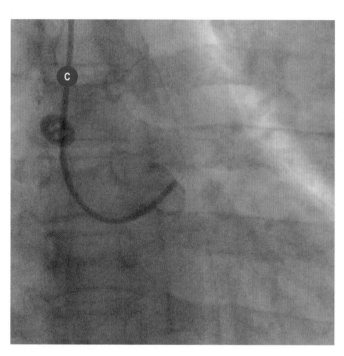

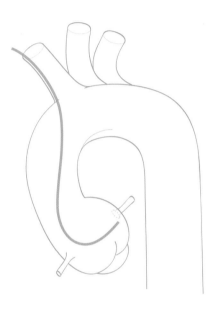

**1** We advanced the guiding catheter over a standard 0.035" guidewire to keep it in the left coronary cusp with the tip facing left.

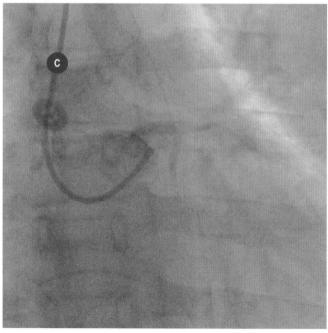

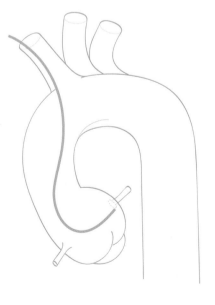

**2** We gradually pushed and rotated the catheter counterclockwise.

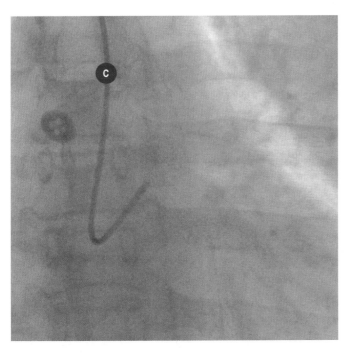

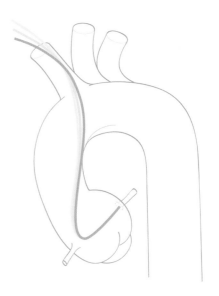

**3** The catheter tip approached the left coronary artery ostium.

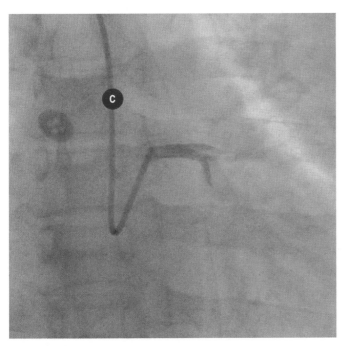

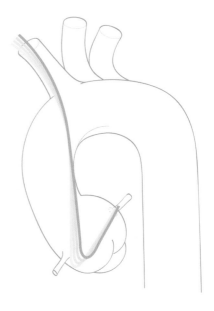

**4** Continuation of the counterclockwise rotation and a gentle push of the catheter resulted in left coronary artery cannulation.

# REMEMBER

■ In most cases, you can cannulate the coronaries by using a regular Judkins, an extra back-up, or a Patel catheter. And in most cases you can use the standard curves and complete the procedure in the usual fashion. In a few selected cases, you may need to use special curves.

■ If there is significant tortuosity in the subclavian region, or there are loops due to dilatation and/or distortion of the aorta, or if there is arteria lusoria, normal torque of the catheter is not preserved. Therefore, rather than fussing about clock or counterclockwise rotation, the operator should concentrate on the movement of the catheter's tip in order to direct it into the coronary ostia. Eye-hand coordination is very important in this situation.

# Recommended Reading

Campeau L. Percutaneous radial artery approach for coronary angiography. Cathet Cardiovasc Diagn. 1989 Jan;16(1):3-7.

Lotan, C, Hasin Y, Mosseri M, et al. Transradial approach for coronary angiography and angioplasty. Am J Cardiol. 1995 Jul 15;76(3):164-7.

Louvard Y, Krol M, Pezzano M, et al. Feasibility of routine transradial coronary angiography: a single operator's experience. J Invasive Cardiol. 1999 Sep;11(9): 543-8.

Saito S, Ikei H, Hosokawa G, et al. Influence of the ratio between radial artery inner diameter and sheath outer diameter on radial artery flow after transradial coronary intervention. Catheter Cardiovasc Interv. 1999 Feb;46(2):173-8.

Gilchrist IC. Transradial technical tips. Catheter Cardiovasc Interv. 2000 Mar;49(3):353-4.

Gobeil F, Lefevre T, Louvard Y, et al. Coronary angioplasty using 5 French guiding catheters: preliminary experience. Catheter Cardiovasc Interv. 2000 Sep;51(1):107-9.

Ochiai M, Ikari Y, Yamaguchi T, et al. New long-tip guiding catheters designed for right transradial coronary intervention. Catheter Cardiovasc Interv. 2000 Feb;49(2):218-24.

Abhaichand RK, Louvard Y, Gobeil JF, et al. The problem of arteria lusoria in the right transradial coronary angiography and angioplasty. Catheter Cardiovasc Interv. 2001 Oct;54(2):196-201.

Grollman JH Jr. The many faces of the anomalous left aortic arch. Catheter Cardiovasc Interv. 2001 Oct;54(2):202-3.

Louvard Y, Lefevre T, Allain A, et al. Coronary angiography through the radial or the femoral approach: The CARAFE study. Catheter Cardiovasc Interv. 2001 Feb; 52:181-7.

Dahm JB, Vogelgesang D, Hummel A, et al. A randomized trial of 5 vs. 6 French transradial percutaneous coronary interventions. Catheter Cardiovasc Interv. 2002 Oct;57(2):172-6.

Sanmartin M, Goicolea J, Meneses D, et al. Coronary angiography with 4 f catheters by the radial: minimally invasive catheterization. Rev Esp Cardiol. 2003 Feb;56(2):145-51.

Gobeil F, Bruck F, Louvard Y, et al. Comparison of 5 French versus 6 French guiding catheters for transradial coronary intervention: a prospective, randomized study. J Invasive Cardiol. 2004 Jul;16(7):353-5.

Ikari Y, Kakajima H, Iijima R, et al. Initial characterization of Ikari Guide catheter for transradial coronary intervention. J Invasive Cardiol. 2004. Feb;16(2):65-8.

Ikari Y, Nagaoka M, Kim JY, et al. The physics of guiding catheters for the left coronary artery in transfemoral and transradial interventions. J Invasive Cardiol. 2005 Dec;17(12):636-41.

Lange HW, von Boetticher H. Randomized comparison of operator radiation exposure during coronary angiography and intervention by radial or femoral approach. Catheter Cardiovasc Interv. 2006 Jan;67(1):12-6.

# RIGHT OR LEFT RADIAL ARTERY: DOES IT MATTER?

Most transradial procedures are performed through the right radial artery, but an operator may use the left radial approach just as effectively when the right radial approach is not suitable.

There is little evidence that there is significant advantage to using the left radial approach. Some operators prefer it, however, explaining that the anatomical relationship between the left subclavian artery, aortic arch, and ascending aorta are more similar to the femoral route and thus make routine catheters (i.e., Judkins) easier to maneuver. (See Chapter 12: "Understanding the Catheter's Course: Radial vs. Femoral".) ■

# DISCUSSION

Our Cath Lab team prefers to use the left radial approach:

- When the right radial artery pulse is absent
- When the Modified Allen's Test on the right side is negative (abnormal)
- For cannulation of a LIMA bypass graft (provided the left radial artery has not been used for the bypass graft)
- For diagnostic and interventional procedures in cases of infradiaphragmatic pathology
- For left subclavian, left vertebral, LIMA diagnostic and interventional studies
- For right common and right internal carotid artery interventions

In the first two situations, the rationale for choosing the left radial approach is obvious and is the only available route.

Cannulating and performing interventions on a LIMA bypass graft is very straightforward from the left radial approach.

For infradiaphragmatic pathologies, we always prefer the left radial approach because there is no need to traverse the arch of the aorta from the left side, thereby saving almost 10 cm of catheter length. Entering the descending aorta is easier and straighter when we approach from the left radial artery. This is an important point given that long catheters and other hardware are still not widely available. Another option in such cases is to go for a high radial puncture which saves an additional 5 to 10 cm of catheter length.

For left-sided arteries (left subclavian, left vertebral, and LIMA), the approach from the left radial artery is more straightforward. However, in the case of right common and right internal carotid artery interventions, the guiding catheter support is much better from the left radial artery because there is no acute bend in the catheter.

As far as anatomical variations, spasms, or passage challenges go, there is not much difference between the right or the left radial artery. Thus, the right is right in most cases. ■

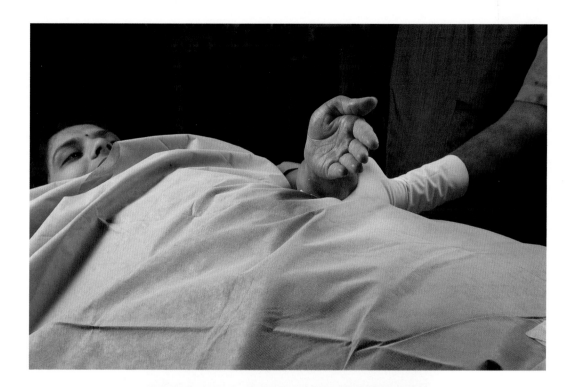

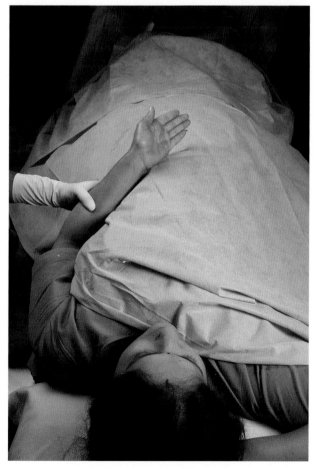

Whenever the left radial approach is used, the patient must rest the left arm across the chest for the duration of the procedure. If necessary, the patient's arm may be supported manually by a Cath Lab staff member.

## RECOMMENDED READING

Spaulding C, Lefevre T, Funck F, et al. Left radial approach for coronary angiography: results of a prospective study. Cathet Cardiovasc Diagn. 1996 Dec;39(4):365-70.

Mann T, Cubeddu G, Schneider J, et al. Left internal mammary artery intervention: the left radial approach with a new guide catheter. J Invasive Cardiol. 2000 Jun;12(6):298-302.

Abhaichand RK, Louvard Y, Gobeil JF, et al. The problem of arteria lusoria in the right transradial coronary angiography and angioplasty. Catheter Cardiovasc Interv. 2001 Oct;54(2):196-201.

Saito S. Right or left side? Catheter Cardiovasc Interv. 2003 Mar;58(3):301-4.

Kawashima O, Endoh N, Terashima M, et al. Effectiveness of right or left radial approach for coronary angiography. Catheter Cardiovasc Interv. 2004 Mar;61(3):333-7.

# HOW & WHY I STARTED MY TRANSRADIAL PROGRAM

**John T. Coppola**

As director of a catheterization laboratory and interventional cardiology program in New York City for thirteen years, it is my job to regularly review all complications and deaths that arise from our Lab.

Several years ago, this involved reviewing over 15,000 interventional procedures. During the process it became apparent that groin complications accounted for significant morbidity, delay in hospital discharge and, on occasion, mortality.

One particular case struck me hard. It involved an angioplasty done on a patient in cardiogenic shock three years after she had undergone a bypass of her left anterior descending and circumflex arteries. She had a new lesion in the right coronary artery in the context of pre-existing left ventricular dysfunction.

Within 24 hours of routine, successful angioplasty through the femoral approach, she developed a pseudoaneurysm of the right femoral artery that led to bleeding, hypotension, successful resuscitation, and with recent exposure to contrast, renal failure that required dialysis. She then developed sepsis from a dialysis catheter and died two months after a successful angioplasty.

In other words, "The operation was a success, but the patient died."

This experience depressed me profoundly and started me on an 8,000-mile journey to India to find a safer way to cannulate the coronary arteries. The two most important things I took to India were an open mind and a trusted colleague.

Our initiation into the transradial procedure was made easier by a concentrated exposure to 100 cases performed by experienced operators over the course of five days. This learning experience gave me and my colleague the information and confidence we needed to start a transradial program of our own.

The selection of our first 100 cases was based on Dr. Patel's beginners' formula for success. We choose patients with large wrists and, therefore, large radial arteries. Our first patients were under age 70 to help avoid the tortuosity of the innominate artery and the elongated aortic arch that is often seen in elderly, hypertensive patients.

Having another budding radialist in the Cath Lab gave me confidence, helped me concentrate, and helped me persevere. We worked together for the second 100 cases, too, which allowed us to move through the learning curve more rapidly.

Once satisfied with our ability to cannulate the radial artery and move the catheter into the coronary arteries, we began teaching our Fellows.

Later, our Fellows were taught the puncture technique.

When our department's nursing and technical staff saw the many advantages of early ambulation, and no sheath removal or bleeding complications, they became roving ambassadors for the transradial approach. It significantly relieved their workload and the recovery rooms became stress-free.

In order to start your own radial program, you must first be passionate about finding a better way. You must believe that one femoral complication, one blood transfusion, one unnecessary death is one too many. And you must have the courage to leave the old and embrace the new.

Agreed, the learning curve for transradial intervention is real, but it is surmountable if you take it step-by-step, just as the experts did when they were first learning. As Dr. Patel often says, "If I can do it, you can do it."

As a beginner, be aware that you must fight impatience and the desire to cross over to the femoral approach the moment a challenge is encountered. In 2003, virtually none of our cases was performed through the radial approach. Today, 85% of our cases are radial procedures and we hope to increase this even more soon.

One of the most rewarding aspects of our training program is that the Fellows who have graduated since 2004 are now performing the majority of their interventions through the transradial approach.

Our hospital and Cath Lab staff members overwhelmingly prefer the radial approach. More important, our patients prefer it and prospective patients ask for it by name! ■

**John T. Coppola, MD, F.A.C.C., F.S.C.A.I.**
St. Vincent's Hospital (Manhattan)
Chief, Cardiac Catheterization Laboratory and
Interventional Cardiology Program;
Director, Interventional Cardiology Fellowship Program
New York, New York, USA

# HOW & WHY I STARTED
# MY TRANSRADIAL PROGRAM

**Samir B. Pancholy**

Coronary intervention has come a long way since I started training—from simple balloon angioplasty to one-session, three-vessel, drug-eluting stenting.

Yet, despite these significant technological refinements, day-to-day groin complications, a product of catheter-based femoral procedures, have continued to plague us. We have updated our pharmacotherapy and tried various (expensive) closure devices, but improvements have been mediocre, at best.

The shame is that femoral complications shake patient confidence and create problems that frequently negate the benefits of minimally invasive coronary interventions.

Despite the great care our Cath Lab took in preventing femoral problems, they were becoming a concern. I felt like NASA which is still using crude, unpredictable rocket blasts to send high-tech payloads into space.

So I started a journey that became the pursuit of the transradial option—the superiority of which was obvious after studying the literature and observing the technique.

The first hurdle was to get hands-on experience, which led me to Tejas Patel who allowed me to observe a large number of procedures over a few days. I returned home eager to set up a transradial intervention program of my own.

The next hurdle was to obtain the proper equipment. To my astonishment, I discovered that most of the specialized hardware Dr. Patel uses for transradial access was not readily available in the United States, but we approached vendors and were able to get substitute equipment. Our Cath Lab staff was now convinced that we were determined to start our own program.

Initial resistance from the staff was expected given that they were also required to learn a new technique. During the effort to work through my own learning curve, I realized I also had to convince my staff to persevere.

But to my surprise, I discovered everyone had been as fed up with the femoral approach as I had been. Their enthusiasm for transradial intervention skyrocketed when they witnessed its "Walk In, Walk Out" simplicity.

We were now in the second phase of the learning curve and were using the transradial approach for all low-risk procedures. Our next step was to master the aortocoronary relationships and develop a "sixth sense" for catheter selection and manipulation from the radiosubclavian viewpoint.

Our Cath Lab developed a unique arm-support system and made other small modifications which resulted in improved operator comfort.

After that, we quickly transitioned from performing 50% of our cases through the radial approach to more than 95%. As our experience grew, our procedure time, radiation exposure, and turnover speed improved. We were now an up-and-running, hard-core transradial program.

Patient feedback was the icing on our cake. Patients who had previously undergone transfemoral procedures became our biggest word-of-mouth advertisers. They could not stop talking to their physicians, families, and friends about the difference. New patients started calling about "the heart procedure through the wrist."

So this is our Cath Lab's success story, but we are a candle in the darkness. In the United States, only 5% of percutaneous coronary interventions are performed through the transradial route.

To turn this statistic around, we need to identify the roadblocks to its acceptance, provide training and support, and communicate its many benefits to the public, referring physicians, hospitals, and third-party payers. When more patients begin demanding this "better, faster, cheaper" technique, the medical community will be forced to respond.

We also need to expose beginning interventionalists to transradial intervention and make it a categorical component of cardiology Fellowship training.

The transradial approach is hardly new. It has been embraced for decades by interventional cardiologists worldwide. But refinement and simplification of the procedure have begun and there is now a critical mass of literature that proves its superiority. I look forward to continued fine-tuning and improved hardware, and predict that in a very few years we will be astounded by how long it took us to make the switch. ∎

**Samir B. Pancholy, MD, F.A.C.C., F.S.C.A.I.**
Mercy Hospital
Interventional Cardiologist
Scranton, Pennsylvania, USA

# TRANSRADIAL INTERVENTION: TODAY AND TOMORROW

In India, approximately 12% of all coronary interventions are performed through the transradial approach. Five years ago, this figure was near zero. We have noticed that younger cardiologists are especially excited about mastering this elegant procedure. Last year, over 350 interventionalists from around the world attended our annual transradial intervention course in India. (See www.trico.in.)

In France and Japan, more than 40% of interventions are performed through the transradial approach. Western Europe, Canada, and certain Asian countries are also moving in this direction. Transradial intervention is slowly catching on in the United States where it is recommended that low-volume interventionalists work in groups so they can master the learning curve together.

We have observed that the number of transradial courses is increasing and many major cardiology conferences have long sessions on transradial intervention. Everything is pointing to the fact that the transradial approach will soon be the approach of choice the world over.

The medical device industry has not yet zeroed in on this technique. Interventionalists need radial route-friendly hardware—from puncture needles to guidewires to sheaths to guiding catheters. At present, radialists do not have a "Judkins curve" for coronary cannulation. Once technology is on our side, the transradial approach will become even more streamlined.

It should be noted that we and many other radialists are already using the radial approach to address peripheral arterial lesions—subclavian, vertebral, carotid, renal, illiac, and even superficial femoral arteries, in spite of hardware constraints.

Patient safety and comfort aside, third-party payers in Western Europe, Canada, and the United States are taking note of transradial intervention due to its significant cost savings.

Out-patient PCI was first floated by radial pioneer, Ferdinand Kiemeneij, of the Netherlands. Hospitals worldwide, including ours, are moving toward out-patient PCI for selected patients. Everyone will benefit when we can safely reduce the typical hospital stay to 12 hours simply by switching to the transradial approach.

But for transradial intervention to take over, a critical mass of interventionalists must make the effort to change their mindsets and learn something new. They must study the literature and realize that this approach is clearly "better, faster, cheaper" and that patients overwhelmingly prefer it.

Actually, it is not a matter of whether femoralists will make the switch to the transradial approach; it is only a matter of when. ■

# RECOMMENDED READING

Kiemeneij F, Laarman GJ, Slagboom T, et al. Outpatient coronary stent implantation. J Am Coll Cardiol. 1997 Feb;29(2):323-7.

Cooper CJ, El-Shiekh RA, Cohen DJ. Effect of transradial access on quality of life and cost of cardiac catheterization: a randomized comparison. Am Heart J. 1999;138(3 Pt 1):430-6.

Eisenhauer M, Moore JA. Transradial coronary stenting: ready for prime time? Catheter Cardiovasc Interv. 2000 Feb;49(2):157-9.

Slagboom T, Kiemeneij F, Laarman GJ, et al. Actual outpatient PTCA: results of the OUTCLAS pilot study. Catheter Cardiovasc Interv. 2001 Jun;53(2):204-8.

Gilchrist IC, Nickolaus MJ, Momplaisir T. Same-day transradial outpatient stenting with a 6-hr course of glycoprotein IIb/IIIa receptor blockade: a feasibility study. Catheter Cardiovasc Interv. 2002 May;56(1):10-3.

Archbold RA, Robinson NM, Schilling RJ. Radial artery access for coronary angiography and percutaneous coronary intervention. BMJ. 2004 Aug 21;329(7463):443-6.

# FREQUENTLY ASKED QUESTIONS

TEJAS PATEL, JOHN COPPOLA, and SAMIR PANCHOLY

■ **What is the best way to approach the transradial learning curve?**
A learning curve precedes every new endeavor, but less effort is required if you keep the benefits in mind. Learning to play the piano is enjoyable when you remember the music you will be making.

Making medical procedures safe, comfortable, and cost-effective is our music. Finding a partner who is as excited as you are about the benefits of the transradial approach will make the learning curve less lonely.

In the beginning, select patients with large wrists and well-palpable radial pulses. Avoid elderly (over age 70), hypertensive patients since they often have an elongated aortic arch and a tortuous subclavian system.

As you perfect the puncture technique and the cannulation of the coronary arteries, you can move on to smaller wrists, weaker pulses, and more interesting subclavian systems.

In the beginning, prepare the femoral area to increase your comfort level. In our experience, it takes about 200 cases to overcome the initial challenges of the transradial approach.

■ **How does the radiation exposure with the transradial approach compare to that of the transfemoral approach?**
All beginning interventional cardiologists face a relatively higher level of radiation when they are training. Once they pass the learning curve, radiation exposure is minimized.

Although one study has shown higher radiation exposures for radial operators as compared to femoral operators, we have found that this is only a problem in hospitals where the patient's arm is kept perpendicular to the table. The proximity of the X-ray tube increases radiation exposure. At our Cath Lab and at many other hospitals, the arm is kept parallel to the table.

When the radial puncture site is lower than the femoral puncture site, the question of a higher radiation exposure does not arise.

Second, our Cath Lab uses Optitorque TIG (Terumo) catheters for diagnostic procedures—left ventricular angiograms and left and right coronary cannulation. Because there is no need to use three catheters and there is no catheter exchange-related radiation exposure, the radial operator has an advantage over the femoral operator.

Third, whether the radial or the femoral route is used, interventional procedures are the same. When the radial operator is well-versed in the tricks of catheter maneuvering, radiation exposure is a non-issue.

### ■ What about radial-artery occlusion?

Radial-artery occlusion is rare and has no clinical consequences. It is seen in 3% to 6% of cases. Limb-threatening ischemia has never been documented.

Short procedure time, an adequate dose of heparin, and immediate removal of the sheath after the procedure are key in preventing radial-artery occlusion.

### ■ Can devices other than balloons and stents be used in the transradial approach?

Most radial arteries are able to accommodate 6F catheters. The 6F large-lumen catheters have an inner diameter of at least 0.070" which allows the use of distal-protection devices using PercuSurge or filter wire.

The 6F catheter also allows bifurcation stenting and the use of extraction catheters. Because most rotablation is now performed for lesion modification and not debulking, large burrs are rarely used. One can easily use a 1.75 mm and even a 2.0 mm rotablator burr through a 6F large-lumen guiding catheter that can be placed transradially in most patients.

Except for patients of short stature, 7F guiding catheters can also be used transradially.

The bottom line is that the transradial approach does not limit device use.

### ■ Can the radial route be used to treat infradiaphragmatic lesions (i.e., renal, iliac, superficial femoral)?

For patients who are shorter than 160 cm, regular-length catheters can be used through the right-radial route for renal interventions. For taller patients, it is better to use the left-radial approach and to puncture the radial artery higher. This eliminates about 10 to 12 cm of length from the arch of the aorta and another 8 to 10 cm from the length of the forearm.

So infradiaphragmatic lesions can be approached with the usual hardware. However, 125 cm long catheters are available for diagnostic and interventional procedures. Long-shaft balloons and stents are also available.

■ **Can a radial artery that has been used for a transradial procedure be used as a bypass graft?**

There are several issues regarding using a radial artery for CABG surgery.

The conclusions of three major studies from the United States, the United Kingdom, and Australia have raised major concerns about the usefulness and patency of the radial artery even over the saphenous vein graft.

LIMA grafts are unquestionably the preferred conduit. Arterial grafts are generally preferred over venous grafts because it is assumed that medium-sized arteries are less prone to atherosclerosis. This is true for the LIMA, but it is not true for the radial artery.

In our own study (results to be published soon), we were surprised to find atherosclerosis and calcification in native radial arteries harvested during the CABG procedures performed at our hospital.

Moreover, if radial artery grafting is needed, the contralateral radial artery is always available. It is the usual practice to use the right radial artery for percutaneous procedures and the left radial artery for bypass grafts.

The fact the the transradial procedure induces intimal proliferation has been documented in one study, so cardiac surgeons should use the left radial artery if they are forced to use a radial conduit.

■ **The new femoral-closure devices allow early ambulation. So what is the advantage to using the transradial approach?**

Although early ambulation is possible with the latest femoral-closure devices, local vascular complication rates remain high. According to a recent meta-analysis of all major trials (with over 42,000 patients), the complication rates for femoral-closure devices were even higher than for manual compression.

So the advantage of early ambulation with the new femoral-closure devices comes with an increased risk of local vascular complications.

The transradial approach allows early ambulation (the "Walk In, Walk Out" benefit) and even minor vascular complications are extremely rare. Moreover, it is inexpensive; femoral-closure devices can add $250 to the cost of the procedure.

■ **What is the status of the transulnar approach? How do you compare it with the transradial approach?**

Several small feasibility studies establishing the safety of the transulnar approach have been published.

A major feasibility study and a major randomized study comparing the transulnar approach with the transradial approach are needed. We have begun working through this approach and hope to shed more light on this subject soon.

The usual observation is that the ulnar artery has a larger diameter and a straighter course than the radial artery. These would seem to be two major advantages.

The downside is that the ulnar artery is more deeply seated, making the puncture difficult. And the ulnar nerve passes near the ulnar artery at the usual puncture site, increasing the possibility of accidental nerve damage. It is also true that the chance of post-procedure hematoma could be slightly higher because of the ulnar artery's depth. A large study is needed to evaluate these issues.

■ **Why isn't the transradial approach more popular in the United States?**

The primary reason transradial intervention is not usually the approach of choice in the United States is due to lack of adequate exposure during Fellowship training.

American interventionalists also feel they do not need to learn more about the transradial approach because they already know how to cannulate the radial artery.

Transradial intervention is considered a "bail-out" technique so it is not performed frequently enough for skills to be maintained.

Finally, it takes approximately 200 cases to work through the initial learning curve and most solo US interventionalists do not have the annual volume to master the approach.

Just like anywhere else, these things create a "generation gap" where already-practicing interventionalists who are not able to perform front-line transradial intervention become critics of the procedure—exaggerating its difficulty and imagining its complications.

# RECOMMENDED READING

Mann JT 3rd, Cubeddu MG, Schneider JE, et al. Right Radial Access for PTCA: A Prospective Study Demonstrates Reduced Complications and Hospital Charges. J Invasive Cardiol. 1996;8 Suppl D:40D-44D.

Benit E, Missault L, Eeman T, et al. Brachial, radial, or femoral approach for elective Palmaz-Schatz stent implantation: a randomized comparison. Cathet Cardiovasc Diagn. 1997 Jun;41(2):124-30.

Kiemeneij F, Laarman GJ, Odekerken D, et al. A randomized comparison of percutaneous transluminal coronary angioplasty by the radial, brachial and femoral approaches: the access study. J Am Coll Cardiol. 1997 May;29(6):1269-75.

Kayashima Y, Satou T, Ito K. Usefulness of transradial angiography and interventional angiography for abdominal diseases: comparison with transfemoral or transbrachial approach. Nippon Igaku Hoshasen Gakkai Zasshi. 2001 Jan;61(1):25-8.

Matsumoto Y, Hongo K, Toriyama T, et al. Transradial approach for diagnostic selective cerebral angiography: results of a consecutive series of 166 cases. Am J Neuroradiol. 2001 Apr;22(4):704-8.

Buxton BF, Raman JS, Ruengsakulrach P, et al. Radial artery patency and clinical outcomes: five-year interim results of a randomized trial. J Thorac Cardiovasc Surg. 2003 Jun;125(6):1363-71.

Khan NE, De Souza A, Mister R, et al. A randomized comparison of off-pump and on-pump multivessel coronary-artery bypass surgery. N Engl J Med. 2004 Jan 1;350(1):21-8.

Khot UN, Friedman DT, Pettersson G, et al. Radial artery bypass grafts have an increased occurrence of angiographically severe stenosis and occlusion compared with left internal mammary arteries and saphenous vein grafts. Circulation. 2004 May 4;109(17):2086-91. Review.

Aptecar E, Dupouy P, Chabane-Chaouch M, et al. Percutaneous transulnar artery approach for diagnostic and therapeutic coronary intervention. J Invasive Cardiol. 2005 Jun;17(6):312-7.

Mangin L, Bertrand OF, De La Rochelliere R, et al. The transulnar approach for coronary intervention: a safe alternative to transradial approach in selected patients. J Invasive Cardiol. 2005 Feb;17(2):77-9.

Aptecar E, Pernes JM, Chabane-Chaouch M, et al. Transulnar versus transradial artery approach for coronary angioplasty: the PCVI-CUBA study. Catheter Cardiovasc Interv. 2006 May;67(5):711-20.

Lange HW, von Boetticher H. Randomized comparison of operator radiation exposure during coronary angiography and intervention by radial or femoral approach. Catheter Cardiovasc Interv. 2006 Jan;67(1):12-6.

# COMMON TRANSRADIAL INTERVENTION EQUIPMENT & HARDWARE

Following is a non-exhaustive list of equipment and hardware that are commonly used in transradial procedures.

## GUIDEWIRES

| Product | Distributor |
| --- | --- |
| 1. Standard (0.035″ / 0.038″); J tip<br>Standard (0.035″ / 0.038″); J tip | CORDIS / MEDTRONIC / BOSTON SCIENTIFIC |
| 2. Glidewire ( 0.025″ to 0.038″): Angled tip<br>Glidewire (0.025″ to 0.038″): Straight tip | TERUMO |
| 3. 0.014″ PTCA guidewire<br>  a. BMW<br>  b. Whisper<br>  c. Hi torque floppy<br>  d. Choice floppy<br>  e. Fusion | GUIDANT CORPORATION<br><br><br><br>BOSTON SCIENTIFIC<br>MEDTRONIC AVE |
| 4. Super-stiff (0.035″) | CORDIS |

## SHEATHS

| Product | Distributor |
| --- | --- |
| 1. RADIFOCUS INTRODUCER II M<br>Sheath 5F / 6F; 7/10 /16 cm<br>Dilator<br>Guidewire 0.25" Straight tip, 45 cm<br>Entry needle 20G | TERUMO |
| 2. CHECK–FLO Performer Introducer sets<br>Sheath 5F / 6F; 7 cm<br>Dilator<br>Wire: Platinum tipped nitinol 0.18″<br>Bare needle 21G | COOK CORPORATION |
| 3. TRANSRADIAL VASCULAR ACCESS KITS<br>Sheath 4F/5F/6F; 11 cm<br>Dilator<br>Wire 0.021″<br>Entry needle 21G | CORDIS |
| 4. MEDIKIT SLIT SUPER SHEATH<br>Sheath 4F/5F/6F; 17 cm<br>Dilator<br>Wire 0.025″<br>Entry Needle 22G | MEDIKIT<br>(Distributed in Europe by BOSTON SCIENTIFIC) |

# COMPRESSION SYSTEMS/HEMOSTATIC DEVICES

| Product | Distributor |
|---|---|
| 1. TR BAND | TERUMO |
| 2. RADISTOP | RADI MEDICAL SYSTEMS |
| 3. EASY RADIAL | BLUE MEDICAL SYSTEM |
| 4. RADSTAT | MERIT MEDICAL |
| 5. CLO–SYR P.A.D. | MEDTRONIC AVE |
| 6. CHITO–SEAL | ABBOTT |

# ANGIOGRAPHIC CATHETERS

| Product | Distributor |
|---|---|
| 1. Judkins – Left and right<br>Amplatz – Left and right<br>Pig tail<br>Multipurpose<br>Internal Mammary<br>Left and right coronary bypass | MEDTRONIC AVE AND<br>CORDIS AND BOSTON SCIENTIFIC |
| 2. SIM<br>Head Hunter<br>Vertebral | CORDIS |
| 3. Radifocus OPTITORQUE TIG | TERUMO |

# GUIDING CATHETERS

| Product | Distributor |
|---|---|
| 1. Femoral – Left and right<br>Amplatz – Left and right<br>VODA<br>Q Curve<br>Internal Mammary<br>Multipurpose | BOSTON SCIENTIFIC |
| 2. Judkins – Left and right<br>EBU<br>Amplatz – Left and right<br>Left and right coronary bypass<br>Internal Mammary<br>Multipurpose | MEDTRONIC AVE |
| 3. Judkins – Left and right<br>XB Brite tip<br>Amplatz – Left and right<br>Left and right coronary bypass<br>Internal Mammary | CORDIS |
| 4. Patel | Commercially available soon. |

# Accounting Information Systems

**Basic Concepts and Current Issues**

# Accounting Information Systems

**Basic Concepts and Current Issues**   *Fourth Edition*

Robert L. Hurt
*California State Polytechnic University, Pomona*

McGraw Hill Education

ACCOUNTING INFORMATION SYSTEMS: BASIC CONCEPTS AND CURRENT ISSUES,
FOURTH EDITION

Published by McGraw-Hill Education, 2 Penn Plaza, New York, NY 10121. Copyright © 2016 by McGraw-Hill
Education. All rights reserved. Printed in the United States of America. Previous editions © 2013, 2010, and
2008. No part of this publication may be reproduced or distributed in any form or by any means, or stored in a
database or retrieval system, without the prior written consent of McGraw-Hill Education, including, but not
limited to, in any network or other electronic storage or transmission, or broadcast for distance learning.

Some ancillaries, including electronic and print components, may not be available to customers outside the
United States.

This book is printed on acid-free paper.

1 2 3 4 5 6 7 8 9 0 DOW/DOW 1 0 9 8 7 6 5

ISBN 978-0-07-802588-4
MHID 0-07-802588-5

Senior Vice President, Products & Markets: *Kurt L. Strand*
Vice President, General Manager, Products & Markets: *Marty Lange*
Vice President, Content Design & Delivery: *Kimberly Meriwether David*
Managing Director: *Tim Vertovec*
Executive Brand Manager: *Steve Schuetz*
Lead Product Developer: *Ann Torbert*
Senior Product Developer: *Gail Korosa*
Director of Digital Content Development: *Patricia Plumb*
Digital Product Analyst: *Xin Lin*
Senior Marketing Manager: *Michelle Nolte*
Director, Content Design & Delivery: *Terri Schiesl*
Executive Program Manager: *Faye M. Herrig*
Content Project Managers: *Mary Jane Lampe, Sandy Schnee*
Buyer: *Debra Sylvester*
Cover Designer: *Studio Montage, St. Louis, MO*
Cover Image: *Tetra Images / age fotostock*
Compositor: *Laserwords Private Limited*
Typeface: *10/12 TimesLTStd-Roman*
Printer: *R. R. Donnelley*

All credits appearing on page or at the end of the book are considered to be an extension of the copyright page.

**Library of Congress Cataloging-in-Publication Data**
Hurt, Robert L.
    Accounting information systems: basic concepts and current issues / Robert L. Hurt.—Fourth edition.
        pages cm
    ISBN 978-0-07-802588-4 (alk. paper)
        1. Accounting—Data processing. 2. Information storage and retrieval systems—Accounting.    I. Title.
HF5679.H865 2014
657.0285—dc23                                                                      2014031863

The Internet addresses listed in the text were accurate at the time of publication. The inclusion of a website does
not indicate an endorsement by the authors or McGraw-Hill Education, and McGraw-Hill Education does not
guarantee the accuracy of the information presented at these sites.

www.mhhe.com

# Preface

## MESSAGE FROM THE AUTHOR

### To the Instructor

Greetings, colleagues . . .

In the years since the publication of the third edition, I've had the pleasure of corresponding with many of you on a variety of AIS-related topics. I value your input and have incorporated much of it into this new fourth edition of the text.

As I promised in the third edition, the Table of Contents has not changed. But, you will find a lot of new and updated content within the pages of the fourth edition. Here are a few examples:

- *COSO Internal Control Framework.* The COSO framework was updated in 2013, and those updates are now included in Chapter 3.
- *FASB Conceptual Framework.* I've rewritten the material on the Conceptual Framework in Chapter 2 in the light of its revision; I've also included more explanatory material and end-of-chapter exercises on it.
- *Discussion of business processes.* Although business processes still comprise the fourth part of the text, I introduce them much earlier so that students can become familiar with them at a conceptual level.
- *Excel applications.* Each chapter now includes an Excel application. The problems focus on a wide variety of skills, from statistical tools to time value of money functions and many others.
- *Comprehensive problem.* This new edition has a five-part comprehensive problem based on Big Marker (www.bigmarker.com), a Chicago-based videoconferencing service.

My philosophy for teaching AIS continues to inform this edition and to differentiate it from other AIS textbooks. My goal is to provide students some baseline concepts, ideas, and examples, then provide opportunities for them to apply those concepts.

My thanks to you for using/considering the use of this book for your AIS course. Don't hesitate to share with me constructive criticism, comments, and suggestions for improvement.

*Bob Hurt*
*(robert.hurt@gmail.com)*

# About the Author

**Dr. Robert L. Hurt**   *California State Polytechnic University, Pomona*

Robert L. Hurt is Professor of Accounting in the College of Business Administration at California State Polytechnic University Pomona, where he teaches Accounting Information Systems, Forensic Accounting, and Accounting Ethics. Dr. Hurt received his Ph.D. in Management with a concentration in information science from Claremont Graduate University. He also holds an M.S. in Business Administration (concentration in business education) from Cal Poly Pomona and a B.S. in Business Administration (concentration in accounting) from Southeast Missouri State University.

Hallmarks of Dr. Hurt's classroom approach include utilizing active learning, developing students' critical thinking skills, and helping students apply and connect accounting-related concepts in diverse settings. His courses are also competency based to help students focus their efforts on important skills.

Dr. Hurt is published in the *International Research Journal of Applied Finance*, *Journal of Forensic and Investigative Accounting*, *NACADA Journal*, and *Fraud Magazine*. He is also the author of Global Consulting Corporation: An Accounting Information Systems Practice Case.

# Acknowledgments

We could not produce a textbook of the quality and scope of *Accounting Information Systems: Basic Concepts and Current Issues* without the help of a great number of people.

The efforts of many people are needed to develop and improve a text. Among these people are the reviewers who point out areas of concern and areas of strength and make recommendations for change. The following professors provided feedback that was enormously helpful in preparing *Accounting Information Systems: Basic Concepts and Current Issues.*

**Tanya Benford**
*Florida Gulf Coast University*

**Mark Best**
*The University of Kansas School of Business*

**Dr. Passard C. Dean**
*Saint Leo University*

**Andy Garcia**
*Bowling Green State University*

**Dr. Marina Grau**
*Houston Community College*

**Andrew Griffith**
*Iona College*

**James E. Groff**
*University of Texas–San Antonio*

**Lois S. Mahoney**
*Eastern Michigan University*

**Ann O'Brien**
*University of Wisconsin–Madison*

**Robert L. Osborne**
*Ohio Dominican University*

**Michael Prindle**
*Simpson College*

**Vasant Raval**
*College of Business Administration– Creighton University*

**Michael Ridenour**
*Pennsylvania State University–Fayette Campus*

**Jason L. Smith**
*University of Nevada–Las Vegas*

**Dan Stone**
*University of Kentucky*

**Eileen Z. Taylor**
*North Carolina State University*

**James F. Waegelein**
*Emporia State University*

**Linda Wallace**
*Virginia Tech*

I'd also like to acknowledge the efforts of Steve Schuetz, Executive Brand Manager, Gail Korosa, Senior Product Developer, Michelle Nolte, Marketing Manager, MaryJane Lampe, Content Project Manager, and Sandy Schnee, Media Project Manager. All contributed significantly to the project, and I appreciate their efforts.

# Walkthrough

## What's New in This Edition!

### Features

- *Text organization*. The fourth edition is once again organized in five parts. Each part includes new and revised material in both the chapter text and end-of-chapter exercises.
- The text has been updated to reflect developments in the field, including the COSO Internal Control Framework, FASB Conceptual Framework of Accounting, Audit Clarity Project, and CoBIT 5.
- Every chapter has a brand new "AIS in the Business World" focused on a company students are likely to recognize. Companies include Starbucks, Amazon, Google, Barnes & Noble, and Netflix.
- Every chapter includes an Excel application. Topics covered include the use of common Excel formulas (descriptive statistics, time value of money, depreciation methods), graphs and charts (including pivot tables), and selection of random samples and data analysis tools (regression, ANOVA, and others). Many of the data sets for the Excel applications are available on Bob's AIS blog (bobhurtais.blogspot.com).
- The fourth edition's Online Learning Center features a "progressive problem" for each chapter. Those problems take one topic from the chapter and provide problems/questions/exercises at progressively more challenging levels of Bloom's taxonomy.
- The AICPA Core Competency Framework is mentioned throughout the text, demonstrating the importance and relevance of AIS to students' careers.
- Many of the end-of-chapter exercises and problems have been revised and updated.
- At the end of each part of the fourth edition, you'll find an installment of a "comprehensive problem." All installments are based on Big Marker, a videoconferencing service.
- Ancillaries, including online quizzes, the test bank, and PowerPoint slides, have all been updated for the new edition.

# Overall Features

## Readability

The writing style has been highly praised. Students easily comprehend chapter concepts because of the conversational tone. The author has made every effort to ensure that the writing style remains engaging, lively, and consistent.

## Philosophy

The text emphasizes the art of AIS over its "science." It helps students begin to develop their professional judgment as accountants, rather than encouraging them to memorize examples and solutions.

## Structure

The text puts the most important, fundamental topics first, followed by applications in transaction cycles. Nice-to-know topics are included and can be covered or not at the instructor's discretion.

## Content

The text incorporates modeling techniques and information technology, but at a level appropriate for accountants rather than CIS majors/professionals. While remaining true to its accounting roots, the text moves beyond a strict accounting orientation; it integrates information technology, behavioral issues, management concerns, quantitative reasoning, and ideas from business law and ethics. Thus, students will have a clear grasp of how AIS concepts impact business practice, regardless of the organizational contexts where they pursue their careers.

# Chapter Features

## Real-World Examples

Each chapter's "AIS in the Business World" opening vignette has been rewritten. All of them are based on real-world companies students will recognize, such as Target and Microsoft.

---

## Chapter Thirteen

# Acquisition/Payment Process

### AIS in the Business World

**Krispy Kreme Doughnuts**

The acquisition/payment process can focus on virtually any asset, but most commonly focuses on inventory. Since Krispy Kreme makes its own doughnuts (in the conversion process, which we'll explore in the next chapter), "inventory" refers to the required raw materials—items like flour, yeast, and sugar.

To order raw materials, KKD would issue a purchase order to a vendor. The purchase order includes information like the vendor's identification data (name, address, and so on), the items KKD wants to purchase, the quantities of each item and the expected cost of each item. The purchase order can be electronic or paper-based.

In its relational database, KKD would include an "issue purchase order" table like the one shown below:

| Field Name | Data Type |
|---|---|
| Purchase order number | AutoNumber |
| Purchase order date | Date/Time |
| Inventory ID | Text |
| Employee ID | Text |
| Vendor ID | Text |

Allowing only employees in the purchasing department to issue purchase orders is a form of internal control—specifically, separation of duties.

### *Discussion Questions*

1. What steps, other than "issue purchase order," are included in the acquisition/payment process?
2. How is the acquisition/payment process related to Porter's value chain?
3. List and discuss, within the context of the acquisition/payment process, examples of each generic element of the AIS.

---

## Reflection and Critical Thinking

| Reflection and Self-Assessment | 3.4 |
|---|---|

Consider the internal controls listed below. For each one, explain: (i) the risk it addresses, (ii) the risk category from Brown's taxonomy, (iii) the broad purpose of internal control it achieves, and (iv) the nature of the control (preventive, detective, corrective).

1. Reconciling a bank statement.
2. Requiring that all purchase requisitions are coordinated through a central purchasing department.
3. Encouraging employees to attend annual seminars on ethical behavior in the workplace and related topics.
4. Tearing ticket stubs in half at a movie theater when a patron enters.
5. Collecting cash at one window and delivering the order in a different window at a fast food establishment.

Each chapter presents basic ideas and then encourages students to reflect on those ideas. "Reflection and Self-Assessment" activities throughout each chapter will help students think critically about the material. In addition, each chapter continues to include a "critical thinking" application that gets students started down that path; most of those sections have been rewritten for the new edition.

# End-of-Chapter Activities

The homework material remains a strength of the text. The sheer number of questions, problems, and Internet assignments will test and therefore expand the students' knowledge of chapter concepts. Further, many chapters include questions and problems that refer back to earlier material in the text and earlier courses in the accounting curriculum to discourage students from doing a "memory wipe" once they've studied a particular topic.

---

End-of-Chapter Activities

1. *Reading review questions.*
   a. What activities are accounted for in the sales/collection process?
   b. What are the steps in the sales/collection process?
   c. How are the five generic elements of the AIS exemplified in the sales/collection process?
   d. What recordable transactions are commonly associated with the sales/collection process? How are they recorded in the AIS?
   e. What internal controls do organizations use in the sales/collection process? What risks do they address?
   f. Respond to the questions for this chapter's "AIS in the Business World."

2. *Reading review problem.* Krispy Kreme Doughnuts offers several ways community groups can use its products for fundraising; one such way is via fundraising certificates. Charitable groups fill out a fundraising application on KKD's Web site; the application is evaluated by a store manager, who verifies that the group's purpose is appropriate. The charitable group purchases the desired quantity of fundraising certificates from a local KKD store, then sells them at a higher price. For example, the charitable group might buy the certificates for $2 each and sell them for $5 each. More information about fundraising is available on the company's Web site (www .krispykreme.com) under the "fundraising" tab.
   a. What forms and documents would KKD use in the process described? Which generic step(s) in the sales/collection process would use each form?
   b. In a manner specified by your instructor (e.g., systems flowchart), document the process described from KKD's perspective.
   c. What risks do fundraising groups bear in the process? What internal controls would you recommend to a fundraising group to address those risks?
   d. Consider the following tables KKD might maintain for the process: fundraising group table, sell fundraising certificates table, redeem fundraising certificates table, redeem fundraising certificates/inventory table. What fields would you include in each table? Indicate primary keys by underlining and foreign keys with brackets.
   e. Based on the tables you laid out in (d), suggest one simple query and one complex query KKD might use. For each query, explain its purpose and indicate the fields you would incorporate.

3. *Multiple choice review*
   1. In a well-designed sales/collection process, the customer's credit should be evaluated:
      a. As the first step.
      b. Immediately after taking the customer's order.
      c. Immediately before billing the customer.
      d. By the salesperson taking the order.
   2. A remittance advice:
      a. Is the source document used to record cash receipts from a customer.
      b. Is the same as a sales invoice.
      c. Is not needed if payments are accepted only with checks.
      d. Is deposited in the bank.

---

# Comprehensive Problem

The fourth edition includes this comprehensive problem as a new feature; you'll find one part of the problem at the end of each part of the text—that is, after Chapters 5, 8, 11, 14, and 17. Each installment of the comprehensive problem will ask you to refer back to the narrative below; each installment will have application questions based on the material in the associated part of the text. As with all aspects of the book, I'm eager to hear your feedback via email or comment in my AIS blog.

---

Comprehensive Problem
Part 3 of 5

Each part of the comprehensive problem is based on Big Marker (www.bigmarker.com). Consider the narrative in Part 1 as you respond to the following questions on XBRL, e-business and ERP systems, and computer crime and IT security.

**Part Three Questions**

1. Consider the following list of transactions Big Marker might record in its AIS. Indicate the journal entry required for each transaction, then use XBRL's Global Ledger taxonomy to find the correct tags for any five of the indicated accounts.

| Transaction Date | Transaction |
|---|---|
| 9 Feb 20x4 | Purchased a new computer server. List price, $7,700. Paid 30% down and financed the remainder with a 2%, 6-month note payable |
| 14 March 20x4 | Paid employees, $18,000 |
| 18 March 20x4 | Paid in advanced for six months' advertising that will start in April 20x4, $3,000 |
| 24 July 20x4 | Billed monthly communities for the 30 days ended 15 July 20x4, $25,000 |
| 23 Nov 20x4 | Received required portion of community dues, $8,000. (Community dues total was $80,000) |

2. Most observers would agree that Big Marker is engaged in e-business.
   a. Which e-business categories apply to Big Marker? (e.g., B2B)
   b. Which benefits of e-business does Big Marker provide to its customers? Which costs apply?

3. Could Big Marker be considered an application service provider? Justify your response. If Big Marker is an ASP, which category (e.g., enterprise, specialist) best describes it?

4. Consider the material in Chapter 11 on computer crime and information technology security.
   a. Which business risks/threats impact Big Marker? Explain your response.
   b. How does the narrative presented at the end of Part One demonstrate one or more of CoBIT's processes and enablers?

# Supplements

## For the Instructor

**Instructor's Online Learning Center** (www.mhhe.com/hurt4e) includes:

**Instructor's Resource and Solutions Manual** includes the solutions to all the discussion questions, end-of-chapter questions and problems, and reflection and self-assessment questions.

**Test Bank** includes a substantial number of questions in each chapter offering a large pool of material to choose from when creating a test.

**EZTest Computerized Test Bank** can be used to create different versions of the same test, change the answer order, edit and add questions, and conduct online testing.

**PowerPoint Presentations** deliver a complete set of slides covering many of the key concepts presented in each chapter. The instructor's versions of the slides include classroom assessment and feedback exercises.

## For the Student

**PowerPoint Presentations** (www.mhhe.com/hurt4e) are available on the Student Center of the text's Online Learning Center. These presentations accompany each chapter of the text.

# Technology

## Online Learning Center

www.mhhe.com/hurt4e

For instructors, the book's Web site contains, the Instructor's Solutions Manual, Power-Point slides, Test Bank, EZTest software, Text and Supplement Updates, and links to professional resources.

The student section of the site features online chapter quizzing activities, including a multiple-choice quiz to accompany each chapter of text. PowerPoint presentations are also available to download. The author has listed several important links relating to text and professional material. The student section also includes a progressive problem for each chapter, designed primarily as a study aid. Progressive problem solutions appear on the blog.

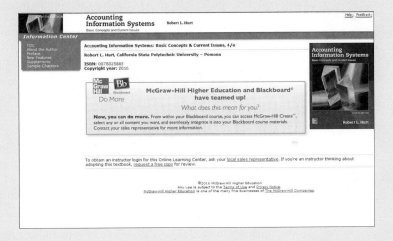

# Message from the Author

## To the Student

Many students are attracted to accounting as a major because they believe at least some of the following:

- Accounting is fundamentally about numbers.
- Accounting problems always have a right answer.
- Success in accounting is achieved by memorizing rules and procedures.
- Accounting is the most important function in a business.

As you'll see in your AIS course, most of those beliefs are (at best) skewed—in some cases, they are patently untrue. Therefore, you're likely to find your AIS course challenging, and very different from other accounting courses—particularly different from introductory accounting.

In my view, success in an AIS course (and in the broader field of accounting) is a matter of:

- Mastering a few fundamental principles and ideas, such as the purposes of internal control, database design, and the accounting cycle, and applying them in diverse contexts.
- Relating new material to previously learned material, both within and between courses. You'll often note, for example, that this book discusses relationships between accounting, finance, information systems, quantitative methods, management concepts, and many other areas.
- Evaluating information and thinking critically in responding to textbook problems, course assignments and exam questions. Pay particular attention, therefore, to the material in Chapter 1 on AIS Information Sources and Information Literacy Concepts, as well as to each chapter's "critical thinking" section.

I appreciate the comments, questions, and observations I've received from student users of previous editions, and have done my best to address them in this revision. If you'd like to share your thoughts on the book, please drop me an e-mail any time (robert.hurt@ gmail.com). You're also most welcome to leave comments on my AIS blog (www .bobhurtais.blogspot.com).

*Dr. Bob Hurt, C.F.E.*

# Brief Contents

**Preface    v**

## PART ONE
**AIS Fundamentals    1**

1  Role and Purpose of Accounting Information Systems    2

2  Transaction Processing in the AIS    20

3  Internal Controls    39

4  Management Concepts    63

5  Information Systems Concepts    80

## PART TWO
**Documentation Techniques and Database Design    101**

6  Flowcharting    102

7  Data Flow Diagramming    119

8  REA Modeling    140

## PART THREE
**Information Technology in the AIS    161**

9  XBRL    162

10  E-business and Enterprise Resource Planning Systems    178

11  Computer Crime and Information Technology Security    196

## PART FOUR
**Business Processes    215**

12  Sales/Collection Process    216

13  Acquisition/Payment Process    238

14  Other Business Processes    260

## PART FIVE
**Other Topics in AIS    281**

15  Decision-Making Models and Knowledge Management    282

16  Professionalism, Ethics, and Career Planning    300

17  Auditing and Evaluating the AIS    316

**Answers    337**

**Glossary    338**

**Comprehensive Chapter References    344**

**Index    347**

# Contents

**Preface**   v

## PART ONE
## AIS Fundamentals   1
Look at topics that form the foundation of most AIS courses.

### Chapter 1
### Role and Purpose of Accounting Information Systems   2

AIS in the Business World   2
Definition and Importance of AIS   4
AIS Structure   7
AIS Information Sources and Information
Literacy Concepts   8
Critical Thinking   11
Text Structure and Content   12
Summary   13
Key Terms   14
Chapter References   14
End-of-Chapter Activities   15

### Chapter 2
### Transaction Processing in the AIS   20

AIS in the Business World   20
Accounting and Bookkeeping   21
Accounting Cycle   22
Coding Systems   28
Human Judgment and Information Technology   30
Critical Thinking   30
Summary   32
Key Terms   33
Chapter References   33
End-of-Chapter Activities   33

### Chapter 3
### Internal Controls   39

AIS in the Business World   39
Internal Control Definition and Importance   40
Risks   42
COSO's Internal Control Integrated Framework   44
Internal Control Examples   47
Internal Control Applications   50

Critical Thinking   53
Summary   54
Key Terms   55
Chapter References   55
End-of-Chapter Activities   55

### Chapter 4
### Management Concepts   63

AIS in the Business World   63
Enterprise Risk Management   64
Nature of Business Process Management   66
Basic Principles   68
Behavioral Issues in AIS   69
Critical Thinking   71
Summary   73
Key Terms   74
Chapter References   74
End-of-Chapter Activities   74

### Chapter 5
### Information Systems Concepts   80

AIS in the Business World   80
Systems Development Life Cycle   81
Capability Maturity Model   84
Information Technology Selection   86
Critical Thinking   89
Summary   91
Key Terms   92
Chapter References   92
End-of-Chapter Activities   92
Comprehensive Problem   96

## PART TWO   101
## Documentation Techniques and Database Design   101
Look at common ways accountants create models of accounting information systems and explore database design.

### Chapter 6
### Flowcharting   102

AIS in the Business World   102
Flowchart Types and Conventions   103

Flowcharting Tools and Symbols    105
Flowchart Design Steps    106
Flowcharting and Accounting Information
Systems    108
Critical Thinking    110
Summary    111
Key Terms    112
Chapter References    112
End-of-Chapter Activities    112

## Chapter 7
### Data Flow Diagramming    119

AIS in the Business World    119
DFD Symbols and Design Considerations    120
Data Flow Diagrams and Flowcharts    123
Leveled Sets of DFDS    125
Database Design    127
Critical Thinking    131
Summary    133
Key Terms    134
Chapter References    134
End-of-Chapter Activities    134

## Chapter 8
### REA Modeling    140

AIS in the Business World    140
Types of Accounting Information Systems    141
REA Modeling    143
Cardinalities    145
Database Creation from an REA Model    147
Critical Thinking    149
Summary    152
Key Terms    153
Chapter References    153
End-of-Chapter Activities    153
Comprehensive Problem    159

## PART THREE
### Information Technology in the AIS    161
Look at ways various forms of information technology
are used.

## Chapter 9
### XBRL    162

AIS in the Business World    162
Terminology    163
History and Structure    165

Global Taxonomies and Tagging Tools    168
Organizational Benefits    169
Internal Control    170
Critical Thinking    171
Summary    172
Key Terms    172
Chapter References    172
End-of-Chapter Activities    173

## Chapter 10
### E-business and Enterprise Resource Planning Systems    178

AIS in the Business World    178
E-Business    179
ERP Systems    184
Application Service Providers    187
Critical Thinking    188
Summary    190
Key Terms    190
Chapter References    191
End-of-Chapter Activities    191

## Chapter 11
### Computer Crime and Information Technology Security    196

AIS in the Business World    196
Business Risks and Threats to Information
Systems    197
Information Security    200
CoBIT    202
Critical Thinking    205
Summary    206
Key Terms    207
Chapter References    207
End-of-Chapter Activities    207
Comprehensive Problem    214

## PART FOUR
### Business Processes    215
Look at various business processes that cut across
organizations.

## Chapter 12
### Sales/Collection Process    216

AIS in the Business World    216
Process Description    218
AIS Structure    219

Internal Controls    223
Systems Documentation    225
Critical Thinking    226
Summary    226
Key Terms    228
Chapter References    229
End-of-Chapter Activities    229

## Chapter 13
### Acquisition/Payment Process    238

AIS in the Business World    238
Process Description    239
AIS Structure    241
Internal Controls    245
Systems Documentation    247
Critical Thinking    247
Business Process Relationships    248
Summary    250
Key Terms    252
Chapter References    252
End-of-Chapter Activities    252

## Chapter 14
### Other Business Processes    260

AIS in the Business World    260
Conversion Process    261
Financing Process    265
Human Resource Process    267
Critical Thinking    270
Process Relationships    271
Summary    271
Key Terms    272
End-of-Chapter Activities    272
Comprehensive Problem    279

## PART FIVE
### Other Topics in AIS    281
Look at other areas of interest and provide an
opportunity to apply some fundamental topics.

## Chapter 15
### Decision-Making Models and Knowledge Management    282

AIS in the Business World    282
Information Overload and Other Barriers to Good
Decisions    283

Decision Models and Knowledge
Management    286
Critical Thinking    291
Summary    292
Key Terms    293
Chapter References    293
End-of-Chapter Activities    293

## Chapter 16
### Professionalism, Ethics, and Career Planning    300

AIS in the Business World    300
Professionalism    301
Ethics    303
Ethics Cases    305
Career Planning    306
Critical Thinking    307
Summary    308
Key Terms    309
Chapter References    309
End-of-Chapter Activities    309

## Chapter 17
### Auditing and Evaluating the AIS    316

AIS in the Business World    316
Types of Audits    317
Audit Clarity Project    319
Generally Accepted Auditing Standards    321
Generic Audit Steps    322
Accounting Information Systems and
Auditing    325
Critical Thinking    326
Summary    328
Key Terms    329
Chapter References    329
End-of-Chapter Activities    329
Comprehensive Problem    334

**Answers    337**

**Glossary    338**

**Comprehensive Chapter References    344**

**Index    347**

# AIS Fundamentals

1. Role and Purpose of Accounting Information Systems

2. Transaction Processing in the AIS

3. Internal Controls

4. Management Concepts

5. Information Systems Concepts

The ideas in these chapters are fundamental to the study of accounting information systems, regardless of approach or philosophy. They define the nature of accounting information systems, review the accounting cycle, and provide a firm foundation in internal controls. They also begin developing the idea that accounting information systems (AIS) is a multidisciplinary field by examining relevant concepts from both management and information systems. While these chapters present the topics at a basic level, the material is reinforced and applied in various contexts throughout the rest of the text.

## Chapter One

# Role and Purpose of Accounting Information Systems

## AIS in the Business World

### Starbucks

If you're like the students in my accounting information systems courses, you've probably purchased coffee and snacks at a local Starbucks. Starbucks is a vast worldwide operation; according to the corporate Web site (www.starbucks.com), it has more than 18,000 stores in 62 countries. Its stock is publicly traded under the symbol SBUX.

Through the Web site, prospective owners can apply to open a licensed Starbucks store. Menus include everything from traditional coffee to more exotic offerings like iced cinnamon dolce latte; various holidays have their own special offerings, too.

To create value for its stakeholders, a typical Starbucks retail store would engage in activities like:

1. Purchasing capital equipment.
2. Buying inventory.
3. Making beverages on demand.
4. Selling those beverages to customers.
5. Paying employees.
6. Reporting financial results to the corporate office.

To accomplish those activities, Starbucks needs an accounting information system.

The purpose of this text is to help you understand how companies like Starbucks account for their various transactions—not just the debits and credits, but the documents, tools, and controls they use that ultimately produce general-purpose financial statements and other reports. Each chapter opens with a short vignette like this one, followed by some discussion questions to stimulate your thinking.

### Discussion Questions

1. What are the essential elements of an accounting information system?
2. How do examples of those elements change for different businesses?
3. Does the presence or absence of computers and other forms of information technology determine whether or not a business has an accounting information system?

We'll explore various kinds of audits and their relationship to the AIS in Chapter 17.

Welcome to the study of accounting information systems (AIS)! AIS is a critically important area of study for future accountants. It ties together what accounting students often see as separate, unrelated areas of accounting: financial, managerial, tax, and governmental. Additionally, AIS brings in considerations from management, finance, and information systems. Finally, a deep, fundamental comprehension of accounting information systems is a great help in the study of auditing.

You'll often hear the phrase "single, correct, deterministic responses" throughout this text—that's another way of saying there is "one right answer."

Many accounting students are drawn to the discipline because of its perceived objectivity; they like solving problems that have "right answers." And your prior study of accounting may have focused on such problems. But, in practice, such problems are few and far between. And even when they exist, you won't be able to look up the right answer in a textbook or solutions manual. Problems and issues in accounting information systems seldom have single, correct, deterministic responses. So, to get you ready to confront and respond to those kinds of problems in practice, I'm including many of them in this textbook. One of this book's main purposes is to help you develop professional judgment and confidence in your ability to analyze **unstructured problems.**

Examples of structured questions with deterministic responses include the following: How much cash is in the bank at a given point in time? What are the three parts of a balance sheet? Unstructured, nondeterministic questions, on the other hand, require critical thinking. They include questions like this: What documentation tool should I use to design an AIS and/or to describe a business process? What internal controls should be implemented for a business process?

You'll find a paragraph like this one at the beginning of every chapter in the book. The enumerated items are often referred to as "learning objectives" or "expected student outcomes."

When you've finished studying this chapter, and completing the activities at its conclusion, you should be able to:

1. Define "accounting information systems."
2. Discuss why AIS is an important area of study for future accountants.
3. Compare and contrast AIS with other areas of study in accounting.
4. Explain the structure of most accounting information systems.
5. Locate and evaluate information sources on accounting information systems.
6. Describe the structure and content of the remainder of this text.

Different university accounting curricula place the AIS course differently. In some schools, AIS is the first course accounting majors take after the introductory sequence. In other programs, AIS is near the end of the required sequence. And you'll find some schools allow students discretion in the timing of AIS study. In my university, students study AIS early in their accounting education—within one or two terms of completing their introductory sequence. But this book can be used in any of the three frameworks mentioned above.

As you can probably tell already, I tend to write in a conversational tone—as if I'm talking to you. I've found students appreciate such an approach, and that it motivates them to read the text more systematically and regularly. If something in the text seems unclear, or could be stated differently to enhance your understanding, I encourage you to contact me with your thoughts. My e-mail is RLHurt@csupomona.edu. While I can't promise a response to every e-mail I receive, I can promise each one will receive serious consideration in any future edition of the text. You're also welcome to leave comments about the text on my AIS blog (www.bobhurtais.blogspot.com).

## DEFINITION AND IMPORTANCE OF AIS

You've probably heard of the FASB by this time in your accounting education. It develops the rules we use to prepare financial statements. You can learn more about them at their Web site (www.fasb.org).

An **accounting information system** is a set of interrelated activities, documents, and technologies designed to collect data, process it, and report information to a diverse group of internal and external decision makers in organizations. AIS is an important area of study for future accountants for at least three reasons:

- Developing a strong accounting information system helps achieve some of the components of the FASB conceptual framework of accounting.
- Studying AIS helps students develop many of the core competencies suggested by the American Institute of Certified Public Accountants (AICPA).
- Acquiring knowledge about AIS helps students learn more about common business processes.

The test bank for this book includes some questions on the conceptual framework. If some of the terms in it are unfamiliar to you, you'll want to research them as part of studying the chapter. My AIS blog is a good place to start.

Let's take a closer look at each of the three reasons.

The Financial Accounting Standards Board (FASB) developed the **conceptual framework** in the late 1970s as a guide for the development of future accounting principles; the conceptual framework was revised and updated in 2010.

Detailed study of the conceptual framework often comprises the first part of intermediate accounting, so we won't go into great detail on it here. But, you can see a summary of it in Figure 1.1.

# Reflection and Self-Assessment                                    1.1

Which terms in the conceptual framework do you recognize from your previous accounting courses? Which ones are unfamiliar? Do some research and define or give examples of at least three of the latter.

A well-designed accounting information system relates to the conceptual framework by

- *Capturing data on the elements of financial statements.* No matter what form they take or information technologies they use, accounting information systems document changes in the 10 elements of financial statements identified in the conceptual framework. Those elements are organized into four general-purpose financial statements: income statement, statement of shareholders' equity, balance sheet, and statement of cash flows.
- *Transforming those data into relevant and reliable information.* Well-designed accounting information systems can also gather data beyond the elements of financial statements. Items like sales by geographic area, customer characteristics and transaction histories, demand for inventory items, and vendor quality ratings can improve decision making by enhancing the elements of relevance: predictive value, feedback value, and timeliness. Additionally, internal controls in the accounting information system promote reliability (verifiability, neutrality, and representational faithfulness), as you'll see in later chapters.
- *Recognizing and adapting to the cost–benefit constraint.* Accounting information systems are all about choices and trade-offs: What data should I capture? What information technologies should I use to process them? What information should I report? Looking at the conceptual framework diagram in Figure 1.1, you'll see "cost-effectiveness" as one

**FIGURE 1.1**
**FASB Conceptual Framework**

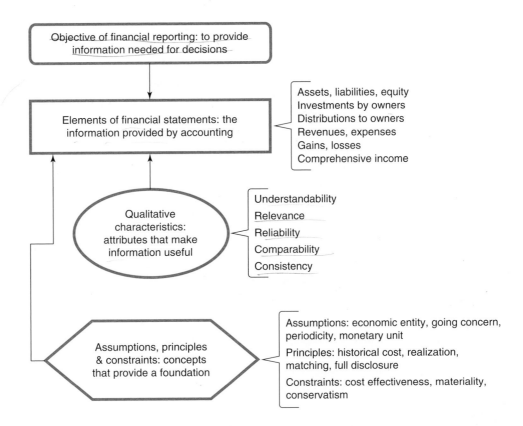

of the constraints on accounting information. Cost-effectiveness reminds us that we can't design the world's perfect accounting information system. Even in the best organizations with the most effective systems, you'll find managers who want more data or different data, who question the system's integrity, and/or who want business processes to be structured differently. As a designer, implementer, and interpreter of accounting information systems, always keep in mind that the benefit of having data, processes, and information must outweigh the costs of obtaining or implementing them. Those costs and benefits might be economic, behavioral, psychological, or financial, but they should always be considered.

The AICPA (www.aicpa.org) has suggested a very comprehensive list of competencies most accounting professionals will need—whether those professionals are practicing in public accounting or some other area. The **AICPA core competencies** are divided into three broad groups; here are some that are particularly related to accounting information systems (AICPA, 2013):

- Broad business perspective competencies
  - *Strategic/critical thinking.* "Critical thinking encompasses the ability to link data, knowledge and insight together from various disciplines to provide information for decision making. Being in tune with the 'big picture' perspective is a necessary component for success."
  - *Resource management.* "Individuals entering the accounting profession should be able to apply management and human resources development theories to human resource issues and organizational problems."

- Functional competencies
  - *Risk analysis.* "The understanding of business risk . . . affects how business strategy is created and implemented."
  - *Research.* "The individual preparing to enter the accounting profession needs to have strong research skills to access relevant guidance or other information, understand it, and apply it."
- Personal competencies
  - *Problem solving and decision making.* "Accounting professionals are often asked to discern the true nature of a situation and then determine the principles and techniques needed to solve problems or make judgments. Thus, individuals entering the accounting profession should display effective problem solving and decision-making skills, good insight, and judgment, as well as innovative and creative thinking."
  - *Communication.* "Accounting professionals are called upon to communicate financial and non-financial information so that it is understood by individuals with diverse capabilities and interests. Individuals entering the accounting profession should have the skills necessary to give and exchange information within a meaningful context and with appropriate delivery. They should have the ability to listen, deliver powerful presentations and produce examples of effective business writing."

Finally, AIS study will also help you understand **business processes** from an accounting point of view; business processes are a very common way of organizing AIS courses. We'll take an in-depth look at various business processes in Part Four of the text; for now, though, here's a brief overview of a few:

- *Sales/collection process.* This process comprises activities from taking a customer's order to collecting payment from the customer. It involves documents such as a remittance advice and customer invoice; common transactions include sales on account and collecting cash on account.
- *Acquisition/payment process.* This process can apply to just about any resource an organization needs, but is most commonly discussed in the context of inventory. In our later discussions of the acquisition/payment process, you'll learn about documents like purchase orders and receiving reports. Common transactions include purchasing inventory on account and paying vendor invoices.
- *Conversion process.* When an organization manufactures a product, it has a conversion process. You may recall from previous study that product costs come in three groups: direct material, direct labor, and overhead. In the conversion process, organizations combine these three resources to create a finished product; they then sell that product through their sales/collection process.
- *Financing process.* Virtually no organization can obtain all the cash it needs to operate simply by selling goods and services; most periodically need to acquire external financing in the form of debt (such as bonds payable) and equity (such as capital stock). The financing process deals with that aspect of the company.
- *Human resources process.* The human resource process encompasses activities such as hiring new employees, evaluating employee performance, paying employees, and managing their separation from the company. This process is heavily regulated by federal and state law.

I hope this section has demonstrated to you that AIS is an important area of study, worthy of your best attention and effort. Next, let's think about the structure of a "typical" accounting information system.

# AIS STRUCTURE

I often refer to "organizations" rather than "companies" or "businesses." That's because every organization needs an AIS, but not all organizations are "businesses."

An accounting information system is a set of interrelated activities, documents, and technologies designed to collect data, process them, and report information to a diverse group of internal and external decision makers in organizations. Most accounting information systems comprise five parts, as shown in Figure 1.2.

Each part of the **AIS structure** plays a vital role in its overall efficiency and effectiveness. And each part is filled with the kinds of design choices and cost–benefit trade-offs mentioned earlier. Consider the questions below to illustrate them:

1. *Inputs.* Inputs to an AIS might include documents such as sales invoices and purchase orders. Accountants would also need to ask questions like these to design and/or audit the system:
   a. What kinds of source documents will system users need?
   b. Should the source documents be paper-based, electronic, or both?
   c. How many copies of each source document will be required?
   d. What information should the documents contain?
2. *Processes.* Processing tools can include computers and satellites; however, please keep in mind that an AIS does not necessarily have to use information technology (IT). In smaller organizations, accounting tasks may still be completed with paper and pen. Here are some questions you might ask about processing tools:
   a. Which processing tools should the AIS use?
   b. Should the tools be manual, computer-based, or both?
   c. If computer-based tools are used in the AIS, which software and hardware packages should be implemented?
3. *Outputs.* System outputs for most organizations would include the general-purpose financial statements as well as internal reports such as variance analyses. Other considerations include:
   a. Beyond the general-purpose financial statements, what other reports will managers and system users need?
   b. How should the AIS be designed to facilitate their production?
4. *Storage.* Data in an accounting information system could be stored in paper form, electronically, or a mix of both. If the data are stored electronically, they are often broken down into three broad file types. Master files typically contain data about "things," such as inventory, customers, and vendors. Transaction files usually focus on "activities," such as earning revenue and incurring expenses. Junction files link other files together, as you'll see later in the text. Relevant questions about storage include:
   a. How should data be stored? On paper? Electronically? Both?
   b. Where should data be stored? Locally? Remotely? Both?
   c. How long should data be stored?
   d. Under what conditions can/should data be destroyed?

**FIGURE 1.2**
**Generic AIS Structure**

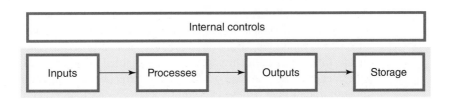

5. *Internal controls.* We'll explore internal controls in much greater depth later in the text. Most organizations employ internal controls such as daily backup of data and separation of duties (custody, authority, and recordkeeping) to maintain control over specific assets. Other questions might be:

a. What controls are necessary to promote information integrity in the AIS?

b. What behavioral effects are the controls likely to have?

c. Are the controls cost-effective?

The preceding questions don't have clear-cut, easy, simplistic answers. They do have "common" or "usual" answers, and that's part of what you'll learn throughout this course. But the rest of what you'll learn may be even more important. You'll learn how to make choices and judgments within the context of accounting information systems—choices and judgments that may not be perfect but that you'll be able to explain, along with their costs and benefits. Additionally, you'll be able to critique and evaluate the choices made by others. At first blush, that kind of thinking may seem daunting. Try to set aside your anxiety so you can think critically. Recognize that even seasoned professionals have to discuss and debate ideas to solve problems.

# Reflection and Self-Assessment                                    1.2

How do you feel about starting a course that doesn't have clear-cut, easy, simplistic answers? What study tools and techniques could you use to develop your ability to respond to open-ended questions?

So, to move you forward toward that goal, let's examine places (other than this book) where you can find information about AIS, as well as some guidelines for evaluating that information.

## AIS INFORMATION SOURCES AND INFORMATION LITERACY CONCEPDTS

If you're like some of my students, you may have heard about information literacy in a philosophy or English class. So, you may be wondering why we're talking about it in AIS. Here's the connection: Accounting information systems is a rapidly changing field; with the possible exception of forensic accounting and fraud examination, it may be the newest field of study for accounting students. And, to a greater degree than with other areas of accounting, practitioners and professors alike take different approaches to it. So, throughout the course, you'll often be called upon to do research as part of answering questions/responding to problems/preparing projects.

According to Dictionary.com, "validity" refers to something that is well grounded or something that is binding. Although validity doesn't appear formally in the conceptual framework, it is definitely implied—particularly by the qualitative characteristics of accounting information.

When your professor assigns a research or current article project, where is the first place you look? If you're like most accounting students, you answered, "the Internet." And, since AIS is such a "hot topic" in today's business world, you're bound to find tons of information on it there. But you're probably not surprised to learn that not all information on the Internet is valid, trustworthy, or reliable. In other words, you can't necessarily believe everything you read on the Internet. You should evaluate information critically for yourself, rather than believe everything you read on the Internet.

Society is full of urban legends that may or may not be true. For example, some people believe the Earth is flat. Others believe that the first U.S. landing on the moon was nothing more than a hoax. Choose one of those urban legends or some other you prefer. Find an information source that attempts to assess its validity, and comment on the believability of the source.

Depending on the kinds of assignments your instructor gives you this term, you may find yourself doing a lot of research for this class. The point of this section of the chapter is to give you tools to evaluate the information you find during your research—to think about it critically, rather than assuming it's all "true" on its face.

If you'd like to learn more about information competence in general and assess the degree to which you have it, I encourage you to visit the American Association of School Librarians' Web site on the topic: www.ala.org/ala/aasl/aaslproftools/informationpower/informationliteracy.htm.

Your university library probably has numerous materials on information literacy as well; most librarians are well versed in the topic and eager to share their knowledge with students.

You'll also find a lot of resources about this important topic at www.calstate.edu/LS/Tutorials.shtml.

Evaluating information reliability, whether on the Internet or from other sources, comes under the broad heading of "information literacy" or "information competence." For ease of discussion, I'll use the term **information competence** (IC) here, but you're likely to hear both terms in conversation about this topic. IC is much, much broader than the evaluation of information reliability, but we'll limit our discussion here to that aspect of it. According to the California State University's Work Group on Information Competence (Curzon, 1995), it is "the ability to find, evaluate, use, and communicate information in all of its various formats."

Why is information competence important in the study of accounting information systems? AIS is full of emerging concepts, ideas, and issues. Answers to the problems you'll confront in this class are not always found in textbooks but may require significant research. Evaluating the validity of sources you encounter in that research is a critical skill for reaching reliable conclusions and finding genuinely valuable information.

Many sources can assist you in evaluating information, but I've found the checklist developed by the University of Maryland's University College (UMUC) to be especially helpful. You can find the checklist at http://umuc.edu/library/guides/evaluate.html. The UMUC site presents five evaluation criteria, each with several specific questions you can use in your research. The five criteria are:

1. *Authority.* Can you tell who created the information? The purpose of its creation? Can you contact the author or creating organization, or otherwise establish their credentials? For example, authors published in *Strategic Finance* (the monthly publication of the Institute of Management Accountants) are required to provide background and contact information as part of their articles. Reading that information carefully can help you make decisions about authority as you evaluate information for AIS course projects.

2. *Accuracy.* Does the site/article/source tell you where the information came from? Does it contain any obvious errors of fact or misleading graphs, charts, or statistics? Consider, for instance, information presented in a graph. Differences can be exaggerated simply by changing the graph's scaling. Consider Figure 1.3 as an illustration of this point. Notice how the differences appear more pronounced in graph (a) than in graph (b), although the only difference between the two graphs is the scaling on the vertical axis.

3. *Objectivity.* Does the information contain advertising? Is it available freely? By this time in your accounting education, you have probably heard of the Sarbanes-Oxley Act of 2002. We'll explore the details of SOX later in the text, but consider www.soxlaw.com in terms of this information criterion. Figure 1.4 gives you a partial screen shot of the Web site. Although I've found the information there to be objective and valuable in learning about SOX, notice the "Contact Us" link on the left side. Clicking that link reveals the name of the consulting firm that compiled the information, offering its services to help companies comply with SOX.

4. *Currency.* Can you tell when the source was created/written? When was the last time it was updated? Does the page contain any "dead links"? Earlier in this chapter, I introduced you to the AICPA core competency framework. In researching this chapter, I came

**FIGURE 1.3**
**Data Displays**

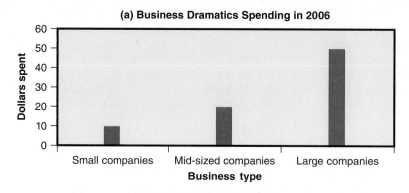

(a) Business Dramatics Spending in 2006

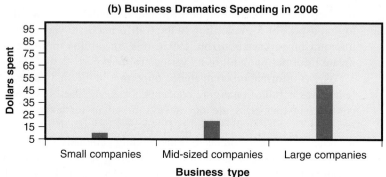

(b) Business Dramatics Spending in 2006

**FIGURE 1.4**
**Sarbanes-Oxley**
**Information Web**
**Site, www.soxlaw.com**

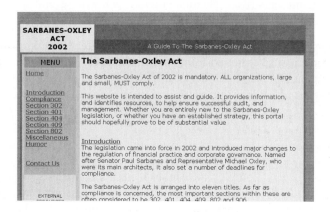

across a *Journal of Accountancy* article written by Paula Thomas in October 2000 that discussed the framework. Is that article current enough to be valuable as an information source? Probably so, as the competencies identified there are still as important today as they were when they were first developed. On the other hand, a discussion of the FASB conceptual framework dated that same month is likely not current enough; the framework was revised in 2010.

5. *Coverage.* Is the source still under construction? Does it cover the subject with sufficient depth? In some sense, all Web sites are always "under construction." In most cases, they have to be updated periodically to stay current and relevant. But if a page is perpetually "under construction," you should consider whether it would be a valuable, trusted source for research and problem solving.

I encourage you to point your Web browser to the University of Maryland Web site and see the full list of questions and other guidelines there; as a reminder, you'll find it at http://umuc.edu/library/guides/evaluate.html.

# Reflection and Self-Assessment                                              1.4

Use your university's library to find an article reasonably related to accounting. Evaluate the article based on the five criteria listed previously, or some other set your instructor prefers.

Again: how is the information you just read related to your study of accounting information systems? It's related in at least two important ways: (a) it gives you some guidance about the kinds of information you may need to consult in doing research and responding to problems throughout the text and (b) it gives you a set of criteria you can use to evaluate that information, rather than treating all information you find as the full and absolute "truth."

## CRITICAL THINKING

By this time in your university education, you've probably heard at least one professor talk about the need to "think critically." But what exactly does that mean? Dictionary.com defines critical thinking as "the mental process of actively and skillfully conceptualizing, applying, analyzing, synthesizing, and evaluating information to reach an answer or conclusion." And the Critical Thinking Community (www.criticalthinking.org) says that someone who thinks critically does five things:

- Raises vital questions and problems, formulating them clearly and precisely.
- Gathers and assesses relevant information, using abstract ideas to interpret it effectively.
- Comes to well-reasoned conclusions and solutions, testing them against relevant criteria and standards.
- Thinks open-mindedly [*sic*] within alternative systems of thought, recognizing and assessing, as needs be, their assumptions, implications, and practical consequences.
- Communicates effectively with others in figuring out solutions to complex problems.

Every area of accounting requires critical thinking; every day, accountants make judgments and respond to questions that may have more than one acceptable answer. Throughout this book, I'll often ask you to think critically so you can develop the skills you'll need to succeed in our profession; recall that critical thinking is one of the broad business perspective competencies identified in the AICPA core competency framework. To help you toward that goal, each chapter in the text will contain a section like this one. I hope that studying them will help you develop your critical-thinking skills.

For this chapter, I'd like to focus on the "statement evaluation" exercises you'll find throughout the text. In each of them, I'll give you 10 statements; your job will be to determine if each one is (a) always true, (b) sometimes true, or (c) never true. For those that are "sometimes true," you'll need to provide an explanation; your instructor may include similar exercises on quizzes and exams.

Consider the following statements, which talk about the role of computers in accounting information systems:

1. Computers can be an important processing tool in the AIS.
2. Computers are always an important processing tool in the AIS.
3. Computers are important processing tools in the AIS.

At first blush, without thinking critically, all three statements may seem alike to you—but they're not. Each statement has a unique phrase that differentiates it from the others: "can be," "are always," and "are."

The first statement (Computers can be an important processing tool in the AIS) is always true. When you see the phrase "can be," think of it as meaning "have the potential to be." It's always true that computers have the potential to be an important processing tool—even though they are not used in every AIS.

The second statement (Computers are always an important processing tool in the AIS) is never true. The phrase "are always" means that there are no exceptions. Here's a parallel example: People with blonde hair always have blue eyes. While it's true that people with blonde hair often have blue eyes, the two don't always go together; some people with blonde hair, for example, have green eyes. Similarly, some accounting information systems employ computers as processing tools—but some don't. So it is never true that computers are always an important processing tool in the AIS.

The third statement (Computers are important processing tools in the AIS) is sometimes true. In other words, in some accounting information systems, computers are important processing tools; but in other systems, they are not.

Take a look at the statement evaluation exercise at the end of this chapter. Statement (a) (Data in an accounting information system are stored electronically, such as on a disk) is sometimes true. Statement (b) ("Truth" is one of the qualitative characteristics identified by the FASB conceptual framework) is never true.

I often tell my students that accounting really isn't about numbers at all; it's really about the use of language. And becoming a critical thinker means, in part, that you're able to use language accurately and precisely. The statement evaluation exercise at the end of each chapter will be challenging for you at first, I'm sure. But, as you practice thinking critically, the exercise will make more sense. If you ever find yourself "stumped" by one of those statements, don't hesitate to drop me an e-mail (RLHurt@csupomona.edu) and let me know; I'll do my best to clarify and point you in the right direction.

## TEXT STRUCTURE AND CONTENT

This book is structured into five parts:

*AIS fundamentals.* In this section, we'll look at topics that form the foundation of most AIS courses. Here in Chapter 1, we examined the basic nature of accounting information systems; we also looked at information literacy and critical thinking. Chapter 2 reviews the accounting cycle and talks about how human judgment and information technology are involved in its activities. Chapter 3 introduces you to internal control. The last two chapters in Part One emphasize the multidisciplinary nature of AIS. Chapter 4 looks at three important management-related topics and their relationship to AIS: enterprise risk management, business process management, and behavioral issues. Chapter 5 introduces you to a similar set of ideas related to information systems: the systems development life cycle, the capability maturity model, and software selection. The topics from all five chapters reappear later in the text, where they are applied in various contexts.

*Documentation techniques.* Whether you're designing a completely new accounting information system, making changes to an existing system, or auditing a system, documentation techniques are important. In these three chapters, we'll look at three common ways accountants create models of accounting information systems: flowcharts (Chapter 6), data flow diagrams (Chapter 7), and REA models (Chapter 8). In Chapters 7 and 8, we'll also explore database design. Later chapters on business processes will give you the chance to apply the skills you acquire in systems documentation in more specific contexts.

*Information technology in the AIS.* The three chapters in the third part of the book look at ways various forms of information technology are used in accounting. Chapter 9 discusses the eXtensible Business Reporting Language (XBRL). XBRL is used to tag accounting-related data so it can be interpreted by a wide variety of software and hardware combinations. In Chapter 10, we'll take a look at e-business and enterprise resource planning systems. Chapter 11 provides an overview of an area my students find especially interesting: computer crime and IT security.

*Business processes.* The chapters in this part of the book take a look at various business processes that cut across organizations: sales/collection (Chapter 12), acquisition/ payment (Chapter 13), and other business processes (Chapter 14). We'll take many of the ideas from previous sections and apply them within the context of those business processes: internal control, systems documentation, the SDLC, risk management, business process management, behavioral issues, and information technology.

*Other topics in AIS.* I've included three chapters in the last part of the text: decision-making models and knowledge management (Chapter 15), professionalism, ethics, and career planning (Chapter 16), and auditing and evaluating the AIS (Chapter 17). I've included these topics, which are not often part of other AIS texts, for several reasons: (a) they are areas my own students have been interested in, (b) they provide an opportunity to apply some fundamental topics (internal control, database design, and information technology) in new areas, (c) they connect accounting with other areas of business (such as management), and (d) they connect AIS with other areas of accounting (such as auditing).

Earlier in this chapter, I referenced my accounting information systems blog. You'll find it at bobhurtais.blogspot.com. In addition to providing another way for us to communicate, you'll also find more detailed discussion of the topics from the text (such as critical thinking), comprehensive case studies, and a host of other materials. As always, I encourage you to communicate with me, either on your own or through your professor, about aspects of the book that are working well for you and those that could use some improvement.

## Summary

Each chapter in the text ends with a brief summary of its major points, structured in terms of the learning objectives at the beginning of the chapter.

1. *Define "accounting information systems."* An accounting information system (AIS) is a collection of interrelated parts, some of which may incorporate information technology. Its purpose is to collect data, process it into information, and report the information so it can be used by internal and external decision makers.

2. *Discuss why AIS is an important area of study for future accountants.* AIS is important for at least three reasons: (a) a well-designed AIS helps fulfill many of the ideas advanced

by the FASB conceptual framework of accounting, (b) studying AIS helps you develop some of the competencies identified in the AICPA core competency framework, and (c) AIS provides important insights into common business processes, including their steps, documents, transactions, and internal controls. In summary, AIS is important because it cuts across traditional functional lines in accounting. It provides the "big picture" and allows students to develop their critical-thinking and problem-solving skills.

3. *Compare and contrast AIS with other areas of study in accounting.* AIS is like other areas of accounting in that it includes consideration of financial statements and internal reports. It is different, though, from other parts of accounting. AIS typically includes more open-ended problems that do not have deterministic responses. It also cuts across traditional accounting subdivisions (financial, managerial, and the like) and incorporates material from disciplines outside accounting (such as management and information systems).

4. *Explain the structure of most accounting information systems.* Most AIS incorporate five main parts. Inputs are used to collect data and get them into the system; they include source documents such as checks and invoices. Processing tools transform the data into information; processing tools can be manual or automated. Outputs provide some of the information decision makers need in organizations. Typical outputs of an AIS include the general-purpose financial statements. Internal controls are the policies and procedures established in an AIS to promote information integrity and safeguard assets. And storage refers to the methods for keeping data secure and available.

5. *Locate and evaluate information sources on accounting information systems.* Information on AIS can be found in both traditional and online sources. All information, regardless of source, should be evaluated for validity. One useful checklist for information evaluation is provided by the University of Maryland: authority, accuracy, objectivity, currency, and coverage. The ability to find, evaluate, and use information appropriately is often referred to as information competence.

6. *Describe the structure and content of the remainder of this text.* The text is structured into five main parts: (a) AIS fundamentals, (b) systems documentation techniques, (c) information technology in the AIS, (d) business processes, and (e) other topics in AIS.

So, as you can see, you're in for a fascinating, highly relevant, diverse study this term in your AIS course. I hope you'll approach your study with enthusiasm and commitment, knowing that what you learn this term will serve you very well in your career as a professional accountant.

## Key Terms

These terms are defined in the glossary at the end of the text, as well as in the chapter.

accounting information system, *4*

AICPA core competency framework, *5*

AIS structure, *7*

business processes, *6*

FASB conceptual framework, *4*

information competence, *9*

unstructured problems, *3*

## Chapter References

AICPA. 2013. *Core Competency Framework and Educational Competency Assessment.* http://www.aicpa.org/interestareas/accountingeducation/resources/pages/corecompetency.aspx (December 7, 2013).

Curzon, S. 1995. *Information Competence in the CSU.* www.calstate.edu/LS/Archive/info_comp_report.shtml (May 25, 2005).

## End-of-Chapter Activities

1. *Reading review questions.* These questions will help you assess your understanding of the text readings. If you've studied the chapter thoroughly, you should be able to answer them without reference to the text itself. Although these questions appear first, you may find them easier to answer after completing the rest of the end-of-chapter assignments. I urge you to answer them in your own words, rather than with quotations from the text itself.

   a. What is an accounting information system?

   b. Explain three reasons AIS is an important area of study for future accountants.

   c. List and discuss the five parts of a generic accounting information system.

   d. Identify five broad criteria you can use to evaluate information on the Internet and in other sources.

   e. In a manner specified by your instructor (e.g., individually or with a group, as a written paper or as an oral presentation), prepare an original response to one or more of the questions for this chapter's "AIS in the Business World."

2. *Multiple choice review questions.* You'll find five questions like these in every chapter. They're "low-context" multiple choice questions, which means you should be able to answer them based on a careful reading of the text. You'll find the answers to these questions at the end of the book.

   1. Which of the following is not essential to the definition of an accounting information system?

      a. Software

      b. Documents

      c. Decision makers

      d. Financial data

   2. The FASB conceptual framework links accounting information systems with what other area of accounting?

      a. Taxation

      b. Auditing

      c. Cost accounting

      d. Financial accounting

   3. Most accounting information systems comprise _____ parts.

      a. Two

      b. Four

      c. Five

      d. Some other number

   4. Terms like "master file" and "transaction file" are most commonly associated with which generic element of the AIS?

      a. Inputs

      b. Storage

      c. Outputs

      d. Internal controls

   5. All of the following are assumptions in the FASB Conceptual Framework except:

      a. full disclosure

      b. monetary unit

      c. periodicity

      d. going concern

3. *Reading review problem.* Richie's Diner is a 1950s style restaurant chain with locations throughout southern California; you can learn more about them at www.richiesdiner .com/. Richie's has a fairly standard process for serving food that goes something like this:

   1. Seat customers.
   2. Give each customer a menu.
   3. Take the customer's drink order.
   4. Take the customer's food order.
   5. Prepare the food.
   6. Deliver the food to the table.
   7. Present the bill at the end of the meal.
   8. Collect payment.

   Servers record drink and food orders on paper; the kitchen uses those orders to prepare the food. Servers use copies of the orders to prepare the bill. Customers are supposed to pay at the cash register, but many give their credit card or cash to the server for processing.

   a. Consider the five business processes described in the chapter. Which one best applies to the activities described? Why?
   b. Does Richie's need an accounting information system? Why or why not?
   c. If you were an accountant for Richie's, how might you demonstrate the AICPA core competencies discussed in the chapter in your interaction with management?
   d. Suggest one example of each generic AIS element within the context of Richie's. The generic elements are input, process, output, storage, and internal control.
   e. Do a Google search on "operating a successful restaurant." Pick one of the articles it produces and evaluate it using the UMUC criteria.

4. *Making choices and exercising judgment.* As you read in the chapter, AIS is all about making choices and evaluating their costs and benefits. These questions and exercises are designed to help you develop those skills. When I give exercises like these to my own students, they frequently say, "So does this mean there's no right or wrong answer?" You may be thinking the same thing, so I'll tell you what I tell them: The point isn't whether your answer is "right" or "wrong," or even if such answers exist. The point here is for you to make choices and create answers you can defend in the face of other alternatives.

   a. RKH Company is a small consulting service based just outside Los Angeles. It has two partners, Sebastian and Viola, and average monthly sales revenue of $25,000. At any one time, Sebastian and Viola have up to three consulting engagements running simultaneously. Monthly expenses include office rent, supplies, utilities, professional magazine subscriptions, and automobile expenses. What form(s) of information technology, if any, should Sebastian and Viola use in their accounting information system? Explain the costs and benefits of your recommendation.
   b. Do a Google search for characteristics of good information. Compare and contrast one of the sources you find to the UMUC criteria discussed in the chapter. "Compare" means identify and describe similarities, while "contrast" means identify and describe differences.

5. *Field exercises.* These exercises will require you to go out "into the field" to interview an accountant, observe a business process, do library research, or collect other kinds of data. Your instructor may ask you to complete one or more field exercises with a group of students; they also could be used as the basis for a major course writing assignment or presentation.

   a. Interview an accountant or other financial professionals in an organization of your choice. Ask what information technologies (if any) are used in the accounting information system and about the costs and benefits of their use. If time permits, also ask for examples of internal controls in the organization. Don't forget to write a thank-you note or e-mail after your interview.

    b. Visit a movie theater, retail store, fast-food outlet, or other business organizations near your home or campus. Carefully observe the process of making sales and collecting payments. What processes and tools does the organization use to keep its cash safe?

    c. Point your Web browser to the site for the AICPA core competency framework. In addition to the six core competencies discussed in the chapter, what other competencies does it identify?

    d. Talk to one of your university's librarians about information competence/information literacy. Find out, from a librarian's perspective, why it's important. Identify two resources available on your campus to help you learn more about information competence.

**6.** *Information competence.* Look up the following references online or in your school's library. Using the criteria and specific questions from the UMUC Web site referenced in the chapter, evaluate and discuss the quality of each reference. (*Note:* To do a thorough evaluation of these references, you *must* get the list of questions from the UMUC Web site. You won't be able to rely on my summary in the chapter to do your best work.)

"Xelltec Reports Laptop Security Microchip." *Wireless News*, 25 February 2011.

Bollinger, M. "Implementing Internal Controls." *Strategic Finance*, January 2011.

Cascone, J., et al. "Equipped to Sustain." *Internal Auditor*, December 2010.

Johansmeyer, T. "Top 4 Small Business Accounting Software for 2008." *CPA Magazine*, November 2008.

Weisman, A., and M. Brodsky. "Fighting Fraud with Both Fists." *The CPA Journal*, January 2011.

**7.** *Terminology.* Each chapter in the book includes a problem like this one; beyond helping you master each chapter's vocabulary, you may encounter similar problems on your class exams and on accounting professional exams (like the CPA exam). Please match each item on the left with the most appropriate item on the right; each item on the right will be used only once, and each item on the left has only one best answer.

| | |
|---|---|
| 1. Activities, documents, and technologies | a. The generic AIS element associated with master/transaction/junction files |
| 2. AICPA core competency framework | b. The ability to find, evaluate, use, and communicate information |
| 3. Balance sheet | c. One way to organize the study of AIS |
| 4. Business processes | d. One of the four general-purpose financial statements |
| 5. Comprehensive income | e. Interrelated parts of an accounting information system |
| 6. Criteria for evaluating information | f. Authority, accuracy, objectivity, currency, and coverage |
| 7. Critical thinking | g. An element of financial statements in the FASB conceptual framework |
| 8. Information literacy | h. A structure that explains skills needed by accounting professionals |
| 9. Internal control | i. A generic AIS element that helps an organization control its assets |
| 10. Storage | j. A broad business perspective competency |

**8.** *Multiple choice questions (high context).* The multiple choice questions presented in Question 2 are "low context." You should be able to answer them simply by a careful reading of the chapter. These questions, on the other hand, are "high context." They will require critical thinking and reasoning on your part.

    1. Which of the following is an example of an internal control in the accounting information system?

       a. Bank reconciliation

       b. Sales order

       c. Balance sheet

       d. Steps in the accounting cycle

2. Which of the following provides the best example of "materiality" as the term is used in the FASB conceptual framework?

   a. Preparing an operating budget

   b. Expensing the cost of a wastebasket

   c. Reporting investments at their fair market value

   d. Providing information for decisions

3. All of the following are facts about accounting information systems except:

   a. They should all involve some form of internal control.

   b. They always incorporate information technology.

   c. They usually provide general-purpose financial statements as outputs.

   d. They can involve three types of storage files.

4. Which of the following best pairs a generic element of the AIS with a specific example of that element?

   a. Input, balance sheet

   b. Internal control, general ledger software

   c. Internal control, balance sheet

   d. Input, general ledger software

5. Which of the following statements shows the strongest level of information competence?

   a. Never using Wikipedia to do research

   b. Consulting the AICPA Web site for information on fraud examination

   c. Investigating an author's professional background

   d. Using only scholarly information as the basis for a paper

9. *Statement evaluation.* As you learned in the chapter, designing and implementing accounting information systems requires judgment and critical thinking. Each chapter will include an exercise like this one to help you develop those skills. Several statements related to the material in the chapter are listed below; your job is to explain whether each statement is (i) always true, (ii) sometimes true, or (iii) never true. If you answer (ii), explain when the statement is true.

   a. Data in an accounting information system are stored electronically, such as on a disk.

   b. "Truth" is one of the qualitative characteristics identified by the FASB conceptual framework.

   c. The FASB conceptual framework identifies ten elements of financial statements.

   d. Information you find on the Internet is reliable.

   e. Cost-effectiveness is an important criterion in the design of accounting information systems.

   f. A Web site that is "under construction" may have a problem with adequate coverage according to the UMUC information criteria.

   g. Both internal and external parties can use information provided by the accounting information system.

   h. Most companies have two different accounting information systems: one for internal use and one for external use.

   i. In an AIS, source documents are paper-based.

   j. Problems and questions in accounting information systems are open-ended; they do not have "right" or "wrong" answers.

10. *Excel application.* Every chapter in this edition has an Excel application problem; I've included them based on feedback from other AIS faculty and my own approach to teaching AIS. As you complete each problem, ensure that your spreadsheet is logically laid out and that the information it presents is clear and understandable.

The accounting information system of RRP Corporation revealed the following account balances at the end of December 2013; each account has a normal balance.

| | |
|---|---:|
| Accounts payable | $ 5,300 |
| Accounts receivable | 6,100 |
| Accumulated depreciation—equipment | 5,800 |
| Additional paid-in capital | 6,300 |
| Cash | 7,700 |
| Common stock | 6,600 |
| Cost of goods sold | 4,600 |
| Deferred service revenue | 800 |
| Depreciation expense | 700 |
| Equipment | 9,100 |
| Inventory | 8,000 |
| Land | 9,300 |
| Notes payable | 6,400 |
| Retained earnings | 15,860 |
| Sales | 6,810 |
| Sales discounts | 470 |
| Supplies | 200 |
| Treasury stock | 1,700 |
| Wages expense | 6,000 |

a. Use Excel to prepare a trial balance in good form based on the balances provided. (Check figure: $53,870.)

b. Use appropriate Excel formulas to determine:

  i. The average balance of all accounts with a debit balance

  ii. The average balance of all accounts with a credit balance

  iii. The largest and smallest balances of all accounts with a debit balance

  iv. The largest and smallest balances of all accounts with a credit balance

11. *Conceptual framework of accounting.* A well-designed accounting information system can help an organization's financial reporting fulfill many parts of the conceptual framework of accounting. Please complete each statement below with an appropriate word/phrase from the conceptual framework.

  a. All changes in equity during a period other than investments by and distributions to owners are called ___.

  b. Although a wastebasket is expected to last for three years, it is treated as an expense in the AIS because of the ___ constraint.

  c. An ___, such as cash, is something that has probable future economic value to an organization.

  d. Because of the ___ assumption, the accounting records of a business are kept separate from the accounting records of its owners.

  e. Certain short-term investments in securities are reported at their fair market value, thus demonstrating the qualitative characteristic of ___.

  f. Collectively, qualities that make information helpful in decision making are called ___.

  g. Outflows or uses of assets during a period from delivering goods, such as cost of goods sold, are ___.

  h. Regardless of changes in market value, land is reported at its historical cost, an application of the qualitative characteristic of ___.

  i. The ___ of financial reporting is to provide information needed for decisions.

  j. The ___ principle is the main justification for depreciating assets like equipment.

# Chapter **Two**

# Transaction Processing in the AIS

## AIS in the Business World

### Amazon

According to its Web site (www.amazon.com), Amazon seeks "to be Earth's most customer-centric company for four primary customer sets: consumers, sellers, enterprises, and content creators." And, if its stock price is any indication, Amazon is doing a pretty good job of achieving that goal. As of the end of 2013, Amazon's market capitalization was over $180 billion, and its stock price was just under $400/share.

Amazon is involved in many different lines of business: merchandise sales, cloud computing, publishing, and others. So, its accounting information system processes a huge number of transactions every day. As a publicly traded company, Amazon must periodically file reports with the Securities and Exchange Commission (www.sec.gov), such as 10-Qs, 10-Ks, and 8-Ks. Amazon's capital stock trades under the symbol AMZN.

### Discussion Questions

1. What steps does Amazon complete to process its transactions?
2. What internal controls does Amazon have in place?
3. How might Amazon structure its chart of accounts to facilitate transaction processing?

As I mentioned in Chapter 1, you may be studying accounting information systems near the start or near the finish of your formal accounting education. If you're taking this course before intermediate accounting, you'll likely want to devote significant attention to this chapter, which talks about the steps in the accounting cycle. If you're studying AIS after completing one or more courses in intermediate accounting, your instructor may use this chapter as a review, or skip it altogether.

When you've finished studying this chapter, and completing the activities at its conclusion, you should be able to:

1. Differentiate *accounting* and *bookkeeping*.
2. List, discuss, and complete, in order, the steps in the accounting cycle.
3. Identify common internal controls associated with the accounting cycle.
4. Describe common coding systems and how they are used in the AIS.
5. Explain how human judgment and information technology affect the accounting cycle.

Understanding the steps in the accounting cycle is important in the study of AIS; the AICPA core competency framework lists "measurement" and "reporting" as functional competencies. Both of those are related to transaction processing. Without grasping the "big picture" of transaction processing, you'll be at a significant disadvantage when we begin talking in later chapters about documentation, internal controls, business processes, and current trends in AIS.

## ACCOUNTING AND BOOKKEEPING

Many students and business professionals confuse bookkeeping with **accounting.** Before the advent of information technology, most accountants spent considerable time on book-keeping tasks. Thankfully, we have tools available to us today that allow us to focus on more interesting and important areas, such as using accounting information for competitive advantage and management decision making.

You can find more information about AAA on its Web site: http://aaahq.org/index.cfm.

The American Accounting Association (AAA) is a group of accounting educators with members all over the world. A committee of the AAA developed the following definition of accounting:

> Accounting is the process of identifying, measuring, and communicating economic
> information to permit informed judgments and decisions by users of the information.

Note that the definition has three principal elements: identifying, measuring, and communicating.

Implied within the AAA's definition is the **bookkeeping** process: that part of accounting devoted to identifying and measuring the economic information. So you may be able to see why bookkeeping is often confused with accounting. A solid understanding of bookkeeping is essential for any practicing accountant, but knowing the rules and procedures of bookkeeping is by no means sufficient to guarantee success in the accounting profession! Several years ago, a student told me that, upon graduation, she wanted a job where she could "sit in a room and make journal entries all day." I said: "First, you'll need to visit the Physics Department and ask them to invent a time machine. Jobs like that haven't existed in accounting for at least the last two decades."

As an undergraduate accounting student at Southeast Missouri State University (www.semo.edu), I had a friend named Gary. Gary, like me, started his higher education as an accounting major. But, after only one semester (and before taking his first accounting course), Gary changed his major to computer science. When I asked him why, his reply was simple: by the time we graduate, all accountants are going to be replaced by computers. That was in 1977 and the accounting profession is still alive and well. Gary was clearly confusing accounting with bookkeeping. Most bookkeeping today is handled via information technology; accountants can then take the summarized information and complete the remaining tasks in the AAA definition: communicating, facilitating informed judgments, and making decisions.

Write your own definition of accounting based on your prior study of the field. What attracted you to the accounting profession? How have your impressions of accounting changed since you were first exposed to it?

Next, we'll look at the steps in the accounting cycle—the process of identifying and measuring economic events that leads to communication and decision making.

## ACCOUNTING CYCLE

The **accounting cycle** comprises 10 steps (Spiceland, Sepe, and Tomassini, 2001, p. 60):

1. Obtain information about external transactions from source documents.
2. Analyze transactions.
3. Record the transactions in a journal.
4. Post from the journal to the general ledger accounts.
5. Prepare an unadjusted trial balance.
6. Record adjusting entries and post to the general ledger accounts.
7. Prepare an adjusted trial balance.
8. Prepare financial statements.
9. Close the temporary accounts to retained earnings (at year-end only).
10. Prepare a post-closing trial balance (at year-end only).

*Some descriptions of the accounting cycle include an 11th step: prepare reversing entries. But the cycle isn't our primary focus here, so we'll omit it. You'll learn about reversing entries in intermediate accounting.*

Notice how the 10 steps relate to the five elements of the AIS we talked about in Chapter 1. Obtaining information from source documents is an input. Steps 2 through 7 of the accounting cycle relate to processes, as well as Steps 9 and 10. Step 8 focuses on one type of output from the AIS: the general-purpose financial statements.

Transactions come in two basic types in most accounting information systems: external and internal. **External transactions,** appropriately enough, are those that involve exchanges of goods and services with other individuals and business entities—suppliers, shareholders, government agencies, employees, and the like. **Internal transactions** include adjusting entries, closing entries, and reversing entries. Accountants become aware of external transactions, in most cases, through the use of **source documents,** which can be paper-based, electronic, or both. They can include purchase orders, remittance advices, and invoices, for example. Common internal controls associated with source documents include:

- *Sequential numbering.* For example, the checks in your checkbook are numbered sequentially. Thus, you would know if a check had been used out of sequence, which may indicate an internal control breach. Other source documents may also be sequentially numbered, including purchase orders and receiving reports.

- *Physical security.* Keeping important source documents physically secure is also important. For example, a company should not keep its blank checks in an easily accessible location; rather, they should be secured (such as in a locked filing cabinet) to prevent unauthorized use.

- *Transaction limits.* A new purchasing agent, for example, might not be authorized to issue purchase orders over a certain amount. Requiring a second signature or supervisory approval can cut down on errors and potential misuse of assets.

Source documents themselves would be a cumbersome way to capture transaction information, so accountants distill the essential information from them and use the principles of transaction analysis to enter them into the accounting information system. Transaction analysis involves five steps:

- Identify the accounts affected by the transaction.
- Identify the effect of the transaction on each account (i.e., increase or decrease).
- Determine the element of financial statements represented by each account. The FASB conceptual framework identifies 10 elements of financial statements. We'll confine our discussion here to the five most common: assets, liabilities, equity, revenues, and expenses. The five elements are related through the expanded accounting equation:

$$\text{Assets} = \text{Liabilities} + \text{Equity} + \text{Revenue} - \text{Expense}$$

- Based on the **principles of debit and credit,** determine which kind of entry is required for each account. *Debit* is accounting shorthand for the left side of an account; *credit* is accounting shorthand for the right side. Because the terms *debit* and *credit* have other meanings in general usage, many students have difficulty remembering the principles of debit and credit in an accounting context. But the rules are actually quite straightforward if you relate them back to the equation. On the left side of the equation, the "plus" is on the left, so assets increase with debits and decrease with credits. On the right side of the equation, the "plus" is on the right. Liabilities, equity, and revenue, then, increase with credits and decrease with debits. Because expenses have a minus sign in front of them, the rules are reversed again: expenses increase with debits and decrease with credits.
- Verify that, for each transaction, the total debits equal the total credits. The equality of debits and credits is at the heart of a double-entry accounting system; you may recall from prior study that double-entry accounting was developed in the late 15th century by Luca Pacioli. Without it, we revert to a single-entry system similar to your checkbook. Single-entry systems have no internal checks and balances; they also fail to provide all the meaningful information of double-entry systems. Ensuring that debits and credits are equal is a form of internal control; even if a bookkeeper makes errors in account names and/or amounts, the errors can be corrected if the entries balance.

After they've been analyzed, transactions are recorded in a journal. The journal may be paper-based or computerized; it is often referred to as the "book of original entry," since it

**FIGURE 2.1**  **General Journal Illustration**

| | DATE | | ACCOUNT TITLE | DOC. NO. | POST. REF. | DEBIT | CREDIT | |
|---|---|---|---|---|---|---|---|---|
| 1 | | | | | | | | 1 |
| 2 | | | | | | | | 2 |
| 3 | | | | | | | | 3 |
| 4 | | | | | | | | 4 |
| 5 | | | | | | | | 5 |
| 6 | | | | | | | | 6 |
| 7 | | | | | | | | 7 |
| 8 | | | | | | | | 8 |
| 9 | | | | | | | | 9 |

GENERAL JOURNAL                    PAGE

You may have heard of "special journals" in your previous study of accounting. Sales journals, for example, have a special structure that facilitates the recording of sales on account only. Very few organizations still use special journals, however, so they are not a major topic of discussion here.

is the first place a transaction is formally recorded in the accounting information system. The most common form of journal is the general journal, illustrated in Figure 2.1. Recall from our discussion of the five elements of an AIS in Chapter 1 that journal entries are commonly stored in transaction files.

In a general journal, debits are recorded first. Credits are indented slightly, as shown below:

| | | | |
|---|---|---|---|
| 8/18/14 | Equipment | $80,000 | |
| | Cash | | $ 8,000 |
| | Notes payable | | 72,000 |

In the preceding transaction, the company purchased equipment with a 10 percent down payment and notes payable for the rest. If a transaction is particularly complex, accountants often will write a short description of it in the journal for clarification.

# Reflection and Self-Assessment                              2.4

Think of two events that would be important to a business organization that would *not* be recorded in the accounting information system. Explain why they would not be recorded; refer to the FASB conceptual framework as needed to justify your responses.

Then, record each of the following transactions in general journal format:

1. DMN Corporation issued 10,000 shares of $1 par capital stock for $15 per share.

2. Purchased inventory on account, $30,000.
3. Sold inventory with a cost of $6,000 on account for $9,000.
4. Paid current period's salaries, $12,000.
5. Paid creditors on account, $4,000.
6. Received cash from clients on account, $6,000.

In most computerized AIS, a transaction that has been posted to the general ledger cannot be changed or deleted. To promote good internal control, posted transactions can only be corrected with an additional journal entry.

The journal, then, is a chronological listing of all the organization's recordable transactions. But, to produce financial statements and other reports, data in the AIS need to be organized according to the account(s) they affect. The process of posting from the journal to the ledger reorganizes the transactions in that way. Posting by hand takes a lot of time and opens up the AIS to all sorts of errors: transposing numbers, recording in the wrong account, recording on the wrong side, and/or omitting part of a transaction are only a few. In most modern accounting information systems, posting is handled via information technology. While IT doesn't eliminate the possibility of incorrect transaction recording, it does cut down on the time and types of errors noted above. As a form of internal control, most IT-based accounting information systems do not allow users to delete transactions once they have been posted to the ledger; rather, errors must be corrected with a journal entry, thus preserving the audit trail.

Preparing a trial balance is the next step in the accounting cycle. A trial balance is a listing of all the accounts in an organization's general ledger, with their balances, that demonstrates the equality of debits and credits in the ledger. Note that the trial balance does not warrant that the AIS is error-free. If, for example, a transaction is posted to the wrong account, but on the correct side, the trial balance will still be in balance. Table 2.1 shows a trial balance.

# Reflection and Self-Assessment                                    2.5

Use the trial balance in Table 2.1 and the journal entries you prepared in Reflection and Self-Assessment 2.4 to prepare a new trial balance for DMN Corporation.

**TABLE 2.1**

**Trial Balance**

**DMN CORPORATION**
**Trial Balance**
**September 30, 2013**

| | Debit | Credit |
|---|---|---|
| Cash | $15,800 | |
| Accounts receivable | 5,200 | |
| Inventory | 4,800 | |
| Equipment | 5,000 | |
| Accumulated depreciation | | $ 1,400 |
| Accounts payable | | 2,000 |
| Notes payable | | 800 |
| Bonds payable | | 6,000 |
| Capital stock | | 12,000 |
| Additional paid-in capital | | 7,400 |
| Retained earnings | | 2,500 |
| Sales | | 13,800 |
| Cost of goods sold | 6,300 | |
| Advertising expense | 5,000 | |
| Depreciation expense | 2,800 | |
| Supplies expense | 1,000 | |
| Totals | $45,900 | $45,900 |

**TABLE 2.2   Adjusting Entries**

| Type | Description | Example | General Format of Adjustment |
|------|-------------|---------|------------------------------|
| Accrued revenues | An organization provides service to its customers before collecting cash | Unbilled client fees | Debit an asset<br>Credit a revenue |
| Accrued expenses | An organization receives service before paying cash | Unpaid employee wages | Debit an expense<br>Credit a liability |
| Deferred revenues | An organization receives cash before providing services to clients | Insurance premiums | Debit a liability<br>Credit a revenue |
| Prepaid expenses | An organization uses up assets that have previously been paid for | Supplies | Debit an expense<br>Credit an asset |
| Uncollectible accounts | Estimates of amounts clients will be unable or unwilling to pay | Bad debts | Debit an expense<br>Credit a contra-asset |
| Depreciation | Periodic allocation of an asset's cost to the periods that benefit from its use | Equipment | Debit an expense<br>Credit a contra-asset |

The basic idea behind the matching concept is simple: it costs money to make money. But, although simple, the matching concept is profoundly important in accounting. It gives us the theoretical basis for things like depreciation and pension accounting.

Once again, information technology is used in most accounting information systems to prepare a trial balance. And a trial balance can serve as an additional form of internal control, ensuring that the ledger accounts balance before preparing the financial statements.

The sixth step in the accounting cycle requires accountants to record adjusting entries and post them to the general ledger accounts. In this context, adjusting entries refer to internal journal entries made to account for timing differences in the flow of cash and the recognition of accrual-basis revenues and expenses. Adjusting entries are required by the matching concept in the FASB conceptual framework. Six types of **adjusting entries** are common in most accounting information systems as shown in Table 2.2. When I discuss adjusting entries with my students, I frequently group the six types into three parts: accruals, deferrals, and estimates.

Notice that each adjusting entry requires one account for the income statement and one account for the balance sheet. "Cash" is not involved in any of the preceding types of adjustments. The specific account titles will change depending upon the exact item being adjusted.

# Reflection and Self-Assessment                                    2.6

Describe a specific transaction for each adjustment type noted above. For example, an accrued revenue description might say: "DMN Corporation had unbilled client fees of $2,000." Then, explain how the adjustment would be recorded in the accounting information system. For example, debit Accounts Receivable and credit Sales.

After adjusting entries are journalized and posted, it's a good idea to prepare an adjusted trial balance. The purpose and nature of an adjusted trial balance are the same as for an ordinary trial balance; the only difference is the timing of its preparation. An adjusted trial balance reflects the status of the ledger accounts after the adjusting entries have been posted.

The accounting cycle continues with the preparation of the **general-purpose financial statements.** They are four in number and include:

- The *income statement,* which summarizes the results of business operations on the accrual basis for a specified period of time. The income statement reports revenues, expenses, gains, and losses from the accounting information system.

- The *statement of changes in shareholders' equity* reports changes in capital stock and retained earnings accounts for the same period of time as the income statement. Net income increases retained earnings; net losses and declaration of dividends decrease retained earnings. Capital stock can increase or decrease for a variety of reasons, the most common of which is issuance of new shares.

- The *balance sheet* shows the financial position of an organization at a specific point in time. It contains assets (listed in order of their liquidity), liabilities (listed with the most current due dates first), and equity (which comes from the statement of changes in shareholders' equity). Naturally, the assets must equal the liabilities plus equity on the balance sheet.

- The *statement of cash flows* is the relative newcomer to the general-purpose financial statements. Developed in the late 1980s by the Financial Accounting Standards Board, the statement of cash flows reports inflows and outflows of cash for a specified period of time. Cash flows on the statement fall into three categories: operating, investing, and financing. Accountants can choose between the direct and the indirect methods of calculating operating cash flows.

You'll probably have an entire course in auditing as part of your accounting program; we'll also discuss auditing in the last chapter of this text. Audits are important forms of internal control. Internal audits can help promote organizational efficiency and encourage compliance with management directives; external audits ensure that financial statements are prepared in accordance with generally accepted accounting principles.

You can access the financial statements of publicly traded companies online via EDGAR. EDGAR is administered by the Securities and Exchange Commission; its URL is www.sec.gov/edgar.shtml.

# Reflection and Self-Assessment                                    2.7

Use EDGAR or some other source to access the financial statements of Amazon. What is your assessment of the corporation's financial position and performance based on the statements?

After preparing financial statements, the accounting information system must be readied for the next fiscal period's entries. That objective is accomplished via closing entries. Balances from temporary (nominal) accounts on the income statement are transferred into retained earnings (a real, permanent account in the equity section of the balance sheet). Finally, then, the accounting information system produces a post-closing trial balance. Similar in form to the other trial balances discussed above, the post-closing trial balance differs in content. Because all the nominal accounts have been closed, the post-closing trial balance contains only balance sheet accounts. See the illustration in Table 2.3 for an example.

**TABLE 2.3**
**Post-closing Trial Balance**

| DMN CORPORATION Post-closing Trial Balance September 30, 2013 | | |
|---|---|---|
| | **Debit** | **Credit** |
| Cash | $15,800 | |
| Accounts receivable | 5,200 | |
| Inventory | 4,800 | |
| Equipment | 5,000 | |
| Accumulated depreciation | | $ 1,400 |
| Accounts payable | | 2,000 |
| Notes payable | | 800 |
| Bonds payable | | 6,000 |
| Capital stock | | 12,000 |
| Additional paid-in capital | | 7,400 |
| Retained earnings | | 1,200 |
| Totals | $30,800 | $30,800 |

Broadly speaking, accounting information systems fall into one of two types: view-driven systems or event-driven systems. View-driven systems are the more traditional; they are focused on providing a particular "view" of the data and information—the view provided by the general-purpose financial statements. The steps in the accounting cycle are primarily focused on collecting data and reporting information in view-driven systems.

We'll talk about event-driven systems later in the text. Event-driven systems focus on capturing more comprehensive information about business events. A view-driven system would be concerned about which accounts and amounts to debit and credit; an event-driven system would capture those data and other details, such as sizes and colors of merchandise ordered. Event-driven systems use relational database technology to provide various ways of viewing the data—it's possible to get the general-purpose financial statements from an event-driven system, but it's also possible to get a much greater variety of reports as well.

You may be able to imagine how much time accountants spent simply completing the steps in the cycle before the advent of information technology. Later in the chapter, we'll take a look at how IT has facilitated the accounting cycle, as well as ways in which human judgment is still paramount in its 10 steps.

## CODING SYSTEMS

In both manual and automated accounting information systems, each account typically has both a name and a number; account numbers facilitate transaction recording and posting, particularly when the AIS relies heavily on information technology. In most cases, you'll walk into an organization with an established chart of accounts; however, at some point in your career, you may need to create a chart from scratch. At a minimum, you'll need to be able to understand your company's and/or clients' charts of accounts. In this section, we'll look at some of the systems used in practice to establish and modify charts of accounts and other items.

Williamson (2006) lists five important reasons for maintaining a clear, logical chart of accounts:

- efficiency of data capture, entry, and analysis . . .
- frequency of use and familiarity . . .
- consistency and understanding of use within the organization . . .
- saving on computer processing time and storage . . .
- similar items can be related by means of a coding system, whereas a verbal description could be very inefficient . . .

In addition, Williamson identified several common coding systems often used in organizations; while they are not exhaustive, they do provide a comprehensive overview. So, let's look at four of them briefly.

- *Sequential coding,* as the name implies, simply numbers items in sequence. Think of the checks in your checkbook when you think of sequential coding. In automated accounting information systems, transactions might be assigned sequential numbers by a computer as a method of internal control.
- *Block coding* is quite common in a chart of accounts. Numbers are assigned in blocks; each block is reserved for a particular kind of account. For example, all current asset accounts might start with "1," while equity accounts might start with "5." Thus, you can tell what kind of account you're dealing with simply by looking at its first digit.
- *Hierarchical codes* are a more sophisticated form of block coding. In hierarchical coding, each digit/block of digits conveys important information to people who know the code. Many enterprise resource planning systems, such as PeopleSoft, use hierarchical coding. Hierarchical coding is also very common in government AIS. They use a system called "fund accounting."
- *Mnemonic codes,* by their nature, help people remember the meaning of the code. At my university, as at most universities, course prefixes are mnemonic. ACC is the code for courses in the accounting department, while CIS stands for computer information systems. In an accounting information system, product and customer codes might be mnemonic in nature. Keep in mind that data about products and customers are commonly stored in master files, as noted in Chapter 1's discussion of the elements of the AIS.

See Table 2.4 for examples of coding systems.

**TABLE 2.4    Chart of Accounts Coding**

| Coding System | Example | Format |
| --- | --- | --- |
| Sequential | Purchase order numbers | 101, 102, 103 |
| Block | Quickbooks standard chart of accounts for retail companies | Current assets: 101, 105, 109<br>Plant assets: 202, 206, 208<br>Current liabilities: 301, 303, 305 |
| Hierarchical | State university | 101-11-08-81<br>101: Big City campus<br>11: academic affairs division<br>08: college of business<br>81: accounting department |
| Mnemonic | Inventory items | DVR: digital video recorder<br>FSTV: flat-screen television |

# HUMAN JUDGMENT AND INFORMATION TECHNOLOGY

Susan Wolcott, of Wolcott Lynch Associates, has developed a methodology for enhancing critical thinking and judgment skills. Called the "Steps for Better Thinking," you can find more information about it at www .wolcottlynch.com. We'll be exploring SBT in more depth in the chapter on decision-making models and knowledge management.

Using information technology tools to assist in the collection, processing, and dissemination of accounting information is the norm in most modern organizations. And, while IT has had a profound impact, it has only increased the need for and opportunity to exercise human judgment.

**Human judgment** comes into play in the AIS in at least the following ways:

- *Designing source documents.* Source documents should be clear and easy to read, omit unnecessary information, and provide plenty of space for filling in required data. Sequential numbering, such as in your checkbook, is also important for strong internal control.
- *Recognizing recordable transactions.* Not every document in an AIS indicates a recordable transaction; further, not every recordable transaction is represented by a source document. Therefore, accountants must exercise professional judgment in recognizing recordable transactions. For example, the market value of land may increase significantly over time; however, such increases are not recordable transactions.
- *Estimating amounts and interpreting accounting rules.* Many journal entries, particularly adjusting entries, require the use of estimates. For example, accountants must estimate the useful economic life and salvage value of fixed assets to calculate depreciation. Further, FASB pronouncements and other authoritative accounting documents require significant interpretation. As principles-based accounting standards, such as International Financial Reporting Standards (IFRS), become the norm, interpretation will become even more important.

At the same time, **information technology** has cut down on the tedium associated with many steps in the accounting cycle. Transactions can be posted automatically or with the touch of a button; the same applies to closing the accounts at the end of the period. Reports, including the general-purpose financial statements, can easily be generated with the "touch of a button" as well.

# CRITICAL THINKING

I'd like to explore two topics with you in this chapter's critical thinking section: recognizing transactions that should be recorded in the AIS and creating a coding system for a chart of accounts.

As you read earlier in the chapter, human judgment is important in several areas of the accounting cycle—one of which is recognizing transactions that should (and should not) be recorded. Consider the three items that follow, along with their explanations:

1. *FNF Corporation sold merchandise with a cost of $800 to customers on account for $1,000.* This transaction should be recorded in the AIS; goods were exchanged between two willing parties, and the evidence of it (source documents) is clear and objective. Assuming the use of a perpetual inventory system, this transaction would be recorded as follows: debit Accounts Receivable, $1,000; debit Cost of Goods Sold, $800; credit Sales, $1,000; credit Inventory, $800.

2. *During 20x3, FNF Corporation purchased temporary investments with a cost of $10,000. The market value of those investments at the end of 20x3 was $12,000; FNF classified them as trading securities.* Of course, the initial purchase of the investments should be recorded in the AIS. But the increase in market value also should be recorded. According to FASB No. 115, trading securities should be reported at their fair value. At first, this idea may seem to violate the objectivity principle of the FASB conceptual

framework. The key here, though, is that the market value of the investments is readily determinable by looking at the financial press. An accountant couldn't simply decide to increase the market value based on his/her own judgment; but, if the market value of the investments can be looked up, then the investments must be increased. The $2,000 difference would be referred to as an *unrealized gain,* which means that it hasn't been "economically experienced" by FNF. To experience (realize) the gain, FNF would have to sell the investments. In your intermediate accounting courses, you'll learn a lot more about which elements of financial statements are reported at their market value. Other valuation bases include historical cost, net realizable value, and present value.

3. *FNF purchased the land for its headquarters 10 years ago at a cost of $65,000. In 20x3, a real estate investor offered to purchase the land for $165,000.* In this case, the $100,000 would not be recorded in the AIS unless FNF actually sold the land. The fact that they've had an offer to buy it isn't objective enough; in addition, the land is not held as an investment—it's used for their headquarters. So, unlike item 2, the increase in market value would not result in an "unrealized gain" for FNF.

So, as you can tell, recognizing which transactions to record in an AIS requires critical thinking and a solid understanding of accounting principles.

When it comes to designing a chart of accounts, critical thinking is important. Whatever coding system an organization uses (sequential, block, hierarchical, or mnemonic), it must be easily understood and rational. Consider the example below, which used a random number generator to assign account numbers in an AIS:

**Poorly Designed Chart of Accounts**

| | |
|---|---|
| 252 | Cash |
| 256 | Accounts receivable |
| 311 | Accounts payable |
| 698 | Wages payable |
| 461 | Capital stock |
| 507 | Retained earnings |
| 824 | Sales |
| 617 | Interest earned |
| 633 | Cost of goods sold |
| 924 | Depreciation expense |

There's no "rhyme or reason" to that chart of accounts; you would practically have to memorize each number and account name individually. On the other hand, the chart of accounts could be made much more understandable with a block-coding system:

**Block Coded Chart of Accounts**

| | |
|---|---|
| 101 | Cash |
| 103 | Accounts receivable |
| 301 | Accounts payable |
| 305 | Wages payable |
| 402 | Capital stock |
| 406 | Retained earnings |
| 501 | Sales |
| 633 | Cost of goods sold |
| 635 | Depreciation expense |
| 701 | Interest earned |

In the block-coded chart, current assets begin with "1," while current liabilities begin with "3." Equity accounts start with "4." Operating revenue (such as sales) is differentiated from nonoperating revenue (such as interest earned) easily with block coding.

Consider these additional account titles and suggested numbers that would conform to the block-coding system:

| | |
|---|---|
| 105 | Inventory |
| 201 | Land |
| 203 | Equipment |
| 213 | Accumulated depreciation—equipment |
| 405 | Treasury stock |
| 801 | Interest expense |

Inventory, as a current asset, has a number starting with "1." Because current assets start with "1" and current liabilities with "3," what kinds of accounts should start with "2"? Long-term assets, such as land and equipment. Notice the numbering similarity between equipment (203) and its related accumulated depreciation account (213). As an equity account, treasury stock has a number that starts with "4." Interest expense starts with an "8" because it would normally be considered a nonoperating expense.

Is block coding the only way to organize a chart of accounts? Definitely not. Is it the best way? In some cases, sure—but not every time. And you could come up with completely different numbers even using a block-coding system. The important idea is being able to explain the coding system to others so that they can use it effectively.

## Summary

This chapter has presented a review of the steps in the accounting cycle. Here is the usual summary based on the chapter's learning objectives:

1. *Differentiate accounting and bookkeeping.* Bookkeeping is the part of accounting concerned with recording transactions in the AIS. Accounting goes far beyond that, concerning itself with identifying those transactions and communicating information for decision making.

2. *List, discuss, and complete, in order, the steps in the accounting cycle.* The chapter examined 10 steps in the accounting cycle:

   a. Obtain information about external transactions from source documents.

   b. Analyze transactions.

   c. Record the transactions in a journal.

   d. Post from the journal to the general ledger accounts.

   e. Prepare an unadjusted trial balance.

   f. Record adjusting entries and post to the general ledger accounts.

   g. Prepare an adjusted trial balance.

   h. Prepare financial statements.

   i. Close the temporary accounts to retained earnings (at year-end only).

   j. Prepare a post-closing trial balance (at year-end only).

3. *Identify common internal controls associated with the accounting cycle.* Internal controls include sequentially numbered documents, physical security, transaction limits, equality of debits and credits, trial balances, and audits.

4. *Describe common coding systems and how they are used in the AIS.* The chapter discusses four common systems: sequential, block, hierarchical, and mnemonic. Most charts of accounts use block or hierarchical coding. Source documents, such as checks, should be sequentially coded; inventory items may use mnemonic coding.

5. *Explain how human judgment and information technology affect the accounting cycle.* Accountants exercise their judgment in deciding which transactions are recordable in the accounting information system. Information technology can be used for a variety of tasks in the cycle: recording transactions, posting them to the ledger, preparing trial balances and financial statements, and closing the accounts.

Accounting education has typically emphasized transaction processing throughout the undergraduate curriculum; understanding this topic is important in your education as an accountant. We'll use it as a foundational topic, exploring more advanced issues throughout the rest of the text.

| | | | |
|---|---|---|---|
| **Key Terms** | accounting, *21* | general-purpose financial | principles of debit |
| | accounting cycle, *22* | statements, *27* | and credit, *23* |
| | adjusting entries, *26* | human judgment, *30* | source documents, *22* |
| | bookkeeping, *21* | information technology, *30* | |
| | external transactions, *22* | internal transactions, *22* | |

**Chapter References**

Spiceland, J. D., J. F. Sepe, and L. A. Tomassini. 2001. *Intermediate Accounting.* Updated 2nd ed. New York: Irwin/McGraw-Hill.

Williamson, D. 2006. *Coding Systems for Accountants: An Introduction.* www.duncanwil.co.uk (June 20, 2006).

**End-of-Chapter Activities**

1. *Reading review questions.*

   a. In your own words, explain the similarities and differences between accounting and bookkeeping.

   b. What systems do accountants use to create and modify a chart of accounts?

   c. What internal controls are common in the accounting cycle?

   d. How is human judgment involved in the accounting cycle?

   e. How has information technology been employed in the accounting cycle?

   f. List and discuss the six common types of adjusting entries found in most accounting information systems.

   g. Explain the purpose and structure of each general-purpose financial statement.

   h. Respond to the questions for the chapter's "AIS in the Business World."

2. *Multiple choice review questions.* Please indicate the best answer for each question.

   1. Which of the following best explains the relationship between bookkeeping and accounting?

      a. Bookkeeping is one activity involved in accounting.

      b. Accounting is one activity involved in bookkeeping.

c.  Bookkeeping and accounting are two terms for the same thing.

d.  Bookkeeping never involves human judgment, while accounting always does.

2.  How many trial balances are commonly prepared as part of the 10 steps in the accounting cycle?

   a.  One

   b.  Two

   c.  Three

   d.  More than three

3.  Which of the following is the best example of an accrued revenue?

   a.  Interest earned but not received on a note receivable

   b.  Interest received but not earned on a note receivable

   c.  Sales on account

   d.  Purchases on account

4.  All of the following chart of accounts coding systems typically use numbers except:

   a.  Block

   b.  Hierarchical

   c.  Mnemonic

   d.  Sequential

5.  Human judgment can be involved in the AIS via:

   a.  Designing source documents

   b.  Recognizing recordable transactions

   c.  Estimating amounts

   d.  All of the above

3.  *Reading review problem.* According to the investor relations section of its Web site (www.regmovies.com), Regal Entertainment Group "operates the largest and most geographically diverse theatre circuit in the United States, consisting of 7,342 screens in 576 theatres in 42 states." Common transactions in Regal's accounting information system include selling tickets, paying employees, purchasing snack foods, advertising new films, and declaring dividends on its capital stock. Regal's stock trades under the symbol "RGC."

   a.  How should Regal code its chart of accounts to facilitate financial reporting? Create account numbers for cash, capital stock, and advertising expense for the following Regal theatres: Regal O'Fallon Stadium 14 (O'Fallon, Missouri), Regal Windward Stadium 10 (Kaneohe, Hawaii), and Regal Goldstream Stadium 16 (Fairbanks, Alaska).

   b.  Suggest three source documents that Regal would use to complete the steps in the accounting cycle.

   c.  What journal entries would Regal make to record the transactions indicated above?

   d.  What roles would human judgment and information technology play in Regal's transaction processing activities?

4.  *Making choices and exercising judgment.*

   a.  Which of the following would be recordable transactions in an accounting information system? For each item that would not be a recordable transaction, explain why not.

      i.  Purchasing land with a down payment and a note payable.

      ii.  Verifying an increase in the market value of land.

    iii. Establishing an exclusive relationship with a raw material supplier.

    iv. Estimating the amount of warranty expense for the next accounting period.

    v. Negotiating with an employee union for wage increases.

  b. How will principles-based accounting influence the design of accounting information systems and the steps in the accounting cycle?

  c. Use EDGAR to obtain the 10-K reports for Barnes & Noble dated 29 July 2013 and 27 June 2012. Compare their financial statements and comment on which company is stronger. Barnes & Noble's stock ticker symbol is BKS.

**5.** *Field exercises.*

  a. Point your Web browser to **www.download.com**. Investigate BS1 Accounting and NolaPro Free Accounting—two general ledger packages that can help companies with the steps in the accounting cycle. Compare and contrast the two software packages.

  b. Point your Web browser to my AIS blog (**www.bobhurtais.blogspot.com**). Check out the entry dated 6 January 2014 titled "chart of accounts coding systems." What system does Harvard Law School use?

  c. Contact an accounting professional at a local organization such as your university, a bank, or a retail store. Find out how he/she employs human judgment and information technology in completing the steps of the accounting cycle.

**6.** *Journal entries.* Record each of the following transactions in general journal format.

  a. Issued 50,000 shares of $1 par capital stock for $35 each.

  b. Billed customers for services provided, $10,000.

  c. Purchased supplies on account, $3,000.

  d. Paid monthly utility bill, $1,500.

  e. Verified 20 percent increase in market price of stock.

  f. Paid wages for the current month, $6,000.

  g. Purchased equipment with a list price of $50,000 by making a 20 percent down payment and financing the remainder with a six-month, 12 percent note payable.

  h. Collected cash from customers, $5,000.

  i. Paid vendors, $1,400.

  j. Recorded one month's accrued interest on note payable.

**7.** *Adjusting entries.* The unadjusted trial balance for GLP Corporation appears on the next page.
End-of-period analysis revealed the following:

  a. The market value of equipment had decreased by 30 percent of its original cost. Depreciation for the quarter totaled $1,000.

  b. The note payable was signed on 1 August 20x4. Its interest rate was 10 percent, and no interest had been recorded since the signing.

  c. Unpaid employee wages at 30 September totaled $1,000.

  d. Deferred fees represented a consulting contract signed at the beginning of September. The contract's duration is three months, and the work is spread evenly throughout the contract period.

  e. Supplies on hand totaled $150.

  f. The market value of capital stock had increased by 15 percent.

  g. Actual bad debt write-offs during September were $300; 1 percent of sales will likely become uncollectible in the coming period.

**GLP CORPORATION**
**Trial Balance**
**30 September 20x4**

|  | Debit | Credit |
|---|---|---|
| Cash | $ 6,000 | |
| Accounts receivable | 2,500 | |
| Allowance for bad debts | | $ 200 |
| Inventory | 4,500 | |
| Supplies | 800 | |
| Equipment | 15,000 | |
| Accumulated depreciation—equipment | | 10,000 |
| Accounts payable | | 1,200 |
| Notes payable | | 6,000 |
| Deferred fees | | 900 |
| Capital stock | | 7,000 |
| Additional paid-in capital | | 8,000 |
| Retained earnings | | 11,000 |
| Sales | | 16,000 |
| Cost of goods sold | 13,500 | |
| Advertising expense | 5,000 | |
| Wages expense | 12,000 | |
| Miscellaneous expense | 1,000 | |
| Totals | $60,300 | $60,300 |

Prepare the required adjusting entries based on the preceding information. Then, prepare an adjusted trial balance.

8. *Financial statements.* Use the adjusted trial balance from Problem 7 to prepare an income statement for the quarter ended 30 September 20x4 and a balance sheet as of 30 September 20x4 for GLP Corporation.

9. *Coding systems.* Which type of coding system is indicated in each of the following independent situations? Be prepared to explain your reasoning.
    a. Airport codes (LAX, OGG)
    b. Automatically assigned transaction numbers in a cash register
    c. Consecutively numbered purchase orders (101, 102, 103, and so on)
    d. State of Kentucky (consult the blog post referenced in Problem 5b above)
    e. Invoice numbers
    f. National Association of Home Builders chart of accounts (consult the blog post again)
    g. Standard chart of accounts included with QuickBooks
    h. Telephone numbers
    i. Universal Product Codes (UPCs)
    j. ZIP codes (91768, 63135)

10. *Terminology.* Please match each item on the right with the most appropriate item on the left.

| | |
|---|---|
| 1. Accrued revenue | a. Book of original entry |
| 2. Credit | b. Cash is received before service is provided |
| 3. Debit | c. Decreases to revenue |
| 4. Deferred revenue | d. Increases to liabilities |
| 5. Human judgment | e. Purchase orders, invoices, and receipts |
| 6. Information technology | f. Service is provided before cash is received |
| 7. Journal | g. Simplifies the bookkeeping process |
| 8. Posting | h. Transferring information from the journal to the ledger |
| 9. Source document | i. Used to recognize recordable transactions |
| 10. Trial balance | j. Verifies the equality of debits and credits in the ledger |

11. *Multiple choice questions.*

1. BRN Corporation has two divisions: California and Nevada. Both divisions have the same basic chart of accounts, which numbers current assets in the 100s, plant assets in the 200s, and so on. BRN differentiates them with an appended "C" or "N" after the account number. From BRN's point of view, the chart of accounts coding system would best be described as:

   a. Block

   b. Hierarchical

   c. Mnemonic

   d. Sequential

2. Consider the data from Question 1. From the divisions' point of view, the chart of accounts coding system would best be described as:

   a. Block

   b. Hierarchical

   c. Mnemonic

   d. Sequential

3. Which of the following is a characteristic of all adjusting entries?

   a. They are written in the journal, but not posted to the ledger.

   b. They always involve an entry to Cash or Retained Earnings.

   c. They always include one nominal account and one permanent account.

   d. They always involve estimates.

4. Consider the trial balance of DMN Corporation shown in Table 2.1. Based on that trial balance alone, which of the following income statement items would total $7,500?

   a. Revenue

   b. Gross profit

   c. Net income

   d. Net loss

5. Consider the trial balance of DMN Corporation shown in Table 2.1. Based on that trial balance alone, DMN's income statement would report:

   a. Net income of $7,500

   b. Net loss of $7,500

   c. Net income of $1,300

   d. Net loss of $1,300

12. *Statement evaluation.* Determine whether each of the following statements is (i) always true, (ii) sometimes true, or (iii) never true. For those that are (ii) sometimes true, explain when the statement is true.

    a. Bookkeeping and accounting are two ways of referring to the same thing.

    b. If a transaction increases a liability, it will also increase an expense.

    c. The accounting cycle involves human judgment.

    d. A company's chart of accounts should use block coding.

    e. Information technology has eliminated the need for human judgment in the accounting cycle.

    f. An "accrual" refers to a situation where a company provides service before receiving cash.

    g. An adjusting entry for depreciation recognizes an asset's loss in market value over time.

    h. Adjusting entries involve one balance sheet account and one income statement account, but never cash.

    i. In automated accounting information systems, block coding facilitates closing entries.

    j. The complete accounting cycle incorporates three different forms of a trial balance.

13. *Excel application.* On 10 January 20x4, TPL Corporation purchased equipment for use in its operations. TPL made a down payment on the equipment of $25,000 and financed the remainder of its $65,000 total cost with a 6 percent, one-year note payable. TPL expects to use the equipment for five years and plans to sell it for $3,000 at the end of that time. Use appropriate Excel formulas to create depreciation schedules for the equipment using both straight-line and sum-of-the-years' digits depreciation. (Check figures: Year 3 book value using straight-line = $27,800. Year 4 depreciation expense using SYD = $8,267.)

# Chapter **Three**

# Internal Controls

## AIS in the Business World

### Bank of America

According to its 2012 annual report, Bank of America (BofA)

> is headquartered in Charlotte, N.C. As of December 31, 2012, we operated in all 50 states, the District of Columbia and more than 40 countries. Through our banking and various nonbanking subsidiaries throughout the United States and in international markets, we provide a diversified range of banking and nonbanking financial services and products through five business segments: Consumer and Business Banking, Consumer Real Estate Services, Global Banking, Global Markets and Global Wealth, and Investment Management.

Like all banks, BofA must maintain strong internal control over its cash. In this chapter, we'll consider the role and purpose of internal control in all types of organizations. We'll look at how to create a strong internal control plan, and recognize strengths and weaknesses in those plans.

### *Discussion Questions*

1. What is internal control? What are its fundamental purposes?
2. How are internal controls related to an organization's risk exposures?
3. How would BofA (and other organizations) use COSO's Internal Control—Integrated Framework to develop and maintain strong internal control?

Internal controls have been at the heart of accounting information systems practically since AIS emerged as a separate field of study for accounting students. A lack of sound internal controls can have serious consequences for a company—particularly with the advent of Sarbanes-Oxley and the Public Companies Accounting Oversight Board. In this chapter, we'll lay a foundation in the study of internal control; later chapters will apply the basic ideas you learn here to specific contexts within your study of accounting information systems.

When you complete your study of this chapter, you should be able to:

1. Define *internal control* and explain its importance in the accounting information system.
2. Explain the basic purposes of internal control and its relationship to risk.
3. Describe and give examples of various kinds of risk exposures.
4. Prepare a simple risk/control matrix.
5. Summarize and explain the importance of COSO's 2013 "Internal Control—Integrated Framework."
6. Critique existing internal control systems and design effective internal controls.

A solid understanding of internal controls is important in any area of accounting. Risk analysis, which should precede the development and implementation of an internal control plan, is one of the functional competencies listed in the AICPA core competency framework. In addition, most accounting professional exams (such as the CPA exam) have questions about internal control.

## INTERNAL CONTROL DEFINITION AND IMPORTANCE

You can find COSO's Web site at www.coso.org. Click the "publications" link for executive summaries of the reports discussed here.

So what is internal control? In ***Internal Control—Integrated Framework*** (2013), the Committee of Sponsoring Organizations of the Treadway Commission **(COSO)** defined **internal control** as "a process, effected by an entity's board of directors, management and other personnel, designed to provide reasonable assurance regarding the achievement of objectives relating to operations, reporting, and compliance." Notice these important elements of the COSO definition:

- *Internal control is a process.* Because internal control is a process, it is subject to process improvement; single correct answers to control problems seldom exist. Accountants must use judgment and experience in designing and implementing internal controls; the controls must be periodically reviewed to ensure their continued effectiveness.
- *Internal control necessarily involves people throughout the organization.* The COSO definition positions internal control firmly and broadly within the organization. Thus, internal control is not the sole responsibility of accounting professionals, information technology professionals, or financial statement auditors. Internal controls, therefore, require discussion during design, implementation, and evaluation. They impact human behavior, and control systems designers, as far as possible, must anticipate their behavioral effects. In addition, internal controls are subject to a cost/benefit constraint, similar to the constraint identified in the FASB Conceptual Framework of Accounting.
- *Internal controls are designed to provide reasonable assurance.* Dictionary.com defines reasonable as "governed by or being in accordance with reason or sound thinking; being within the bounds of common sense; not excessive or extreme." So, internal controls should not, and probably cannot, be designed to provide absolute assurance of anything. Almost any internal control can be circumvented/thwarted/foiled through collaboration or collusion. For example, if a warehouse employee works with a receiving clerk, it may be possible to steal inventory in spite of strong separation of duties.

Why are internal controls important? One answer certainly lies with the purposes of internal control (as shown in Table 3.1). Most managers, stockholders, employees, and other organizational stakeholders want a company to operate as effectively and efficiently as possible, to have financial statements that are reliable, and to make sure their assets are safe. Apart from those issues, though, internal control is also legally mandated by several important pieces of legislation.

You can find out more about the FCPA on its Web site: www.usdoj .gov/criminal/fraud/ fcpa.html. Another great source I've often used for FCPA information is Mike Koehler's FCPA Professor blog. You'll find it at www .fcpaprofessor.com.

The **Foreign Corrupt Practices Act (FCPA)** was passed by the U.S. Congress in 1977. U.S. businesses had begun expanding internationally in the mid-1970s. And, in some foreign countries, bribery is an acceptable way of doing business. In fact, an SEC investigation in the 1970s showed that over 400 U.S. companies had paid bribes to foreign officials for a variety of reasons. Although bribery is an acceptable business practice in some countries, it is not in the United States. So, the FCPA was enacted to stop those practices by U.S. businesses and to restore some confidence in U.S. business practices around the world. The FCPA requires corporations covered by its provisions to maintain an adequate system of internal accounting controls. The act also states, "no person shall knowingly circumvent or knowingly fail to implement a system of internal accounting controls or knowingly falsify any book, record, or account." The legislation also mentions the concept of reasonable assurance, defining it as "such level of detail and degree of assurance as would satisfy prudent officials in the conduct of their own affairs." Companies failing to comply with the Foreign Corrupt Practices Act can be subject to both fines and imprisonment. You may be familiar with the 2012 scandal involving Walmart de Mexico's alleged violations of the FCPA.

Details of SOX are available all over the Internet. One site I've found useful is www .soxlaw.com. It is a proprietary site, but the information is accurate and easy to read.

In response to the corporate scandals of the late 20th century, Congress passed the **Sarbanes-Oxley Act of 2002 (SOX)**. SOX is the most sweeping accounting-related legislation business professionals have seen since the FCPA. It is a broad-reaching act that significantly changed the way U.S. companies do business, as well as impacting the roles of top management, the board of directors, independent auditors, and audit committees. Provisions of SOX related to internal controls include:

- Management and the external auditors must assess the company's internal controls on an annual basis.

- Management has certain required disclosures when reporting to the SEC. They include acknowledgment that management is personally and organizationally responsible for the design and implementation of internal controls, particularly as they relate to reasonable assurance of reliable financial statements. Management also must disclose any internal control changes since the last reporting cycle, if those changes are likely to have a noticeable effect on internal controls over financial reporting. Finally, management must certify that they have informed the auditors and the board of directors' audit committee of any significant problems or weaknesses in internal control.

- Management must personally sign the required certifications and reports related to the preceding items. The signature cannot be delegated, even via a power of attorney.

**TABLE 3.1   Purposes (and Examples) of Internal Control**

| |
|---|
| Safeguarding assets (daily deposits of cash in a bank) |
| Ensuring financial statement reliability (supervisory review of complex transactions) |
| Promoting operational efficiency (maintaining a centralized purchasing department) |
| Encouraging compliance with management's directives (distributing a company procedures manual) |

Many of the SOX requirements related to internal control are found in section 404 of the act. In practice, people often refer to conducting/having a "404 audit."

So, internal controls are very important for organizations of all types. As an accounting professional, you may be involved in the design, implementation, or evaluation of internal controls as an external (independent) auditor, internal auditor, controller, or consultant.

## Reflection and Self-Assessment                                    3.1

Compare the content and purpose of the FCPA and SOX. What similarities and differences do you notice? If a non-accountant asked you how you know that financial statements are fair and reliable, what would you say?

To design effective internal controls, accountants and managers should consider the risks associated with doing business. By identifying risks, we can develop controls to mitigate them successfully.

## RISKS

Risk is a part of everyday life—both personally and professionally. The question is, are businesses taking risks unnecessarily, to the point that they cannot operate effectively or rely on their accounting systems to produce reliable information? Inappropriate risk-taking behavior is at the heart of many fraud cases, such as Enron and Bernie Madoff.

Most business professionals, including accountants, find it easier to think about risk if they have some organizational structure for doing so. An organizational structure for knowledge, like types of risk, is sometimes referred to as a *taxonomy*.

Brown (2001) takes a very practical view toward the management of risk. He identified four categories of risk and suggested eight specific risks within the four categories, as shown in Figure 3.1. Here are some definitions and examples of the elements of **Brown's taxonomy of risk:**

1. *Financial risks* are related to monetary activities. Let's look at some examples that Bank of America might face.
   a. *Market risk* refers to changes in a company's stock prices, investment values, and interest rates. For the year ended 3 January 2014, BofA's stock price ranged from a low of $10.98 to a high of $16.50. Any publicly traded organization is subject to market risk.
   b. *Credit risk* is associated with customers' unwillingness or inability to pay amounts owed to the organization. As you may recall from your earlier study of accounting, a bank's assets are actually its loans to customers. If BofA fails to evaluate loan applications carefully and/or establish appropriate qualifying criteria, it will experience the negative impact of credit risk.
   c. *Liquidity risk* involves the possibility that a company will not have sufficient cash and near-cash assets available to meet its short-term obligations. According to the 10-K it filed with the SEC dated 28 February 2013, BofA's cash balance as of 31 December 2012 was $110,752 million. Whether that exposes BofA to significant liquidity risk is a matter of judgment.

Think about risks you have taken today. For example, you risked that your car wouldn't start when you came to school. You may have taken a risk in leaving your house, residence hall, or apartment later than usual. List six additional risks you've taken today and organize them in some way that makes sense to you.

**FIGURE 3.1**
**Brown's Risk Taxonomy**

| | |
|---|---|
| Financial risk<br>◇ Market risk<br>◇ Credit risk<br>◇ Liquidity risk | Strategic risk<br>◇ Legal and regulatory risk<br>◇ Business strategy risk |
| Operational risk<br>◇ Systems risk<br>◇ Human error risk | Hazard risk<br>◇ Directors' and officers' liability risk |

2. *Operational risks* concern the people, assets, and technologies used to create value for the organization's customers.

   a. *Systems risk* relates directly to information technology (IT). Like all major banks, BofA relies heavily on information technology in its operations. Systems risks include malware, data theft, and server crashes.

   b. *Human error risk* recognizes the possibility that people in the organization will make mistakes. If a BofA teller cashes a check without an authorized signature, BofA experiences the serious consequences of human error risk.

3. *Strategic risks,* according to Brown (2001, p. 44), "relate to the entity's decision-making process at the senior management and board of directors level."

   a. *Legal and regulatory risk* is concerned with the chance that those parties might break laws that result in financial, legal, or operational sanctions. In addition to being subject to the provisions of the FCPA and SOX, banks are also subject to the Bank Secrecy Act and the USA Patriot Act. If BofA violates the provisions of those laws (or others), it will be exposed to legal and regulatory risk.

   b. *Business strategy risk* comprises poor decision making related to a company's basis for competing in its markets. As noted in this chapter's AIS in the Business World, BofA operates in all 50 states, the District of Columbia and more than 40 countries. In making strategic decisions about where to operate, BofA must consider many factors, such as economic stability, workforce availability, and the presence of other banks.

4. *Hazard risk,* in Brown's taxonomy, has a single category: *directors' and officers' liability.* Organizations in which directors and officers are accused of mismanagement by shareholders, government agencies, employees, or other stakeholders bear this risk in a very direct way. We talked about SOX in relation to legal and regulatory risk, but it is also related to hazard risk. The legislation provides both organizational AND personal penalties for violation.

Brown's taxonomy of risk is not the only one available for risk assessment. In the 2013 framework, COSO discusses risk in terms of the three categories of objectives it identifies: operations, reporting, and compliance. Using an established taxonomy to identify risks helps organizations ensure that they've "covered all the bases" as they begin to develop internal control plans.

## Reflection and Self-Assessment                                          3.3

The Institute of Internal Auditors (www.theiia.org) publishes a monthly newsletter called "Tone at the Top." Look up an article from the February 2002 edition titled "The Lessons that Lie Beneath." List three ways the information in the article relates to the material you just read on risk assessment and internal control.

Many students ask me about the risk of fraud. The Association of Certified Fraud Examiners (www.acfe.com) provides outstanding tools for assessing the risk of fraud in organizations. In terms of the Brown taxonomy, fraud can manifest itself as liquidity risk, systems risk, legal and regulatory risk, and/or hazard risk.

## COSO'S INTERNAL CONTROL INTEGRATED FRAMEWORK

COSO comprises five professional accounting organizations: the American Accounting Association, the American Institute of Certified Public Accountants, the Financial Executives Institute, the Institute of Internal Auditors, and the Institute of Management Accountants. Originally published in 1992, COSO's Internal Control Integrated Framework was updated in 2013.

COSO laid out the similarities and differences between the original and updated frameworks as follows:

- Similarities
  - Internal control definition
  - Objective categories: operations, reporting, and compliance
  - Components of a strong internal control plan
  - Necessity for all plan components to work together
  - Importance of judgment in establishing sound internal control
- Differences
  - Environmental changes, such as economic conditions and legal considerations
  - Expanded objectives for operations and reporting
  - Creation of fundamental concepts that support the components
  - Additional examples and approaches

Figure 3.2 specifies the five components of the COSO Internal Control Integrated Framework.

**FIGURE 3.2**
**Components of the COSO Internal Control Framework**

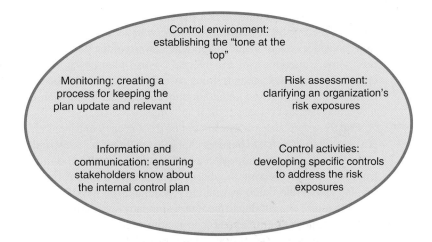

To create a strong, viable internal control plan, organizations must establish an appropriate *control environment*. Often referred to as the "tone at the top," the control environment ensures that internal control is seen as a serious, important, worthy topic throughout the organization. Top management can start creating a good control environment by mentioning internal control in organizational communications, providing training and development opportunities, and maintaining open lines of communication regarding internal control effectiveness (or lack thereof).

Well-developed internal control plans are predicated on a sound *risk assessment*. Earlier in this chapter, we looked at Brown's risk taxonomy as a way of categorizing and discussing risk. Whether that or some other taxonomy, it's critical to identify an organization's risk exposures as a precursor to creating internal controls. Risk exposures should be based on an organization's goals and objectives. For example, if a company's goals include increasing the percentage of sales from new customers, it must consider things that could interfere with that goal, such as insufficient advertising.

After identifying its risks, the organization is in a good position to establish *control activities*—policies, processes, and procedures that will address the risks in a cost-effective way and provide reasonable assurance that the goals will be achieved. Organizations can "address" risks in at least three ways: prevention, detection, and correction. To address the risk of insufficient advertising, an organization might allocate more money to the advertising budget and/or conduct a survey to assess the effectiveness of current advertising methods.

## Reflection and Self-Assessment                                    3.4

Consider the internal controls listed below. For each one, explain: (i) the risk it addresses, (ii) the risk category from Brown's taxonomy, (iii) the broad purpose of internal control it achieves, and (iv) the nature of the control (preventive, detective, corrective).

1. Reconciling a bank statement.
2. Requiring that all purchase requisitions are coordinated through a central purchasing department.
3. Encouraging employees to attend annual seminars on ethical behavior in the workplace and related topics.
4. Tearing ticket stubs in half at a movie theater when a patron enters.
5. Collecting cash at one window and delivering the order in a different window at a fast food establishment.

Even the best internal control plans will be less than effective if no one knows about them. In the *information and communication* section of the COSO framework, organizations consider how to make stakeholders aware of the plan. For example, a company might post some components of the internal control plan on its Web site; it might also require employees to participate in training sessions to familiarize them with the plan. Please keep in mind that information and communication refers to the plan in its totality—not to each individual risk and related control activities.

Finally, establishing a *monitoring* process is critical to maintain strong internal control. An organization's risk exposures change over time, so its internal control plan must change as well. Unless the organization establishes an effective monitoring plan, its internal controls will quickly become outdated. Establishing a monitoring plan should, at minimum, involve a timeline (such as quarterly or annually), assignment of responsibility (such as with the internal audit department or a company-wide committee), and suggested activities (such as surveys or employee focus groups).

In the 2013 revision, COSO elucidated 17 principles to provide more detail about the five components. Here are some examples (COSO, 2013):

- *Control environment.* "The board of directors demonstrates independence from management and exercises oversight of the development and performance of internal control."
- *Risk assessment.* "The organization specifies objectives with sufficient clarity to enable the identification and assessment of risks relating to objectives."
- *Control activities.* "The organization deploys control activities through policies that establish what is expected and procedures that put policies into action."
- *Information and communication.* "The organization communicates with external parties regarding matters affecting the functioning of internal control."
- *Monitoring.* "The organization selects, develops and performs ongoing and/or separate evaluations to ascertain whether the components of internal control are present and functioning."

You can see the other principles in the Executive Summary on COSO's Web site (www .coso.org). In summary, COSO offered the following explanation of effective internal control:

Each of the five components and relevant principles is present and functioning. "Present" refers to the determination that the components and relevant principles exist in the design and implementation of the system of internal control to achieve specified objectives. "Functioning" refers to the determination that the components and relevant principles continue to exist in the operations and conduct of the system of internal control to achieve specified objectives.

The five components operate together in an integrated manner. "Operating together" refers to the determination that all five components collectively reduce, to an acceptable level, the risk of not achieving an objective. Components should not be considered discretely; instead, they operate together as an integrated system. Components are interdependent with a multitude of interrelationships and linkages among them, particularly the manner in which principles interact within and across components.

Next, we'll turn our attention to a discussion of some common internal control procedures.

ISACA (Information Systems Audit and Control Association, www.isaca.org) developed another control framework, often referred to as COBIT (Control Objectives for Information and Related Technology). We'll explore COBIT in more depth in our discussion of computer crime later in the text.

Explain why COSO's Internal Control Integrated Frame-work is important to you as an accounting professional. Also check out the COSO Web site (www.coso.org).

What additional internal control publications has COSO issued?

## INTERNAL CONTROL EXAMPLES

Internal control systems are as unique and different as the organizations and managers that utilize them. But some internal controls are so common that they merit a closer look. While the list below does not represent the "universe" of internal controls, it does give you an introduction to some you're likely to encounter in practice. (The items are listed in alphabetical order so you can refer to them easily later.)

1. *Adequate documentation.* Understanding how things are supposed to happen in an accounting information system is an important first step in designing and assessing internal controls. Process documentation, often in the form of flowcharts (Chapter 6) and/or data flow diagrams (Chapter 7), can help you critique internal controls and determine if they are functioning effectively. Employee manuals frequently include descriptions of internal controls as well.

2. *Background checks.* People are the heart of most organizations today. Particularly for employees in sensitive positions, such as those who deal with large amounts of money, background checks are essential. For example, they may reveal financial difficulties or criminal convictions that may create pressure to breach internal controls. Increasingly, employers look at prospective employees' uses of social media (e.g., Facebook and Twitter) as part of a background check.

3. *Backup of computer files.* If done regularly, backing up computer files takes only a few minutes—a smaller inconvenience compared to the alternative of recreating files from scratch. Daily backups ensure that no more than one day's work is lost in an event of a systems failure. To be most effective, backup copies should be stored in a different electronic/physical location; for example, if a company keeps its data files on a local network, it might consider backing them up to a cloud-based server.

4. *Backup of power supplies.* A few years ago, California was subject to power blackouts when the state's electrical grid was overloaded. During that time, backup power supplies were commonly employed as an internal control. While a computer cannot run indefinitely on a backup power supply, the backup supply can give the user time to save any open files, ensuring they are not lost.

5. *Bank reconciliation.* You probably learned how to reconcile a bank statement in your introductory accounting course. The basic purpose of a bank reconciliation is to account for timing differences between the account holder's records and the bank's records of a cash account. Reconciling the bank statement at least monthly can be helpful in spotting out-of-sequence checks, fraudulent signatures, and errors in the information system. Now that organizations can access their banking records electronically, those reconciliations can (and should) be performed much more frequently—such as once a week or even daily.

6. *Batch control totals.* When an accounting information system is processing a group (batch) of documents, users can calculate various control totals to promote data integrity. For example, you could add up the invoice numbers for a group of sales invoices. Would the total have any meaning in the AIS? Probably not. But, as the invoices move through the AIS, the total should remain the same.

7. *Data encryption.* In today's world of wireless networks, data encryption is critically important. Without it, hackers and other computer criminals can easily access, change, and/or steal data, compromising data integrity and privacy throughout the accounting information system. Data can be encrypted with software and / or with hardware.

8. *Document matching.* Whether electronic or paper-based, document matching helps ensure that vendor invoices are only paid when merchandise has been properly ordered and invoiced. The purchasing department would send a copy of all purchase orders to the accounting department; the receiving department would likewise send a copy of the receiving report. Then, when the vendor mails the invoice, an accountant will match the three documents before initiating payment. In practice, we often use the term "three-way match" to describe such an arrangement.

9. *Echo checks.* You've seen echo checks in operation if you've ever purchased books or airline tickets online. The information system "echoes" the data you've entered back to you before it completes final processing. That process allows you to edit the data for any errors or other changes.

10. *Firewalls.* Along with data encryption, a firewall is an important element of AIS security—particularly in a wireless environment. Firewalls are also useful in wired environments. They can prevent unauthorized intrusions into an accounting information system and warn users when such intrusions are detected.

11. *Insurance and bonding.* While insurance and bonding cannot prevent internal control breaches, they can help organizations correct any financial losses they experience as a result. If you've ever hired contractors to work in your home, they were probably bonded. Companies often bond key employees to address human error and other forms of risk.

12. *Internal audits.* We'll look more closely at audits, including internal audits, in the last chapter of the text; your university may even offer a course in internal auditing. Internal audits can reveal indications of fraud, waste, and inefficiency, thus strengthening internal control. You can also learn more about internal auditing from the Web site of the Institute of Internal Auditors (www.theiia.org).

13. *Limit checks.* An accounting information system can incorporate various kinds of limit checks; for example, if a manager is authorized for purchases less than $1,000, a limit check can ensure that the manager doesn't violate the limit for a specific transaction. Most general ledger packages limit transaction dates to the current year; they don't allow users to pre- or post-date transactions.

14. *Lockbox systems.* Lockbox systems help promote strong internal control over cash. Rather than remitting payment directly to an organization, customers send their payment to a lockbox. An independent company, for a fee, monitors the lockbox and deposits cash receipts daily in the bank. (See Figure 3.3 for an illustration of how a lockbox system works.)

15. *Physical security.* Internal control doesn't have to be extraordinarily sophisticated. Simple actions such as locking doors and securing computers and related equipment can go a long way in safeguarding assets.

**FIGURE 3.3**
**Typical Lockbox System**

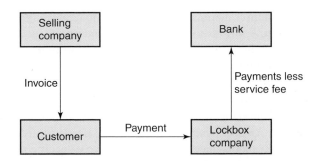

**FIGURE 3.4**
**Preformatted Data Entry Screen** www .giveanything.com

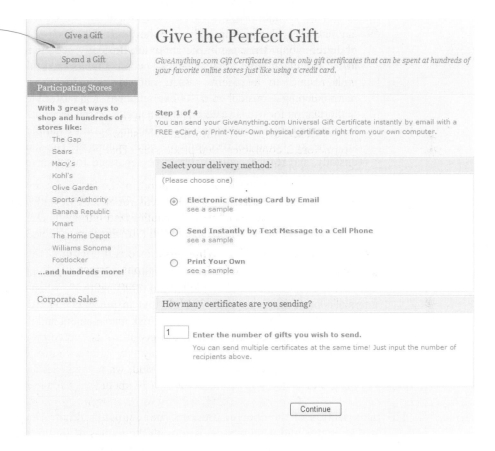

16. *Preformatted data entry screens.* Remember that one of the purposes of internal control is promoting operating efficiency. Using preformatted data entry screens for things like customer orders and cash disbursement processing greatly improves data entry efficiency. Check out Figure 3.4 for an illustration of a preformatted data entry screen. If your AIS instructor incorporates material on relational databases in your course, you may learn how to design such a screen—usually referred to as a "form."

17. *Prenumbered documents.* Checks, purchase orders, sales invoices, and other documents should be prenumbered to promote strong internal control. If an accounting

information system is automated, the numbers may be assigned using an "auto numbering" function. A seriously out-of-sequence document (such as a check numbered in the 400s when others are in the 100s) can be a warning sign for internal control breaches and/or fraud.

18. *Restrictive endorsement and daily deposits of checks received.* You endorse checks when you deposit them in your bank account; you may use a "blank endorsement," which means your signature alone. Here's the problem: blank endorsements weaken internal control. An unethical person with a fake ID can easily cash such a check at the bank. Restrictive endorsements give the bank more specific instructions that limit the uses of the endorsed check; the most common is "for deposit only," often with an account number included. In addition, all cash receipts (coin, currency, and checks) should be deposited daily in the bank to keep them secure.

19. *Segregation of duties.* Although all of the controls in this list are important, segregation of duties may be the most important of all. Basically, segregation of duties means that, to the extent possible, three different people should each take on one responsibility with respect to a specific asset: authorization for use, physical custody, and recordkeeping. Consider cash, for example: physical custody rests with the bank, while authorization for use is vested with signatories on the account. Recordkeeping refers to both journal entries and bank reconciliations. So, for example, someone authorized to sign checks should not reconcile the bank statement. The same duties (authorization, custody, and recordkeeping) should be separated for other assets, such as inventory, plant assets, and supplies.

20. *User training.* Finally, let's consider user training. All the internal control processes in the world are virtually worthless if people don't know how to apply them. Thus, employees should receive periodic training/reminders about appropriate internal control procedures, their rationales, and the reasons they exist.

Remember: the controls we've just considered are not the sum total of available choices. They are a good beginning, but you should think creatively when designing and critiquing internal control systems—both in class and in practice. Let's conclude this chapter by looking at some ways to apply the ideas of risk management and internal control in various organizational settings.

# INTERNAL CONTROL APPLICATIONS

This section of the chapter presents four vignettes illustrating various internal control strengths and weaknesses. Although the names of the individuals and companies involved have been disguised, they represent actual internal control issues in actual organizations.

### Vignette #1: Internal Control over Cash

Alphabet Soup Consulting employs a staff of 50 consultants and is managed by a three-person board of directors: Robbie (president), Vicki (vice president), and Richard (treasurer). The company's bylaws specify that checks over $500 require the signatures of two directors to be valid. However, if an invoice over $500 is due and Robbie or Vicki cannot be reached, Richard frequently writes two (or more) smaller checks to cover the total amount. For example, if an invoice totals $900, Richard might write three checks for $300 each or two checks for $450 each. Richard feels justified in his actions because of increased efficiency.

Clearly, Richard's actions constitute a breach of internal controls. Recall the four basic purposes of internal control, and you'll realize that Richard is not fulfilling two of them: safeguarding assets and ensuring compliance with management directives. By implication, he also is interfering with financial statement reliability. To keep Richard from circumventing controls, Alphabet Soup Consulting could take a number of actions, including (i) restricting Richard's access to checks; (ii) asking an independent third party, such as the firm's CPA, to handle check writing and bill paying; or (iii) removing Richard as a signatory on the account. Each of those controls has a cost, as shown in the table below:

| Control | Type | Cost |
|---|---|---|
| Restricting Richard's access to checks | Preventive | Decreased efficiency |
| Asking an independent third party to handle check writing and bill paying | Corrective | Increased monetary cost; time delays in paying bills |
| Removing Richard as a signatory on the account | Preventive | Extra burden on Robbie and Vicki |

So what really happened in this situation? Vicki and Robbie continued to allow Richard to circumvent the company's controls. Richard had no external controls over his spending of the company's money, and Alphabet Soup Consulting eventually went out of business due to poor liquidity.

### Vignette #2: Embezzling

Gary and Dan were psychologists in private practice. They employed Christina as a receptionist, and a local CPA firm to handle many (but not all) financial matters. Christina opened the mail, collected cash payments from clients, and wrote checks for Gary's or Dan's signature each month. Each month, the practice would get a bank statement in the mail; Christina was supposed to pass on the bank statement to the CPA firm for reconciliation. Unfortunately, Christina got into a personal financial dilemma. Having access to the company's checks and knowing what Gary's and Dan's signatures looked like, she began forging checks written to her husband. The checks were stored in boxes in an unlocked filing cabinet; Christina would take checks to forge from the bottom of the box so they would not be missed until much later. Additionally, although she had regularly been forwarding the bank statements to the CPA firm, the CPAs had not reconciled them for at least six months. One Saturday, Gary came into the office and noticed the bank statement sitting on Christina's desk. Thinking to save himself and his partner some money, he decided to reconcile the bank statement on his own rather than sending it to the CPA firm. He noticed the out-of-sequence checks with signatures that resembled his and Dan's but were not exactly "right." Christina had embezzled a total of $250,000 before Gary and Dan caught onto her scheme.

The preceding vignette illustrates several important internal controls for cash: sequential numbering of checks (preventive), separation of duties (check writing, check signing, and reconciliation—both preventive and detective), and sequentially numbered documents (preventive). But the system broke down when the CPAs did not do their job by balancing the checkbook monthly (a detective control). In addition, the checks were kept in an unlocked filing cabinet; the company would have achieved stronger internal control by locking up the blank checks more securely (a preventive control).

So what happened? Gary and Dan confronted Christina about her embezzlement. At first, she denied it, but later she confessed when confronted with the evidence. Gary and Dan fired her and she was prosecuted for embezzlement; the bank restored the embezzled funds into Gary and Dan's account, and they hired a new CPA firm.

**Vignette #3: Information Technology**

The College of Business at Southern State University has over 200 faculty and four information technology staff members. The college's e-mail is maintained on a central server; each administrator, staff member, and professor can check his/her e-mail from any computer in the world that has Internet access. When a new hire comes to work for the college, his/her e-mail password is the same as the e-mail user name. For example, if Dr. J. M. Ortiz is hired as a professor, both his user name and initial e-mail password are *jmortiz.* A small group of students figured out that connection and started hacking into faculty members' e-mail accounts for illicit purposes. David, the lead information technology staff member, therefore introduced several new policies related to e-mail security:

- *Random creation of initial passwords.* Rather than establishing the initial password as the user name, David's staff now uses a password generator to create new passwords for new hires.
- *Mandatory password changes every six months.* New passwords must contain at least six characters. The six characters must contain at least two of the following: capital letters, lowercase letters, or numbers. The passwords cannot be recycled for a period of two years. So, for example, if someone establishes a password of PhdCma1977 for six months, that password cannot be used again for two years after the six-month period ends.
- *Daily file backup.* David and his staff back up the files from the e-mail server every day.
- *Virus, spyware, and spam protection.* The e-mail server, as well as other information technology assets, is equipped with extensive software to prevent, detect, and correct those problems.

The college has experienced no significant internal control problems with information technology since those policies were instituted.

**Vignette #4: Inventory**

John is the purchasing manager for The Village Bookstore in Claremont, California. He monitors inventory, prepares purchase orders to send to book publishers, and receives the books when they arrive at the store. The bookstore uses a perpetual inventory system, in which inventory records in the accounting information system are updated with every purchase and sale. For example, when books are purchased, the accountant debits inventory and credits accounts payable; when books are sold, the accountant debits cost of goods sold and credits inventory. John also handles merchandise returns when books arrive in unacceptable condition. Since Village uses a perpetual inventory system, John sees no need for periodic counts of inventory—he views them as a waste of time, since the accounting information system is always up-to-date.

Possibly the biggest internal control problem for The Village Bookstore is the separation of duties. To safeguard assets and ensure financial statement reliability, three important duties should be borne by different people in most organizations: (i) physical custody of an asset, (ii) recordkeeping for the asset, and (iii) authorization to use the asset. In this example, John has both physical custody of inventory and authorization for its use. By vesting both those important responsibilities in a single person, it becomes far too easy for John to steal books and tell the accountant they were returned to, or never received from, the publisher. In addition, although the company uses a perpetual inventory system, they still need an annual inventory to promote financial statement reliability.

Thankfully, John was a trustworthy employee. Although he had multiple opportunities to defraud The Village Bookstore, he never did so. An external consultant from a local accounting firm pointed out the bookstore's internal control weaknesses and the company corrected them before they experienced significant financial losses.

# CRITICAL THINKING

In Chapter 1, I suggested three reasons why AIS is an important area of study for future accountants; one of those reasons was that AIS provides an important introduction to an organization's business processes. Here's a brief review of the processes I laid out there:

- *Acquisition/payment process.* In this process, organizations acquire and pay for assets such as inventory and equipment. Associated documents include purchase requisitions, purchase orders, and receiving reports.
- *Conversion process.* For organizations that manufacture a product, the conversion process encompasses activities related to the manufacturing operation. Direct material, direct labor, and overhead are combined to create finished goods that are sold to customers. Documents associated with the conversion process include materials requisitions and labor time tickets.
- *Financing process.* In the financing process, organizations issue debt and equity securities to meet some of their cash needs. If an organization is issuing its stock for the very first time, they must use a prospectus as part of their initial public offering.
- *Human resources process.* All employee-related activities are part of the human resources process: interviewing, hiring, paying, evaluating, and managing separation from the company. In the payroll function, we use documents like Form W-2 and the payroll register.
- *Sales/collection process.* An organization wouldn't survive long if it didn't sell goods and services to its customers. The sales/collection process encompasses those activities, as well as related cash collections. Associated documents include customer invoices, remittance advices, and bank deposit slips.

Each process has its own set of risks that should be addressed with various internal controls. And, many organizations use a risk/control matrix like the one in Table 3.2 to lay them out. Table 3.2 is just one good way to organize a risk/control matrix; in other words, it is illustrative, not definitive.

**TABLE 3.2   Risk/Control Matrix**

| Risk | Risk Category (Brown) | Internal Control | Internal Control Purpose | Comments* |
|---|---|---|---|---|
| Theft of inventory | Liquidity risk | Separation of duties | Preventive | Acquisition/payment process |
| Spoiled raw materials | Liquidity risk | Establish proper storage conditions | Preventive | Conversion process |
| Dividends paid to the wrong shareholders | Human error risk | Internal audit of shareholder database | Detective | Financing process |
| Disclosure of the database of employees' Social Security numbers | Systems risk | Data encryption and firewalls | Preventive | Human resource process |
| Granting credit inappropriately | Credit risk | Established procedures for granting credit, including a separate credit department | Preventive | Sales/collection process |

*The "Comments" column can include virtually any text you'd like; it doesn't have to be limited to the name of the associated business process.

Identifying risks and establishing internal controls require strong critical thinking skills and some experience in organizations. I encourage you, as you go about your normal tasks, to think about how both you and the organizations with which you interact are exposed to risk, and consider the internal controls needed to address them.

## Summary

Here is the usual chapter summary, structured according to the learning objectives:

1. *Define* internal control *and explain its importance in the accounting information system.* Internal control refers to the ways an organization keeps its assets safe and ensures that everyone follows established organizational procedures. Without solid internal control in the AIS, an organization can open itself up to fraud. Weak internal controls also necessitate more extensive auditing procedures.

2. *Explain the basic purposes of internal control.* Internal control has four basic purposes: (*i*) to safeguard assets, (*ii*) to ensure financial statement reliability, (*iii*) to promote operational efficiency, and (*iv*) to encourage compliance with management's general and specific directives.

3. *Describe and give examples of various kinds of risk exposures.* Taxonomies for classifying and describing organizational risks are numerous in the literature and in practice. Brown advanced a four-part structure: financial risk, operational risk, strategic risk, and hazard risk. Financial risks include not having sufficient cash on hand to meet short-term obligations. Operational risks concern (among other things) the possibility that people will make mistakes. Strategic risks include entering a market not aligned with organizational strategy. Hazard risks relate to fraud and errors committed by the board of directors and/or company management.

4. *Prepare a simple risk/control matrix.* Table 3.2 in this chapter's "Critical Thinking" section illustrates a simple risk/control matrix.

5. *Summarize and explain the importance of COSO's 2013 Internal Control—Integrated Framework.* The framework has five parts: control environment, risk assessment, control activities, monitoring, and information and communication. It gives managers comprehensive guidance on internal control by defining internal control, explaining the five parts and laying out principles to follow for each part. The COSO framework is widely used in all types of organizations.

6. *Critique existing internal control systems and design effective internal controls.* This process starts with a comprehensive risk assessment. Managers must then consider various responses to risk, as well as the cost–benefit relationship of various internal controls. As with most issues we study in accounting information systems, the design, implementation, and evaluation of internal controls is at least as much "art" as "science." The question most managers face in most organizations is not Which internal controls are the "right" ones? but Which internal controls can I implement in a cost- effective way to provide reasonable assurance of information integrity, asset safety, and procedural compliance?

As you consider the end-of-chapter materials that follow, try not to "second guess" me or your AIS instructor; try, instead, to put yourself in each situation and come up with the most original solutions you can.

**Key Terms**

Brown's taxonomy of risk, *42*
COSO, *40*
Foreign Corrupt Practices
Act, *41*

internal control, *40*
*Internal Control—Integrated
Framework,* 40

Sarbanes-Oxley Act
of 2002, *41*

**Chapter
References**

Brown, B. 2001. "Step-by-Step Enterprise Risk Management." *Risk Management,* September,
pp. 43–49.
Committee of Sponsoring Organizations of the Treadway Commission. 2013. *Internal Control—
Integrated Framework.* New York: Committee of Sponsoring Organizations of the Treadway
Commission.

**End-of-Chapter
Activities**

1. *Reading review questions.*
   a. What is internal control? Why is internal control important in organizations?
   b. What are the four basic purposes of internal control? Give an example of each one.
   c. List and discuss four broad categories of organizational risk exposures. For each broad
      category, suggest two examples.
   d. What is COSO? Why is the work of COSO important in internal control?
   e. Prepare a response to the questions for this chapter's "AIS in the Business World."

2. *Multiple choice review questions.* Please select the best answer for each question.
   1. Which of the following legally requires management to assess a company's internal controls
      annually?
      a. Foreign Corrupt Practices Act
      b. Brown's risk taxonomy
      c. COSO *Internal Control* framework
      d. Sarbanes-Oxley Act
   2. Which of the following is a type of financial risk according to Brown's taxonomy?
      a. Credit risk
      b. Systems risk
      c. Legal and regulatory risk
      d. Business strategy risk
   3. In the COSO *Internal Control* framework, the "tone at the top" is most closely related to:
      a. Monitoring.
      b. Control environment.
      c. Control activities.
      d. Information and communication.
   4. To develop and sustain a strong control environment, managers and others should:
      a. Be committed to integrity and ethical behavior.
      b. Demonstrate a commitment to competence in carrying out their duties and responsibilities.
      c. Maintain a consistent, appropriate management philosophy.
      d. All of the above.
   5. All of the following are basic purposes of internal control except:
      a. Eliminating fraud.
      b. Ensuring reliable financial statements.
      c. Promoting operating efficiency.
      d. Safeguarding assets.

3. *Reading review problem.* Enron was one of the most publicized fraud cases of the late 20th century; it was so serious that it not only led to its own demise, but to the dissolution of Arthur Andersen, one of the (then) "Big Five" CPA firms. Enron and related cases led to the most sweeping legislation impacting the accounting profession since the 1930s: the Sarbanes-Oxley Act of 2002. In "Trials and Tribulations of Enron and S-Ox" (*Forbes*, 23 January 2006), Pitt stated: "The principal deficiencies that led to Enron's demise are easy enough to catalog. They include . . . a serious lack of meaningful internal controls."

   a. What is internal control?

   b. Explain the importance of COSO's 2013 Internal Control—Integrated Framework in establishing strong internal control.

   c. Consider the following risk exposures at Enron: insufficient cash for operations, fraudulent accounting, too close a relationship with auditors, declines in stock price. For each risk exposure, indicate the relevant category of the Brown taxonomy; suggest at least one internal control to address the risk.

4. *Making choices and exercising judgment.*

   a. Consider the four vignettes presented in the last section of the chapter. For each one, suggest one additional internal control procedure. Discuss whether the procedure you suggest is preventive, detective, or corrective; also identify the type of risk it is designed to control based on the risk categories discussed in the chapter.

   b. Hassan and Ashok are employed by one of the Big Four CPA firms. Both have recently earned their CPA licenses, however, and are considering starting their own practice. Using Brown's risk taxonomy, identify and describe at least five risks Hassan and Ashok must be aware of if they start their own business. For each risk you identify, suggest one or more internal controls that could ameliorate it.

5. *Field exercises.*

   a. Through observation and/or interview, collect information about internal control over inventory from a local retail establishment such as a bookstore, coffee shop, or discount store. How does the information you collected about processes, procedures, and documents align with the information presented in the chapter?

   b. Read the articles listed below about actual internal control breaches. In each case, suggest at least two internal controls the company needs to institute.

      i. "Big Banks Face Fines on Role of Servicers," *The Wall Street Journal Online*, 16 February 2011.

      ii. G. Heslop and L. Kapp, "An Institutional Response to Fraud, Scandal and Embarrassment—The Dallas Independent School District Procurement Card Case," *Journal of Leadership, Accountability and Ethics*, December 2010.

      iii. B. Leonard, "When HR Goes Bad," *HR Magazine*, January 2011.

   c. Consider one or more of the following cases. Identify the internal control weaknesses and suggest internal controls to address them. (The dates in parentheses are for posts on my AIS blog where you might start your research.)

      i. Bernie Madoff (28 June 2012)

      ii. First Priority Credit Union (9 November 2012)

      iii. Graduate Assistance and Consolidation (6 November 2012)

      iv. Olympus Camera (26 September 2013)

   d. Access the executive summary of the COSO internal control framework on the COSO Web site (www.coso.org). For each section of the framework, summarize the associated principles of internal control.

6. Internal control has four basic purposes: safeguarding assets, ensuring financial statement reliability, promoting operational efficiency, and encouraging compliance with management's

directives. Consider each of the internal control procedures described below. For each procedure, indicate which purpose(s) of internal control it is designed to address.

   a. Conducting surprise cash counts.

   b. Creating a policy manual.

   c. Creating separate departments for purchasing inventory and receiving inventory.

   d. Deleting an employee's computer account when the employee retires or is fired.

   e. Employing internal auditors.

   f. Installing virus cleaning software on all computers.

   g. Locking filing cabinets with sensitive documents.

   h. Performing background checks on employees.

   i. Reconciling the bank statement monthly.

   j. Requiring all management employees to take annual vacations.

**7.** Visit the Web site of the Wild Cat Zoo in southern California (www.cathouse-fcc.org). Classify each of the following risks using Brown's taxonomy. Also suggest one or more internal controls to address each risk. For each internal control you suggest, specify which broad purpose(s) of internal control it satisfies, as well as whether it is preventive/detective/corrective in nature. Explain your responses.

   a. The zoo fails to attract a sufficient number of visitors.

   b. One or more animals get sick.

   c. The zoo's Web site becomes unavailable due to a computer virus.

   d. Promotional and educational literature contain errors of fact about the animals and the zoo's operating hours.

   e. One of the animals escapes because a keeper fails to lock its cage securely.

   f. An employee falsifies his/her credentials to obtain a position as a veterinarian.

   g. The zoo's admission prices are prohibitively high for school groups.

   h. The zoo loses its 501(c)(3) status with the Internal Revenue Service.

   i. The gift shop runs out of a popular souvenir item.

   j. A disgruntled former volunteer attempts to set a fire at the zoo.

**8.** Do a Google search for the Fortune 100 companies. Choose two of the companies from the list and prepare a risk/control matrix similar to the one illustrated in the chapter. Include five to seven risks for each company you choose. (You'll find an example for Walmart Stores in the 25 September 2011 post on my blog.)

**9.** (CMA adapted, December 1992) In each of the following independent situations, identify internal control deficiencies and make suggestions regarding their correction/improvement.

   a. Many employees of a firm that manufactures small tools pocket some of these tools for their personal use. Since the quantities taken by any one employee were immaterial, the individual employees did not consider the act as fraudulent or detrimental to the company. As the company grew larger, an internal auditor was hired. The auditor charted the gross profit percentages for particular tools and discovered higher gross profit rates for tools related to industrial use than for personal use. Subsequent investigation uncovered the fraudulent acts.

   b. A company controller set up a fictitious subsidiary office to which he shipped inventories and then approved the invoice for payment. The inventories were sold and the proceeds deposited to the controller's personal bank account. Internal auditors suspected fraud when auditing the plant's real estate assets. They traced plant real estate descriptions to the assets owned and leased and could not find a title or lease for the location of this particular subsidiary.

   c. The manager of a large department was able to embezzle funds from his employer by carrying employees on the payroll beyond actual termination dates. The manager carried each terminated employee for only one pay period beyond the termination date so the employee would not easily detect the additional amount included on the W-2 reporting of wages to the Internal Revenue Service. The paymaster regularly delivered all checks to the department manager, who then deposited the fraudulent checks to a personal checking account. An internal auditor discovered the fraud from a routine tracing of sample entries in the payroll register to the employees' files in the personnel office. The sample included one employee's pay record whose personnel file showed the termination date prior to the pay period audited. The auditor investigated further and discovered other such fraudulent checks.

10. (CMA adapted, June 1994) MailMed Inc. (MMI), a pharmaceutical firm, provides discounted prescription drugs through direct mail. MMI has a small systems staff that designs and writes MMI's customized software. Until recently, MMI's transaction data were transmitted to a third party for processing on their hardware.

    MMI has experienced significant sales growth as the cost of prescription drugs has increased and medical insurance companies have been tightening reimbursements in order to restrain premium cost increases. As a result of these increased sales, MMI has purchased its own computer hardware. The computer center is installed on the ground floor of its two-story headquarters building. It is behind large plate-glass windows so that the state-of-the-art computer center can be displayed as a measure of the company's success, attracting customer and investor attention. The computer area is equipped with high-tech fire suppression equipment and backup power supplies.

    MMI has hired a small computer operations staff to operate the computer center. To handle the current level of business, the operations staff is on a two-shift schedule, five days per week. MMI's systems and programming staff, now located in the same building, have access to the computer center and can test new programs and program changes when the operations staff are not available. As the systems and programming staff are small and the work demands have increased, systems and programming documentation are developed only when time is available. Periodically, MMI backs up its programs and data files, storing them at an off-site location.

    Unfortunately, due to several days of heavy rains, MMI's building recently experienced serious flooding, which reached several feet into the first floor level and affected the on-site hardware, data, and programs.

    Based on the preceding narrative, describe at least two specific computer weaknesses for MMI. For each weakness you identify, suggest a way to compensate for it.

11. (CMA adapted, June 1994) Richards Furniture Company is a 15-store chain, concentrated in the southwest, that sells living room and bedroom furniture. Each store has a full-time manager and an assistant manager, who are paid on a salary basis. The cashiers and sales personnel typically work part-time and are paid an hourly wage plus a commission based on sales volume. The company uses cash registers with four-part sales invoices to record each transaction; the invoices are used regardless of the payment type (cash, check, credit card).

    On the sales floor, the salesperson manually records his/her employee number and the transaction, totals the sales invoice, calculates any appropriate discount and the sales tax, and calculates the grand total. The salesperson then gives the sales invoice to the cashier, retaining one copy in the sales book.

    The cashier reviews the invoice and inputs the sale into the cash register. The cash register automatically assigns a consecutive number to each transaction. The cashier is also responsible for obtaining credit authorization approval on credit card sales and approving sales paid by check. The cashier gives one copy of the invoice to the customer and retains the second copy as the store copy. Returns are handled in exactly the reverse manner with the cashier issuing a return slip when necessary.

At the end of each day, the cashier sequentially orders the sales invoices and provides cash register totals for cash, credit card, and check sales, as well as cash and credit card returns. These totals are reconciled by the assistant manager to the cash register tapes, the total of the consecutively numbered sales invoices, and the return slips. The assistant manager prepares a daily reconciled report for the store manager's review.

Cash sales, check sales, and credit card sales are reviewed by the manager, who then prepares the daily bank deposit. The manager physically deposits these at the bank and files the validated deposit slip. At the end of the month, the manager performs the bank reconciliation. The cash register tapes, sales invoices, return slips, and reconciled report are then forwarded daily to the central Data Entry Department at corporate headquarters for processing. The Data Entry Department returns a weekly Sales and Commission Activity Report to the manager for review.

Please respond to the following questions about Richards Furniture Company's operations based on the preceding narrative:

a. What risks does Richards face?

b. If you were an unethical customer and/or employee of Richards, how could you defraud the company given their current procedures?

c. What internal control strengths does the company possess? What risks are those strengths designed to address?

d. How could internal control be improved at Richards?

12. (CMA adapted, June 1993) PriceRight Electronics Inc. (PEI) is a wholesale discount supplier of a wide variety of electronic instruments and parts to regional retailers. PEI commenced operations a year ago, and its records processing has been on a manual basis except for stand-alone automated inventory and accounts receivable systems. The driving force of PEI's business is its deep-discount, short-term delivery reputation that allows retailers to order materials several times during the month to minimize in-store inventories. PEI's management has decided to continue automating its operations, but, because of cash flow considerations, this needs to be accomplished on a step-by-step basis.

It was decided that the next function to be automated should be sales order processing to enhance quick response to customer needs. PEI's systems consultants suggested and implemented an off-the-shelf software package that was modified to fit PEI's current mode of operations. At the same time, the consultants recommended and installed a computerized database of customer credit standings to permit automatic credit limit checks as the lingering recessionary climate has resulted in an increase in slow paying or delinquent accounts. The new systems modules are described below:

*Marketing.* Sales orders are received by telephone, fax, mail, or e-mail and entered into the sales order system by marketing personnel. The orders are automatically compared to the customer database for determination of credit limits. If credit limits are met, the system generates multiple copies of the sales order.

*Credit.* On a daily basis, the credit manager reviews new customer applications for creditworthiness, establishes credit limits, and enters them into the customer database. The credit manager also reviews the calendar month-end accounts receivable aging report to identify slow-paying or delinquent accounts for potential revisions to or discontinuance of credit. In addition, the credit manager issues credit memos for merchandise returns based on requests from customers and forwards copies of credit memos to Accounting for appropriate accounts receivable handling.

*Warehousing.* Warehouse personnel update the inventory master file for purchases and disbursements, confirm availability of materials to fill sales orders, and establish back-orders for sales orders that cannot be completed from stock on hand. Warehouse personnel assemble and forward materials with corresponding sales orders to Shipping and Receiving. They also update the inventory master file for merchandise returns that are received by Shipping and Receiving.

*Shipping and Receiving.* Shipping and Receiving accepts materials and sales orders from Warehousing, packs and ships the order with a copy of the sales order as a packing slip, and forwards a copy of the sales order to Billing. Merchandise returns received from customers are unpacked, sorted, inspected, and sent to Warehousing.

*Accounting.* The Accounting Department comprises three functions relevant to this narrative: Billing, Accounts Receivable, and General Accounting. Billing prices all sales orders received, which takes approximately five days after order shipment. To spread the work effort throughout the month, customers are segregated and placed in 30-day billing cycles. There are six billing cycles for which invoices are rendered during the month. Monthly statements, prepared by Billing, are sent to customers during the cycle billing period. Outstanding carry-forward balances reported by Accounts Receivable and credit memos prepared based on credit requests received from the credit manager are included on the monthly statement. Billing also prepares sales and credit memo journals for each cycle.

Copies of invoices and credit memos are forwarded to Accounts Receivable for entry into the accounts receivable system by customer account. An aging report is prepared at the end of each billing cycle and forwarded to the credit manager.

The accounts receivable journal reflecting total charges and credits processed through the accounts receivable system for each cycle is forwarded to General Accounting. General Accounting compares this information to the sales and credit memo journals and posts the changes to the general ledger.

Based on the preceding narrative:

a. Identify at least two internal control strengths of PEI's system. Indicate why each is a strength.

b. Identify at least three internal control weaknesses in PEI's system. Explain the nature of each weakness and recommend a way to address it.

13. *Terminology.* Please match each item on the right with the best item on the left.

| | |
|---|---|
| 1. Business strategy risk | a. 1977 legislation |
| 2. Foreign Corrupt Practices Act | b. 2002 legislation |
| 3. Information and communication | c. A section of the COSO framework |
| 4. Legal and regulatory | d. Internal control example |
| 5. Liquidity | e. A group that offers advice about internal control |
| 6. Reasonable assurance | f. Organizational risk example |
| 7. Sarbanes-Oxley Act | g. Poor decision making related to market competition |
| 8. Separation of duties | h. Strategic risk category |
| 9. Systems | i. Type of financial risk |
| 10. COSO | j. What internal controls provide |

14. *Multiple choice questions.*

1. Which of the following best explains the relationship between "monitoring" and "information and communication" as the terms are used in the COSO *Internal Control* framework?

   a. Monitoring must be done by an individual, while information and communication must be done by a group.

b. Information and communication must be done by an individual, while monitoring must be done by a group.

c. Monitoring involves ongoing changes to an organization's internal control plan; information and communication focuses on letting stakeholders know about current internal controls.

d. Information and communication involves ongoing changes to an organization's internal control plan; monitoring focuses on letting stakeholders know about current internal controls.

2. Which of the following best pairs a specific risk exposure with a category from Brown's taxonomy?

a. Company sanctions for violation for the Foreign Corrupt Practices Act, legal and regulatory risk

b. Failure to follow proper imprest systems procedures for petty cash, systems risk

c. Failing to give employees proper credit for their accomplishments, credit risk

d. Fundamental flaws in an entity's marketing plan, market risk

3. A quarterly internal control newsletter published by the CEO's office would most likely be related to which element(s) of the COSO *Internal Control* framework?

a. Risk assessment, monitoring

b. Control environment, information and communication

c. Risk assessment, control environment

d. Monitoring, information and communication

4. Which of the following is most likely to benefit from a lockbox system as a form of internal control?

a. Mortgage lender

b. Convenience store

c. The IRS

d. Home Depot's corporate office

5. All of the following have a responsibility for promoting strong internal control in organizations except:

a. Independent auditors.

b. Internal auditors.

c. Executive management.

d. Stockholders.

15. *Statement evaluation.* Indicate whether each of the following statements is (i) always true, (ii) sometimes true, or (iii) never true. For those that are (ii) sometimes true, explain when the statement is true.

a. Audits are less time consuming and less expensive in organizations with strong internal control systems.

b. Document matching concepts can be applied to purchases of and payments for office supplies.

c. In companies with strong internal control, only one person has the authority to sign checks.

d. In the COSO *Internal Control* framework, control activities can be preventive, detective, or corrective.

e. Information technology eliminates the need for internal control systems.

f. Internal controls prevent fraud.

g. Liquidity risk is more important than other types of risk.

h. Preventive controls are more expensive than detective or corrective controls.

i. Properly implemented lockbox systems eliminate the need for bank reconciliations.

j. Reported weaknesses in internal control will lead to reductions in stock prices.

**16.** *Excel application.* The internal audit department of JTJ Corporation set up an anonymous hotline for reporting suspected internal control breaches. After receiving several tips through the hotline alleging breaches in JTJ's purchasing department, internal auditors decided to investigate. They collected the following data on purchase orders issued in March 20x4:

| Date | P.O. Number | Amount | | Date | P.O. Number | Amount |
|------|-------------|--------|---|------|-------------|--------|
| 1 | 5001 | $ 5,680 | | 17 | 5020 | $ 10,837 |
| 1 | 5002 | 6,936 | | 18 | 5021 | 9,700 |
| 4 | 5003 | 6,346 | | 18 | 5022 | 11,350 |
| 5 | 5004 | 6,360 | | 18 | 5023 | 7,984 |
| 5 | 5005 | 5,524 | | 19 | 5024 | 8,040 |
| 6 | 5006 | 6,863 | | 19 | 5025 | 7,901 |
| 6 | 5007 | 5,058 | | 20 | 5026 | 8,571 |
| 6 | 5008 | 6,753 | | 21 | 5027 | 11,311 |
| 6 | 5009 | 6,675 | | 22 | 5028 | 7,256 |
| 7 | 5010 | 6,583 | | 23 | 5029 | 11,821 |
| 7 | 5011 | 6,595 | | 24 | 5030 | 8,453 |
| 9 | 5012 | 6,485 | | 25 | 5031 | 10,924 |
| 9 | 5013 | 5,555 | | 26 | 5032 | 11,418 |
| 11 | 5014 | 6,631 | | 27 | 5033 | 7,309 |
| 12 | 5015 | 6,906 | | 28 | 5034 | 7,211 |
| 12 | 5016 | 6,479 | | 29 | 5035 | 11,135 |
| 14 | 5017 | 6,568 | | 29 | 5036 | 11,880 |
| 14 | 5018 | 6,485 | | 30 | 5037 | 8,495 |
| 15 | 5019 | 5,418 | | 31 | 5038 | 7,782 |

Internal auditors suspect that purchase orders issued in the last half of the month are significantly larger than those issued in the first half of the month.

Use Excel's *t*-test function to determine if further investigation of a potential internal control breach is justified.

Additional information and hints

- Access the data set on my AIS blog in the 3 February 2014 post.
- Do a two-sample test assuming equal variances.
- Check figure: calculated t statistic = −7.37.

# Chapter **Four**

# Management Concepts

## AIS in the Business World

### Papa John's International

Even in today's health-conscious society, pizza is still a dietary staple for many college students. And, according to the Motley Fool (www.fool.com), three companies dominate the market; one of those three is Papa John's International. (The other two are Pizza Hut and Domino's.) Papa John's trades its shares under the symbol PZZA, and holds about 7% of the market. As of 6 January 2014, Papa John's stock was trading at just over $45/share, with a total market capitalization of $1.96 billion.

For an international company like Papa John's, consistency is very important. Customers want consistent food, prepared in a consistent way, regardless of where they purchase it. In addition, Papa John's faces a multitude of risks, many of which are associated with its international operations. The company's annual report of 2012 (http://ir.papajohns.com/annuals.cfm) listed several risks, including:

- changes in consumer preferences or discretionary consumer spending could adversely impact our results;
- food safety and quality concerns may negatively impact our business and profitability;
- our expansion into emerging or under-penetrated domestic and international markets may present increased risks.

In this chapter, we'll consider how organizations like Papa John's accomplish three important tasks: managing risk, managing business processes, and motivating employees.

### Discussion Questions

1. Why is the study of management concepts relevant to accounting information systems?
2. How could Papa John's use COSO's enterprise risk management framework to address the risks it faces?
3. What considerations should Papa John's keep in mind when it comes to ensuring process consistency throughout its operations?
4. How can Papa John's employ expectancy theory in motivating its employees?

One of the fascinating and interesting things about AIS is its interdisciplinary nature. AIS draws from accounting, to be sure, but also has connections to other areas of business, such as information systems, management, and finance. In fact, I often point out to my own students that there is almost no such thing in modern organizations as an "accounting problem." Rather, there are "organizational problems" that can, in part, be informed by accounting. The next two chapters look at two areas with clear connections to AIS: management and information systems.

In this chapter, we'll look at three major topics: enterprise risk management (ERM), business process management (BPM), and behavioral issues in AIS. When you've finished studying the chapter, and completing the activities at its conclusion, you should be able to:

1. Summarize and explain the importance of COSO's *Enterprise Risk Management— Integrated Framework.*
2. Define business process management, including a generalized model of BPM.
3. List and discuss some basic principles of business process management.
4. Explain expectancy theory.
5. Apply all three topics within the context of accounting information systems.

## ENTERPRISE RISK MANAGEMENT

In Chapter 3, you learned about COSO and its *Internal Control—Integrated Framework.* If you visited the COSO Web site (www.coso.org), you probably noticed that COSO has many other publications beyond the internal control framework. In this section, we'll take a look at a second major COSO publication: the **Enterprise Risk Management Integrated Framework.** The AICPA Core Competency Framework states that risk analysis is one of the functional competencies all accountants need. According to COSO:

> Enterprise risk management is a process, effected by an entity's board of directors, management and other personnel, applied in strategy setting and across the enterprise, designed to identify potential events that may affect the entity, and manage risk to be within its risk appetite, to provide reasonable assurance regarding the achievement of entity objectives.

Notice that the definition of ERM mentions entity objectives. COSO discusses five categories of objectives for most organizations: strategic, operations, reporting, compliance, and safeguarding of resources. The objectives and categories overlap, of course; also, not all categories are always under the direct control of management. Strategic and operations objectives, for example, can be profoundly influenced by political and economic events around the world. (You may recall similar language in COSO's definition of internal control.)

Whereas the integrated framework for internal control had five components, the ERM framework has eight, as shown in Figure 4.1. Like the five elements of the internal control framework, the eight ERM elements are intimately linked to one another. Here's the way COSO describes them in the executive summary of the ERM documents:

> **Internal Environment**—The internal environment encompasses the tone of an organization, and sets the basis for how risk is viewed and addressed by an entity's people, including risk management philosophy and risk appetite, integrity and ethical values, and the environment in which they operate.

> **Objective Setting**—Objectives must exist before management can identify potential events affecting their achievement. Enterprise risk management ensures that management has in place a process to set objectives and that the chosen objectives support and align with the entity's mission and are consistent with its risk appetite.

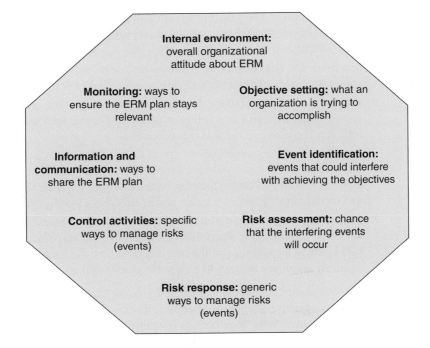

**FIGURE 4.1**
**Enterprise Risk Management Framework**

**Event Identification**—Internal and external events affecting achievement of an entity's objectives must be identified, distinguishing between risks and opportunities. Opportunities are channeled back to management's strategy or objective-setting processes.

**Risk Assessment**—Risks are analyzed, considering likelihood and impact, as a basis for determining how they should be managed. Risks are assessed on an inherent and a residual basis.

**Risk Response**—Management selects risk responses—avoiding, accepting, reducing, or sharing risk—developing a set of actions to align risks with the entity's risk tolerances and risk appetite.

**Control Activities**—Policies and procedures are established and implemented to help ensure the risk responses are effectively carried out.

**Information and Communication**—Relevant information is identified, captured, and communicated in a form and time frame that enable people to carry out their responsibilities. Effective communication also occurs in a broader sense, flowing down, across, and up the entity.

**Monitoring**—The entirety of enterprise risk management is monitored and modifications made as necessary. Monitoring is accomplished through ongoing management activities, separate evaluations, or both.

The objectives (strategic, operations, reporting, compliance, and safeguarding assets) represent what the organization is trying to accomplish. The eight components of the enterprise risk management framework help managers formulate plans for accomplishment. Let's consider what an ERM plan might look like for Papa John's International.

1. *Internal environment.* Papa John's could establish a strong internal environment for risk management in many ways. For example, management could discuss the importance of risk management with staff; Papa John's might also consider establishing a "risk management" department to demonstrate its commitment to ERM.

2. *Objective setting.* As part of its strategic plan, Papa John's might set a goal of expanding into more international locations.

3. *Event identification.* One thing that could interfere with the goal of expanding into more international locations is lack of knowledge about language and culture.

4. *Risk assessment.* The inherent (unmitigated) risk is high; even after employing some risk management techniques, the residual (mitigated) risk is likely to be moderate.

5. *Risk response.* If Papa John's decided to pursue its objective, it would necessarily be accepting the risk of lack of knowledge; additionally, however, the company could choose to reduce the risk through one or more control activities.

6. *Control activities.* To reduce the risk of not knowing about language and culture, Papa John's might establish and follow a policy of issuing international franchises only to long-term residents of the relevant countries.

7. *Information and communication.* As in COSO's Internal Control—Integrated Framework, information and communication refers to how Papa John's informs people of the plan in its entirety. Posting the plan on its Web site, referring to it in employee manuals and mentioning it in press releases are all effective ways to communicate the plan.

8. *Monitoring.* The final part of the ERM framework also shares similarities with the internal control framework. Papa John's could delegate responsibility for monitoring the ERM plan to a committee of the board of directors; the board committee might conduct quarterly employee surveys to ensure the plan is still effective.

Notice that three elements of the ERM framework are concerned with the "big picture" view: internal environment, information and communication, and monitoring. The remaining five elements "hang together" as demonstrated in the example above. For each individual objective (#2), an organization would identify one or more risks (#3). It would assess the chance that the risks might happen (#4), then choose one or more generic risk responses to manage those that are most likely (#5). Finally, the organization would get more specific about implementing the generic risk responses (#6).

COSO's internal control framework was well received in the business community; in fact, many organizations (including Papa John's) use the COSO internal control framework as part of Sarbanes-Oxley Act of 2002 (SOX) compliance and SEC reporting. The ERM framework was more sharply criticized because it was much more general. From my point of view, the ERM framework had to be more general: The kinds of risks organizations face and the ways they respond to them are much more diverse than matters related to internal control. While not every organization has identical internal controls, all internal control systems are attempting to respond to the same four purposes we discussed in Chapter 3.

As with the internal control framework, you'll find additional COSO ERM publications on its Web site (www.coso.org).

# NATURE OF BUSINESS PROCESS MANAGEMENT

**Business process management** has been defined in different ways, including:

- A business improvement strategy based on documenting, analyzing, and redesigning processes for greater performance (SmartDraw.com, 2008).
- A systematic approach to analyzing, redesigning, improving and managing a specific process (Harmon and Wolf, 2008, p. 12).

Notice the important ideas in each definition of BPM: improving performance, promoting efficiency, responding to the needs of clients, and analyzing processes systematically and strategically. BPM is relevant to the study of AIS because both are connected to an organization's business processes. You may recall, from Chapter 1, that understanding business processes is one of the reasons AIS is an important area of study for future accountants. The AICPA Core Competency Framework mentions many skills related to BPM: research, critical thinking, resource management, and others.

Consult at least two other sources that provide definitions of business process management. Based on those sources and what you've just read, develop your own definition of BPM.

Although every BPM project is unique in some way, certain generic activities are common to most of them. Seppanen, Kumar, and Chandra (2005) suggested the following sequence as a generalized model of BPM.

1. Select the process and define its boundaries.
2. Observe, document, and map the process steps and flow.
3. Collect process-related data.
4. Analyze the collected data.
5. Identify and prioritize potential process improvements.
6. Optimize the process.
7. Implement and monitor process improvements.

Here's an example of how Papa John's might employ those seven steps in managing its business processes.

1. *Select the process and define its boundaries.* Let's suppose Papa John's wanted to improve its process for evaluating franchise applications in the United States. Notice that the boundary is established in two ways: by naming the exact process itself and by limiting it to a specific geographic region. (Later in the book, when we talk about flowcharting, you'll again encounter the idea of a "boundary.")

2. *Observe, document, and map the process steps and flow.* Papa John's Web site (www .papajohns.com) has an entire section devoted to describing the U.S. franchising process. They would certainly use that material as a starting point; they would also want to talk to some recent franchise operators to determine if the generic description is how things "really" work.

3. *Collect process-related data.* As part of those interviews, Papa John's would collect data about how long the process takes. They could use an activity-based system to calculate the cost of processing a new U.S. franchise application.

4. *Analyze the collected data.* Papa John's would next look for bottlenecks in the process— steps that are taking longer than necessary. They could also use the information collected from interviewing franchise operators to identify places where the process could be improved.

5. *Identify and prioritize potential process improvements.* Real-time and/or virtual focus groups would yield some ways to improve the process of evaluating franchise applications. Papa John's would prioritize those, perhaps based on their cost or their potential impact.

6. *Optimize the process.* The team tasked with improving the process would redesign the franchise application process based on one or more of the suggested improvements from the prioritized list. Think of this step as designing the new process.

7. *Implement and monitor process improvements.* Once the new process was designed, Papa John's would implement it. Just as ERM and internal control plans must be monitored, process improvements must also be monitored.

How is BPM related to your study of accounting information systems? Good question!

Consider the following points to help understand why AIS students should know something about business process management:

1. BPM can assist managers in providing accounting information that conforms to elements of the FASB Conceptual Framework. Refer back to Figure 1.1, which illustrates the conceptual framework. Managing business processes can ensure that relevant, reliable information is furnished in a cost-effective way.

2. BPM can help managers promote strong internal control. You probably recall that internal control has four main purposes, one of which is enhancing operating efficiency. Periodically examining business processes to see how they can be improved helps achieve that goal.

3. BPM frequently involves strategic uses of information technology, such as relational databases, enterprise resource planning systems, and general ledger software. In the Papa John's example, the redesigned process might involve designing a relational database that would monitor U.S. franchise applications.

4. BPM is a natural outgrowth of accountants' intimate involvement with business processes. As a future accounting professional, your work will frequently focus on business processes: documenting them (flowcharts, data flow diagrams, REA models), designing inputs and outputs for them (sales invoices, purchase requisitions, production cost reports), and auditing them (financial, operational, compliance).

Next, let's turn our attention to some fundamental ideas associated with business process management.

## BASIC PRINCIPLES

As part of my background research for this chapter, I interviewed my friend and former student, Robert J. Eppele II. Robert is the chief information officer (CIO) for ERP Solutions LLC; you can learn more about his company on its Web site: www.erpsolutions.net. He shared these important ideas about business process management:

1. *Understand how business processes interact with/support organizational strategy.* As you may have learned in a management class, "strategy" refers to the ways an organization gains a competitive advantage in its markets. In today's on-demand, knowledge-driven economy, an organization's business processes can be the keys in creating and sustaining a competitive advantage in the marketplace.

2. *Move away from the "we've always done it this way" mentality. Be open to alternatives.* Business processes often originate based on some organizational need. For example, many medical offices have historically relied on paper documents for things like patient charts and prescriptions; in the last decade, however, IT professionals have developed cost effective, efficient ways to maintain those records electronically.

3. *Enlist top management support; ensure that top management can describe current business processes before trying to reengineer/maintain/modify the processes.* We've already talked about the COSO frameworks for internal control and enterprise risk management; in both frameworks, the "tone at the top" is an important factor. The same is true for BPM: Without top management support, most efforts will be doomed to failure. In addition, to support and lead BPM efforts effectively, top management needs to understand the way things currently work in the organization.

4. *Managing business processes is fundamentally about people, not technology or documents. It's important to hire people who can think beyond their little pieces of the world*

*and see how what they do fits into the "bigger picture."* BPM requires a holistic view of the organization—one that moves beyond thinking about what's best for your department to thinking about how the organization as a whole can create value for its stakeholders. Notice the connection between this principle and the AICPA Core Competency Framework, which includes an entire category on "broad business perspective" competencies.

5. *Don't rely on external consultants to the exclusion of internal employees; value the experience of people in the organization who are close to the process.* This point might strike you as a bit odd, since both Robert and I have worked as external consultants in many organizations. But it is 100 percent true! Far too many managers, when confronted with a complex problem, advocate hiring an external consultant as a first step. While doing so has many advantages, external consultants rarely have the intimate familiarity of internal employees when it comes to BPM. I've often found that a team approach, combining both employees and consultants, produces very positive results.

6. *When using consultants, make sure the task is well defined, with specific deliverables defined by the company.* This idea reminds me of something Lewis Carroll wrote in *Alice's Adventures in Wonderland:* "If you don't know where you are going, any road will take you there." In other words, outcomes for a BPM project should be defined in advance; otherwise, the project may grow out of control, costing both time and money without achieving solid results.

7. *Communicate early; communicate often. Deal immediately with objections/issues as they arise.* BPM, like most important organizational initiatives, needs to be an open, transparent process. The best plans are developed by a team of people through a process of dialogue and feedback, not by one or two people sitting in an office for several hours.

We'll take a closer look at how the steps and principles of BPM are applied later in the text.

## BEHAVIORAL ISSUES IN AIS

In Chapter 1, we took a brief look at the FASB conceptual framework; you'll probably recall "cost effectiveness" as one of the constraints on financial reporting. Costs associated with an accounting information system come in at least three forms: behavioral, psychological, and financial. In this section of the chapter, we're going to take a quick look at behavioral issues in AIS. People have been trying to understand and explain human behavior in organizations practically since organizations first existed. While this section alone won't make you an expert on the matter, it will provide a framework for understanding some of the behavioral issues you'll face in designing, implementing, and using accounting information systems.

So what are some of the behavioral issues associated with AIS? Consider the following list:

• Many people are uncomfortable with change. So, if you are moving an AIS from paper-based to technology-based, making a business process more efficient, or introducing new internal controls, some folks will resist "on principle."

• Fraud is a serious problem in all types of organizations. In its 2012 Report to the Nations on Occupational Fraud and Abuse, the Association of Certified Fraud Examiners (www .acfe.com) "estimated that the typical organization loses 5% of its annual revenue to fraud. Applied to the estimated 2011 Gross World Product, this figure translates to a potential global fraud loss of more than $3.5 trillion" (ACFE, 2012).

- Business today is a global endeavor. So, people in organizations must learn new languages, cultures and customs. Violating a country's/culture's behavioral norms can be both embarrassing and detrimental to conducting business there.
- When elements of an AIS change, people need to be trained in new technologies, processes and procedures to be effective. Whether the training is done in a classroom or online format, it involves human behavior.

Dozens, perhaps hundreds, of theories exist to help us understand human behavior. One I've used a lot is Vroom's expectancy theory (1964). It has stood the test of time both in research and in practice—probably because it is easy to understand and is practical. **Expectancy theory** says that motivation is the product of three factors:

- *Expectancy:* If I put in the effort toward achieving a goal, will I be successful?
- *Instrumentality:* If I achieve the goal, will I be rewarded?
- *Valence:* Do I value the reward?

Vroom put them together in a simple, yet elegant, formula to emphasize their relationship:

$$\text{Motivation} = \text{Expectancy} \times \text{Instrumentality} \times \text{Valence}$$

Notice that the three factors are *multiplied,* not added, to achieve motivation. So, if just one of the three factors is zero, motivation will be zero as well.

How would Vroom's expectancy theory be applied within the context of accounting information systems? Earlier in this chapter, you read about applying the COSO ERM framework at Papa John's International. Table 4.1 shows how the three elements of expectancy theory might look in that context:

**TABLE 4.1   Application of Expectancy Theory**

| Factor | General Question | Application to Papa John's |
|---|---|---|
| Expectancy | If I put in the effort toward achieving a goal, will I be successful? | If we work with a consultant, will we be able to develop an ERM plan? |
| Instrumentality | If I achieve the goal, will I be rewarded? | If we successfully develop the ERM plan, will we manage risk and achieve our goals? |
| Valence | Do I value the reward? | Will managing risk and achieving our goals give us something we want? |

# Reflection and Self-Assessment                                4.2

Think about a goal you have tried / are presently trying to achieve—perhaps earning your accounting degree. Use the elements of Vroom's expectancy theory to analyze your motivation for achieving it. Be as honest as you can be.

# CRITICAL THINKING

We've explored three related, but diverse, topics in this chapter: enterprise risk management, business process management, and expectancy theory. Rather than trying to tie all the three together in a case study, let's relate each topic to something nearly every AIS student considers important: taking exams. The test bank that accompanies this book includes three question types for each chapter: multiple choice, problems, and short answer. Within each question type, I've prepared questions at different levels of difficulty; the harder the question, the less it relies on memorization and the more it requires critical thinking. Many times, AIS students are a bit confused about how to "reason through" questions that require critical thinking, since prior accounting courses may have relied a lot on memorization of textbook material. I hope the following three examples will help demystify the process of preparing for exams.

*Example 1: Multiple choice **application** question on ERM.* An "application" question requires you to use a concept in a new situation. To respond to an application question, you need a firm foundation in the subject matter (ERM, in this case), but you need to do more than simply memorizing facts. Here's the question:

The COSO enterprise risk management framework comprises eight parts. If the second part of an ERM plan based on the framework includes "increase inventory turnover," which of the following should be included in the third part of the plan?

    a. Monitor inventory.

    b. Inform and communicate with management about the problem.

    c. Two vice presidents are fired for committing fraud.

    d. Inventory is outdated.

The best answer is "d." The second part of an ERM plan is "objective setting," and the third part is "event identification." As you'll recall from earlier in this chapter, "event identification" is the part of the plan where we consider risk exposures—things that could happen that would reduce our ability to achieve a goal. Notice how "a" and "b" use language that appears in the ERM framework (monitor, inform, communicate). But, neither of those choices identifies a risk exposure, which is what the question requires. Answer "c" does identify a risk exposure, but it's not related to increasing inventory turnover; in other words, two vice presidents being fired will probably not interfere with the company's ability to increase inventory turnover. "D" is the best choice; if inventory is outdated, the company may not be able to increase its inventory turnover.

*Example 2: Fill in the blank **analysis** problem on business process management.* An "analysis" question requires you to separate a large block of material into distinct parts. Analysis questions are more advanced than application questions; not only do they require a firm foundation in the subject matter, but they also require you to differentiate relevant and irrelevant material. Here's a sample question:

Fei and Hassan were working on project with the goal of streamlining their company's payroll processing. The following were part of their initial conversations about the project:

1. First, we should decide what kind of information technology the new process will use.

2. Let's keep the payroll supervisor informed as we develop a plan.

3. I wonder if streamlining the payroll process will allow us to compete more effectively in our markets.

Indicate which statement(s) violate one or more of the principles of business process management discussed in the chapter; for those that do, indicate which principle is violated in your own words. Record your answers in the table below. (The table below includes the answers, as you can see. In an exam, of course, it would have just the column headings and statement numbers filled in; your job would be to complete the remaining columns.)

| Statement | Violates BPM Principle (Yes or No)? | Principle Violated (If Applicable) |
|---|---|---|
| 1 | Yes | BPM should focus more on people than on technology. |
| 2 | No | Not applicable |
| 3 | No | Not applicable |

This question requires more critical thinking than the "application" question. Not only do you have to know the principles of BPM discussed in the text, but you also have to be able to determine, through critical thinking, which statements exemplify them and which violate them. Then, you should be able to summarize the principles in your own words, rather than simply memorizing and repeating them. Statement 2 does not violate any of the principles; rather, it upholds the idea that communication is critical in any BPM project. Likewise, Statement 3 links the BPM project to strategy, aligning it with the first of Eppele's BPM principles.

*Example 3: Short answer **synthesis** question on expectancy theory.* In some ways, synthesis questions are the opposite of analysis questions. Synthesis questions require you to consider some material and organize it in a coherent way. They require you to create something from what may appear to be disparate parts—sort of like having the parts of a computer spread out on a table, and building a working computer from them.

Here's an example question:

Lee is an audit manager for a local CPA firm. Most of the members of Lee's team are highly motivated and do excellent work, but Marie frequently makes mistakes and slacks off. Lee had a conversation with Marie in which Marie made the following comments: "I know I've been messing up too much, Lee, and that's no way to get promoted in the firm. I really want to get promoted, though. So, if I really focus and start making fewer errors, will I get promoted?"

Consider Marie's comments through the lens of expectancy theory. Indicate which of her comments provide examples of expectancy theory components; for any element not represented, suggest a question or comment Lee should include in responding to Marie. Record your answers in the table below. (As before, an exam problem would give you just the table; your job would be to fill in the answers.)

| Expectancy Theory Element | Example |
|---|---|
| Expectancy | What is your plan for focusing and making fewer errors? |
| Instrumentality | If I really focus and start making fewer errors, will I get promoted? |
| Valence | I really want to get promoted. |

This question is definitely the most advanced of the three. It requires that you know the elements of expectancy theory, but it also requires you to recognize examples of each (an "analysis" task). Because only two elements of expectancy theory are represented in Marie's comments (instrumentality and valence), you must also be able to create (synthesize) the third element (expectancy). And, that synthesis must be from Lee's perspective—not Marie's. (Of course, the example I've included is not the only good response. See if you can come up with another one on your own, and ask your AIS professor about it.)

I hope this section will help you understand the chapter's topics more deeply *and* help you prepare more effectively for exams.

## Summary

This chapter has been all about the management issues you'll need to consider in AIS work. Here is a summary of its main points, organized based on the expected outcomes from the beginning of the chapter:

1. *Summarize and explain the importance of COSO's Enterprise Risk Management— Integrated Framework.* COSO's ERM framework comprises eight elements: internal environment, objective setting, event identification, risk assessment, risk response, control activities, information and communication, monitoring. The framework is important because it gives business professionals a structured, concrete way to manage risk throughout the organization. It also allows them to change and adapt their risk management procedures over time as internal and external environments change.

2. *Define business process management, including a generalized model of BPM.* BPM has been defined in many different ways. Fundamentally, it is a set of ideas associated with making virtually any business process more effective and efficient—helping ensure that it creates value for organizational stakeholders. The generalized model of BPM discussed in the chapter comprises seven steps:

   a. Select the process and define its boundaries.
   b. Observe, document, and map the process steps and flow.
   c. Collect process-related data.
   d. Analyze the collected data.
   e. Identify and prioritize potential process improvements.
   f. Optimize the process.
   g. Implement and monitor process improvements.

3. *List and discuss some basic principles of business process management.* The chapter also presented seven basic principles of BPM:

   a. Understand how business processes interact with/support organizational strategy.
   b. Move away from the "we've always done it this way" mentality.
   c. Enlist top management support.
   d. Managing business processes is fundamentally about people, not technology/ documents.
   e. Don't rely on external consultants to the exclusion of internal employees.
   f. When using consultants, make sure the task is well defined, with specific deliverables defined by the company.
   g. Communicate early; communicate often.

4. *Explain expectancy theory.* Vroom's expectancy theory is a way to understand and explain human motivation in organizations. It comprises three elements: expectancy, instrumentality, and valence. Motivation is the product of the three; if any one of the factors is zero, motivation will also be zero.

5. *Apply all the three topics within the context of accounting information systems.* All the three areas can be applied in various ways when working with accounting information systems. The ERM framework can be used to assess and respond to the various types of risk discussed in Chapter 3 (financial, operational, strategic, hazard). Business processes are central to AIS, you read in Chapter 1. (You'll learn a lot more about business processes in later chapters.) The principles of BPM outlined in this chapter can be used to make those processes more effective and efficient. Since every AIS involves people in some way, expectancy theory can be used to assess and increase motivation.

Key Terms

basic BPM principles, *68*
business process management, *66*

Enterprise Risk Management—
Integrated Framework, *64*

expectancy theory, *70*
generalized model of BPM, *67*

Chapter
References

Association of Certified Fraud Examiners. 2012. *Report to the Nations on Occupational Fraud and Abuse.* Downloaded 6 January 2014 from www.acfe.com.
Committee of Sponsoring Organizations of the Treadway Commission. 2004. *Enterprise Risk Management—Integrated Framework.* New York: Committee of Sponsoring Organizations of the Treadway Commission.
Harmon, P., and C. Wolf. 2008. *The State of Business Process Management.* San Francisco: Business Process Trends.
Seppanen, M., S. Kumar, and C. Chandra. 2005. *Process Analysis and Improvement: Tools and Techniques.* 1st ed. New York: Irwin/McGraw-Hill.
SmartDraw.com. 2008. "Standards and Methodologies." www.smartdraw.com/tutorials/bpm/methodologies.htm (August 27).
Vroom, V. H. 1964. *Work and Motivation.* Jossey-Bass.

End-of-Chapter
Activities

1. *Reading review questions.*

   a. What are the elements of COSO's enterprise risk management framework?

   b. What is business process management? List and discuss the steps managers often use to change a business process.

   c. List and discuss seven principles of business process management.

   d. What are the elements of expectancy theory? Give examples of each one.

   e. In a format specified by your instructor, respond to the questions for this chapter's "AIS in the Business World."

2. *Reading review problem.*

   For better or worse, McDonald's locations can be found all over the world. The corporate Web site (www.aboutmcdonalds.com) states: "At McDonald's, we strive to be more than just a restaurant—we're a first job for many, a community partner, a model for other restaurants around the world, and a company seeking new ways to fulfill our brand promise of Quality, Service, Cleanliness, and Value." Although most folks think of McDonald's as a place to buy fast food, the corporation itself is principally concerned with establishing new locations; at present, McDonald's operates in almost 120 countries around the world.

   As with Papa John's and other large, multinational organizations, consistency is very important for McDonald's. The company profile on the corporate web site states: "McDonald's customer-focused Plan to Win provides a common framework for our global business yet allows for local adaptation. Through the execution of initiatives surrounding the five elements of our Plan to Win—People, Products, Place, Price, and Promotion—we have enhanced the restaurant experience for customers worldwide and grown comparable sales and customer visits in each of the last 8 years. This plan, combined with financial discipline, has delivered strong results for our shareholders."

   a. Use COSO's framework to develop an enterprise risk management plan for McDonald's corporate office. Ensure that the risks you identify are focused on the corporate office, not individual locations.

   b. The corporate office has many business processes, including establishing new franchises, paying dividends to shareholders and communicating with news agencies. Choose one of those processes and at least three of Eppele's basic principles of business process management. Explain how the process you chose should be aligned with the principles you chose. Here's an example:

Process: establishing new franchises

Principle: managing business processes is fundamentally about people

Alignment: in evaluating applications for new franchises, McDonald's should consider the education and experience of the person making the request.

c. Consider the process of establishing a new franchise from two perspectives: the person requesting the franchise and the McDonald's employee evaluating the application. In a format similar to Table 4.1 in the chapter, apply the elements of expectancy theory to explain each party's motivation.

3. *Multiple choice review.*

1. All of the following are elements of COSO's enterprise risk management framework except:
   a. Fraud detection.
   b. Objective setting.
   c. Control activities.
   d. Monitoring.

2. Which of the following steps typically occurs first in business process management?
   a. Analyzing collected data.
   b. Monitoring process improvements.
   c. Defining process boundaries.
   d. Optimizing the process.

3. When considering a business process management project, managers should:
   a. Understand how business processes interact with organizational strategy.
   b. Be open to alternatives.
   c. Ensure that top management can describe current business processes before the project starts.
   d. All of the above.

4. All of the following are elements of expectancy theory except:
   a. Expectancy.
   b. Instrumentality.
   c. Valence.
   d. Conditioning.

5. Which of the following best exemplifies expectancy theory?
   a. Motivation = Expectancy × Instrumentality − Valence
   b. Motivation = Expectancy + Instrumentality + Valence
   c. Motivation = Expectancy × Instrumentality × Valence
   d. Motivation = Expectancy × Instrumentality/Valence

4. *Making choices and exercising judgment.*

America Online's corporate Web site (http://corp.aol.com) states: "At AOL, we're in the business of making the Internet better—period. Through innovation and creativity, we've raised the bar and set the standard for what we believe high quality content is on the Internet." AOL's competitors include companies like Google and Yahoo.

a. Use COSO's enterprise risk management framework to develop an ERM plan for AOL. For "event identification," include two events that have a "moderate" or "high" risk assessment.

For the first event, suggest a control activity that will **reduce** the risk; for the second, suggest a control activity that will **share** the risk.

b. AOL uses an electronic funds transfer system (EFTS) to process employee expense reimbursements and vendor invoices. Respond to the following questions based on some of the steps in the generalized model of business process management:

　i. Suggest two pieces of process-related data AOL might collect if it wants to revise the process of reimbursing employee expenses.

　ii. Explain what tools and techniques you would use to analyze the data you collect.

　iii. Give one example of how AOL might improve its employee expense reimbursement process.

c. Use the elements of expectancy theory to develop a brief summary you could use to present your ideas to AOL's corporate officers and motivate them to accept your ideas.

5. *Field exercises.*

a. The chapter discussed expectancy theory as a way of explaining motivation. But, researchers and practitioners have suggested many other theories, such as Maslow's hierarchy of needs, Herzberg's two-factor theory, and McClelland's needs theory. Research one or more of those theories (or others suggested by your instructor). Compare and contrast them to expectancy theory.

b. Search the Internet and/or your school's library to find an example of a successful BPM project. Summarize the project. To what extent does the case follow the seven basic steps suggested by Seppanen, Kumar, and Chandra? The BPM principles suggested by Eppele?

c. If you're like students at my university, you may be frustrated by some of your school's processes—such as the process of registering for classes, purchasing textbooks, or paying fees. Use the steps and principles of business process management to suggest a way to improve a process that frustrates you.

6. *Enterprise risk management.* Which element of the COSO ERM framework is most closely associated with each of the following?

　a. ALG Corporation bonds key employees.

　b. Based on previous experience, TRG Corporation's management believes the risk of inventory shortages is moderate.

　c. BPC Corporation implements a profit-sharing plan as a way to motivate managers to control costs.

　d. BRN Corporation's board of directors hires a consultant to explain ERM.

　e. CNV Corporation's managers accept the risk of stock price decreases.

　f. DTI Corporation holds quarterly staff lunches where employees discuss how they manage risk.

　g. EIV Corporation's president organizes monthly meetings for managers to discuss books and articles related to ERM.

　h. FLM Corporation operates manufacturing plants on three continents.

　i. FPO Corporation follows a top-down model for strategic planning.

　j. HRP Corporation's internal audit department assesses and tracks the effectiveness of its ERM plan.

　k. Management at CNV Corporation determines the probability of a decrease in stock value is very high.

　l. MGG Corporation occasionally hires a consultant to provide feedback on its ERM plan.

　m. RCH Corporation's enterprise risk management department prepares and distributes a monthly ERM newsletter.

　n. SSO Corporation reviews and revises its strategic plan annually.

　o. TRG Corporation's managers want to avoid inventory shortages.

　p. WRL Corporation does not use data encryption in its wireless network.

**7.** *Expectancy theory elements.* Which element of expectancy theory is described in each of the following independent scenarios?

    a. Anh completed the steps for licensure as a Certified Public Accountant and received a pay raise. *instrumentality*

    b. Claudia completed a BPM project early; her boss said she could either have extra time off or a small pay raise. Claudia chose the pay raise. *valence*

    c. Ethan put in many extra hours in January and was pleased to be named "employee of the month." *instrumentality*

    d. Lupe believes her company's new general ledger software is too complex to master. *expectancy*

    e. Mark changed his major from finance to accounting because he heard jobs are plentiful in accounting. *valence*

    f. Richard has stopped suggesting business process improvements because his ideas are never implemented. *expectancy*

**8.** *Expectancy theory and employee motivation.*

In the previous problem, you identified one relevant element of expectancy theory. Consider each scenario again; "fill in" the other two elements. Here's an example:

> Expectancy: Anh studied hard and took a review course that enabled her to pass the CPA exam on her first attempt. Instrumentality: Anh completed the steps for licensure as a Certified Public Accountant and received a pay raise. Valence: Anh celebrated her pay raise with her family and close friends.

**9.** *Business process management principles.*

Which of Eppele's seven principles is violated in each of the following independent cases? Justify your responses. (Each case may violate more than one principle.)

    a. Amanda objected to her company's new approach to training because they had never used it before.

    b. Esther started a BPM project by looking for appropriate information technology tools.

    c. Eugene, an entry-level employee, implemented a new system for taking inventory.

    d. Jeff decided to change his company's purchasing process because the current process seemed too cumbersome.

    e. Minh told the consultants for a BPM project to prepare and submit reports as they felt appropriate.

    f. Molly told her employees that all their concerns would be addressed at the end of the BPM project.

    g. Raul argued strongly that a proposed BPM project be managed by a consulting firm.

**10.** *ERM plan.*

In Chapter 3, Exercise 8, you developed a risk/control matrix for two of the Fortune 100 companies. Develop a full enterprise risk management plan for one of them; use the COSO framework to structure your plan.

**11.** *Terminology.* Match each item on the left with the most appropriate item on the right.

| | |
|---|---|
| 1. Behavioral issues | a. First step in BPM |
| 2. Control activities | b. Fraud & resistance to change |
| 3. Define boundaries | c. Key idea when using consultants |
| 4. Expectancy | d. Reduce, accept, avoid, share |
| 5. Instrumentality | e. Second step in BPM |
| 6. Internal environment | f. Specific actions taken to respond to risk |
| 7. Map steps and flow | g. The belief that effort will lead to success |
| 8. Risk responses | h. The idea that goal achievement leads to reward |
| 9. Valence | i. The value placed on a reward |
| 10. Well-defined tasks | j. Tone at the top |

**12.** *Multiple choice questions.*

1. In business process management, decision makers must collect and analyze data. Which of the following tools would best be used to collect useful data?
   a. Journal entries
   b. Interviews
   c. Financial statements
   d. Expectancy theory

2. Employees of BRN Corporation are trying to convince the CEO of the importance of enterprise risk management. The CEO comments: "I can't really support this idea. Too many organizations develop ERM plans, then put them on the shelf instead of implementing them." Which element of expectancy theory is reducing the CEO's motivation?
   a. Expectancy
   b. Valence
   c. Instrumentality
   d. Motivation

3. The first step in business process management is to select the process and define its boundaries. Which of the following is the best defined process within the context of BPM?
   a. Selling assets
   b. Posting journal entries to the ledger
   c. Purchasing inventory
   d. Financing operations

4. Which of the following is a key idea in both business process management and enterprise risk management?
   a. Defining the boundary
   b. Accepting things as they are
   c. Increasing efficiency
   d. Involving company executives

5. Which of the following statements best exemplifies one of the principles of BPM?
   a. First, we need to think about the software we're going to use.
   b. Let's develop a proposal, then inform the CFO.
   c. We'll need to select the BPM team carefully.
   d. This project should be quick and easy; we can wait and let everyone know about it when we're done.

**13.** *Statement evaluation.* Please indicate whether each of the following statements is (i) always true, (ii) sometimes true or (iii) never true. For those that are sometimes true, explain when/under what circumstances they are.

a. Accountants are in the best position to determine reward valence.
b. Both BPM and ERM require strong support from top management to be successful.
c. Both the COSO internal control and ERM frameworks include monitoring.
d. BPM projects result in lower costs because they use information technology strategically.
e. Companies should avoid external consultants at all costs in BPM projects.
f. Cost variance analysis can be used to analyze data in BPM.
g. In developing an ERM plan, managers should always attempt to reduce risk.
h. Production workers are in the best position to add value to a BPM project.
i. The COSO ERM framework is the only viable way of managing risk.
j. Vroom explained that human motivation depends on three factors.

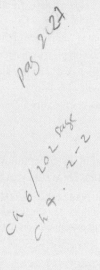

**14.** *Excel application.* THN Corporation wants to reorganize the process of issuing purchase orders to make it more efficient. As part of collecting process-related data, the purchasing manager generated the following:

| P.O. Number | Employee Number | P.O. Dollar Amount | Processing Time (min) |
|---|---|---|---|
| 801 | 234 | 388 | 41 |
| 802 | 234 | 289 | 46 |
| 803 | 234 | 156 | 38 |
| 804 | 237 | 132 | 36 |
| 805 | 237 | 166 | 41 |
| 806 | 237 | 129 | 42 |
| 807 | 240 | 300 | 23 |
| 808 | 240 | 149 | 25 |
| 809 | 240 | 328 | 47 |
| 810 | 240 | 423 | 40 |

Use Excel to prepare a pivot chart and pivot table that show the average amount of processing time for each employee number. (You may consult the 3 February 2014 post on my AIS blog to download the data set if you don't want to enter it yourself.) Here's a sample of how the pivot chart might look:

## Chapter Five

# Information Systems Concepts

## AIS in the Business World

### Google

As recently as 50 years ago, most people could not have imagined the technology that is available to us today—technologies that are considered commonplace in today's world. Indeed, over 50% of the "millennial generation" has said they would rather give up their sense of smell than give up their technology!

Google has been an "information technology staple" for many years. The company did its initial public offering (IPO) in 2004, and has increased its stock price from $85 at the IPO to over $1000 per share today! The company's stock trades under the symbol GOOG. Among the many information technology innovations associated with Google are things like Chromecast, Google Glasses, Google Hangouts, and many others. You can find a lot more information about Google's history and operations at http://www.google.com/about/company/.

Although Google prides itself on its culture of innovation, developing new forms of information technology requires discipline and structure along with creative thinking. In this chapter, we'll look at three important information technology concepts, often using Google as an example for how to use them. The three concepts are: the systems development life cycle, the capability maturity model, and factors to consider in software selection.

### Discussion Questions

1. What are the steps in the systems development life cycle? How might a company like Google use them to develop a product like Gmail?
2. What is the purpose of the capability maturity model (CMM)? What are its levels and why are they important from a systems perspective? Based on your own use of Google products, how would you characterize Google's business processes using the CMM?
3. What factors should an organization consider in evaluating Google products for their own use?

Early in your study of accounting information systems, you learned that most AIS have five parts: inputs, processes, outputs, storage, and internal controls. But did you ever wonder how those elements of the AIS come into existence in the first place? After all, they don't "spring full blown" like Minerva from the brow of Jupiter! (That's your multicultural, interdisciplinary lesson for this chapter. Hope you liked it.) And once the elements are in place, how can we judge, in a macro sense, the extent to which an organization's processes need improvement? Finally, what factors should professionals take into account when choosing which information technology to implement?

In this chapter, we're going to explore three topics that help answer those questions: the systems development life cycle (SDLC), the capability maturity model (CMM), and software selection.

When you've finished studying this chapter, you should be able to:

1. List and discuss, in order, the steps in the systems development life cycle.
2. Explain the advantages and disadvantages of using the SDLC.
3. Apply the SDLC in accounting contexts.
4. List and discuss the levels of the capability maturity model.
5. Classify organizations' processes according to the CMM.
6. Explain factors managers should consider when choosing IT for an AIS.

## SYSTEMS DEVELOPMENT LIFE CYCLE

As the name implies, the **systems development life cycle** (SDLC) is a methodology for designing, implementing, and maintaining virtually any kind of information system. It's certainly not the only such methodology; it may not even be the best methodology. But many organizations use the SDLC in their systems projects, so you're highly likely to run across it in your career.

The SDLC comprises seven parts (see Figure 5.1):

1. Initiation/planning
2. Requirements analysis
3. Design
4. Build
5. Test
6. Implementation
7. Operations and maintenance

Although the seven steps appear very linear in nature, the SDLC is actually highly **iterative** in practice—similar to systems documentation. In other words, information systems professionals don't move from one step to another in a rigid way. Rather, they move back and forth between the steps as needed in a specific project. So, for example, an organization might be engaged in testing, only to find that it must change the way a system is built; or, a team might be partially done designing a system when it discovers that the requirements analysis needs additional work.

Let's look at each of the seven steps in more detail, along with how you might apply them in an accounting information system:

1. *Initiation/planning.* Most systems development projects start because someone in an organization recognizes an unfilled need. For example, a small organization might

**FIGURE 5.1**
**Systems Development Life Cycle**

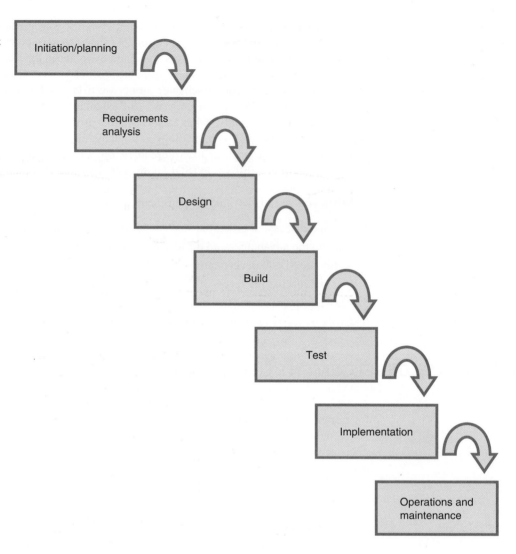

have been using a checkbook as its only accounting information system. But if the organization is growing, its needs for accounting information will quickly outpace the capabilities of a simple checkbook. This first phase of the SDLC often includes a feasibility study to determine if the project is possible from economic, operational, and technical perspectives. The feasibility study results may be used to try to get the project funded.

2. *Requirements analysis.* In requirements analysis, systems designers figure out what the new system needs to accomplish. They may use a variety of tools at this stage, including flowcharts and interviews with system users. The fundamental goal of requirements analysis is to develop a clear set of objectives for the new system—in much the same way that every chapter in this book starts with a set of objectives. The requirements analysis for our fictional small organization, which we'll call MCL Company, could include objectives like "produce general purpose financial statements" or "prepare end-of-year tax returns."

3. *Design.* With the requirements analysis in hand, systems designers can begin to think about how the system should look—how will screen layouts look, what kinds of documents are

Enterprise resource planning systems come in different versions based on generic organizational types. For example, PeopleSoft has one version designed for the needs of colleges and universities.

needed, what forms of internal control will be involved. Very often, the overall AIS is broken down into modules for design purposes; modules could be based on business processes (e.g., sales/collection) and/or stakeholders (such as customers and employees). At this point, MCL may decide to build a system "from scratch" or to evaluate "off-the-shelf" software. Both approaches have costs and benefits. Building a system from scratch takes time and may be expensive; off-the-shelf software may not be completely customizable to a specific organization.

4. *Build.* If the system is being built "from scratch," this phase involves writing the actual computer code. If an organization is using off-the-shelf software, like Peachtree, building probably includes customizing it to the particular organization. If you've worked with general ledger software in your AIS course, you probably customized things like the chart of accounts, inventory records, and personnel information. As a small organization, MCL Company may be more likely to use off-the-shelf software, particularly if its needs are as generic as those mentioned in (2) above.

5. *Test.* You probably wouldn't want to buy a new car without test driving it first, right? The same holds true for information systems! During the testing phase, users can critique the system and make suggestions for its improvement. One of my former students works for the U.S. Navy; when the Navy was preparing to implement new software for procurement/purchasing, the software was installed on a few machines. Users had the opportunity to work with the new software and make suggestions about it. If MCL's management decided to build a system from scratch using relational database software, testing would involve setting up the database so users could "check it out" before starting to use it. It's much easier to make design changes at this stage than it would be after the system has been implemented. If the information system has been designed in modules, testing also helps ensure that the modules work well together.

This step may help you understand the iterative nature of systems development more clearly, as it may involve revisiting earlier phases of the SDLC.

6. *Implementation.* After any revisions based on testing, the system is at last ready for implementation—for actual use by the organization to achieve the purposes set out in requirements analysis. Managers have many choices when it comes to systems implementation. They may, for example, run the old system and the new system simultaneously for a time (parallel implementation). They may completely take down the old system and put the new system in its place (direct cutover or "big bang"). They may implement the system in modules, as well. MCL's management could continue using its simple checkbook system alongside its newly developed/purchased system for a time. Even with such a parallel approach, MCL could use modular implementation for the new system. Every implementation approach has costs and benefits; there's no "one right way" or even "one best way" to approach this important task.

7. *Operations and maintenance.* Information systems, particularly accounting information systems, are dynamic. As people, processes, products, and services of the organization change, the AIS should change along with them. For example, MCL's management might decide to incorporate at some point; at a minimum, incorporation would require a change in the chart of accounts. Other issues to consider over the life of a new system include internal control, accessibility for the disabled, and hardware and software requirements.

Some descriptions of the SDLC break it down into more than seven phases. The U.S. Department of Justice lists 10 steps in its SDLC (www.usdoj.gov/imd/irm/lifecycle/ch1.htm#para1.2); regardless of the level of detail, the same basic tasks are involved.

Now, we'll turn our attention to the capability maturity model.

## CAPABILITY MATURITY MODEL

Humphrey first wrote about the CMM in Managing the Software Process.

The **capability maturity model** (CMM) was first suggested by **Watts Humphrey** in the late 1980s. Humphrey was a software engineer, and he developed the CMM as a framework to assess business processes in an objective way—with particular reference to government contractors and software projects. In the intervening years, the CMM has been applied in many other organizational contexts: project management, software maintenance, risk management, and business school accreditation. Whatever the context, the CMM has five levels: chaotic, repeatable, defined, managed, and optimized (see Figure 5.2). Let's look at each level's characteristics and apply them to accounting information systems.

- *Level one: chaotic.* These processes are unstable and noncohesive; think of this level as an "every person for him/herself" mentality, or like a bunch of Lone Rangers in an organization. Individuals may be highly motivated and put forth extraordinary effort in making a process "work," but the organization's processes as a whole are jumbled and confused. As a graduate student, I did some consulting with small businesses that often had chaotic

**FIGURE 5.2**
**Capability Maturity Model**

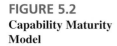

Level five
optimized

Level four
managed

Level three
defined

Level two
repeatable

Level one
chaotic

accounting information systems. I recall one client, a marine supply business, in which the AIS consisted of a shoebox full of receipts, check stubs, and other documents. And, as a reviewed them, I discovered that the collection was incomplete. Hopefully, in your professional career, you won't run across an organization with such a chaotic AIS.

- *Level two: repeatable.* This level involves some planning; it may result in consistent results over time. One way to recognize this maturity level is the development of "major milestones" for projects and/or processes, with specific deliverables at each milestone. If the marine supply business wanted to move from its chaotic AIS to this level, managers might focus on producing monthly financial statements. They could establish a process for collecting source documents, making journal entries, and keeping accounting records up-to-date to achieve that goal.

- *Level three: defined.* In describing this level, Hurst (2007, p. 4) noted:

   At maturity level 3, the standards and procedures for an individual project are derived from organizational standards to suit that particular project. This is a key distinction between levels 2 and 3. Both levels require project standards, procedures, and process descriptions. In level 2, they might be unique to a project. In level 3, they are tailored from broader organizational standards. It is expected in level 3 that processes will be described in more detail and with more rigor. Management is expected to understand relationships between processes and to collect detailed metrics of performance.

   So, in the marine supply business, the accounting information system moves from being a "necessary evil" to something that supports the organization in other ways. The business would likely develop a procedures manual to standardize the way the AIS is maintained; such a manual would be particularly useful during times of transition and expansion.

- *Level four: managed.* In level three, processes are defined but not measured. When an organization moves to level four, its management develops metrics to establish goals and control processes. When a process doesn't achieve those goals, management can look for ways to improve the process. The management of the marine supply business might, for example, set a goal of producing quarterly financial statements within one week of the end of each quarter. If the quarterly financials took longer than a week, management would look for ways to improve the process to achieve that goal.

The idea of continuous improvement is called *kaizen* in Japan. You may have encountered this idea in a cost accounting or operations management course.

- *Level five: optimized.* This level is characterized by a "continuous improvement" mentality in the organization. At this level, organizations look at the "big picture" of process improvement. Hurst (2007, p. 4) offered these comments: "A key distinction between level 4 and level 5 is the types of process variation that are addressed. At level 4, the concern is with individual projects experiencing delays and variations. Level 5 organizations develop processes to address the common causes of process delay and variation, and to change processes to improve performance." If our marine supply business moved to this level, managers would think beyond the accounting information system, considering ways to improve other business processes. Level five is really about an attitude of improvement—one that permeates the organization and affects nearly everything it does.

# Reflection and Self-Assessment                                    5.2

You've started the process of entering the accounting profession by going to college. Based on the CMM levels, how would you describe that process? Why? In formulating your response, consider that most practicing accountants today follow a process similar to your own. For example, most earned a college degree in accounting; many pursued certification/licensure as well.

We'll look more closely at business processes in Part Four of the text. Chapter 1 listed five common processes as part of discussing why AIS is an important area of study for future accountants.

Ideally, an organization will move all of its business processes sequentially through the levels. Since each level builds on those that precede it, skipping levels can be frustrating and counterproductive. At the same time, processes at different levels within the same organization can create problems; for example, a sales/collection process at level four would be problematic if the acquisition/payment process was at level two.

## INFORMATION TECHNOLOGY SELECTION

The eight issues here are but a small subset of many considerations managers must weigh in IT decisions. Later, you'll have a chance to research and/or brainstorm additions.

Managers need to consider two kinds of issues when they think about selecting an appropriate form of information technology for their AIS: macro-level issues and micro-level issues. Figure 5.3 provides a list of all the factors we'll consider in this section.

Managers must first specify the *need* they are trying to meet with a new form of information technology. Often, company personnel want the "latest and greatest" form of information technology just because it looks cool or is fun to play with. But IT resources represent a major investment of time and money for most firms, so establishing a clear need is critical. Johnston (2003) offered the following insights in this area:

Notice how Johnston's comments tie into the phases of the SDLC.

> Assign the managers . . . to prepare a [needs analysis] for their sections. It should include all the things they do—from invoice preparation to inventory operations. Using the data, ask them to prepare flowcharts to diagram how they perform those tasks . . . or even how they get bottled up. During this analysis have the managers gather samples of every form . . . and every report the current software produces. From this analysis you will be able to develop a requirements definition—a detailed document that defines what your business needs.

*Strategic fit* is also important when investing in new information technology. As you may know, a strategy indicates how an organization competes in its markets. Most good strategic plans begin with a strong, yet concise, mission statement. For example, the mission of the McGraw-Hill Companies (www.mcgraw-hill.com) is to provide essential information and insight that help individuals, markets, and societies perform to their potential. A mission statement, as part of a strategic plan, explains why an organization exists; it outlines how the organization plans to differentiate itself from its competitors. Investments should align with (support) the organization's strategic plan; that is, managers and employees should be able to state clearly how a given information technology fulfills the organizational mission.

*Personnel involvement* is another key factor in new IT investments. Johnston (2003) recommended two items in this area: a technology advisory committee and independent consultants. While he considers a technology advisory committee essential, he states that hiring an independent consultant may or may not be a good idea. A technology advisory committee should, according to Johnston, comprise five to seven members from various

**FIGURE 5.3**
**Factors to Consider in IT Selection**

| Macro-Level Factors | Micro-Level Factors |
|---|---|
| Need | Cost |
| Strategic fit | Adaptability |
| Personnel involvement | Training |
| Financing | Vendor reliability |

departments/functions/offices of the organization. Subcommittees also may be in order to manage more focused tasks and involve more personnel. Employees on the committee need not necessarily be technology experts, but they should be able to think globally for the good of the company, rather than representing the (perhaps) parochial interest of their own area.

# Reflection and Self-Assessment                                    5.3

Under what circumstances would you want to hire an independent consultant for an IT investment project? Suggest three questions you would ask during a selection interview for an independent consultant; also, identify and discuss three adjectives that would describe the ideal consultant.

Finally, on the macro side of the equation, managers need to consider *financing*—how do they plan to pay for the IT? Key questions here include

- Will external funding be required for the investment?
- If so, how will the company raise it: debt or equity?
- Is leasing an option? If so, what are its advantages and disadvantages?
- Are any tax credits available based on the investment?

Well-developed, detailed operational and capital budgets will help address those issues.

Now, let's look at some of the *micro-level issues* involved in IT investments. Most managers will immediately consider *cost* when they think about micro-level issues. Cost, however, is much broader than just the money spent for the investment. Managers need to consider the total cost of information technology: its upfront cost, training, maintenance, and customization, to name a few.

*Adaptability* is another micro-level issue managers need to consider. In other words, can the proposed information technology be adapted effectively to the organization? Or will its adoption involve major business process redesign? Investments in new IT are challenging under most circumstances. But, if they disrupt or create change in the way a company does business, they become even more so.

Employees need to learn to use a new information technology, so *training* becomes another issue. How easy will it be to learn to use new hardware and/or software? Will the training be provided by the vendor as part of the contract, or will the company have to pay extra for it? Can the training be made available online, or does it require classroom attendance to be effective? While a hardware or software vendor will certainly have answers to most of those questions, many organizations seek answers from companies that have already implemented the same or similar systems.

Finally, what about *vendor reliability?* Is the supplier of the technology a well-established, reputable company? You don't want to make a significant investment with a company only to find them bankrupt or out of business within a few months or years. Naturally, no one can predict those kinds of events with perfect certainty, so managers have to rely on their judgment and independent data collection as assessment tools.

Sylla and Wen (2002) proposed a **three-stage process** for evaluating information technology investments; their ideas are depicted in Figure 5.4.

**FIGURE 5.4**
**Sylla and Wen**
**Framework**

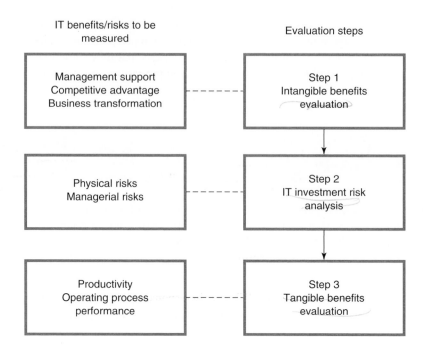

So how can you make sense of all those factors in an IT investment situation? I've often used a **weighted-rating technique** as a guide. Here's how it works:

1. Develop a list of factors that are important in your decision. I generally stick with around five factors, but you could use fewer or more depending on the circumstance.
2. Weight each factor on a scale from 1 to 10 based on its importance, with higher numbers assigned to factors that are more important.
3. Evaluate each piece of hardware and/or software on each factor. Assign each item a score (again from 1 to 10) based on how well it fulfills the factor.
4. Multiply the weightings by the ratings and add everything up to determine an overall "score" for an individual item.
5. Use the weighted ratings as one input to your investment decision.

Here's an example:

| Factor | Factor Weighting |
|---|---|
| Adaptability | 7 |
| Cost | 8 |
| Strategic fit | 9 |
| Training | 9 |

| Software package | Ratings | | | | |
|---|---|---|---|---|---|
| | Adaptability | Cost | Strategic Fit | Training | Weighted Score |
| 1 | 6 | 10 | 8 | 5 | 239 |
| 2 | 10 | 10 | 9 | 7 | 294 |
| 3 | 8 | 7 | 10 | 9 | 283 |

So, in the preceding analysis, the numeric results argue in favor of software package 2. Notice, though, that its "score" is very close to that of package 3. In cases such as this, where the scores are so close, managers need to use judgment in making the final choice—rather than slavishly following the numeric results.

## CRITICAL THINKING

Vitalics is an internal control software application designed specifically for small business. You can get more information about it in the 15 August 2013 post on my AIS blog, as well as on the Web site of the company that developed it (Business Fraud Prevention LLC, http://www.businessfraudprevention.org/vitalics.html). See Figure 5.5 below for a Vitalics screen shot.

Let's consider the three topics we've discussed in this chapter (SDLC, CMM, software selection) through the lens of Vitalics.

A company considering adopting Vitalics to strengthen its internal controls might complete the steps in the SDLC like this:

1. *Initiation/planning.* Whether in response to internal control breaches, recommendations from auditors, or for some other reason, management of RCV Corporation recognizes a need to improve internal control.

2. *Requirements analysis.* RCV could use one or both COSO frameworks (internal control and/or enterprise risk management) to determine more specifically what it needs from an internal control IT application. Those requirements could include items like these:

   a. Costs under $300

   b. Requires little or no specialized training

   c. Specifically designed for small business

   d. Updated regularly without cost

**FIGURE 5.5**
**Vitalics Menu**

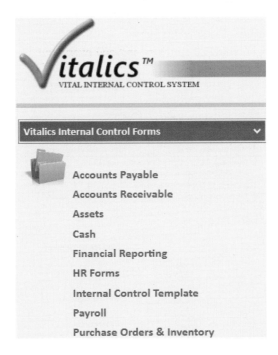

3. *Design.* RCV has at least two options at this stage. They can develop software on their own or look for a suitable product. Clearly, that decision would be based on many factors, including both cost and availability of the required expertise. For this example, let's assume that RCV decides to look for a suitable product. Through personal networking, Internet searches, and/or professional associations, RCV would identify a few "candidates" based on the requirements analysis. The candidates would go through RCV's search process, and RCV would select one; let's suppose Vitalics is chosen.
4. *Build.* RCV would use the forms built into Vitalics and/or create its own forms, customizing as necessary for its own operations. See Figure 5.6 below for an example of a Vitalics form.
5. *Test.* RCV would give a few employees access to the Vitalics software and ask them to use it. The employees would provide feedback to make the software more effective for RCV.
6. *Implementation.* After testing, RCV would "roll out" the software to the rest of the company.
7. *Operations and maintenance.* RCV would receive periodic updates to maintain the software and, as needed, make additional changes to the forms and/or its own internal control processes to align them more completely.

Where would RCV (or any other organization) need to be on the CMM to benefit from software like Vitalics? At the minimum, its internal control processes should be at Level three: defined. When a process is "defined," as the term is used in the CMM, it is widely understood and used throughout the organization. Prior to implementing Vitalics, RCV should have a clear internal control plan, perhaps based on the COSO framework. If RCV's internal control processes were more sophisticated ("managed" or "optimized" in the CMM), they would benefit even more from using Vitalics.

Notice how the macrolevel and microlevel factors identified in Figure 5.3 are incorporated in the SDLC steps. The "micro-level factors" are part of requirements analysis; some of the macro-level factors (e.g., need) are included in other steps (e.g., initiation/planning).

**FIGURE 5.6**
**Vitalics Form**

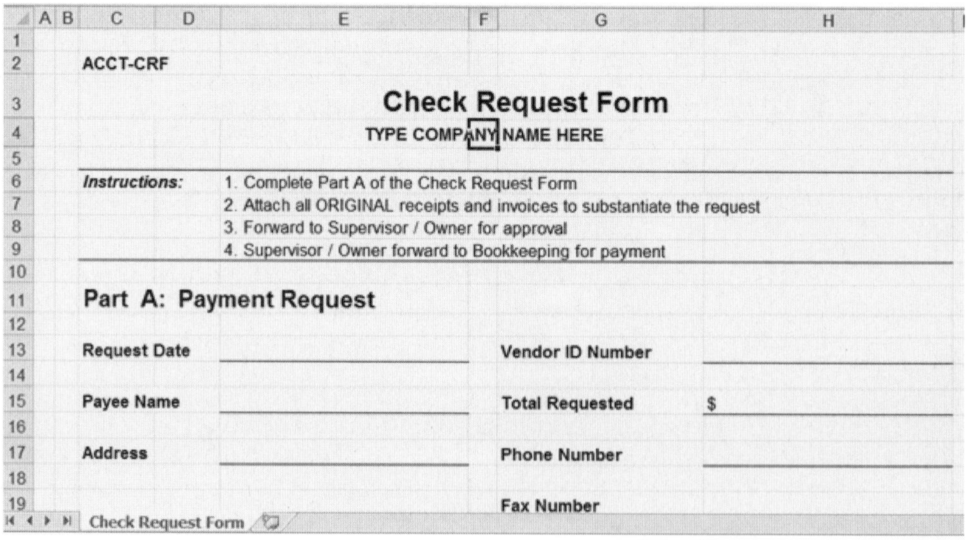
ACCT-CRF

Check Request Form

TYPE COMPANY NAME HERE

Instructions:
1. Complete Part A of the Check Request Form
2. Attach all ORIGINAL receipts and invoices to substantiate the request
3. Forward to Supervisor / Owner for approval
4. Supervisor / Owner forward to Bookkeeping for payment

Part A: Payment Request

Request Date ____________ Vendor ID Number ____________

Payee Name ____________ Total Requested $ ____________

Address ____________ Phone Number ____________

Fax Number

Check Request Form

## Summary

Here's a look back at what we've covered in this chapter:

1. *List and discuss, in order, the steps in the systems development life cycle.* The SDLC is a methodology many organizations use to develop and implement information systems. It comprises seven steps, which are highly iterative in nature: initiation/planning, requirements analysis, design, build, test, implementation, and operations and maintenance.

2. *Explain the advantages and disadvantages of using the SDLC.* The SDLC is very structured and offers organizations a lot of control over information systems projects; in addition, it is widely recognized and used in business. On the other hand, the steps in the SDLC can take a lot of time to complete, thereby resulting in high costs relative to other systems development strategies.

3. *Apply the SDLC in accounting contexts.* Since accounting is fundamentally an information system, the SDLC steps can be applied to it. In the *initiation/planning* stage, an organization would recognize the need for changes in its AIS—for example, the need to generate a variance analysis or consolidate results from subsidiary companies. *Requirements analysis* focuses on what the system needs to accomplish; staying with the variance analysis example, the system would probably need to generate quantity and cost variances for product costs. *Designing* such a system gets still more specific: What would a user see on the screen? Which source documents, paper or electronic, would be required to collect the data? How would the data be input? Systems professionals would move next to *building* the system—actually putting together the screens, documents, and programming code for computing variances. Users would have the opportunity to *test* the system prior to it being *implemented* with a parallel approach, direct cutover approach, or some other approach. Finally, in *operations and maintenance,* the system would be changed as the organization and its information needs change.

4. *List and discuss the levels of the capability maturity model (CMM).* The capability maturity model consists of five levels, each more sophisticated than the previous level: chaotic, repeatable, defined, managed, and optimized.

5. *Classify organizations' processes according to the CMM.* When an organization's processes are *chaotic,* they lack cohesion; each individual in the organization does what seems best to him/her. *Repeatable* processes involve some standards and procedures, but they are probably applied to a single project. When processes are *defined,* they are connected to broader organizational standards; standards are developed and data are collected about the process. Processes move to the *managed* stage when the collected data are used to improve and control the process. When the idea of managing and improving business processes is ingrained in the organization, becoming part of its culture, it moves to the last level of the CMM: *optimized.*

6. *Explain factors managers should consider when choosing IT for an AIS.* The chapter considers both macro- and micro-level factors. Macro-level factors include need, strategic fit, personnel involvement, and financing. Micro-level factors are cost, adaptability, training, and vendor reliability. The weighted-rating technique can be used to balance the factors.

When accounting information systems courses started becoming a part of undergraduate accounting programs, they often focused on ideas common to all information systems like the SDLC. Although the content of AIS courses has become more specific over time, those ideas can still be an integral part of AIS study.

| Key Terms | | | |
|---|---|---|
| capability maturity model, *84* | micro-level issues, *86* | three-stage process, *87* |
| iterative, *81* | systems development life | Watts Humphrey, *84* |
| macro-level issues, *86* | cycle, *81* | weighted-rating technique, *88* |

## Chapter References

Hurst, J. 2007. *The Capability Maturity Model and Its Applications.* www.giac.org/resources (last visited September 26, 2014).

Johnston, R. 2003. "A Strategy for Finding the Right Accounting Software." *Journal of Accountancy,* September, pp. 39–46.

Sylla, C., and H. J. Wen. 2002. "A Conceptual Framework for Evaluation of Information Technology Investments." *International Journal of Technology Management,* pp. 236–61.

## End-of-Chapter Activities

**1.** *Reading review questions.*

   a.  What are the steps in the systems development life cycle? What activities does each step involve?

   b.  What are the costs and benefits of using the SDLC?

   c.  How can the SDLC be useful in accounting information systems?

   d.  What are the levels in the capability maturity model? What characteristics distinguish each level?

   e.  What factors should managers consider when choosing information technology resources?

   f.  Respond to the questions for this chapter's "AIS in the Business World."

**2.** *Reading review problem.*

This chapter's "AIS in the Business World" focused on Google. But, Google is not "the only game in town" when it comes to information technology. According to "Apple, Amazon and Google: The Competition Is Heating Up" by John Macris (30 April 2013, http://beta.fool.com):

> Fast-forward to present date, and Apple, Amazon, and Google are fiercely competing to become the most powerful name in technology. The concrete borders that once separated one company from another have been knocked down, and the areas of distinction are becoming fewer (*sic*) as these businesses increasingly overlap. Consumers frequently use the names of all three companies in the same conversation.

Products like Amazon Cloud and Amazon Prime compete very directly with products like Google Drive and Google Shopping.

Consider the list of Google products at http://www.google.com/intl/en/about/products/. Choose **one** as the basis for answering the following questions:

   a.  Use the steps in the systems development life cycle (SDLC) to explain how a company like Amazon, Apple or some other firm would develop a product or service to compete with the Google product you chose.

   b.  Does using the SDLC correspond to any particular level of the capability maturity model (CMM)? Why, or why not?

   c.  Consider at least one macrolevel and one microlevel factor from Figure 5.3 in the context of the product/service you suggested in (a). Prepare a short written summary and/or oral presentation relating the factors to your product/service. (For example, how would you demonstrate the "need" for your product/service?)

**3.** *Multiple choice review questions. Please select the best answer for each question.*

   1.  Which of the following SDLC steps occurs first?

      a.  Build

      b.  Design

      c.  Test

      d.  Operations/maintenance

2. Which phase of the SDLC is most likely to include a feasibility study?

   a. Initiation/planning

   b. Requirements analysis

   c. Design

   d. Operations and maintenance

3. At which level of the CMM are project standards first derived from broader organizational standards?

   a. Chaotic

   b. Repeatable

   c. Defined

   d. Managed

4. Which of the following phrases is most closely associated with the "optimized" level of the CMM?

   a. Lone Ranger

   b. Continuous improvement

   c. Necessary evil

   d. Information technology

5. All of the following are macro-level issues to consider in IT selection except:

   a. Financing

   b. Need

   c. Strategic fit

   d. Training

**4.** *Making choices and exercising judgment.*

   a. Business professionals have debated whether or not an organization should strive to ensure that all its processes are "optimized" according to the CMM. What do you think? Regardless of your response, what benefits might an organization realize at the earlier levels?

   b. Common forms of information technology in AIS include spreadsheets, databases and general ledger software. List and discuss three AIS-related tasks you could accomplish with each type of software; for example, you could develop a budget with spreadsheet software.

   c. FTP (file transfer protocol) software is used to transfer files between a computer and the Internet. In considering an FTP package, managers might consider factors such as cost, popularity, documentation, and ease of use. Point your Web browser to www.download.com and identify three FTP software packages available there. Evaluate them using the weighted-rating technique described in the chapter.

**5.** *Field exercises.*

   a. The SDLC is only one methodology for designing and implementing information systems. Others include rapid application development, open source development, joint applications design, and prototyping. Investigate one or more of those alternatives. Describe it, then compare and contrast it to the systems development life cycle.

   b. Arrange an interview with an accounting or information systems professional in an environment where you'd like to work after earning your degree. Ask your interviewee to describe a business process in his/her organization. On your own, based on that description, classify the process according to the capability maturity model. Explain your classification.

   c. Read "Commercializing the Back Office at Lloyds of London: Outsourcing and Strategic Partnerships Revisited" in *European Management Journal* (April 2004, pp. 127–40). Summarize the article's contents in no more than one single-spaced page. Did Lloyds use IT strategically? Justify your response.

6. *Capability maturity model classification.* Several business processes are described below. Which CMM level best characterizes each one?

   a. Alastor owns a lawn care business. Each time he mows a client's lawn, he sets a goal for how long it should take.

   b. Big State University was engaged in three building projects simultaneously: an addition to the library, a new parking structure, and upgrades to the student center. Although each project was over budget for both time and money, the university president focused on analyzing the situation for the parking structure only.

   c. CHL Corporation's management team meets monthly to address issues of process improvement and product quality.

   d. Christina is a sales representative with clients all over eastern Michigan. At the beginning of each day, she decides which clients she will contact that day and whether she will contact them in person, over the phone, or via e-mail.

   e. Hong and Meihua build wooden doghouses based on requests from clients. They frequently disagree about the best way to build each one.

   f. Magdy is the vice president of finance at TCH Corporation. At the end of each year, he consults with the president and other vice presidents to determine the corporation's optimal capital structure. He then compares the optimal structure to the actual one, making recommendations for needed changes.

   g. Rodrigo, Miguel, and Ana own a mobile pet grooming service with eight employees. Every quarter, as part of their overall quality improvement plan, they send two employees to a continuing education seminar.

   h. Sebastian is a manager at PPK Corporation. The last time he hired a new employee, he asked his favorite current employee if any of her relatives were looking for a job; he then hired one based on that conversation.

   i. The payroll manager at BHN Corporation has proposed outsourcing part of the payroll function. In accordance with BHN policy, the manager prepared a flowchart of how the new process would work.

   j. When the production manager at STK Corporation suggested converting from a process-costing system to a job-costing system, the vice president of operations asked how the change would affect the amount of inventory available for sale.

7. *Systems development life cycle.* Which phase of the SDLC is described by each independent case below?

   a. Dolores used design specifications to create database tables for employee records.

   b. Eric works at a "help desk" answering questions about patching issues in World of Warcraft.

   c. Esther must decide how many "action buttons" to put on an Access form for entering purchase requisitions.

   d. Liliane completed several simulations of a new inventory control system, then made recommendations for changes in how the system was designed and built.

   e. Marcel prepared a leveled set of data flow diagrams for a new sales/collection process, then used the set as a basis for discussion with the sales staff.

   f. Tony wants to move from incremental budgeting to zero-based budgeting.

   g. When the accounting staff of CHF Corporation arrived at work on Monday morning, their old manual accounting system had been replaced.

8. *Requirements analysis.*

   a. Jeff is the warehouse manager for Alta Pasa Unified School District; he wants an online inventory tracking system for computers and other technology resources in the warehouse. List and discuss at least five questions you would ask Jeff and his staff as part of the requirements analysis for the project.

b. Amanda is a hypnotherapist in Dallas, Texas. She currently maintains her appointment schedule in a paper-based calendar but wants to start using information technology for that purpose. List and discuss at least five questions you would ask Amanda as part of the requirements analysis for the project.

9. **AICPA Top Technology Initiatives.** Do a Google search for the AICPA Top Ten Technologies. Investigate the most recent list; describe the process used to develop the list. Work with a group of students to investigate one or more of the technologies, summarizing your work in a form specified by your instructor.

10. *Terminology.* Match each item on the left with the most appropriate item on the right.

| | |
|---|---|
| 1. "Ad hoc" processes | a. Test (SDLC) |
| 2. Business rules | b. Risk of SDLC |
| 3. Consistent project standards | c. Repeatable (CMM) |
| 4. Cost overrun | d. Optimized (CMM) |
| 5. Discrete project standards | e. Managed (CMM) |
| 6. Feasibility study | f. Initiation/planning (SDLC) |
| 7. Improvement part of organizational culture | g. Design (SDLC) |
| 8. Modular programming code | h. Defined (CMM) |
| 9. Simulations | i. Chaotic (CMM) |
| 10. Statistical project control | j. Build (SDLC) |

11. *Multiple choice questions.*

1. As a future accounting professional, which phase of the SDLC are you least likely to be involved in?

   a. Build

   b. Requirements analysis

   c. Operations/maintenance

   d. Test

2. If a system does poorly during the testing phase of the SDLC, it may be due to issues in

   I. Requirements analysis.

   II. Design.

   III. Build.

   a. I and II only

   b. II and III only

   c. I and III only

   d. I, II, and III

3. Which of the following is the best example of the "initiation/planning" stage of the SDLC?

   a. "We need to use XBRL to produce financial statements."

   b. "We should adopt Peachtree as our general ledger software."

   c. "Let's compare PeopleSoft with SAP."

   d. "Our inventory controls are weak."

4. Which of the following statements is most true?

   a. Failure of a new system is a bigger risk in direct cutover implementations than in parallel implementations.

   b. Failure of a new system is a bigger risk in parallel implementations than in direct cutover implementations.

   c. Smaller organizations should use parallel implementation more often than direct cutover.

   d. Larger organizations should use direct cutover implementation more often than parallel.

5. John plans to use the SDLC to develop a balanced scorecard for his department. Which stage of the capability maturity model is John's organization in?

a. Chaotic

b. Repeatable

c. Managed

d. Cannot be determined from the information given

12. *Statement evaluation.* Indicate whether each of the following statements is (i) always true, (ii) sometimes true, or (iii) never true. For those that are (ii) sometimes true, explain when the statement is true.

a. The systems development life cycle is the best way to develop new information systems.

b. The SDLC can never be used as a tool for managing business processes.

c. Interviews with system users can be an important element of requirements analysis.

d. Results in the build stage of the SDLC may require an organization to revisit its requirements analysis.

e. Cost growth and schedule delays are risks associated with using the SDLC.

f. If the business processes in Department X are optimized, the business processes in Department Y are also optimized.

g. An organization can move from repeatable processes to managed processes without having defined processes.

h. An organization should move through the stages of the CMM sequentially.

i. An organization using activity-based management is at the managed stage of the CMM.

j. Publicly traded corporations are required to optimize their business processes for SOX and the Foreign Corrupt Practices Act.

13. *Excel application.* AGN Corporation uses the systems development life cycle to develop/select new forms of information technology for its operations; its technology acquisition process is considered "managed" based on the capability maturity model. AGN is considering purchasing new software to track its sales and marketing function. Relevant data about the software appear below:

| | |
|---|---|
| Software cost | $ 80,000 |
| Additional revenue generated annually | 12,000 |
| Annual cost savings | 6,000 |
| Anticipated life of the software | 5 years |

AGN uses a discount rate of 3% in decisions of this type. Additional revenue and cost savings are "net of tax."

a. Use Excel's NPV and IRR functions to calculate the net present value and internal rate of return on the software. (Check figure: NPV is between $2,000 and $2,500.)

b. Should AGN buy the software? Why, or why not?

**Comprehensive Problem**

**Part 1 of 5**

The fourth edition includes this comprehensive problem as a new feature; you'll find one part of the problem at the end of each part of the text—that is, after Chapters 5, 8, 11, 14, and 17. Each installment of the comprehensive problem will ask you to refer back to the following narrative; each installment will have application questions based on the material in the associated part of the text. As with all aspects of the book, I'm eager to hear your feedback via email or comment in my AIS blog.

The comprehensive problem is based on Big Marker, a videoconferencing service based in Chicago, IL. Their Web site is www.bigmarker.com. The narrative is divided into the following sections: company description, internal controls, and business processes.

## Company Description

Big Marker was started in 2010 by Mr. Zhu-Song Mei. Zhu was inspired to start the company by the need to communicate with his mother during a period of illness. The company was initially financed by a group of angel investors and Zhu-Song; over time, it has attracted additional investors. Big Marker is organized as a limited liability company, and has 11 employees. Its organizational structure is fairly "flat," as shown in the organizational chart below:

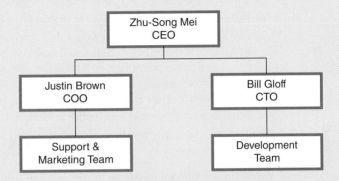

Zhu-Song handles the financial recordkeeping using Quickbooks, and McGladrey (www.mcgladrey.com) does an annual "compilation and review" for Big Marker. Big Marker uses the standard service company chart of accounts built into Quickbooks for its transaction processing. (The chart of accounts is block coded.)

Big Marker is organized into a collection of "communities," which are based on common interests/goals. Each community has at least one organizer; for example, my community is called "Bob Hurt Education Community." Additionally, one organizer can participate in/create multiple communities. Communities host meetings and webinars at the organizer's discretion; meetings are designed for collaboration, while webinars are typically structured as interactive presentations. As of early 2014, Big Marker had between 5,000 and 10,000 communities, and hosted 1,000–2,000 meetings/webinars monthly.

## Internal Controls

Big Marker employs several internal controls to safeguard its assets, ensure reliable financial reporting, promote operating efficiency and encourage compliance with management directives. Here are some controls Big Marker employs, presented in alphabetic order:

1. *Asset tracking.* If a Big Marker employee wants to remove an asset from the office temporarily, one of the C-suite officers must authorize it. Additionally, approved assets must be signed out with the building's security staff. (Big Marker is one office in a large office building.) Finally, all assets are logged in both QuickBooks and a locally maintained spreadsheet.

2. *Cash handling.* Big Marker employs several internal controls to help safeguard its cash. For example, the office handles no actual cash; everything, from cash collections to payroll, is handled electronically. Big Marker maintains two separate cash accounts: one for the payroll at Chase (www.chase.com) and one for the operating expenses at Bank of America (www.bankofamerica.com).

3. *Employee expense reimbursements.* Zhu-Song personally reviews all requests for employee expense reimbursements; common requests include office supplies, party supplies, laptop accessories, and travel and entertainment costs. Approved reimbursements are processed as part of the payroll with ADP; employees log into the system and enter the data. (See "payroll processing" later in this list for details.)

4. *Employee manual.* All new hires get an employee manual. The manual lays out a few "common sense, minimal policies," but the overall atmosphere at Big Marker is very friendly and casual. Employees are very passionate about the work they and the company do.

5. *Information technology.* Big Marker uses state of the art computer servers for its operations. It uses both colocation and cloud computing for its servers.

6. *Payroll processing.* In addition to maintaining the dedicated payroll account at Chase, Big Marker promotes strong internal control over the payroll process by outsourcing it to ADP (www.adp.com). Individual employees log into ADP's system to submit their hours and other information; ADP processes the payroll on a monthly basis, and all Big Marker employees are required to have checks direct deposited in their bank accounts. No paper checks change hands for payroll. The company offers a standard benefits package, including health insurance.

7. *Staff meetings.* Big Marker holds weekly staff meetings to discuss issues and priorities facing the company.

You'll find additional elements of internal control in Big Marker's terms of use at https://www.bigmarker.com/terms.

## Business Processes

In addition to the payroll process described above, common business processes at Big Marker include purchasing servers, starting communities, monitoring communities, and paying company bills (such as advertising and rent).

When Big Marker wants to purchase a new server, employees first develop their requirement specifications (e.g., processing speed, available memory). They use those specifications to choose a server from a vendor such as Dell (www.dell.com). Big Marker orders the server online, and accepts delivery when the server is ready.

When an organizer starts a new community, Big Marker sends an automatically generated email with details about how to host events and related matters. Each community is assigned a "community hero"—a Big Marker employee available to answer questions and guide the organizer in relevant tasks. All new communities receive a free 14-day trial of Big Marker, after which their credit card (submitted during the community creation process) is billed for a nominal monthly fee of $20. Big Marker then attempts to charge the credit card each month for the fee. If billing fails, Big Marker sends another automatically generated email stating that they will try to bill the credit card every three days for 15 days; if billing still fails, the community is suspended. Community organizers have the option of selling tickets to their events; if they do, Big Marker retains 10% of the total ticket revenue. Similarly, community organizers may charge community dues to members; Big Marker also retains 10% of that revenue. Big Marker also will attempt to find "corporate sponsors" for communities; a corporate sponsor would contribute funds to maintain and help run the community, and all those funds go directly to the community itself.

Big Marker also monitors each community's activity. If a community hosts no events for two months, the organizer(s) receive an email offering assistance. Big Marker queries its database to determine which communities fall into that category. The "average" member of Big Marker belongs to three or four communities; communities have no upper limit as to membership. Similarly, each member may join as many communities as he/she wishes. Although each community has just one "community hero," the same community hero may serve in that capacity for multiple communities.

All bill-paying activity at Big Marker happens electronically in one of the three ways: via the company's credit card, via automatic debit from the Bank of America operating account, or via electronic check from the Bank of America operating account.

## Part One Questions

1. Accounting information systems have five generic parts. Based on the preceding narrative, information on the Big Marker Web site and your own critical thinking, provide two examples of each of the five generic parts.

2. Big Marker uses the standard chart of accounts in QuickBooks to maintain its financial records.

   a. Suggest specific account titles and account numbers for at least three accounts in each of the following categories: current assets, plant assets, current liabilities, long-term liabilities, equity, revenue, and expense.

   b. Use the account titles and account numbers from (a) to suggest at least 10 transactions Big Marker would commonly process. Indicate, using the account names and numbers, how Big Marker would record each transaction you suggest.

3. Consider the list of internal controls presented in the narrative. For each one, discuss:

   a. Whether it is primarily preventive/detective/corrective in nature.

   b. Which of the four purposes of internal control it is designed to achieve.

4. Use the relevant COSO frameworks to develop internal control and enterprise risk management plans for Big Marker. For both plans, suggest control activities that are not mentioned in the narrative.

5. Create a risk/control matrix for Big Marker using some combination of the internal controls discussed in the narrative and any you created in the previous question.

6. How would you describe Big Marker's business processes using the Capability Maturity Model? Explain your classification.

## Part Two

# Documentation Techniques and Database Design

**6.** Flowcharting

**7.** Data Flow Diagramming

**8.** REA Modeling

Part One presented some fundamental ideas about accounting information systems. In Part Two, we'll look at ways to document the AIS.

In this context, "document" means to "prepare a graphic representation" of the AIS. Fundamentally, accountants document business processes for two major reasons: (i) to understand a business process more completely and/or (ii) to understand the database that underlies the AIS.

In your career, you'll need to understand an organization's business processes for a variety of reasons, including (but not limited to) evaluating internal control as part of a financial statement audit, training new employees, making processes more efficient and effective using the principles of business process management, and conducting a forensic audit (fraud examination). Likewise, you'll need to understand the database that underlies the AIS to audit it effectively, query it to provide information to management and others and prepare various reports (such as an aging of accounts receivable).

Although accountants may use many different methods to document the AIS, we'll focus in this part of the book on three: flowcharts, data flow diagrams, and REA models. Because systems documentation helps us understand the database that underlies the AIS, we'll also look at database design when we consider data flow diagrams, and REA models.

# Chapter **Six**

# Flowcharting

## AIS in the Business World

### Barnes & Noble

In Chapter 1, you read brief descriptions of five common business processes, including the sales/collection process. Consider the systems flowchart below, which depicts part of that process for Barnes & Noble (www.barnesandnoble.com). The process would be very similar for most online booksellers.

Barnes & Noble online book sales process prepared by A. Student 17 January 20x4
Page 1 of 2

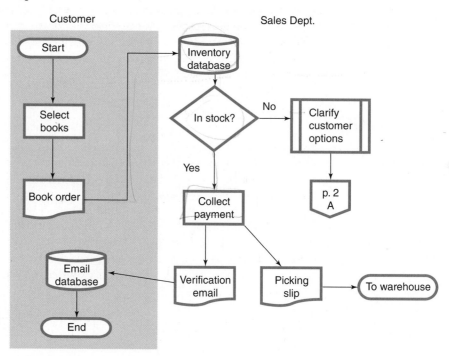

### *Discussion Questions*

1. What differentiates systems flowcharts from other flowchart types?
2. What conventions (i.e., common practices) are illustrated in the flowchart above?
3. Identify and describe the symbols used in the flowchart above. What other symbols are commonly used in systems flowcharts?
4. Create a narrative description of the process illustrated in the flowchart.

In practice, you may often be called upon to evaluate a system's risk exposures; recommend ways to achieve stronger internal control; and/or suggest one or more ways to make a system more efficient and effective. In those situations, you'll want a way to encapsulate the essential features of an accounting information system: its documents, personnel involved, information flows, and related technologies. As you read in the opening comments for Part Two, we call that process "systems documentation." In this chapter, we look at the documentation used most widely in accounting practice: flowcharting.

When you complete your study of this chapter, you should be able to:

1. List and discuss the purpose and use of systems flowcharts, document flowcharts, program flowcharts, and hardware flowcharts;
2. Explain the basic parts of and design considerations common to all types of flowcharts;
3. Identify and describe common symbols and information technology tools used in flowcharting;
4. Discuss ways flowcharts impact the design, implementation, and evaluation of accounting information systems;
5. Create and interpret systems flowcharts.

A good flowchart is like a snapshot of an information system. It can tell you, at a glance, where information originates, who handles the information, and how it is summarized for decision making. Like most of the rest of AIS, flowcharting is at least as much art as science. The keys are to make your flowcharts as easy to read and as understandable as possible and to develop them in sufficient detail to provide an accurate picture of what's going on in an accounting information system. In terms of the two broad purposes of systems documentation (understanding business processes and understanding the database), flowcharts are focused on the first (understanding business processes).

## FLOWCHART TYPES AND CONVENTIONS

Basically, a flowchart is a graphical representation of some part of an information system. The information system might be focused on accounting, production, human resources, or marketing; it might be related to a particular business process (such as the sales/collection process) or project (such as hiring new employees). As you'll learn in Chapter 17, understanding business processes is a key element of financial statement auditing, so you'll often run across flowcharts in an audit. Flowcharts have been used by information technology professionals for years to document computer programs; they also can be used to depict the hardware associated with a computer information system. According to Bradford, Richtermeyer, and Roberts (2007), at least 60% of practicing management accounting professionals use flowcharts in their work.

Flowcharts often are classified by their overall purpose and function:

- **Systems flowcharts** give the user a "big picture" look at an information system. Consider, for example, the process you use to register for classes each term. You use certain documents and types of information technology to select and register for classes; a systems flowchart would combine all of those resources with their related business processes. The partial Barnes and Noble flowchart in this chapter's AIS in the Business World is a systems flowchart.

- **Program flowcharts** show the logic associated with a computer program. As an accountant, you probably won't have much to do with program flowcharts.

- **Document flowcharts,** as you might expect, show the various documents involved in a system; they also portray the procedures performed on those documents. So, for example, a document flowchart might show your federal income tax return from the time you receive a blank form through its eventual disposition with the Internal Revenue Service.

- **Hardware flowcharts** will probably be a minor concern in your accounting career as well. They show the computers, printers, monitors, input devices, and other hardware elements associated with an information system.

## Reflection and Self-Assessment                                    6.1

What type of flowchart would be most appropriate in each of the following situations?

1. Steps in a Visual Basic program for producing financial statements.

2. Steps associated with purchasing inventory.

3. Relationships between a central server and desktop computers.

4. Path of a sales invoice through an information system.

5. Origination, processing, and termination of a payroll check.

6. Local area network configuration.

7. Employee evaluation process.

Although two different people can look at the same business process and draw flowcharts that are significantly different, they should generally observe some very common conventions (habits) associated with good flowcharting:

1. Flowcharts should generally be read from top to bottom and left to right—the same way you read a page in a book. Flowcharting, though, is a highly iterative process, meaning that most folks don't "get it right" the very first time. So, the design may not proceed in such a neat and orderly fashion. But, when the final flowchart is produced, users should be able to follow it easily.

2. Flowcharts should have plenty of "white space." In other words, they shouldn't be too crowded on the page. If you're like most accounting students, you're thinking, "How do I know if it's too crowded? Is there a rule?" Well, no. Generally, if you think a flowchart looks too crowded, it probably is. In that case, it needs to be broken up into more than one page for easier reading.

3. Flowcharts should have a title. A bunch of symbols on a page can be confusing to read and evaluate if you don't know what they're trying to present. So, it's a good idea to title your flowchart based on what it represents; for example, "Systems flowchart of the employee evaluation process." The title should also include the name of the company, the date the flowchart was prepared, and the preparer's name. If the flowchart spans multiple pages, they should be numbered as "1 of x, 2 of x," and so on.

4. Flowcharts should be organized in columns that depict areas of responsibility. For example, purchasing inventory in most organizations involves departmental managers, purchasing agents, and vendors. So, a systems flowchart that shows the purchasing process would typically have three columns—one for each area of responsibility. Areas of responsibility will most commonly be the names of departments/functions/job titles within the organization; we don't typically use a person's name as a column heading.

5. Documents involved in a business process should have a clear origin and a clear termination. They shouldn't appear "by magic" in the middle of a flowchart, nor should they disappear from the system. Documents typically originate in one of two ways: (i) they

enter the system from outside the system boundary or (ii) they are created by some process within the system. They typically terminate in one of two ways, as well: (a) they are filed (electronically or on paper) or (b) they cross out of the system boundary. (We'll talk about what a 'system boundary' is in a few pages.)

6. Rough drafts of flowcharts should be discussed by people involved in the process. Such discussions serve as a "reality check." They also help ensure that the flowchart is easily understood by someone other than the designer.

Adhering to those six conventions will make your flowcharts a lot easier to read and understand; they'll also be considerably more useful in the design, evaluation, and implementation of accounting information systems.

## FLOWCHARTING TOOLS AND SYMBOLS

Flowcharts can be designed using a variety of tools, both high-tech and low-tech. On the low-tech end, you can draw a flowchart with paper and pencil. You also can use a flowcharting template, which includes many common flowcharting symbols. While manual methods are useful for "quick and dirty" starts at a flowchart, they can become tedious and messy over time.

You can find more information about Visio at http://support .microsoft.com/ph/2529. Check out SmartDraw on its Web page: www .smartdraw.com.

Fortunately, numerous software programs facilitate the preparation of good flowcharts. Two programs I've found useful are **Microsoft Visio** and **SmartDraw.** Visio is part of the Microsoft Office Suite, so it interfaces fairly well with other programs such as Word, PowerPoint, and Excel. SmartDraw is an independent software program, but it also does a good job with designing all kinds of flowcharts; generally, they also can be read by Office software. Of course, you can use just about any software package that has some graphics capability to design a flowchart—even something as simple as PowerPoint! The advantage of using a program specifically designed for flowcharting, like SmartDraw or Visio, is its adherence to the flowcharting conventions discussed earlier. Additionally, flowcharting programs typically have a wider variety of flowcharting symbols in their libraries than other programs designed for different purposes. In most of Microsoft Office, you'll find flowcharting symbols under the "Shapes" command of the "Insert" tab.

## Reflection and Self-Assessment                6.2

Point your Web browser to www.download.com. Search for flowcharting programs. Identify and describe two other programs you could use to create flowcharts.

Because flowcharts represent a kind of "universal language" in information systems design, implementation, and evaluation, they have some common symbols with specific meanings. According to the American National Standards Institute (ANSI), flowchart symbols can be divided into four groups: data, process, line, and special. Consider the **symbols** shown in Figure 6.1, which are just a small subset of the many symbols associated with flowcharting.

Now, let's take a look at how the symbols are put together to construct an actual flowchart.

**FIGURE 6.1**
**Selected**
**Flowcharting**
**Symbols**

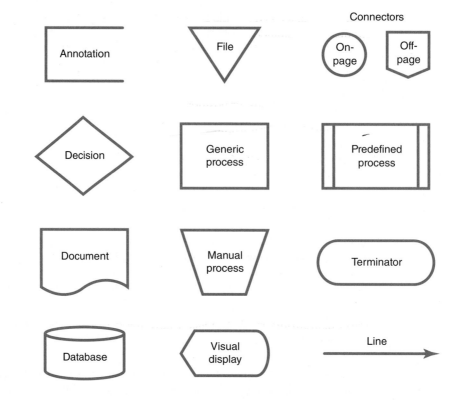

---

# Reflection and Self-Assessment                                    6.3

Consider the flowchart symbols in Figure 6.1. Which would you use for each of the following? (Some symbols may be used more than once; others may not be used at all.)

1. By date
2. Customer check
3. Grant credit?
4. In database?
5. Load merchandise on truck by hand
6. p. 2, A
7. Purchase order
8. Reconcile bank statement
9. Start
10. To bank

---

## FLOWCHART DESIGN STEPS

As you might suspect, there's no "one right way" to design a flowchart. When I prepare a flowchart, I normally follow this seven-step process:

1. *Establish the system boundary*. The system boundary is critical in designing a flow-chart. Without a well-established system boundary, you end up "analyzing the world" every time you draw a flowchart. The system boundary puts a virtual "box" around the system; this process is sometimes called "delimiting."

In this chapter's AIS in the Business World, the system boundary comprises just two entities: the customer and the sales department. Notice the use of the terminator symbol to send the picking slip across the boundary to the warehouse.

2. *Determine column headings*. Column headings, ("customer" and "sales department" in the Barnes and Noble example) should focus on areas of responsibility—usually department names, functions, or position titles.

3. *List actions performed within each column*. In this step, list what each department does within the system. Notice that we haven't yet begun thinking about how to represent those actions with flowcharting symbols. It's important to have a good, clear idea of what goes on in the system before thinking about the symbols. Because flowcharting is a highly iterative process, you might find it necessary to revisit the column headings at this stage—always keeping in mind the system boundary so the flowchart doesn't grow out of control.

    In the Barnes & Noble example, the customer selects books, creates the order and receives the confirmation email. The sales department checks the inventory database to determine if all the merchandise is in stock, collects payment OR clarifies customer options, sends the verification email to the customer and sends the picking slip to the warehouse.

4. *Select appropriate symbols*. Once I have the list of actions, I think about what flowcharting symbols will best represent them. Please refer to Figure 6.1 for a few symbols you'll come across frequently.

    a. Annotation. This symbol is used to add descriptive comments or explanations to a flowchart. For example, an annotation might explain how often a connected process occurs.

    b. *Decision*. Decision symbols are used when a choice has a binary outcome; that is, when it has only two options. Remember, therefore, that a decision symbol is NOT used for every decision! Examples of choices with binary outcomes include "grant credit" or "merchandise in stock."

    c. *Document*. A document can be electronic or paper; remember that a document should always have a clear point of origin AND a clear point of termination. If a document includes an original and one or more copies, layer the document symbols, ensuring that each one is properly differentiated (e.g., Copy A, Copy B).

    d. *File*. Sometimes referred to as "merge," this symbol should always indicate how the documents are filed. Examples include by name or by date.

    e. *Generic process*. This symbol can be used for any process in a flowchart. Because it symbolizes a process, it should always be labeled with a verb phrase, such as "receive applications" or "prepare purchase order."

    f. *Manual process*. If you know a process is manual (i.e., doesn't involve IT), you can use this symbol instead of the generic process.

    g. *On- and off-page connectors*. Readability is a critical feature of flowcharts. To avoid crossed lines on a page, use an on-page connector. To avoid overcrowding and move the action of a flowchart between pages, use an off-page connector. On- and off-page connectors always come in pairs with the same label. You can use letters for on-page connectors and numbers for off-page, or vice versa—just be consistent.

    h. *Predefined process*. Use this symbol to encapsulate a named process with multiple steps. The multiple steps should either be readily understood by the person reading the flowchart, OR they should be specified elsewhere (such as in a separate flowchart). "Complete the steps in the accounting cycle" is an example of a predefined process.

i.  *Terminator.* I tend to use the terminator symbol only to mark the start and end of a flowchart. But, it can also be used to show entry from/exit to some point outside the system boundary.

j.  *Database.* Use this symbol when data are stored/retrieved electronically. The database symbol should be labeled with the name of the database, such as "employee database." An arrow entering a database symbolizes data input, while an arrow exiting the database symbolizes data output—no need for a process symbol for either of those.

k.  *Visual display.* If information is displayed on a computer screen, use this symbol. In general, the visual display symbol should be labeled with the data it depicts, such as "customer record."

l.  *Line.* Lines are used, of course, to indicate the direction of action in a flowchart. Lines in a flowchart should not be labeled.

5.  *Prepare a first draft.* Once the symbols are chosen and correlated with the actions in (3), it's time to draw a first draft of the flowchart, keeping in mind the design conventions listed above.

6.  *Discuss the flowchart with others.* Because flowcharting is somewhat subjective and highly iterative, the first draft is rarely the final product. It's important to get feedback on the draft from other people, because they can tell you what seems unclear from an outsider's point of view.

7.  *Revise as needed.* Based on those suggestions, revise the flowchart as necessary to make it clearer. For your first few flowcharts, you might need several rounds of revision. As you become more experienced, you might be able to cut them down to just one or two.

In the next section, we'll look at how flowcharts are used in AIS contexts. This chapter's "critical thinking" section will walk you through an example of flowchart creation.

## FLOWCHARTING AND ACCOUNTING INFORMATION SYSTEMS

So how does all this material relate to your study of accounting information systems? AIS professionals use flowcharts in many different ways, including confirming how a system is currently operating, suggesting improvements to an accounting information system, evaluating internal control deficiencies, and designing procedures manuals.

In your very first accounting job after you graduate, you'll likely be coming into an unfamiliar environment. You may wonder "how things work" in the accounting information system, especially if you're in charge of a particular function such as accounts payable or accounts receivable. Additionally, if you're working for a CPA firm or as a consultant, you may need to confirm how a system is operating currently before you start an audit or make recommendations regarding operational efficiency. In all those cases, a flowchart can be a useful way to conceptualize the big picture of a system. You'd probably want to look over any existing procedures manuals and talk with employees familiar with the system already. Then, you can try designing a flowchart to model a business process. Once you've completed a first draft, discuss it further with others in the organization. Explain to them what it says and ask if that's the way things "really work" in the company, or if you're misunderstanding something. Remember: The overall goal of a flowchart in this situation is to understand the current state of things—the way they are, not necessarily the way they should be.

If you're looking at a previously constructed flowchart, whether you've created it or not, you can try to spot opportunities for improvement. Critically analyzing a flowchart is a tough job—there are no hard-and-fast rules for doing it. You'll need to draw on your training, experience, and ordinary business sense to identify and describe possible improvements in an accounting information system. Once again, interviewing and other kinds of research will help in this task. Ask employees, for example, what their biggest complaint is about the current process. If they've thought about ways to improve it, listen to those as well. You could ask employees in one-on-one or small group interviews; written surveys, e-mail exchanges, and employee suggestion boxes also can help in gathering ideas about process improvements. In many cases, the employees closest to a process can provide the best suggestions for making things better; in some cases, a system outsider can provide a new, fresh idea based on experience in other organizations. Opportunities for improvements might include redesigning forms, increasing or decreasing the number of copies of a particular form, obtaining authorizing signatures for transactions, filing in a different way (for example, based on date rather than customer name or vice versa), or changing a form from paper-based to electronic (or vice versa).

Systems risk relates directly to information technology. As organizations become increasingly dependent on computers and related IT to deliver goods and services to customers, they risk the possibility that IT resources will fail at a critical moment.

Flowcharts also can be used to spot internal control deficiencies in an accounting information system. A flowchart can enhance a risk analysis by providing a concrete picture of an accounting information system. To use a flowchart to spot internal control deficiencies, start by making a list of the system's risk exposures. Then, look at the flowchart with those risk exposures in mind. Do any of the organization's processes or documents increase its exposure to specific risks? For example, if a company maintains only an electronic record of inventory purchases, you'll see that in a flowchart. In that case, the company is exposed to a systems risk. What controls has the company implemented to reduce its exposure to systems risk? Are the controls strong and adequate given the level of the risk? For example, does the company also maintain a paper file that is not shown on the flowchart? Or is a paper file missing from the flowchart because it doesn't exist?

Finally, flowcharts can be a starting point for the development of procedures manuals. A procedures manual is simply an "instruction book" that explains how everyday tasks in an organization are accomplished. Halbert (2003) recommends that "every staff member . . . document his or her duties and write a procedures manual—a time-consuming effort but worth doing." A well-constructed flowchart can easily be "translated" into regular, step-by-step text for use by future employees.

# Reflection and Self-Assessment                                    6.4

Throughout the previous chapters, I've often pointed out how the text material relates to one or more of the items in the AICPA Core Competency Framework. Explain how the process of developing a systems flowchart relates to the following competencies

1. Broad business perspective: strategic/critical thinking.
2. Functional: decision modeling and risk analysis.
3. Personal: interaction and communication.

# CRITICAL THINKING

As you read earlier in this chapter, developing flowcharts is as much "art" as "science." Therefore, learning to create good, descriptive flowcharts is often a challenge for accounting students—knowing the rules and conventions only takes you part of the way, in just the same way that you can't really learn to drive a car simply by reading a book. So, for this section, I'm going to show you how I usually go about creating a flowchart; please keep in mind that the way I do it is a result of my own experience and training. It's not the "only right way" to develop flowcharts.

In this chapter's "AIS in the Business World," you considered part of the sales/collection process for Barnes & Noble. For this example, let's look at the "flip side" of that process: acquisition/payment. In short, the acquisition/payment process covers activities from recognizing the need for new inventory through paying a vendor's invoice. We'll go through the first five steps of the seven-step process described earlier in the chapter; I'm omitting the last two steps as they are fairly self-explanatory.

1. *Establish the system boundary.* As you'll learn in an upcoming chapter, the acquisition/payment process starts with a request for goods/services based on monitored need; in most cases, it ends when cash is disbursed to pay a vendor's invoice. For the purpose of this example, we'll consider the system boundary as including Barnes & Noble's purchasing department, their receiving department, and the vendor.

2. *Determine column headings.* Our flowchart will therefore have three columns: purchasing department, receiving department, and vendor. The vendor refers to the publisher where Barnes & Noble will buy the books; for example, McGraw-Hill (the publisher of this book) or Bloomsbury (the publisher of Harry Potter). The purchasing department, as its name implies, handles all formal purchases of inventory. To promote strong internal control through separation of duties, the receiving department actually receives the shipped books.

3. *List actions performed within each column.* Here are the actions for each party:
   a. Purchasing Department
      i. Issue purchase order. (predefined process, document)
      ii. File the original for their own records. (database)
      iii. Send copies to the receiving department and the accounting department. (document)
   b. Receiving Department
      i. Receive the books from the vendor. (predefined process)
      ii. Create a receiving report. (document)
      iii. Send a copy of the receiving report to the purchasing department and the accounting department; file the original for their own records. (document, database)
   c. Vendor
      i. Ship the books. (generic process)
      ii. Issue the invoice. (generic process, document)

4. *Select appropriate symbols.* The appropriate symbol(s) for each action above are noted in parentheses.

5. *Prepare a first draft.* The first draft of the flowchart appears in Figure 6.2. In the interest of saving space, I've omitted the formal heading, but you should be sure to include the heading in any flowcharts you create. Consult the flowchart in this chapter's "AIS in the Business World" for an example heading.

**FIGURE 6.2**
**Partial Systems Flowchart of the Acquisition/Payment Process**

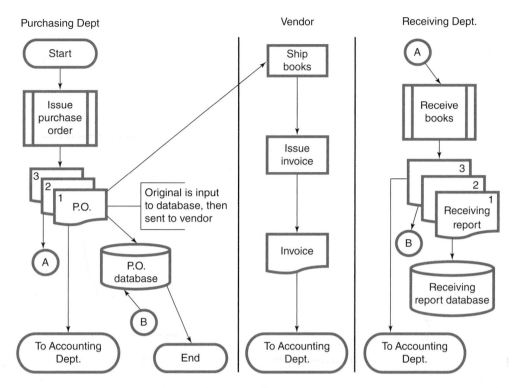

I hope the preceding example has been helpful to you. As you work through the end-of-chapter exercises assigned by your AIS instructor, please remember that drawing good flowcharts takes plenty of practice and discussion. And, like most nondeterministic problems, most cases/problems/situations have more than one "good answer."

## Summary

Here is a summary of the chapter:

1. *List and discuss the purpose and use of systems flowcharts, document flowcharts, program flowcharts, and hardware flowcharts.* A systems flowchart provides a top-level view of an information system; it shows the "big picture" of what is happening. A document flowchart, as the name implies, shows how documents (paper and electronic) flow through an information system, while a program flowchart details the steps in a specific computer program. A hardware flowchart lays out the computers, printers, monitors, and other hardware devices used in an information system.

2. *Explain the basic parts of and design considerations common to all types of flowcharts.* In general, a flowchart should be read from top to bottom and left to right. Since flowcharts are communication tools, they should be easy to read, incorporating plenty of white space. Every flowchart should have a title to make it easier for reference after its creation; flowcharts also should be organized into columns based on areas of responsibility in the information system. Documents should have a clear beginning and ending points as well. Flowcharts are usually the product of discussion among colleagues, rather than the product of a single individual.

3. *Identify and describe common symbols and information technology tools used in flowcharting.* Figure 6.1 shows various flowcharting symbols; your individual research (Reflection and Self-Assessment 6.3) revealed more. Two popular IT tools for flowchart creation are SmartDraw and Visio.

4. *Discuss ways flowcharts impact the design, implementation, and evaluation of accounting information systems.* A well-constructed flowchart can give a new accountant or consultant a quick overview of how a system works. Flowcharts also can be used as part of the auditing process and/or to suggest process improvements in the accounting information system, particularly when combined with a risk/control matrix. They also can inform recommendations regarding internal controls.

5. *Create and interpret systems flowcharts.* Three key ideas are important in creating flowcharts: (*i*) strive to achieve a clear representation of the system, not a deterministic response to a particular problem or case situation; (*ii*) practice will increase your skill in flowcharting; and (*iii*) seldom will your first creation be your final one—flowcharts can almost always be improved via dialogue and consultation with other professionals.

Flowcharting is one commonly used documentation techniques for accounting information systems. For accounting students, who typically like dealing with numbers better than words and symbols, they can be challenging. But, with time, practice, and patience, you can learn the art of developing clear, meaningful flowcharts and using them as analytical tools in the accounting information system.

| | |
|---|---|
| **Key Terms** | document flowcharts, *103*     program flowcharts, *103*     symbols, *105* <br> hardware flowcharts, *104*     SmartDraw, *105*     systems flowcharts, *103* <br> Microsoft Visio, *105* |

**Chapter References**

Bradford, M., S. Richtermeyer, and D. Roberts. 2007. "System Diagramming Techniques: An Analysis of Methods Used in Accounting Education and Practice." *Journal of Information Systems*, Spring, pp. 173–212.

Egerdahl, R. 1995. "A Risk Matrix Approach to Data Processing Facility Audits." *Internal Auditor*, June, pp. 34–40.

Halbert, J. 2003. "Mining Back-Office Operations May Bolster the Bottom Line." *Los Angeles Business Journal*, April 14, www.findarticles.com (last visited November 4, 2004).

**End-of-Chapter Activities**

1. *Reading review questions.*

   a. What is a flowchart? Describe four different kinds of flowcharts and explain the most often used in an accounting information system.

   b. Summarize the rules and conventions commonly observed in the preparation of flowcharts.

   c. List and explain the meaning and use of 10 common flowcharting symbols. What sources would you consult for learning about additional symbols not on your list?

   d. How are flowcharts used in working with accounting information systems?

   e. Respond to the questions for this chapter's "AIS in the Business World."

2. *Reading review problem.*

   This chapter's AIS in the Business World presented a partial flowchart for the sales/collection process at Barnes & Noble; later in the chapter, Figure 6.2 presented a partial flowchart of the acquisition/payment process for the same company.

   Once the picking slip shown in the sales/collection process flowchart reaches the warehouse, warehouse workers pick the books from the shelves. The books are then packed (with a packing slip) and sent to a common carrier (such as UPS) for shipping to the customer. The contract between Barnes & Noble and the common carrier is called a "bill of lading."

In the acquisition/payment process, Barnes & Noble's accounting department matches the information from the purchase order, the vendor invoice, and the receiving report. Provided all information correlates, the accounting department issues a check to the vendor in payment of the invoice; if the information on all the three documents does not match, the accounting department contacts the relevant party to resolve discrepancies. Once done, the accounting department issues the check.

a. Prepare flowcharts of the steps described above—one flowchart for the sales/collection steps, and a separate one for the acquisition/payment steps.

b. Explain how you would use the flowcharts you created and/or those illustrated in the chapter as an independent auditor for Barnes & Noble, and/or as the bookstore's director of training and development.

c. List and discuss at least two internal control strengths/weaknesses based on the flowcharts you created.

3. Multiple choice review questions. Please select the best answer for each question.

1. Which of the following best describes a systems flowchart?
   a. Shows the flow of documents through an information system.
   b. Shows the logic used to create a program.
   c. Shows the "big picture" view.
   d. Shows how hardware elements are configured in a system.

2. Which of the following statements about "white space" in a flowchart is most true?
   a. White space prohibits the use of color in flowcharts.
   b. At least 50 percent of the page should be devoted to white space.
   c. White space is unimportant in document flowcharts.
   d. Adequate white space is a matter of judgment.

3. In a systems flowchart, columns denote:
   a. Areas of responsibility.
   b. People's names and titles.
   c. That the flowchart is unfinished.
   d. A lack of adequate white space.

4. In a systems flowchart, a terminator symbol can be used to indicate: (i) the start or end of a business process or (ii) a destination outside the system boundary.
   a. i only
   b. ii only
   c. Both i and ii
   d. Neither i nor ii

5. In creating a systems flowchart, selecting appropriate symbols comes immediately after:
   a. Determining column headings.
   b. Establishing the system boundary.
   c. Discussing the flowchart with others.
   d. Listing actions performed within each column.

4. *Making choices and exercising judgment.* Compare and contrast SmartDraw and Microsoft Visio. Prepare a paper and/or PowerPoint presentation that includes a recommendation regarding your preferred flowcharting software; justify your recommendation.

5. *Field exercises.* Visit a local restaurant for lunch or dinner. Pay close attention to the steps involved in ordering, receiving, and paying for a meal. Create a flowchart that depicts the process. List and discuss one or two internal controls you observe in the process; also suggest one or two ways the system could be improved.

6. *Flowchart creation.* Create a flowchart based on each of the following independent situations (one flowchart per situation).

   a. *Cori's Catering Services.* Cori is the owner and manager of a catering company. CCS provides complete meals (breakfast, lunch, and dinner), as well as an assortment of hot and cold appetizers and drinks, for groups of 12 to 500. CCS receives orders in three main ways: e-mail, telephone, and personal office consultation. In some cases, the customer has an idea of what he/she wants; in others, the customer relies on Cori's expertise to select appropriate items. For each catering job, Cori prepares an estimate for the client; she files one copy of the estimate and sends the other to the client for approval. The client may make changes to the estimate over the phone, via e-mail, or through a personal consultation. Once the estimate has been finalized, Cori prepares a catering contract for the client's signature. She requires a 50 percent deposit with the signed contract; the remaining catering fees can be paid within 30 days of the catering event. Cori accepts cash and checks; she does not accept credit cards. The client signs the contract and sends it back to Cori. Cori also signs it, files a copy for her own records, and sends a copy with both signatures back to the client. Cori and her staff deliver the catering order as scheduled, and she bills the client for any remaining fees. The client pays the invoice within 30 days and Cori deposits the funds in her bank account.

   b. *University Bookstore.* Ordering textbooks in a university bookstore is a massive undertaking that requires good organizational, communication, and coordination skills. The process begins with faculty deciding which textbooks they want to use. Professors communicate relevant information about the textbook (title, author, ISBN, edition, publisher, copyright date) to a department chair or secretary, who consolidates all the orders. That communication may take place with a paper form or an e-mail. In either case, the departmental representative prepares a standard university book requisition form in triplicate: one copy for the requesting faculty member, one for the department, and one for the bookstore. The bookstore receives and consolidates requisition forms from all across the university and prepares purchase orders for textbook publishers. Each purchase order has three copies: one for the publisher, one for the purchasing department, and one for the accounting department. When the publisher sends the books, the bookstore's receiving department prepares two copies of a receiving report; one is filed to indicate that the goods were received, while the second is forwarded to the accounting department. The publisher sends a billing statement (invoice) directly to the accounting department. Once all three documents have been matched and verified, the accounting department writes a check or sends an electronic funds transfer to the publisher. The bookstore staff then sort the books based on class and stock the shelves, where the books await purchase by students.

   c. Horacio is a college student at Feng Shui University. He rents an apartment from the university for $600 a month. On the 15th of every month, Horacio writes a check for the rent. He mails the check to the Housing Services office on campus; in turn, Housing Services sends an e-mail receipt back to Horacio. The mailroom staff in Housing Services makes a copy of the check for Horacio's file and sends the original, with all the other rent checks for the month, to the bank. Once a month, the treasurer of Housing Services reconciles the bank statement. Prepare a flowchart of the preceding scenario.

   d. Visit the Web site of the International Accounting Standards Board. Summarize the process the Board uses to develop International Financial Reporting Standards (IFRS), then create a systems flowchart of the process.

7. (CMA adapted) *Narrative preparation from a flowchart.*

   a. Consider the Richards Furniture Company flowchart presented in Figure 6.3. Write a narrative description of the business process it depicts.

   b. Consider the PriceRight Electronics Inc. flowchart presented in Figure 6.4. Write a narrative description of the business process it depicts.

**FIGURE 6.3** **Flowchart for Richards Furniture Company**

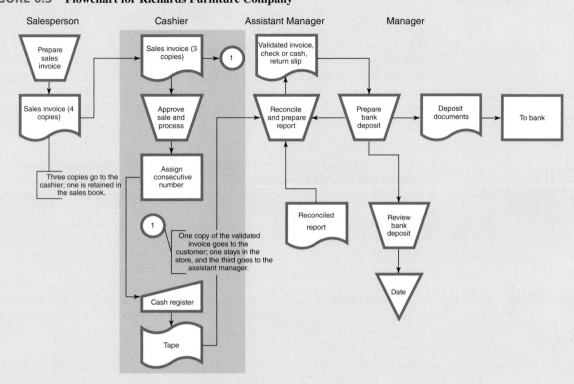

**FIGURE 6.4** **Flowchart for PriceRight Electronics Inc.**

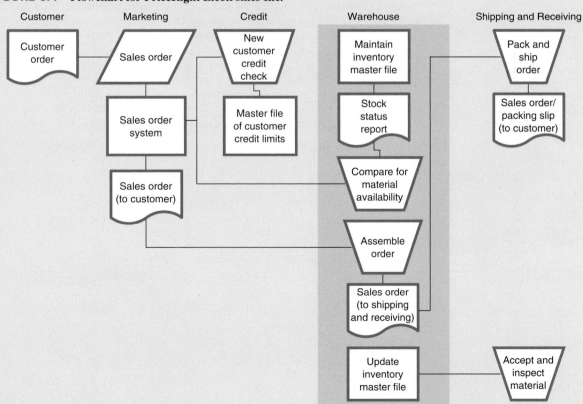

8. *Flowchart and system critiques.*

   a. Consider the Richards Furniture Company flowchart again. Describe at least two strengths and at least two weaknesses of the flowchart itself. Then, identify and describe at least two strengths and at least two weaknesses of the process it depicts. For each process weakness, suggest a way to correct it.

   b. Consider the PriceRight Electronics Inc. flowchart again. Describe at least two strengths and at least two weaknesses of the flowchart itself. Then, identify and describe at least two strengths and at least two weaknesses of the process it depicts. For each process weakness, suggest a way to correct it.

9. *Terminology.* Please match each item on the left with the best item on the right.

   | | |
   |---|---|
   | 1. Areas of responsibility | a. A flowchart depicting the process of buying a car |
   | 2. Document flowchart | b. Based on lines of computer code |
   | 3. Hardware flowchart | c. Can trace remittance advices and invoices through a system |
   | 4. Inverted triangle | |
   | 5. Origin and termination | d. Documents in a flowchart should have these |
   | 6. Overlapping shapes | e. Every flowchart should have one of these |
   | 7. Program flowchart | f. One application of flowcharting in AIS |
   | 8. Spotting internal control deficiencies | g. Represents a file in a flowchart |
   | | h. Shows monitors, input devices, and computers |
   | 9. Systems flowchart | i. Used to show multiple copies of a document |
   | 10. Title | j. What columns represent in a flowchart |

10. *Multiple choice questions.*

    Consider the following narrative as you respond to these questions:

    When staff at IGV Corporation need to travel on company business, they first submit a travel request to their immediate supervisor. The travel request includes the employee's identifying information; dates, location, and purpose of the trip; and a budget. The supervisor compares the travel budget to the department's total travel budget; if sufficient funds are available, the supervisor evaluates the need for the trip by comparing it to the department's strategic plan. If the trip is approved, the supervisor submits the budget to the cash expenditures department, where a staff member issues a travel advance to the employee. After the trip, the employee submits receipts and either pays back any excess advance funds or receives additional reimbursement for expenses incurred. If insufficient funds are available or if the trip does not support the strategic plan, the request is filed by employee name.

    In each question, assume you are creating a systems flowchart of the narrative.

    1. All of the following would be column headings except:
       a. Cash expenditures department.
       b. Department strategic plan.
       c. Staff member.
       d. Supervisor.

    2. Which of the following actions would require the use of this symbol?

    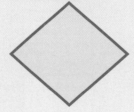

a. Compare travel budget to total budget
b. File request
c. Issue travel advance
d. Prepare budget

3. Which of the following actions would require the use of this symbol?

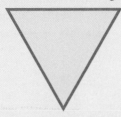

a. Compare travel budget to total budget
b. File request
c. Issue travel advance
d. Prepare budget

4. Which of the following is most likely to fall outside the system boundary?
a. Supervisor
b. Receipts
c. Conference hotel
d. Additional reimbursement

5. Which of the following actions is most likely to be depicted with this symbol?

a. Evaluate the need for the trip
b. File receipts
c. Prepare strategic plan
d. Issue travel advance

11. *Statement evaluation.* Indicate whether each statement below is (i) always true, (ii) sometimes true, or (iii) never true. For those that are (ii) sometimes true, explain when the statement is true.

a. Columns in a systems flowchart denote areas of responsibility.
b. Flowcharts are focused on business documents.
c. Flowcharts should include off-page connectors for easier reading.
d. Monthly bank reconciliations ensure that no one embezzles cash.
e. Once designed, flowcharts do not need to be revised.
f. On-page connectors help keep flowcharts uncluttered and easy to read.
g. Process symbols should be sandwiched between an input and an output.
h. The first step in drawing a flowchart is to decide which software package to use.
i. Two designers would independently create identical flowcharts for the same business process.
j. Visio is the best tool for drawing flowcharts.

**12.** *Excel application.* TNG Corporation has 25 employees in its Accounting department. Based on the results of a standardized exam, TNG has ranked each employee's flow-charting skill as shown in the array below:

| Flowchart Skill Rank | Employee ID | Start Date |
|---|---|---|
| 17 | 100 | 06/08/2008 |
| 20 | 103 | 09/11/2008 |
| 3 | 112 | 04/17/2009 |
| 5 | 117 | 11/05/2008 |
| 15 | 128 | 05/04/2008 |
| 23 | 129 | 08/18/2007 |
| 1 | 131 | 02/11/2008 |
| 12 | 133 | 02/18/2009 |
| 8 | 135 | 06/18/2009 |
| 7 | 137 | 11/05/2007 |
| 18 | 165 | 03/07/2008 |
| 21 | 174 | 12/04/2007 |
| 13 | 178 | 10/10/2008 |
| 16 | 186 | 04/07/2008 |
| 9 | 195 | 12/28/2008 |
| 25 | 196 | 08/11/2008 |
| 2 | 197 | 03/19/2009 |
| 24 | 198 | 07/19/2009 |
| 6 | 205 | 10/09/2007 |
| 14 | 231 | 07/11/2008 |
| 22 | 235 | 01/22/2009 |
| 11 | 237 | 09/14/2007 |
| 19 | 245 | 01/08/2008 |
| 10 | 278 | 12/01/2008 |
| 4 | 293 | 05/20/2009 |

The most skilled employee is ranked 1; the least skilled, 25. (You may access the data array in the 3 February 2014 post on my AIS blog.)

a.  Use Excel's VLOOKUP function to find the ID of the employee with the highest flowcharting skill rank. (Check figure: 131)

b.  Use Excel's YEARFRAC function to determine how long each employee had worked for TNG as of 22 January 2014. Insert a column before "flowchart skill rank" for your results. (Check figure for Employee 100: 5.62 years)

c.  Use Excel's VLOOKUP function to find the ID of the employee who has worked for TNG the longest. (Check figure: 129)

# Chapter **Seven**

# Data Flow Diagramming

## AIS in the Business World

### Barnes & Noble

In the opening vignette for Chapter 6 (flowcharting), we considered a flowchart of the online book sales process for Barnes & Noble. Here in Chapter 7, we'll consider a different method to document the accounting information system: data flow diagrams. The Level Zero data flow diagram (DFD) below presents the same process steps as the flowchart in Chapter 6:

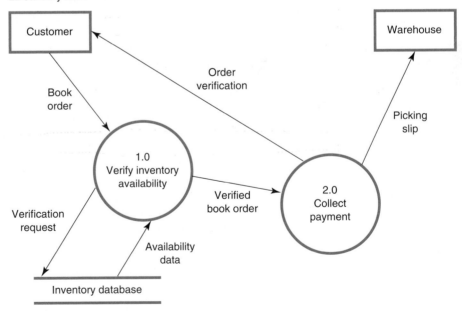

Barnes & Noble
Online book sales process
Level Zero DFD
Prepared by A. Student
22 January 2014

### Discussion Questions

1. What are the basic principles and design considerations for a DFD?
2. What do the four symbols in the DFD mean?
3. How are DFDs similar to flowcharts? How are they different?

In the previous chapter, you learned about the first of the three documentation techniques often used in accounting information systems: flowcharting. In this chapter, we consider the second of the three: data flow diagramming. The third technique, REA modeling, is discussed in the next chapter. In terms of the two broad purposes of systems documentation in AIS, data flow diagrams help us achieve both. But, they are less detailed than flowcharts when describing a business process; they are also a bit more cumbersome than a REA model for understanding the database.

The concepts and ideas of data flow diagramming originated in the broader field of systems analysis and design. Since the accounting information system is a subset of an organization's complete management information system, we can borrow the ideas and techniques for our purposes here. Data flow diagrams (DFDs) incorporate fewer symbols and different "rules" than flowcharts, but they do share many similarities. When you finish studying this chapter, you should be able to:

1. Explain the symbols and design considerations associated with DFDs.
2. Compare and contrast flowcharts and DFDs with regard to purpose, content, structure, and use in accounting information systems.
3. Discuss the ways in which DFDs are used in AIS work.
4. Construct a leveled set of DFDs.
5. Design normalized database tables from a DFD.

Some AIS professionals prefer one documentation method over another, but many use both flowcharts and data flow diagrams depending upon the situation and tasks at hand. In research conducted by Bradford, Richtermeyer, and Roberts (2007), just over 20 percent of respondents reported using data flow diagrams to document information systems. Managers use them to describe business processes, evaluate the current system, design or change a system, and assess the internal control environment.

# DFD SYMBOLS AND DESIGN CONSIDERATIONS

Data flow diagrams can be prepared with the same software tools as flowcharts.

Unlike flowcharts, which incorporate a plethora of symbols, data flow diagrams incorporate only four (DeMarco, 1979), which are shown in Figure 7.1.

A **process** is any set of procedures an organization uses to gather data, change the data into information, or report the information to system users. Every process in a data flow

**FIGURE 7.1**
**Data Flow Diagram Symbols**

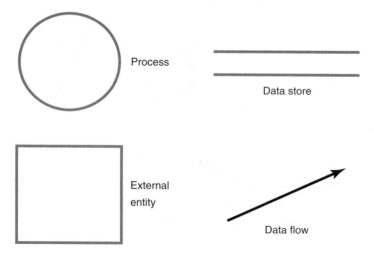

Process

Data store

External entity

Data flow

diagram has two identifying characteristics: a number and a name. Numbers follow specific conventions, which we'll examine later in this chapter. Process names should always be verb phrases; that is, they should start with an "action word," like approve, record, calculate or check.

An **external entity** is any person or organization outside the boundary of an information system. Establishing a clear, appropriate system boundary is essential to the construction of a good data flow diagram; you'll recall the same is true of flowcharts. Without such a boundary, you'll end up analyzing "the world" every time you want to solve a problem in an accounting information system. Boundaries are a matter of management judgment, and external entities lie outside boundaries. So, for example, if you were constructing a data flow diagram for an organization's cash management system, external entities might include customers, suppliers, or the bank. But whether or not a person or an organization is an external entity depends upon your definition of the system, not your definition of the organization. So, for example, if you are processing travel expenses for a marketing staff member, the marketing staff member might be an external entity—even though she is employed in the same organization. You might want to refer back to Chapter 6 for additional comments on establishing the system boundary.

A **data store** is a place for collecting data; you might think of it as a "file," whether paper-based or electronic. Data stores are labeled with noun phrases such as customer data, vendor data, or inventory data. Data stores can be linked to processes or external entities in a data flow diagram; they cannot be linked to one another. Later in this chapter, we'll consider some of the issues involved in creating database files based on the data stores in a DFD.

Finally, a **data flow** is represented by a directional line in a data flow diagram. Data flows should have only one arrow on one end to conform to DFD design conventions. Data flows, like data stores, are labeled with noun phrases: desired information, accounts payable data, customer order data, and the like. When a data flow is labeled in that way, we're referring to the content, not the format. So, for example, a data flow labeled "approved order" could indicate a piece of paper, an e-mail, or an electronic purchase order. Students often try to label data flows with verb phrases—that's a bad idea. Remember, processes are verbs—they tell what happens to data in an information system. A data flow refers to the data itself, not what happens to it.

Hoffner, George, and Valacich (1996) suggested the following **rules/conventions** associated with good data flow diagrams:

1. All processes should have unique names. If two data flow lines (or data stores) have the same label, they should both refer to the exact same data flow (or data store).
2. The inputs to a process should differ from the outputs to a process.
3. Any single DFD should not have more than about seven processes.
4. No process can have only outputs. (This would imply that the process is making information from nothing.) If an object has only outputs, then it must be an external entity.
5. No process can have only inputs. If an object has only inputs, it must be a data store.
6. A process has a verb phrase label. Examples include *prepare check* or *register for classes.*
7. Data cannot be moved directly from one data store to another data store. Data must be moved by a process.
8. Data cannot move directly from an external entity to a data store. Data must be moved by a process that receives data from the entity and places the data into the data store.
9. Data cannot move directly to an external entity from a data store. Data must be moved by a process.
10. A data store has a noun phrase label.

**FIGURE 7.2**
**Issue Purchase**
**Order Process**
**Level Zero DFD**

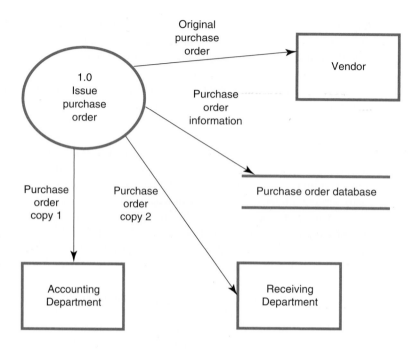

11. Data of any concern to the system cannot move directly from one external entity to another external entity. They must be moved by a process. If data flow directly between external entities without processing, then they are outside the system boundary and omitted from the DFD.

12. An external entity has a noun phrase label.

13. A data flow has only one direction between symbols.

14. A data flow cannot go directly back to the same process it leaves. There must be at least one other process that handles the data flow, produces some new data, and returns the original data to the original process.

15. A data flow can go directly into a data store. When it does, it signifies an update (delete, add, or change). Likewise, a data flow can come directly from a data store; in that context, it refers to a retrieval or use of the data in the store.

16. A data flow has a noun phrase label.

Consider the DFD presented in Figure 7.2. In Chapter 6, I presented a flowchart of Barnes & Noble's book purchasing process; that flowchart had three columns (Purchasing Department, Vendor, and Receiving Department). The DFD in Figure 7.2 encompasses the activities of the Purchasing Department from that flowchart. The DFD has just one process (issue purchase order), corresponding to the predefined process symbol in the flowchart.

Figure 7.2 has three external entities: vendor, receiving department, and accounting department. Notice that, although within Barnes & Noble, the receiving department is considered an external entity because of how the system boundary was established. In the flowchart, the system boundary was established differently; thus, the vendor and the receiving department are shown in the flowchart as columns, while the accounting department is an external entity. The DFD has one data store (purchase order database), shown in the flowchart with the cylindrical database symbol.

The DFD in Figure 7.2 comprises four data flows. Notice how the original purchase order is differentiated from the two copies that are used internally. The annotation in the flowchart indicates that the data from the original purchase order is input to the database, then the original is sent to the vendor. In the DFD, we would make a similar notation in a separate document called the data dictionary.

Data flow diagrams represent a very new way of thinking for most accounting students, so expect a bit of frustration as you become comfortable with this important method of documenting an accounting information system. When my own students experience that frustration, I often remind them of how they may have struggled initially to remember the rules of debit and credit in the AIS. By the time they take an AIS course, however, debiting and crediting accounts seem as routine as driving a car. In time and with practice, you'll develop that same level of comfort regarding designing and interpreting data flow diagrams.

## Reflection and Self-Assessment                                                      7.1

Consider the actions of the receiving department in Barnes & Noble's book purchasing process. Prepare a Level Zero DFD similar to Figure 7.2 for the receiving department.

## DATA FLOW DIAGRAMS AND FLOWCHARTS

So now that you know a bit about both, what are the differences between data flow diagrams and flowcharts? Many of the important differences are summarized in the table below:

| Characteristic | Data Flow Diagram | Flowchart |
|---|---|---|
| Symbols | Four: circle (process), line (data flow), rectangle (external entity), and parallel lines (data store). | Many: rectangle (process), diamond (decision), triangle (file), and others. |
| Organization | Leveled sets, each depicting more detail than the last. | Columns representing areas of responsibility. |
| Numbers | Processes are numbered in the following formats: Level Zero, 1.0; Level One, 1.1; Level Two, 1.1.1; and so on. | Numbers can be used for on- and off-page connectors, not for processes. |
| Focus | DFDs focus on data and how they move between business processes, external entities, and data stores. | Flowcharts are concerned with data, but also with documents and processing tools. |
| Use of "lines" | Lines represent data; they are labeled with noun phrases (e.g., account balance, customer data). | Lines represent movement between processes, areas of responsibility, and the like; they are not labeled. |

Both data flow diagrams and flowcharts are useful in the design and implementation of accounting information systems; but systems flowcharts typically provide more detail about a business process than a data flow diagram. In a data flow diagram, for example, a business process, such as "receive payment," would be represented with a single numbered circle, a single data flow, and a single external entity:

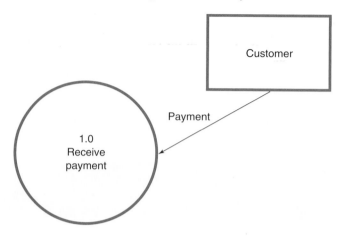

Someone looking at that portion of a Level Zero data flow diagram would not know

- How is the payment transmitted?
- What documents are used in the transaction?
- Who receives the payment?

A flowchart of that same process, on the other hand, might look like this:

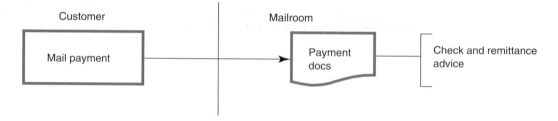

From that flowchart excerpt, we know

- Payments are made through the mail.
- They are received in the company's mailroom.
- Documents include both the customer's check and the remittance advice.

In the DFD, notice that the rectangle denotes the customer (an external entity); in the flowchart, the rectangle denotes a process (mail payment). In the data flow diagram, the process is depicted with a numbered circle. And, in the DFD, the data flow (arrow) has a name; in the flowchart, the data are represented with the document symbol, while the arrow shows the movement of the documents between areas of responsibility.

At this point, you might be wondering why it's necessary to learn more than one systems documentation technique; many students feel that knowing one should be enough. In practice, you might be called upon to create a flowchart as part of a financial statement audit to assess internal controls; you also might need to use a data flow diagram if you want to focus on the data you're auditing, regardless of their format (paper, electronic). Additionally, you will probably need to interpret both kinds of documents at some point in your career. For example, if you were hired by an entrepreneur to design an accounting information system "from scratch," you might first use a data flow diagram to focus on the data and how they are manipulated; the DFD might later be supplemented with a systems flowchart to iron out the details of who is responsible for different tasks, how documents will be named, how many copies of documents will be required, and other detailed issues. In the AICPA Core Competency framework, preparing and interpreting data flow diagrams is related to the broad business perspective competencies. Those competencies emphasize the need to understand how a business functions and how its processes are organized.

# LEVELED SETS OF DFDS

You probably recall from our discussion of flowcharting that flowcharts often span more than one page; the pages are connected with off-page connectors. The point of creating multipage flowcharts is to make them easy to read and interpret.

In the same way, data flow diagrams should be uncluttered and easy to read; but systems analysts use a slightly different method to achieve that goal: **leveled sets** of DFDs. A leveled set of DFDs refers to a collection that models related business processes. The various levels provide increasing detail about the processes in the system.

Table 7.1 shows an overview of the components of a leveled set of DFDs.

The highest level DFD, with the least amount of detail, is called a **context diagram.** Context diagrams show how the process, represented as a single circle, relates to the external entities, represented with rectangles. Consider Figure 7.3, which shows the context diagram for the Barnes & Noble online book sales process illustrated in this chapter's AIS in the Business World.

When creating a leveled set of DFDs, you would normally create the context diagram first, followed by the Level Zero diagram. Every leveled set of data flow diagrams has exactly one context diagram and exactly one **Level Zero diagram.** A leveled set may have more than one Level One diagram, depending on the complexity of the process.

One other important note about leveled sets of data flow diagrams: they must be **balanced.** Consider the context diagram in Figure 7.3 and its related Level Zero diagram in this chapter's AIS in the Business World. Notice that, in both diagrams, there is one data inflow to the customer, one data outflow from the customer and one data inflow to the warehouse. All the data flows are consistently named between the levels. Because those two things are true, the Level Zero diagram is balanced with the context diagram.

**TABLE 7.1**
**Components of a Leveled Set of DFDs**

| Level Name | Number of DFDs in a Leveled Set | Numbering Format |
|---|---|---|
| Context | One | 0 |
| Zero | One | 1.0, 2.0 |
| One | As many as necessary | Process 1.0 is subdivided into 1.1, 1.2, 1.3<br>Process 2.0 is subdivided into 2.1, 2.2, 2.3 |
| Two | As many as necessary | Process 1.1 is subdivided into 1.1.1, 1.1.2<br>Process 2.3 is subdivided into 2.3.1, 2.3.2, 2.3.3 |
| Three | As many as necessary | Process 1.1.2 is subdivided into 1.1.2.1, 1.1.2.2<br>Process 2.3.1 is subdivided into 2.3.1.1, 2.3.1.2 |

**FIGURE 7.3**
**Online Book
Sales Process
Context Diagram**

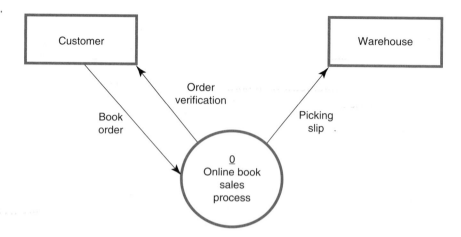

Here are some questions my students often raise when learning how to draw data flow diagrams:

1. *How many processes should a single DFD have?* As you might suspect, this question is open to interpretation. However, most systems analysts would limit the number of processes to seven, as suggested by the third of Hoffner's principles (discussed earlier in the chapter).

2. *How many levels should be in a leveled set of DFDs?* Like the previous question, this one is nondeterministic. However, for your work in class, you shouldn't need to go past Level Three; most of the time, in fact, Level Two will be plenty.

3. *When do you stop breaking down a process?* You stop breaking down (decomposing/exploding) a process when it is **primitive**. In other words, when the process label is fairly self-explanatory. Consider the process in Figure 7.2. "Issue purchase order" would likely be considered primitive, requiring no further decomposition.

4. *Does each process have to be decomposed to the same level?* No.

## Reflection and Self-Assessment  7.2

Every term, you register for classes for the upcoming term. To complete that process, you may interact with your advisor; you probably also consider the courses you've already taken (your academic history) and the published class schedule. Generically, your registration process might comprise three steps: (i) Select preliminary classes. (ii) Meet with advisor. (iii) Preregister for classes. Based on that information, prepare a context diagram and a Level Zero diagram of the course registration process.

## Reflection and Self-Assessment  7.3

In Reflection and Self-Assessment 7.2, you prepared a context diagram and a Level Zero diagram of your course registration process. Suppose the first step (select preliminary classes) can be broken down into: (i) Determine needed classes. (ii) Determine time constraints. (iii) Prepare potential class list for meeting with advisor. Prepare a Level One DFD from that information; ensure that it is balanced with the Level Zero diagram.

# DATABASE DESIGN

The data stores in a leveled set of data flow diagrams represent relational databases. Broadly speaking, a relational database is a collection of components (objects) that allows us to store, retrieve, report, and ask questions about the data it contains. Think of a database as a "big bucket" that we can put things into and take things out of depending on our information needs.

**Database tables** are the fundamental building blocks of relational databases; every relational database must contain at least one table, although most will contain multiple tables. Tables are organized into fields (columns) and rows (records), as shown in Figure 7.4.

The table in Figure 7.4 comprises five fields and three records. Every database table must have a **primary key**—a field that uniquely identifies every record within the table. For example, you probably have a student identification number that uniquely identifies you at your school; government agencies, such as the IRS, use your Social Security Number for that purpose. In Figure 7.4, the primary key is "Inventory ID." Notice that each of the three records has a different, unique entry in that field.

Another common object in a relational database is the **query.** A query is a set of instructions that examines records in one or more tables, then outputs data in accordance with those instructions. Figure 7.5 shows a query that calculates the total cost of each inventory item from the table in Figure 7.4.

Data from tables and/or queries can be formatted as a **report** (a third database object) for easier reading. Finally, relational databases often contain **forms** that allow users to input data to a table and/or look up data in a table. Figure 7.6 illustrates a form based on the inventory table.

To facilitate information processing, database tables must be organized as efficiently and effectively as possible. The process of making a database table efficient and effective

**FIGURE 7.4**
**Relational Database Table**

| inventory table | | | | |
|---|---|---|---|---|
| Inventory ID | Inventory description | Beginning quantity on hand | Cost per unit of beginning quantity | Beginning date |
| LPTP | laptop computer | 15 | $125.00 | 4/1/2014 |
| WBCM | webcam | 20 | $25.00 | 4/1/2014 |
| MIC | microphone | 18 | $10.00 | 4/1/2014 |

**FIGURE 7.5**
**Relational Database Query**

| total cost of BI query | | | |
|---|---|---|---|
| Inventory description | Beginning quantity on hand | Cost per unit of beginning quantity | Total cost |
| laptop computer | 15 | $125.00 | $1,875.00 |
| microphone | 18 | $10.00 | $180.00 |
| webcam | 20 | $25.00 | $500.00 |

**FIGURE 7.6**
**Relational Database Form**

Inventory input form

| | |
|---|---|
| Inventory ID | LPTP |
| Inventory description | laptop computer |
| Beginning quantity on hand | 15 |
| Cost per unit of beginning quantity | $125.00 |
| Beginning date | 4/1/2014 |

is referred to as **normalization.** Database tables are normalized in the three-stage process outlined below:

- Step One: First Normal Form (1NF). A database table is in 1NF if it *eliminates repeating groups*.
- Step Two: Second Normal Form (2NF). A database table is in 2NF if it *eliminates repeating groups* **and** *eliminates redundant data*.
- Step Three: Third Normal Form (3NF). A database table is in 3NF if it *eliminates repeating groups* **and** *eliminates redundant data* **and** *eliminates columns not dependent on the primary key*.

Notice that the normal forms are additive; that is, a table in 2NF is also in 1NF. Similarly, a table in 3NF also has the characteristics of 2NF and 1NF.

To illustrate the process of normalization, let's think about the process of buying inventory. The data you need to track inventory purchases includes:

- Inventory ID
- Inventory description
- Employee ID
- Vendor ID
- Purchase order number
- Date purchased
- Quantity purchased
- Cost per unit purchased

If all that information were organized in a spreadsheet, we would refer to it as a **flat file.** Flat files may be acceptable tools for managing data if the data are fairly simple and straightforward; but most organizations need to manage complex data, so a relational database is a better tool. Figure 7.7 illustrates a flat file with data about inventory purchases.

Even with that small amount of data, consider how cumbersome it would be to answer even the simplest questions, such as "How many purchase orders did Smith01 complete when the total cost of merchandise purchased was more than $500?" Answering such questions would be much simpler if the flat file was organized as a relational database, with all tables in 3NF.

To put the flat file in 1NF, we must eliminate repeating groups. In this context, "repeating groups" refers to any purchase order that has more than one item; so, we need to ensure that each item is listed in a separate row, as illustrated in Figure 7.8:

**FIGURE 7.7**    **Inventory Purchases Flat File**

| Purchase Order Number | Date Purchased | Purchasing Agent ID | Vendor ID | Inventory ID | Inventory Description | Quantity Purchased | Cost per Unit |
|---|---|---|---|---|---|---|---|
| 101 | 1/23/2014 | Smith01 | 5004 | LPTP, WBCM | Laptop computer, webcam | 123, 45 | $125, $20 |
| 102 | 1/23/2014 | Fan03 | 5001 | MIC, WBCM | Microphone, webcam | 109, 149 | $10, $27 |
| 103 | 1/25/2014 | Martinez02 | 5005 | LPTP | Laptop computer | 113 | $125 |
| 104 | 1/27/2014 | Fan03 | 5000 | MIC | Microphone | 121 | $12 |
| 105 | 1/27/2014 | Smith01 | 5000 | LPTP, WBCM | Laptop computer, webcam | 45, 82 | $125, $23 |
| 106 | 1/29/2014 | Martinez02 | 5003 | MIC, PPR | Microphone, paper | 24, 87 | $15, $17 |

**FIGURE 7.8  Inventory Purchases in 1NF**

| Purchase Order Number | Date Purchased | Employee ID | Vendor ID | Inventory ID | Inventory Description | Quantity Purchased | Cost per Unit |
|---|---|---|---|---|---|---|---|
| 101 | 1/23/2014 | Smith01 | 5004 | LPTP | Laptop computer | 123 | $  125 |
| 101 | 1/23/2014 | Smith01 | 5004 | WBCM | Webcam | 45 | 20 |
| 102 | 1/23/2014 | Fan03 | 5001 | MIC | Microphone | 109 | 10 |
| 102 | 1/23/2014 | Fan03 | 5001 | WBCM | Webcam | 149 | 27 |
| 103 | 1/25/2014 | Martinez02 | 5005 | LPTP | Laptop computer | 113 | 125 |
| 104 | 1/27/2014 | Fan03 | 5000 | MIC | Microphone | 121 | 12 |
| 105 | 1/27/2014 | Smith01 | 5000 | LPTP | Laptop computer | 45 | 125 |
| 105 | 1/27/2014 | Smith01 | 5000 | WBCM | Webcam | 82 | 23 |
| 106 | 1/29/2014 | Martinez02 | 5003 | MIC | Microphone | 24 | 15 |
| 106 | 1/29/2014 | Martinez02 | 5003 | PPR | Paper | 87 | 17 |

So now, our array has no repeating groups. But, it has a lot of redundant data! Listing the purchase order number, date purchased, purchasing agent ID, and vendor ID separately for each item purchased on a single purchase order creates that redundancy. To put the table in 2NF, we need to eliminate that redundant data. To do so, we need to split up the data into separate tables, as illustrated in Figure 7.9.

In Figure 7.9, the inventory table is a master table, while the purchases table is a transaction table. The purchases/inventory table is a junction table; its whole purpose is to "marry" the data from the other two tables. Without the junction table, we would have data about inventory (in the inventory table) and about purchases (in the purchases table), but we would have no data about how the two are related to one another!

A junction table, such as the purchases/inventory table, is needed in a database when "many" items from one table can be associated with "many" items from another table. In our case, since each purchase order may contain many items, and each item can be on many purchase orders, we need a junction table. Other situations requiring junction tables include sales/inventory and student/class.

Junction tables commonly have a **compound primary key,** often comprising the primary keys of the tables they join. In Figure 7.9, the inventory/purchases table's compound primary key is the inventory ID and the P.O. number.

Finally, to put the tables in 3NF, we need to eliminate columns not dependent on the primary key. In other words, we need to ensure that every field in a table gives us information about the primary key of that table. In Figure 7.9, the inventory table would also include the following fields: beginning quantity on hand, cost per unit of beginning inventory, and date of beginning inventory. The purchases table needs no additional data; likewise, the inventory/purchases table. Thus, they are already in 3NF.

Although not illustrated above, the database would also include an "employee table" and a "vendor table." The primary key of the employee table would be the Employee ID; the primary key of the vendor table would be the Vendor ID. When the primary key from one table is included as a field in another table, we refer to it as a **foreign key.** So, the purchases table has two foreign keys (Employee ID and Vendor ID). The purchases/inventory table also has two foreign keys (P.O. number and Inventory ID). Together, those two foreign keys comprise the primary key of the junction table.

**FIGURE 7.9**
**Inventory Purchases in 2NF**

| Inventory Table | | | |
|---|---|---|---|
| **Inventory ID** | **Inventory Description** | | |
| LPTP | Laptop computer | | |
| WBCM | Webcam | | |
| MIC | Microphone | | |
| PPR | Paper | | |

| Purchases Table | | | |
|---|---|---|---|
| **P.O. Number** | **Date** | **Employee ID** | **Vendor ID** |
| 101 | 1/23/2014 | Smith01 | 5004 |
| 102 | 1/23/2014 | Fan03 | 5001 |
| 103 | 1/25/2014 | Martinez02 | 5005 |
| 104 | 1/27/2014 | Fan03 | 5000 |
| 105 | 1/27/2014 | Smith01 | 5000 |
| 106 | 1/29/2014 | Martinez02 | 5003 |

| Purchases/Inventory Table | | | |
|---|---|---|---|
| **P.O. Number** | **Inventory ID** | **Quantity** | **Cost per Unit** |
| 101 | LPTP | 123 | $   125 |
| 101 | WBCM | 45 | 20 |
| 102 | MIC | 109 | 10 |
| 102 | WBCM | 149 | 27 |
| 103 | LPTP | 113 | 125 |
| 104 | MIC | 121 | 12 |
| 105 | LPTP | 45 | 125 |
| 105 | WBCM | 82 | 23 |
| 106 | MIC | 24 | 15 |
| 106 | PPR | 87 | 17 |

# Reflection and Self-Assessment                                      7.4

The primary key of the employee table is Employee ID. What other fields would you include in that table? Remember, every field should tell you something important about the primary key.

By now, I'm sure your head is spinning a bit! Learning to create normalized database tables is not an intuitive process for most folks. I'll give you another illustration in this chapter's "Critical Thinking" section; you might also want to consult the 23 January 2014 post in my AIS blog, which has additional resources to help you understand this complex and important topic. We'll also consider database design and table normalization in Chapter 8 (REA Modeling).

# CRITICAL THINKING

According to the investor relations section of its Web site, Netflix (www.netflix.com) "is the world's leading Internet television network with over 44 million members in 41 countries." New clients create an individual account, then add movies and television shows (programming) to their queue (list) for later viewing.

Figure 7.10 shows context diagram of that process from Netflix's point of view.

Remember: any leveled set of data flow diagrams has exactly one context diagram; the context diagram shows how the process depicted relates to external entities, and the process is always represented with a single circle.

The context diagram is decomposed/exploded into a Level Zero diagram, such as the one shown in Figure 7.11.

**FIGURE 7.10**
**Account and List Creation Process Context Diagram**

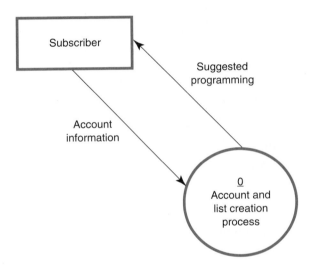

**FIGURE 7.11**
**Account and List Creation Process Level Zero Diagram**

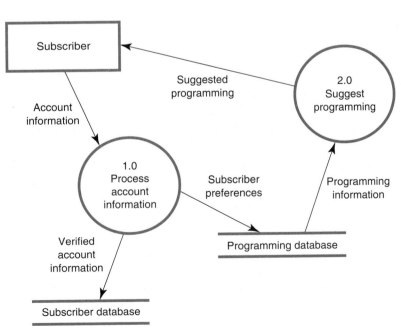

Notice how the Level Zero diagram is balanced with the context diagram: one data outflow from the subscriber to the process (account information) and one data inflow to the subscriber from the process (suggested programming). Everything else in the Level Zero diagram is "inside" the one process symbol found in the context diagram; the Level Zero diagram simply provides additional detail.

Netflix maintains its records in a relational database. At the minimum, the Netflix database would include the tables listed below; in each case, the primary key is underlined, and foreign keys are in brackets.

**Subscriber table**

Subscriber email address

Subscriber password

Subscriber street address

Subscriber city

Subscriber state

Subscriber ZIP code

Subscriber plan type

Subscriber payment type

Subscriber payment account number

**Create account table**

Transaction number

Transaction date

[Subscriber email address]

**Subscriber/programming table**

[Subscriber email address]

[Program title]

Date program added

The "subscriber" table is a master table; it contains data about each individual subscriber. The subscriber email address is its primary key because every account requires a unique email address; arguably, Netflix could require a subscriber to create a unique user name, but the email address fulfills that function effectively.

The "create account" table is a transaction table. Its primary key (transaction number) is likely to be an auto-number field to promote strong internal control. Including the subscriber email address as a foreign key allows the database to access any information it needs about the subscriber **without** repeating the information in the "create account" table. Repeating the account information in multiple tables violates the principles of normalization.

The "subscriber/programming" table is a junction table. Remember, a junction table is required when two things in a database have a many-to-many relationship. In this case, every subscriber can have many programs in their list; every program can be in the list of many subscribers. The junction table has a compound primary key comprising the primary keys of the two tables it joins.

What about the other common database objects: queries, forms, and reports? As you may be aware, Netflix offers three plan types to subscribers: online only, CD only, and online/CD combination. If the company wanted a list of subscriber email addresses for each account type, it would query the subscriber table, grouping the output by plan type. The query results could be output to a report.

Subscribers complete a form when they create their account; the form populates (i.e., records data in) the subscriber table. Similarly, a subscriber would use a form to log into Netflix.

# Reflection and Self-Assessment                    7.5

Netflix bills each subscriber monthly using the payment information in the subscriber's account; Netflix also maintains a programming database from which subscribers add titles to their lists. Create table specifications for the "bill subscriber" table and the "programming" table.

## Summary

Data flow diagrams and relational databases are powerful tools in the design, implementation, use, and evaluation of accounting information systems. Here is the chapter summary:

1. *Explain the symbols and design considerations associated with DFDs.* Data flow diagrams incorporate four symbols. Processes are represented with circles, data flows are depicted by arrows, parallel horizontal lines denote data stores, and rectangles represent external entities. DFDs are prepared in leveled sets, with each set revealing more detail than the one before it.

2. *Compare and contrast flowcharts and DFDs with regard to purpose, content, structure, and use in accounting information systems.* Both flowcharts and DFDs are methods of conceptualizing an information system. Flowcharts incorporate more symbols than DFDs, but both are read from top to bottom and left to right (generally). DFDs can be used more easily to design relational databases.

3. *Discuss ways DFDs are used in AIS work.* DFDs can be used in at least four ways in accounting information systems design, development, and implementation. They can (*i*) ensure an adequate understanding of an accounting information system, (*ii*) help accountants make process improvements to the system, (*iii*) help others understand the flows of data and information, and (*iv*) assist in designing relational database tables that capture data and report information.

4. *Construct a leveled set of DFDs.* As with flowcharting, DFDs are designed iteratively and cooperatively. Two different systems professionals can create two different DFDs based on the same situation; as usual, there is no deterministic solution for most DFD problems.

5. *Design normalized database tables from a DFD.* Many elements of a DFD require database tables in an accounting information system. Tables should be normalized; each must include a primary key that uniquely identifies each record within the table. Foreign keys can link tables together in a database. Junction tables are used when items in two separate tables have a many-to-many relationship, such as the relationship between customers and inventory or purchasing agents and vendors.

As noted in the conclusion for the flowcharting chapter, you will likely be challenged as you develop familiarity and skill in using DFDs. Keep in mind that, like flowcharting, data flow diagramming and database design are at least as much "art" as "science." The point isn't to get to the "one right answer"; it probably doesn't exist anyway. The point here is to produce DFDs and database tables that are both effective and efficient from multiple points of view.

## Key Terms

balanced, *125*
compound primary key, *129*
context diagram, *125*
data flow, *121*
data store, *121*
database tables, *127*
external entity, *121*

flat file, *128*
foreign keys, *129*
forms, *127*
Level Zero diagram, *125*
leveled sets, *125*
normalization, *128*
primary key, *127*

primitive, *126*
process, *120*
query, *127*
report, *127*
rules/conventions, *121*

## Chapter References

Bradford, M., S. Richtermeyer, and D. Roberts. 2007. "System Diagramming Techniques: An Analysis of Methods Used in Accounting Education and Practice." *Journal of Information Systems,* Spring, pp. 173–212.

DeMarco, T. 1979. *Structured Analysis and Systems Specifications.* Englewood Cliffs, NJ: Prentice Hall.

Hoffner, J., J. George, and J. Valacich. 1996. *Modern Systems Analysis and Design.* Reading, MA: Benjamin/Cummings.

Ricciardi, S. 1994. "Database Design: Redundancy and Normalization." *PC Magazine,* January 25, pp. 285–89.

## End-of-Chapter Activities

1. *Reading review questions.*

   a. What is a data flow diagram? How are data flow diagrams used in accounting information systems?

   b. List and discuss the four symbols used in the development of data flow diagrams. Give an example of each symbol in an AIS context.

   c. What rules/conventions should accountants follow when creating DFDs?

   d. Define the following terms as they relate to the material presented in this chapter: relational database, table, primary key, foreign key, field, record, and query.

   e. Respond to the questions for this chapter's "AIS in the Business World."

2. *Reading review problem.* Most major airlines have "frequent flyer" programs. A customer creates a new account, then earns miles in a variety of ways such as purchasing goods and services through a credit card linked to the account, taking paid flights on the airline, and celebrating the annual anniversary of account creation. The miles are later "spent" on flights and other items. An individual account holder may only earn miles for his/her personal account, but miles from multiple accounts may sometimes be used for a single "spending" transaction.

   Consider the following context diagram below as you respond to the questions that follow:

Frequent flyer accounting process
Context diagram

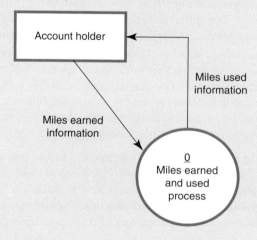

a. Create a Level Zero data flow diagram. Ensure that it is balanced with the context diagram.

b. Create table specifications for the following tables: account holder, miles earned, miles used, miles used/account holder.

c. Suggest at least two queries that would be useful to the airline and/or the account holder based on the tables you created. For each query, indicate its purpose and the tables and fields you would access to create it.

3. *Multiple choice review questions.* Please select the best answer for each question.

1. All of the following are rules for preparing DFDs except:
   a. No process can have only inputs.
   b. A DFD can never have more than seven processes.
   c. External entities and data stores have noun phrase labels.
   d. A data flow can go directly into a data store.

2. How many context diagrams are in a properly prepared leveled set of DFDs?
   a. One, with its process numbered 0
   b. One, with its processes numbered 1.0, 2.0, and so on
   c. No more than seven
   d. As many as the preparer thinks necessary.

3. What term is used to describe the relationship between levels in a set of DFDs?
   a. Primitive
   b. Decomposed
   c. Context
   d. Balanced

4. Every ___ in a database table must be uniquely identified with a ___.
   a. field, primary key
   b. primary key, field
   c. record, primary key
   d. primary key, record

5. The process of making a relational database efficient and easy to use is called:
   a. Normalizing.
   b. Balancing.
   c. Leveling.
   d. Combining.

4. *Making choices and exercising judgment.* Bumble Beasley is a recently enrolled accounting major at your university. In a conversation about accounting information systems, he said: "I don't know why we have to learn about flowcharts *and* data flow diagrams. One documentation technique should be enough; besides, both techniques give basically the same information if you know how to read them." Do you agree or disagree with Bumble? Why?

5. *Field exercises.*

a. Contact an information systems professional such as a professor or systems analyst. Ask him or her about how flowcharts and data flow diagrams could be used in the design and evaluation of an accounting information system.

b. Point your Web browser to www.download.com and search for flowcharting and/or data flow diagramming software there. Identify and describe two pieces of software that are capable of creating *both* flowcharts and data flow diagrams.

c. Use your school's library and/or a Google search to find and read one or more of the following articles on relational databases from the Journal of Accountancy: "What You Better Know about Databases" (January 1999), "Building a Database from Scratch" (November 1999), "Working with Databases" (May 2000), "When Querying Databases, You've Got to Ask the Right Question" (February 2001), and "Put a Database to Work" (January 2002). In a format directed by your AIS instructor, summarize the contents of the article(s) you read.

**6.** *Data flow diagram creation.*

a. The Geek Squad (www.geeksquad.com) offers a variety of telephone, in-office, and in-home computer services. When a call for assistance comes into their 800 number, the Geek Squad determines its geographical origin and routes the call to an agent in the area. The agent confers with the customer by phone, determining the nature of the problem and the type of service desired. The agent also will find out if the customer has previously done business with Geek Squad. The agent will respond to the customer's request and report the problem's resolution to the corporate office. The corporate office bills the customer and collects payment; a fixed fee is remitted to the local agent based on the type and nature of the service call. Point your Web browser to the Geek Squad Web site to get more information about their operations. Then, prepare a context diagram, Level Zero diagram, and one Level One diagram for Geek Squad.

b. Every year, the Institute of Management Accountants sponsors a student case competition to help students build their technical, analytical, and communication skills. In the student case competition, the IMA solicits cases from accounting faculty; an IMA committee chooses the best case and publishes it in an issue of *Strategic Finance*. Teams of students prepare videotaped responses to the case and submit them to the IMA. The videotaped presentations are evaluated and the team with the best presentation in each geographic region presents their case "in person" to a panel of judges at the IMA annual meeting. The team with the best presentation receives an award; all teams presenting at the annual meeting receive an engraved plaque with the members' names on it. The IMA maintains a database of case topics and authors; it also keeps a record of the name and university affiliation of all teams submitting videotapes as well as the status of those submissions. (For more information about the IMA student case competition, point your Web browser to www.imanet.org.) Consider the preceding narrative, and prepare a leveled set of data flow diagrams (context, Level Zero, and Level One).

c. Consider the narratives presented in Problem 6 of Chapter 6 for Cori's Catering Services and University Bookstore. Use those narratives to prepare a leveled set of data flow diagrams.

**7.** *Creating database tables from flat files.* Several independent flat files are shown below. From the fields listed, create the tables indicated. (Not all fields will be used in creating the indicated tables.)

a. Tables to create: purchase inventory table, purchase inventory/inventory table

| **Available Fields** | |
| --- | --- |
| Vendor phone | Inventory description |
| Purchasing agent ID | Cost per item |
| Vendor ID | Vendor code |
| Purchasing agent home address | Invoice total |
| Vendor address (street, city, state, ZIP) | Payment terms (e.g., 2/10, n/30) |
| Purchasing agent name (first, last) | Transaction number |
| Transaction date | Quantity purchased |

b. Tables to create: open bank account table, account holder/account table

| Available Fields | |
| --- | --- |
| Bank account type (e.g., checking) | Account number |
| Current account balance | Account holder name(s) |
| Date account created | Identity verified? |
| Transaction type (e.g., deposit) | Transaction date |
| Transaction amount | Account holder address (street, city, state, ZIP) |
| Employee ID | Annual interest rate |
| Total interest earned in current year | Account holder email |

c. Tables to create: register for courses table, register for courses/courses table

| Available Fields | |
| --- | --- |
| Student ID | Faculty member ID |
| Course ID | Course prefix and number (e.g., Acc 305) |
| Course title | Maximum enrollment |
| Registration transaction number | Registration date |
| Total students currently enrolled | Average GPA of students enrolled |

8. *Creating database tables.*

a. Create at least two database tables for each Level One data flow diagram you created in Problem 6 (data flow diagram creation).

b. In most states, the Department of Motor Vehicles keeps records of individual driver's licenses and vehicle license plates. Create two database tables that capture relevant information for the DMV; information in the driver's license table would include, but not be limited to, an individual's name, license number, and birth date. Information in the vehicle license plate table would include, but not be limited to, the license plate number and information about the vehicle itself. What foreign key(s) would you use to link the two tables together?

c. Robert Half International (www.roberthalf.net) pairs up potential employees with companies seeking accountants and other financial information professionals. Their Web site states: "With 325 offices and 55 years of experience, Robert Half is the world's first and largest specialized financial recruiting firm, placing quality candidates at all levels." Point your Web browser to the company's Web site and click the link for Robert Half United States. What information does Robert Half collect on new job seekers? Organize that information into a database table.

9. *Terminology.* Please match each item on the left with the most appropriate item on the right.

1. Data flow
2. Data store
3. External entity
4. Field
5. Foreign key
6. Level Zero
7. Primary key
8. Process
9. Query
10. Record

a. A compilation of fields in a database
b. A primary key posted to another table
c. Accounts receivable file
d. Customer last name
e. First detailed look at an information system
f. First National Bank
g. Paid invoices
h. Prepare financial statements
i. Uniquely identifies records in a database
j. Which customers have balances over $500?

10. *Multiple choice questions.* Consider the following narrative in responding to the questions that follow:

> The Rancho Cucamonga Humane Society (RCHS) is open from 7 a.m. to 7 p.m., seven days a week. It maintains a computerized inventory of animals available for adoption, which includes animal type (dog, cat, bird), breed (basset hound, parakeet), gender, approximate age, date placed at the shelter, notes, and date adopted. People interested in adopting animals can visit the Society at any time; they complete an application, which is reviewed by the Society staff. A staff member discusses the potential adopters' wants and needs for a pet, then takes them to see appropriate animals. The potential adopter can see and interact with up to five animals in a single visit. If the customer chooses an animal, the staff member fills out appropriate paperwork before the customer takes the pet home. A staff member makes a follow-up call two weeks later to ensure that everything is satisfactory with both the pet and the adopter.

You have been asked to prepare a leveled set of DFDs and database specifications for RCHS.

1. Which of the following is most likely to be an external entity?
   a. People interested in adopting animals
   b. Humane Society staff
   c. Animals
   d. Rancho Cucamonga Humane Society

2. Which of the following is most likely to be Process 1.0?
   a. Open from 7 a.m. to 7 p.m.
   b. Maintain computerized inventory of animals.
   c. Complete application.
   d. Review application.

3. The Level Zero DFD is likely to have how many processes?
   a. Two
   b. Three
   c. Four
   d. Five

4. How many data stores would be depicted in the Level Zero DFD?
   a. One
   b. Two
   c. Three
   d. Four

5. Which of the following is most likely to be the primary key for the "animal" table?
   a. Type
   b. Breed
   c. Name
   d. Intake number

11. *Statement evaluation.* Specify whether each statement below is (i) always true, (ii) sometimes true, or (iii) never true. For those that are (ii) sometimes true, explain when the statement is true.
   a. A context diagram does not include data stores.
   b. A database table in 2NF is in 3NF as well.
   c. A salesperson is an external entity in a data flow diagram.

   d. Data flow diagrams are better than flowcharts for documenting accounting information systems.

   e. Database forms can be used to look up information in a table.

   f. Database queries store instructions, not data.

   g. Database tables are needed for processes, external entities, and data stores in a DFD.

   h. Database tables in 3NF are, by definition, also in 1NF and 2NF.

   i. Decomposing a process numbered 2.0 would lead to numbers like 2.1, 2.2, and so on.

   j. Lines in a data flow diagram should be labeled with verb phrases to show the movement of data.

**12.** *Excel application.* In this problem, you'll be creating a drop-down list in Excel.

   a. Consider the following list of items you might find in a data flow diagram:

| | A |
|---|---|
| 1 | Buy supplies |
| 2 | Class registration |
| 3 | Employee |
| 4 | Employee database |
| 5 | Employee pay data |
| 6 | Issue capital stock |
| 7 | Pay employees |
| 8 | Purchase order |
| 9 | Register for classes |
| 10 | Shareholder |
| 11 | Shareholder database |
| 12 | Shareholder information |
| 13 | Student |
| 14 | Student database |
| 15 | Vendor |
| 16 | Vendor database |

Starting in Cell A1, enter the list of items in the first tab of a blank Excel spreadsheet.

   b. Consider this list of shapes found in a data flow diagram:

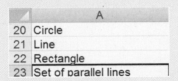

| | A |
|---|---|
| 20 | Circle |
| 21 | Line |
| 22 | Rectangle |
| 23 | Set of parallel lines |

Starting in Cell A20, enter the list of shapes in the same tab of the Excel spreadsheet.

   c. In Cell B1, use Excel's Data Validation tool to create a drop-down list of the four shapes. Copy the drop-down list for the remaining items from (a).

   d. Use the drop down list to indicate which symbol you would use to depict the indicated item in a data flow diagram. The first row should look like this:

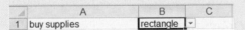

| | A | B | C |
|---|---|---|---|
| 1 | buy supplies | rectangle ▾ | |

## Chapter Eight

# REA Modeling

## AIS in the Business World

### Barnes & Noble

In this final chapter on systems documentation, we'll look at a technique designed primarily to help users design and/or understand the relational database that underlies the AIS; the technique is called REA modeling. Here's an REA model of the Barnes & Noble online book sales process we've been examining:

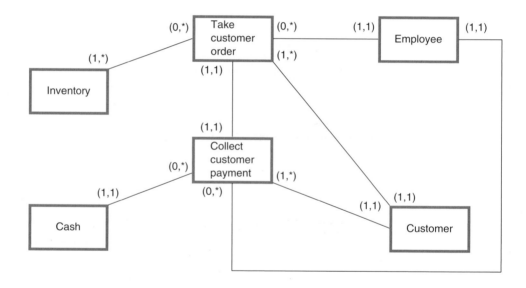

The first column shows two resources, while the middle column shows two events. The rightmost column shows to agents. Notice the order: Resources, Events, and Agents. Hence, the figure is called an REA model. The parenthetical notations, such as (1, 1), are cardinalities; they show the relationship between various elements of the REA model, and also provide guidance for database design.

### *Discussion Questions*

1. What are the steps involved in creating an REA model?
2. How should the cardinalities in the above model be interpreted?
3. What do the cardinalities tell us about the design of the database?

So far, we've looked at two documentation techniques for accounting information systems: flowcharting and data flow diagramming. In this chapter, we'll examine a third technique: REA modeling (we will discuss the meaning of the "REA" term later in the chapter). A relative newcomer to accounting information systems, REA modeling is an important part of designing event-driven accounting information systems. As you read in Chapter 6, systems documentation has two main purposes: understanding business processes and understanding the database. REA modeling is designed primarily for the latter; it depicts only enough of the business process to design, understand, and/or evaluate the database.

Database-focused accounting information systems are sometimes referred to as event-driven systems. **McCarthy** (1982) is considered by many to be the pioneer in the development of event-driven accounting systems. Event-driven systems capture a broader range of data than view-driven systems; relational database technology underlies most event-driven systems. Enterprise resource planning (ERP) systems are a sophisticated version of event-driven AIS. In this chapter, we'll take a closer look at event-driven accounting information systems and REA modeling, the documentation technique often used in their development.

When you finish studying this material, you should be able to:

1. Compare and contrast view-driven and event-driven accounting information systems.
2. Use REA modeling to represent an event-driven AIS.
3. Use a REA model to design a relational database for an event-driven AIS.

In some accounting curricula, professors devote entire courses to the topic of event-driven AIS. Although REA modeling is used less frequently in accounting practice than systems flowcharts, it represents an important way of thinking about the AIS. As with flowcharting and data flow diagramming, two people may come up with slightly different REA models for the same event-driven AIS. And, as with the other two systems documentation techniques, skill in REA modeling is developed with practice over time.

# TYPES OF ACCOUNTING INFORMATION SYSTEMS

At a very basic level, accounting information systems can be divided into two broad groups: view-driven and event-driven. Think of view-driven systems as traditional accounting systems—they may incorporate some forms of information technology, but their defining characteristic is their focus on the general purpose financial statements. If a manager or other decision maker is interested in producing an income statement, a balance sheet, a statement of changes in equity, or a statement of cash flows, the task can be accomplished with a few simple, well-defined steps (i.e., completing the accounting cycle).

Stove piping refers to separating organizational functions and their information systems; for example, treating accounting as though it is unrelated to marketing, operations, or human resource management.

However, managers and other organizational stakeholders frequently need different and/or additional information for effective decision making. For example, a balance sheet can tell you the total accounts receivable balance, and a subsidiary ledger can detail the customer balances that comprise it. However, a balance sheet alone cannot tell you if customers are satisfied, how old the receivables are, or which inventory items were most popular. As business processes have become more integrated, the need for information has grown exponentially. Business professionals no longer have the luxury of "stove piping" the disciplines. And, unfortunately, view-driven accounting systems foster the idea that departments can remain separate and unrelated.

Walker and Denna (1997) summarized five key problems with view-driven accounting information systems:

1. They focus on a very small, well-defined group of important business events—those that are recordable in the accounting information system with debits and credits.
2. They often process data in batches, frequently at the end of the month. Thus, the data in a view-driven accounting system are often outdated.
3. Even for those transactions described in (1), the system captures a very limited set of data—dates, accounts, and amounts. Other transaction details, such as product characteristics, are omitted.
4. Data in a view-driven system are highly aggregated and stored in multiple places. Important data from source documents such as purchase orders and customer invoices are summarized and rearranged to conform to generally accepted accounting principles. Those changes may facilitate the production of financial statements, but they limit the information available for making decisions.
5. In view-driven systems, the internal control process is often protective and expensive. Controls such as separation of duties are focused on preventing collusion in an effort to safeguard assets.

Consider, for example, a simple, common transaction in most businesses: the sale of inventory on account. If the cost of inventory was $100 and the selling price was $150, a view-driven accounting information system would record the sale as follows:

| | | |
|---|---|---|
| Accounts receivable | $150 | |
| Cost of goods sold | 100 | |
| Sales | | $150 |
| Inventory | | 100 |

And, while that information is vital for the production of financial statements, consider the following questions related to the transaction: Was the merchandise delivered on time? Was its quality acceptable to the customer? Has this customer ordered similar merchandise before? How close is the customer to reaching/exceeding its established credit limit? Those questions are virtually impossible to answer with a view-driven accounting information system.

In contrast to view-driven systems that capture, organize, and summarize data by business function, event-driven accounting systems focus on business processes. Processes may cut across disciplinary lines, so the data captured about business processes must be more comprehensive than in a view-driven system. You'll probably recall from Chapter 1 that understanding business processes is one of the reasons AIS is an important area of study for future accountants. In terms of the AICPA Core Competencies, understanding business processes has relationships to having a strong industry/sector perspective (broad business competency), analyzing risk (functional competency), and solving problems/making decisions (personal competency).

Walker and Denna (1997, p. 24) offer the following comments about event-driven accounting information systems:

> The event-driven approach assumes that the purpose of accounting (and other) information systems is to provide information about economic events that is useful in a variety of decision contexts. Events proponents say, "Let's collect raw business data that can be used by a variety of information customers, each with its own set of values and weights to assign to the data." It is the events view that provides an avenue to the next generation of business information systems.

So, in contrast to view-driven systems, event-driven systems

1. Capture more data about individual transactions.
2. Organize the data so that they can be accessed and understood by people from a variety of organizational functions.
3. Are equipped to answer questions like those posed above regarding the inventory transaction.

By their nature, event-driven systems are more complex than view-driven systems. They must be designed to meet the information needs of many groups of users—not just accountants interested in preparing general purpose financial statements. Because of that complexity and the importance of following good design principles, systems professionals needed a new modeling tool. In the next section, we'll look at REA modeling—a documentation technique that facilitates the design and implementation of event-driven accounting information systems.

# REA MODELING

REA is an acronym referring to the *resources, events,* and *agents* in an event-driven accounting information system. Most AIS designers and auditors find it best to start a REA model by identifying its relevant events. In general, "events" come in three broad categories, as shown in Table 8.1:

* *Operating events* focus on activities involved with providing goods and services to customers. Examples include purchasing and selling inventory, paying employees, and converting raw material into finished goods.
* *Information events* deal with recording and maintaining data, as well as reporting information. Think of information events as preparing financial statements or updating accounting records.
* *Decision/management events* are concerned with human decision making. They can range from simple things, such as which software and hardware to buy, to more complex decisions such as changing compensation packages.

As shown in Table 8.1, REA models capture data on strategically significant operating events; they do not incorporate information events or decision/management events. Once strategically significant operating events have been identified, the rest of the details (resources and agents) can be filled in around them.

Agents are the people involved in the information system. Internal agents include employees in all departments; external agents refer to customers, vendors, and other stakeholders "outside" the business. Resources are the things agents need to complete the events: cash, inventory, equipment, supplies, and other assets.

**TABLE 8.1**
**Event Types**

| Event Type | Examples | Depicted in REA Model? |
| --- | --- | --- |
| Operating | Buying supplies, issuing capital stock | Yes |
| Information | Querying a database, posting transactions to the ledger | No |
| Decision/management | Deciding how to allocate budgeted funds, choosing between debt and equity financing | No |

REA models are organized in columns, with the **events** appearing in the middle, **resources** to the left, and **agents** to the right. The REA model presented in Figure 8.1 has one event: rent car. It includes one resource—automobile—and it incorporates two agents: client (an external agent) and a rental agent (an internal agent). That REA model describes the process of renting a car to a client.

So how do you develop an REA model? Hollander, Denna, and Cherrington (2000) recommend a six-step process:

1. *Understand the organization's environment and objectives.* To become trusted business advisors, accounting professionals need to have a thorough grasp of what the organization does. Consider the REA model presented in this chapter's AIS in the Business World. If you had never bought/sold a book online, you would need to understand Barnes & Noble's process before designing the model. The same reasoning holds true about Figure 8.1 and renting a car.

2. *Review the business process and identify the strategically significant operating events.* REA modeling focuses on business processes—the everyday activities employees undertake to create value for their customers and other stakeholders. Every business process is made up of events; the focus in REA modeling is on strategically significant operating events. Barnes & Noble's online book sales process requires a lot of steps, as you'll see when we talk about the sales/collection process later in the text. However, not all of Barnes & Noble's process steps are strategically significant operating events; thus, the REA model depicts only two: take customer order and collect customer payment. Identifying the strategically significant operating events for an REA model is both subjective and iterative. The process is subjective because two different designers might come up with two slightly different sets of events and/or give them different names. The process is iterative because you'll normally need several "tries" to capture all the events.

3. *Analyze each strategically significant operating event to identify the relevant event resources and agents.* Ask yourself: which people have to be involved to carry out (participate in) each event? What resources are needed? In the Barnes & Noble example, we need a customer and an employee for both order taking and payment collecting. Similarly, we need inventory and cash as resources.

4. *Identify the relevant behaviors, characteristics, and attributes of the REA model elements.* This step helps you create database tables. For example, what data would you want/need to capture about a Barnes & Noble employee in your database? Fields in the "employee" table might include last name, first name, social security number, area code, phone number, address, job position, and emergency contact. The resource "cash"

**FIGURE 8.1**
**REA Model Illustration**

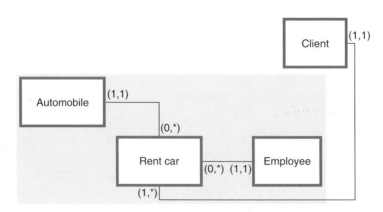

refers to Barnes & Noble's bank account. You would need to know the account number, the bank name, the type of account (e.g., checking), the opening balance, and the date on which the opening balance was valid.

5. *Identify and document the direct relationships among elements of the REA model.* Look again at Figure 8.1; notice the lines between the various REA model elements and the symbols at the end of each line. The lines show which elements are related to one another; the symbols are called *cardinalities.* We'll look at how to establish cardinalities in more detail in the next section. Cardinalities help systems designers, auditors, and fraud examiners (among others) understand how a relational database should be constructed.

6. *Validate the REA model with businesspeople.* Once the REA model is constructed, it should be discussed with people in the organization. Discussing the REA model helps the accounting professional develop a deeper understanding of the organization and its business processes. Those discussions will probably result in changes to the REA model, once again demonstrating that REA modeling is a highly iterative process.

You won't be able to complete this step in homework problems, but it is vital in practice.

You'll need to practice developing REA models to become comfortable and proficient at the process. Try not to become discouraged or frustrated—REA modeling is a new way of thinking for most accounting students. Remember, for example, when you first started making journal entries in introductory accounting? You may have thought you'd never remember that debits are on the left and credits are on the right; now, though, you probably don't give that whole process a lot of conscious thought—it's second nature to you. REA modeling will likely be the same: some initial confusion and discomfort leading to success in the long term.

## Reflection and Self-Assessment 8.1

If you're like most accounting students, you love pizza. Think about the process of ordering and making a pizza. Identify the strategically significant operating events associated with those two processes; then identify the relevant resources and agents. What information would you want to capture in a relational database about each item you identify?

Now, let's take a closer look at establishing relationships between the elements of a REA model by creating cardinalities.

## CARDINALITIES

As you read earlier, **cardinalities** tell an accounting professional about the relationships between elements of a REA model. A well-constructed set of cardinalities is a huge help in using a REA model to create a relational database. Ask yourself four questions when establishing cardinalities for a REA model:

1. *For each x, what is the minimum number of y involved?* Consider, for example, the relationship between "rent car" and "employee" in Figure 8.1. If "rent car" is *x* and "employee" is *y*, you're asking: for each "rent car" transaction, what is the minimum number of employees involved? In this case, the answer is one.

2. *For each x, what is the maximum number of y involved?* Extending that illustration, this question becomes: for each "rent car" transaction, what is the maximum number of employees involved? Assuming that each transaction is handled by only one employee, the answer here is also one. Setting the maximum number of employees to "one" promotes strong internal control; if two or more employees were involved in a transaction, collusion between them could lead to errors and/or fraud.

Once you've answered the first two questions, record the cardinalities on the *y* side of the relationship. So, the (1,1) notation next to the "employee" box in Figure 8.1 explains how many employees are involved in each "rent car" transaction.

3. *For each y, what is the minimum number of x involved?* In our example, this question is asking about the minimum number of rental transactions an employee could complete. To answer this question, consider that a rental car agency has many types of employees; only some of them have the responsibility for renting cars. Other employees may be in charge of cleaning the office, washing the cars, or other tasks. So, the minimum number of rental transactions for a given employee is zero.

4. *For each y, what is the maximum number of x involved?* On the other hand, envision an employee responsible for renting cars who works tirelessly—who handles each rental transaction effectively and efficiently. Would you limit the number of transactions that employee could complete? Probably not. When there's no upper limit on a relationship between two elements of an REA model, we refer to the maximum as *many,* and symbolize it with an asterisk (*).

After answering questions 3 and 4, note the cardinalities on the *x* side of the relationship. So, the (0,*) notation next to "rent car" tells us that each employee can complete from zero to many car rental transactions. Consider Figure 8.2, which shows the same REA model as Figure 8.1, but includes the interpretations of the cardinalities for your reference.

**FIGURE 8.2**
**REA Model with Cardinalities Explanation**

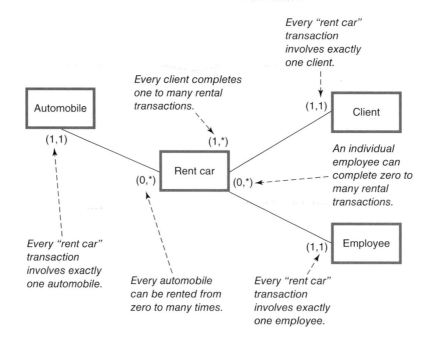

Examine the relationships in this chapter's AIS in the Business World. Write out, in plain English, what each of the following relationships means: customer and take customer order, take customer order and inventory, take customer order and collect customer payment. Use the four questions as a guide.

The final element of our discussion of REA modeling involves how to translate the REA model into a **relational database**. We'll take up that topic in the next section.

## DATABASE CREATION FROM AN REA MODEL

In Chapter 6, we talked a bit about the four common objects found in relational databases: tables, queries, forms, and reports. Since tables are the fundamental building blocks of relational databases, the next few paragraphs focus on how to create tables that are as efficient and effective as possible. In other words, we want to create tables that have only the information required; further, we need to ensure that the information is organized as efficiently as possible.

In general, you're going to need at least one table for each "box" in the REA model. So, in our ongoing rental car example, you'd need the tables listed below and on the next page. Possible fields in each table are indicated, with the primary key signified by an underline. The rules for data normalization, explored earlier in the text, also apply to creating databases for event-driven accounting information systems based on REA models. When finished, database tables should be in third normal form; they should contain neither repeating groups (1NF) nor redundant data (2NF). In addition, every field in the table should provide additional information about its primary key (3NF). As you may recall from your study of data flow diagramming, the rules of **normalization** are:

1. Focus each database table on a single "thing," such as customer data or inventory data. Each table must have a primary key that uniquely identifies each record.
2. Eliminate redundant data in each table. If a table has a compound primary key, each data element in the table must depend on both parts of the primary key. If a data element depends on only one part of the key, it should go in a separate table.
3. Ensure that all fields in a database table contain data that describe the table's primary key. If a field is not dependent on the primary key, it should be moved to a separate table.

- Automobile table

  | | |
  |---|---|
  | <u>Identification number</u> | Model |
  | Make | Year |

- Client table

  | | |
  |---|---|
  | <u>Client last name</u> | City |
  | <u>Client first name</u> | State |
  | Client date of birth | ZIP |
  | Street address | Phone |

- Employee table

  | | |
  |---|---|
  | <u>Employee ID</u> | First name |
  | Address | Job classification |
  | Date of birth | Last name |
  | Emergency contact information | Phone |

- Rent car table

| | |
|---|---|
| <u>Transaction number</u> | [Client last name] |
| [Automobile identification number] | [Employee ID] |
| [Client first name] | Transaction date |

In the "rent car" table, notice the presence of primary keys from the other three tables. Referring to the REA model in Figure 8.1, notice the cardinalities between the automobile table and rental transaction table (as well as the others). The maximum cardinalities between the automobile and rental transaction are one and many, bringing us to the first "rule" of creating database tables from an REA model:

> **When the maximum cardinalities between two elements of an REA model are one and many, include the primary key from the "one side" in the table on the "many side."**

In our example, that rule tells us to put the primary key from the automobile table (the "one side") into the rental transaction table (the "many side").

In some REA models, relationship cardinalities include maximums of many on both sides. Consider, for example, a database that tracks the academic progress of students in your AIS class. Each student can take many classes; each class includes many students. The REA model relationship between student and class would look like Figure 8.3.

Situations like that one bring us to the second important rule of creating database tables from a REA model:

> **When the maximum cardinalities between two elements of an REA model are many and many, create a separate junction table to reflect the combined relationship.**

So, in creating a database to reflect the relationship above, you would need three tables: a "class" table, a "register for class" table and a "class/register for class" table. The class/register for class table is referred to as a **junction table.** Junction tables don't normally contain more than a few fields; many of them will simply comprise the primary keys from the other two tables. Figure 8.4 illustrates the database specifications for all three tables.

Here are a few comments and observations about Figure 8.4:

- In the "Class" table, the field Employee ID refers to the faculty member teaching the course. Elsewhere in the database, you would include an "Employee" table, and its primary key would be Employee ID. Thus, in the "Class" table, Employee ID is a foreign key, denoted by the brackets.
- At many schools, the Class ID also indicates the term the course is offered (e.g., Fall 2014)—a form of block coding, which you may recall from Chapter 2. If the Class ID was not block coded, you would add fields for the term and year to the table.

**FIGURE 8.3**
**Many-to-Many Relationship**

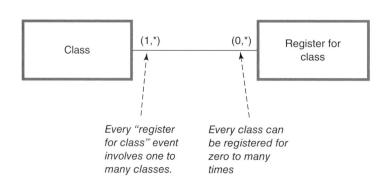

**FIGURE 8.4**
**Database Tables for Figure 8.3**

| **Class table** | **Register for class table** | **Class / register for class table** |
|---|---|---|
| Class ID number | Transaction number | [Transaction number] |
| Course prefix | Registration date | [Class ID number] |
| Course number | [Student ID] | |
| Course title | | |
| Section number | | |
| [Employee ID] | | |
| Meeting days | | |
| Start time | | |
| End time | | |

- In the "register for class" table, the transaction number field is likely to be auto-numbered. Auto-numbering transactions promotes strong internal control, since an out-of-sequence number may indicate a deleted record.
- In the "Register for class" table, Student ID is a foreign key for the same reasons that Employee ID is a foreign key in the "Class" table. No additional data about the student is needed in the "Register for class" table; including it would violate the principles of normalization. If a database user wanted to create a list of student names and their associated transaction numbers, the user would query the two tables involved; they are linked by the Student ID field.
- The junction table (class/register for class) is a relatively simple table, comprising the primary keys of the two tables it joins. Any additional data could be referenced (called) from the linked tables in a query or report.

## Reflection and Self-Assessment                          8.3

Suppose one of the strategically significant operating events for a pizza restaurant is "sell pizza." Assume the agents involved are "customer" and "employee," and the one resource is "pizza." Create a REA model, including cardinalities, for those four items. Then, create specifications for the "sell pizza" database table.

Remember: it takes patience and practice to get comfortable with creating REA models and databases for event-driven accounting systems. The idea is to create a workable model that reflects an organization's **strategically significant operating activities**—not to search for the "one right answer" in any particular situation.

## CRITICAL THINKING

All three chapters in this section of the book have used Barnes & Noble's online book sales process for "AIS in the Business World." We've also looked at the firm's book purchasing process (Figures 6.2 and 7.2). For this chapter's critical thinking application, let's stick with the book purchasing process. I'm going to walk you through the six steps to create a REA model, then consider how to design a relational database.

1. *Understand the organization's environment and objectives.* Barnes & Noble is one of many retail bookstore chains; it also has a strong online presence. Barnes & Noble's e-reader is called the Nook; it has both a standalone version and an app that will run on just about any mobile device. The company's stock trades on the NYSE under the symbol BKS.

2. *Review the business process and identify the strategically significant operating events.* We're going to consider two strategically significant operating events from Barnes & Noble's acquisition/payment process: issue purchase order and pay vendor invoice. The acquisition/payment process has many other steps, but those two will suffice for this example.

3. *Analyze each strategically significant operating event to identify the relevant resources and agents.* With respect to "issue purchase order," the resource would be inventory; the agents would be employee and vendor. For "pay vendor invoice," the resource is cash; the agents are, once again, employee and vendor.

   At this point, the REA model looks like Figure 8.5. (We'll insert the cardinalities in Step 5.)

4. *Identify the relevant behaviors, characteristics, and attributes of the REA model elements.* At this point, we begin to think about how the relational database associated with the REA model will look. Here's a short list of some of the relevant information for each element of the REA model:

   a. Inventory: Inventory ID, book title, beginning quantity on hand, cost per unit of beginning quantity, beginning quantity date.

   b. Cash: Account number, account type, bank, beginning balance, beginning balance date.

   c. Issue purchase order: Purchase order number, purchase order date, vendor, employee.

   d. Pay vendor invoice: Check number, check date, vendor, employee, bank account number.

   e. Employee: Employee ID, employee job title, employee last name, employee first name. (This table would contain many more attributes, such as the employee's address. Refer back to previous examples for a more comprehensive list.)

   f. Vendor: Vendor ID, vendor name, vendor contact person. (Like the employee table, this table would have several more fields, such as vendor address and vendor phone number.)

5. Identify and document the direct relationships among elements of the REA model. Now, we'll create the cardinalities between the elements of the REA model. Remember to use the four questions as a guide until you're comfortable working with cardinalities.

**FIGURE 8.5**
**REA Model without Cardinalities**

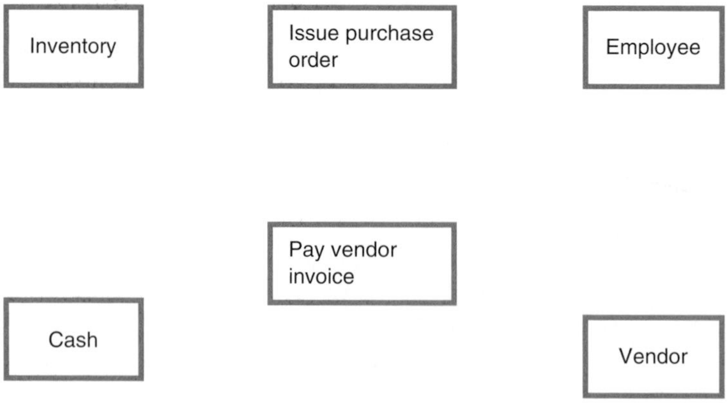

Figure 8.6 depicts the REA model with cardinalities. Notice the cardinalities between the two events. The maximum cardinalities call for a junction table because each "pay vendor invoice" can be associated with many "issue purchase orders," and vice versa. In other words, an invoice (and therefore its related check) may include multiple purchase orders; likewise, a check might include partial payments for one or more purchase orders.

6. Validate the REA model with businesspeople. In practice, you would consult (at minimum) employees in the purchasing and cash payments departments at Barnes & Noble to be sure the REA model accurately reflects the process.

Once the REA model is created, we can design the relational database it depicts. We'll need a total of eight tables: one for each "box" of the REA model, plus two junction tables (inventory/issue purchase order and issue purchase order/pay vendor invoice). Figure 8.7 shows the specifications for some of the tables (you may develop the specifications for the others as part of a homework assignment from your AIS professor).

**FIGURE 8.6**
**REA Model with Cardinalities**

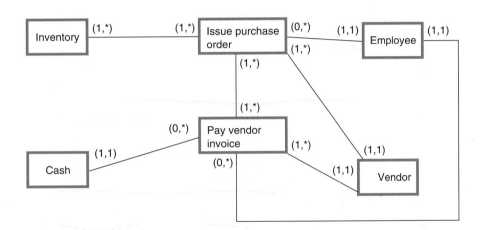

**FIGURE 8.7**
**Selected Tables for Figure 8.6**

**Inventory table**

Inventory ID
Book title
Beginning quantity on hand
Cost per unit of beginning inventory
Beginning balance date

**Issue purchase order table**

Purchase order number
Purchase order date
[Employee ID]
[Vendor ID]

**Vendor table**

Vendor ID
Vendor name
Vendor contact first name
Vendor contact last name
Vendor street address
Vendor city
Vendor state
Vendor ZIP code
Vendor country

**Inventory / Issue purchase order table**

[Purchase order number]
[Inventory ID]
Quantity purchased
Cost per unit

Finally, here are a couple sample exam questions about the example:

1. Consider the REA model presented in Figure 8.6. Which table is likely to have a field called "purchase order total?"

   a. Issue purchase order table.

   b. Inventory/issue purchase order table.

   c. Both A and B.

   d. Neither A nor B.

The best answer is "D." "Purchase order total" is a derivable amount; derivable amounts are never stored in a database table. Rather, to determine the purchase order total, we would create a query to do the computations.

2. Consider the REA model presented in Figure 8.6. Which of the following tables would include Employee ID as a foreign key: (i) employee table, (ii) issue purchase order table, and (iii) pay vendor invoice table.

   a. i and ii only

   b. ii and iii only

   c. i and ii only

   d. i, ii, and iii

The best answer is "B." When the maximum cardinalities between two elements of the REA model are one and many, post the primary key from the "one side" to the table on the "many side." The employee table would include Employee ID, but not as a foreign key; rather, as a primary key.

On a quiz or exam, your instructor might give you only the REA model as the basis for answering those two questions. Therefore, they require more critical thinking since you would not only have to interpret the REA model, but also have to design the tables correctly.

## Summary

In this chapter, then, we've examined event-driven accounting information systems and REA modeling. Here's a summary of the chapter's important points, seen through the lens of its learning objectives:

1. *Compare and contrast view-driven and event-driven accounting information systems.* Both types of systems are designed to collect data and process it into information; both typically involve various forms of information technology. View-driven systems are designed to present that information in one principal way: the general purpose financial statements. Event-driven systems are built on relational database technology; they capture more data and offer greater flexibility in terms of reporting via queries and reports.

2. *Use REA modeling to represent an event-driven AIS.* REA modeling begins by understanding an organization's environment and business processes. Then, for each process, it identifies the resources, events and agents needed to capture the essential nature of transactions. System designers use cardinalities to explain the relationships between the elements of an REA model.

3. *Use a REA model to design a relational database for an event-driven AIS.* Once the REA model has been established and validated, it can be translated into a series of

relational database tables. In most cases, each element of a REA model requires at least one table in a relational database. Where the maximum cardinalities between elements of the model are many to many, system designers create a junction table to denote the relationship.

The relational database technology that forms the basis for REA modeling is also the basis for enterprise resource planning systems. So, a solid understanding of this area of AIS will give you an appreciation for that important technology, as well as help you "speak the same language" as the IT professionals with whom you'll be working.

## Key Terms

agents, *144*
cardinalities, *145*
events, *144*
junction table, *148*

McCarthy, *141*
normalization, *147*
relational database, *147*
resources, *144*

six-step process, *144*
strategically significant operating activities, *149*

## Chapter References

Hollander, A. S., E. L. Denna, and J. O. Cherrington. 2000. *Accounting, Information Technology, and Business Solutions.* 2nd ed. New York: Irwin/McGraw-Hill.

McCarthy, W. E. 1982. "The REA Accounting Model: A Generalized Framework for Accounting Systems in a Shared Data Environment." *Accounting Review,* July, pp. 554–77.

Walker, K. B., and E. Denna. 1997. "Arriveder ci, Pacioli? A New Accounting System Is Emerging." *Management Accounting,* July, pp. 22–30.

## End-of-Chapter Activities

1. *Reading review questions.*

   a. What are the similarities and differences between view-driven and event-driven accounting information systems?

   b. What does the acronym REA stand for? Give examples of each element.

   c. List the six steps for creating a REA model.

   d. Explain how to establish a set of cardinalities between two elements of a REA model.

   e. How would you use a REA model to design a relational database?

   f. Prepare a response to the questions for this chapter's "AIS in the Business World."

2. *Reading review problem.* Most major airlines have "frequent flyer" programs. A customer creates a new account, and earns miles in a variety of ways such as purchasing goods and services through a credit card linked to the account, taking paid flights on the airline, and celebrating the annual anniversary of account creation. The miles are later "spent" on flights and other items. An individual account holder may only earn miles for his/her personal account, but miles from multiple accounts may sometimes be used for a single "spending" transaction.

   a. Which systems documentation technique would you use if your goal was to construct the relational database that supports the narrative? Why?

   b. Regardless of your answer to (a), construct a complete REA model of the process.

   c. Based on your REA model, identify four tables you would need in the relational database—one each for a resource, an event, an agent, and a junction table. What would be each table's primary key?

   d. Based on the tables you created, suggest two queries the airline might create. For each query, indicate its name, its purpose and the fields involved.

3. *Multiple choice review questions.* Please select the best answer for each question.
   1. All of the following are criticisms of view-driven accounting information systems except:
      a. The information technology tools to implement them are not widely available.
      b. They often process data in batches.
      c. They focus on a very small, well-defined group of important business events.
      d. The internal control process is often protective and expensive.
   2. In contrast to view-driven AIS, event-driven systems:
      a. Capture more data about individual transactions.
      b. Organize the data so they can be accessed and understood by people throughout the organization.
      c. Are equipped to answer a broader range of questions relevant to running a business.
      d. All of the above.
   3. Events can be classified into three broad groups. Which of the following is not one of them?
      a. Decision/management events
      b. Financial events
      c. Information events
      d. Operating events
   4. Cardinalities:
      a. Are not necessary in a well-designed REA model.
      b. Are required by GAAP.
      c. Explain relationships between elements of a REA model.
      d. Can be developed without human judgment.
   5. Which of the following statements is (are) true in using cardinalities to construct a relational database?
      a. When the maximum cardinalities between two elements of an REA model are one and many, include the primary key from the "many side" in the table on the "one side."
      b. When the maximum cardinalities between two elements of an REA model are many and many, create a separate junction table to reflect the combined relationship.
      c. Both a and b.
      d. Neither a nor b.

4. *Making choices and exercising judgment.* Coral's See-the-Reef, located on the Gulf of Mexico, is famous for its fast service. Coral's business is renting scuba and snorkeling gear. Coral needs someone to analyze her business and help her use that analysis to plan and design a new information system. Coral employs four fitting clerks, three rental clerks, and four cashiers. The fitting clerks enter equipment items, sizes, and experience codes into the computer. The computer searches the rental inventory, by experience code, for the requested equipment. For example, a beginner is code one, which tells the computer to locate the oldest equipment available in the requested size. Once the requested equipment is located, a duplicate rental invoice is printed. The rental clerk uses the second copy to retrieve the equipment. While this clerk gets the equipment, the customer pays the rental fee to a cashier. A deposit is added to the rental fee, and a code indicating the condition of the equipment is noted.

   *Source:* A. S. Hollander, E. L. Denna, and J. O. Cherrington, *Accounting, Information Technology, and Business Solutions*, 2nd ed. (New York: Irwin/McGraw-Hill, 2000).

   a. Create a REA model for Coral's See-the-Reef. Create database tables for one resource, one event, and one agent.
   b. Suggest two queries Coral should incorporate in her database; justify your suggestions. Which tables and fields would she need to create the queries you suggest?
   c. Design a form a fitting clerk could use for entering equipment items, sizes, and experience codes.

5. *Field work.*

   Relational database software can be used very effectively in detecting fraud in the accounting information system. Use your school's library resources to find and read R. Marden and R. Edwards, "Internal Controls for the Small Business: Skimming and the Fraud Triangle," *Internal Auditing* (January/February 2005). If Pinewoods of the Blue Ridge Mountains (the company discussed in the article) captured transactions in a relational database based on a REA model, what queries and reports would you construct in an attempt to discover the fraud?

6. *Constructing REA models.* (Case situations (*a*) through (*d*) come from Hollander, Denna, and Cherrington, 2000.) In each independent case situation below, construct a REA model and a database structure.

   a. *Tom's Trailers.* Tom owns a small recreational trailer business in a suburban community located close to the mountains. The community is relatively small but growing at a fast rate. Tom's business is growing, not because of his effective sales style and personality, but by growth of the community. Currently, Tom's competition has been nearly nonexistent but, as the area grows, he expects to encounter increasing competition.

   Tom sells mostly trailers for vacationing and camping. When customers arrive on Tom's lot, they are greeted by a salesperson. The salesperson may show the customers the trailers on the lot, but the salesperson need not be present during the entire showing. Depending on customer preference, either the salesperson will take the customer on a tour or the customer may roam the lot freely, inspecting trailers at his or her leisure.

   Since recreational trailers are fairly large-ticket items, customers often will leave the lot without making a purchase, only to return another day after making the decision to purchase a trailer. When a customer decides to make a purchase, the salesperson initiates a series of procedures to properly document the order and sale transaction. First, the salesperson determines the model of the selected trailer and offers the customer a list of options that correspond to the particular model. The customer may (i) purchase a trailer off the lot with no added features, (ii) purchase a trailer off the lot with additional features, or (iii) special order a trailer not currently on the lot.

   In most cases, customers do not pay cash for their trailers. If, however, the customer pays cash, a simple sales contract is prepared and the customer drives off with his or her trailer. The majority of customers use an installment method of purchase. Before an installment purchase is authorized, the customer's credit must be verified to determine creditworthiness.

   With an installment purchase, an installment agreement is prepared in addition to the sales contract. Tom has arranged financing through a local bank for all installment sales. When an installment sale is made, the bank sends Tom a lump-sum payment equal to the price of the trailer. Instead of making a payment to Tom, customers pay the bank plus interest. In either case, Tom receives a lump-sum payment for each trailer sold, whether that lump sum comes from the customer or the bank.

   Once the customer's credit is approved, the customer can take delivery of the trailer. This involves a delivery person who checks the trailer before delivering it to the customer. The customer may pick up the trailer or have it delivered by Tom.

   b. *Maple Bluff Pharmacy.* Maple Bluff Pharmacy sells prescription drugs and over-the-counter medications and supplies. All prescriptions and over-the-counter items are sold using a cash register. Each cash register retains on the cash register's journal tape a record of the transactions and who performed them. This information is subsequently entered into a computer.

   Prescriptions received over the phone are taken by the pharmacist and recorded on a prescription slip. Also, prescriptions received over the phone are entered into a computer that matches the prescription with guideline dosage levels and instruction information and prints the necessary information for the prescription. After entering the prescription information into the computer, the prescription is filled and a hard copy of the prescription slip is filed numerically for future reference.

All sales items are paid for with cash, check, or credit card. On occasion, credit is extended to a customer, but he or she must be approved through the chief pharmacist. If credit is extended, a separate billing account is established. If a customer does not pay the bill within 120 days of the initial billing date, the account is turned over to a collection agency.

At the end of the day, cash in the register till is counted and compared with the total amount of credit card receipts and accounts receivable slips. This check is performed by two employees in the safe room and is always monitored on camera. In addition, total cash receipts recorded in the computer are compared with the deposit totals each day before Deposits Express picks up the money for deposit.

c. *Western Steel Company.* Western Steel Company produces steel for a variety of customers. When customers order steel, an order clerk enters the information into a computer that prepares a purchase order to track the order from production to collection of payment. If the customer's credit has been approved, production of the order begins immediately. If the customer is new, a credit check is performed.

After the order is filled, a tally count is made of the produced steel and the steel is shipped to the customer. If the steel is to be shipped by railroad, rail cars are checked for weight before shipping the order. The weight of the load is then compared to the order to ensure an accurate delivery. Accompanying the shipment is a computer-generated bill of lading and a copy of the purchase order.

Shortly after shipping an order, Western invoices the customer using prices on an approved price list. The invoice total is obtained by multiplying the quantity ordered and shipped by the standard price. Steel prices are set by the Sales department, which determines competitive prices based on market conditions and cost information.

Customers send payments directly to a lockbox account in selected cities across the United States. The bank where a particular customer sends payment is located in the city closest to the customer's location. Western receives no payment, but Western receives a record of customer deposits from the bank maintaining the lockbox account. Accounting personnel maintain the billing and collection accounts, while the Credit department issues credit to customers and follows up on past due accounts.

d. *Payroll process for a CPA firm.* The payroll and personnel function represents a large expense for many companies—especially the audit divisions of accounting firms. Clients are frequently billed based on staff, manager, and partner involvement in the audit. Firms bill clients based on a predetermined rate for each person involved. For example, a company bills a partner's hours at a substantially higher rate than it bills the staff's hours. Partners also trade employees to work on different projects for different clients. Careful tracking and planning go into each audit to maintain both audit quality and the lowest possible cost to the client.

For each client engagement, an audit plan is developed to identify the type and quantity of hours necessary to complete each audit step. For example, the audit plan might specify 30 hours to count warehouse inventory. Each week, auditors record their time on a time-and-expense report and submit it to the audit supervisor. The supervisor compares the actual time to the budgeted time in the audit plan. The time-and-expense reports are then submitted to the Payroll department, which prepares paychecks for the auditors. Each week, the Payroll department calculates pay based on a yearly salary and overtime for each employee. In addition, the Payroll department must track deductions for taxes, insurance, and benefits. Once the deductions are withheld, the net pay is deposited into the employee's checking account, or a check is issued in the name of the employee.

e. *Textbook ordering and purchasing process.* Six weeks before the start of each academic term, accounting instructors at AIS University of America inform the department secretary of the books they're planning to use for each class. Instructors may use one or more books for an individual class; different instructors may use different textbooks for various sections of the same course. The department secretary compiles the instructor-provided data and transmits them via e-mail to the bookstore's purchasing agent. The purchasing agent prepares a purchase order and sends it to the textbook publisher; a single purchase order may combine textbooks for several different courses, so long as all the textbooks come from the same publisher. When the publisher ships the books, the bookstore's receiving department records the shipment; stock clerks put the books on the shelves. The textbook publisher invoices the bookstore, which then writes a check in payment; unused textbooks are returned to the publisher roughly one month after the term begins.

f. *Beta Alpha Psi.* Beta Alpha Psi (www.bap.org) is the international honor society for students and professionals in accounting, finance, and information systems. Each BAY chapter is required to complete certain activities each year; they also may earn extra recognition and rewards by going beyond the minimums specified by the national office. Each BAY chapter tracks its members' participation in the various events, reporting periodically to the national office via BAY's reporting intranet. Thus, a chapter's strategically significant operating events would include: initiate new members, host events, and report to national office.

7. *Interpreting a REA model.* Consider the REA model presented below. Write a narrative description of the business process it depicts.

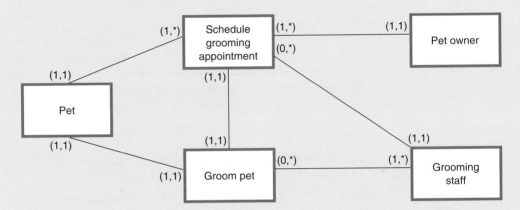

8. *Terminology.* Match each item on the left with the most appropriate item on the right.

| | |
|---|---|
| 1. Cardinality | a. Unique record identifier in a database table |
| 2. Decision/management event | b. Supports the preparation of financial statements |
| 3. Enterprise resource planning | c. Purchasing supplies |
| 4. Information event | d. Preparing journal entries ⸴ |
| 5. Junction table | e. Opening an office in a new city |
| 6. Primary key | f. Internal agent |
| 7. Purchasing agent | g. External agent |
| 8. Strategically significant operating event | h. Combines the primary keys of two tables |
| 9. Vendor | i. A sophisticated form of event-driven AIS |
| 10. View-driven AIS | j. (1,*)—(1,1) |

9. *Multiple choice questions.* Consider the following REA model in responding to the questions below; it represents the system by which members of the accounting club at Big State University are reimbursed when they incur expenses on the club's behalf.

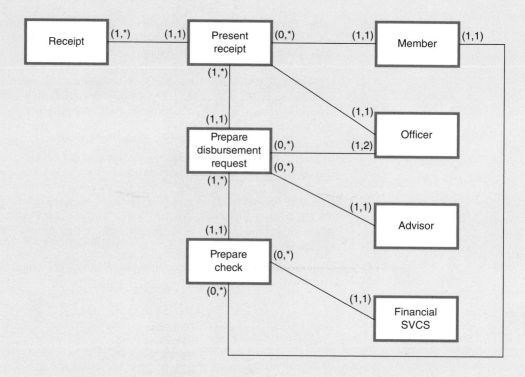

1. Which of the following is an external agent?

   a.  Member
   b.  Officer
   c.  Advisor
   d.  Financial services

2. How many junction tables are indicated in the REA model?

   a.  Zero
   b.  One
   c.  Two
   d.  More than two

3. Which of the following statements is most true?

   a.  A disbursement request can be split into one or more checks.
   b.  A check can cover multiple disbursement requests.
   c.  Neither a nor b.
   d.  Both a and b.

4. All of the following statements are true except:

   a.  An advisor must sign every disbursement request.
   b.  At least one officer must sign every disbursement request.
   c.  All disbursement requests must be signed by two officers.
   d.  Receipts may be presented by either an officer or a member.

5. Which of the following would be a foreign key in the "prepare disbursement request" table?

   a.  The primary key from the "present receipt" table
   b.  The primary key from the "receipt" table
   c.  Both a and b
   d.  Neither a nor b

10. *Statement evaluation.* Please indicate whether each of the following statements is (i) always true, (ii) sometimes true, or (iii) never true. For those that are (ii) sometimes true, explain when the statement is true.

    a. "Choose AIS software" would be included as an event in a REA model.
    b. Events can be related to one another in a REA model.
    c. Events in a REA model are shown in the second column.
    d. If an accountant can construct a REA model, data flow diagrams and flowcharts are unnecessary.
    e. Most REA models will include both internal and external agents.
    f. REA models include decision/management events.
    g. Resources and agents are unrelated in a REA model.
    h. Strong internal controls are evident in a REA model.
    i. Understanding an organization's environment is important in designing a REA model.
    j. View-driven accounting systems do not provide information for decisions.

11. *Excel application.* Consider the following Excel spreadsheet

| Transaction ID | Transaction date | Employee ID | Customer ID |
|---|---|---|---|
| 1 | 2/3/2014 | 178 | 5071 |
| 2 | 2/6/2014 | 157 | 5813 |
| 3 | 2/11/2014 | 183 | 5813 |
| 4 | 2/14/2014 | 157 | 5348 |
| 5 | 2/19/2014 | 178 | 5071 |

    (The spreadsheet is available in the 3 February 2014 post on my AIS blog.)
    Import the Excel data into an Access table. Then, create a query that shows the number of transactions processed by each employee.

## Comprehensive Problem
### Part 2 of 5

Each part of the comprehensive problem is based on Big Marker (www.bigmarker.com). Consider the narrative in Part 1 as you respond to the following questions on systems documentation and database design.

### Part Two Questions

1. Using the technique(s) specified by your AIS instructor, document the process Big Marker uses to purchase new servers.

2. The Big Marker narrative discusses the relationship between corporate sponsors and communities. Consider the REA model below; create specifications for all indicated database tables.

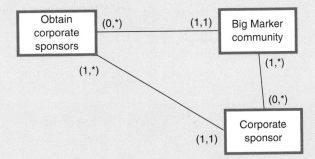

3. Consider the database specifications you created in Question 2. Suggest three queries Big Marker could create to inform decision making about obtaining corporate sponsors. For each query, indicate its name, its purpose, and the fields you would use to create it.

4. The Big Marker narrative explains the process used for starting and monitoring communities. Using the technique(s) specified by your AIS instructor, document that process.

5. Create database specifications for the following tables: create new community, community hero, create new community/community organizer.

# Information Technology in the AIS

As you learned in Part One, information technology is a processing tool in the AIS—the technology is not the system itself. Now that you've learned some fundamental ideas about AIS in Parts One and Two, we'll turn our attention to the role IT can play in the accounting information system.

This part comprises three chapters:

**9.** XBRL

**10.** E-business and Enterprise Resource Planning

**11.** Computer Crime and Information Technology Security

XBRL is an acronym for the eXtensible Business Reporting Language. It is an information technology tool that allows accounting and IT professionals to tag (mark up) financial data. Once marked up, the data and tags can be read and interpreted across diverse hardware and software platforms. All companies that file documents with the SEC are required to use XBRL.

Next, we'll turn our attention to e-business, the essence of which is conducting business via computer networks. Enterprise resource planning systems are often associated with e-business; they are relational databases that capture comprehensive data about an organization and allow managers and others to access that data for improved decisions. New to the 4th edition will be a discussion and illustrations of SAP, a major ERP system used globally by about 75% of the Forbes 500 companies.

Finally in this section, we'll reconsider issues of internal control within an IT-enabled environment. As you can likely imagine, using information technology creates new risks for organizations; thus, they need to create internal controls to address those risks. This chapter also introduces Version Five of the CoBIT framework, a widely used, well-respected framework that informs governance and management processes of company-wide information technology resources. CoBIT 5 focuses on a comprehensive set of principles and enablers; you'll see several similarities between CoBIT and the two COSO frameworks discussed in Part One of the text.

# Chapter **Nine**

# XBRL

## AIS in the Business World

### Microsoft Corporation

Our topic for this chapter is XBRL, an acronym for the eXtensible Business Reporting Language. XBRL is a system for labeling primarily financial information so that it can be interpreted by a variety of software and hardware combinations—regardless of those used to prepare it.

Consider the following excerpt from Microsoft's income statement for the period ended 30 June 2013:

| Revenue | $ 77,849 |
|---|---|
| Cost of revenue | (20,249) |
| Gross profit | $ 57,600 |

Now, consider the following details about the XBRL code that generated the information:

| | Revenue | Cost of Revenue | Gross Profit |
|---|---|---|---|
| Name | us-gaap_SalesRevenueNet | us-gaap_CostOfRevenue | us-gaap_GrossProfit |
| Namespace prefix | us-gaap_ | us-gaap_ | us-gaap_ |
| Date type | xbrli:monetaryItemType | xbrli:monetaryItemType | xbrli:monetaryItemType |
| Balance type | Credit | Debit | Credit |
| Period type | Duration | Duration | Duration |

All publicly traded companies that want to list their stock on US exchanges must use XBRL in their financial reporting to the SEC.

### Discussion Questions

1. What is XBRL?
2. What impact does XBRL have on financial reporting and the accounting information system?
3. What is the XBRL Global Ledger Taxonomy?

One of the really interesting things about accounting information systems is its dynamic nature. Because AIS involves information technology, there are always new ideas, new tools, and new topics to explore. We'll look at one of those topics in this chapter: XBRL. XBRL is an acronym for the eXtensible Business Reporting Language; the basic purpose of XBRL is to facilitate information exchange, particularly financial information, between all different kinds of organizations, regardless of the hardware and software platforms they use individually.

XBRL is a "standard" in the broadest sense of the term. It is not, however, a new accounting standard in the FASB sense. XBRL is simply a way to code information for easier interpretation.

You may have heard of HyperText Markup Language (HTML), the language used to develop Web pages on the Internet. **XBRL** is to financial information what HTML is to Web page development. XBRL is a subset of a much broader language, XML (eXtensible Markup Language). As an accountant, you will likely be called to convert standardized financial statements into XBRL format; you also may have to interact with information technology professionals in organizations about this important standard.

When you've finished studying this chapter, you should be able to:

1. Define the following terms as they relate to XBRL: *extensible, specification, taxonomy, namespace,* and *instance document.*
2. Explain the history and structure of XBRL.
3. Discuss ways XBRL can benefit organizations.
4. Identify software tools for creating XBRL-tagged documents.
5. Discuss internal control issues for XBRL.

According to the Web site of XBRL International (www.xbrl.org):

XBRL is a language for the electronic communication of business information, providing major benefits in the preparation, analysis, and communication of business information. It offers cost savings, greater efficiency, improved accuracy, and reliability to all those involved in supplying or using business information. It is one of a family of "XML" languages which is a standard means of communicating information between businesses and on the internet. XBRL is being developed by an international non-profit consortium of over 600 major companies, organizations, and government agencies. It is an open standard, free of license fees. It is already being put to practical use in a number of countries and implementations of XBRL are growing rapidly around the world.

All publicly traded companies that file reports with the SEC must do so using XBRL.

# TERMINOLOGY

As you may have learned in your very first accounting course, accounting is often referred to as the "language of business." And, like most languages, accounting has some specialized terminology/idiomatic expressions that should be mastered. Consider, for example, the term *depreciation*. If you ask a friend who is a nonaccounting major what depreciation is, he or she likely will talk about a loss in value—as in "when you drive a new car off a lot, it depreciates 50 percent." But, in accounting, *depreciation* takes on a completely different meaning: the periodic allocation of an asset's cost to the periods that benefit from its use. In accounting, we say that depreciation is a process of allocation, not valuation.

In the same way that accounting (and most "regular" languages) involves specialized terminology, so does XBRL. You should understand at least five terms before you begin reading about XBRL in the rest of this chapter.

- *Extensible.* The "X" in XBRL stands for *extensible.* In other words, the XBRL language is "able" to be "extended." The same is true for English. Think about words and expressions we use in the 21st century that hadn't even been invented a decade ago: frenemy, "Google it," or "Like us on Facebook". In the same way that English grows and changes, users can add new ideas and phrases to the basic XBRL without changing its fundamental purpose, structure, or existing terminology. This idea is critically important in any discussion of XBRL. The original creators of the language could not possibly have anticipated every term needed by every organization over the course of even a few years—let alone a longer time period.

- *Specification.* Think of a specification as a particular (specific) example of a larger group. For example, "California" is a specification of "United States." Or "goodwill" is a specification of "assets." XBRL is part of a larger group of languages referred to as XML (eXtensible Markup Language). One common feature of all XML specifications is their "extensible" nature; another is their use as "markup" languages. So, XML consists of a series of descriptors added to various kinds of information that help users make sense of the information. As a specification of XML, XBRL is focused on descriptors of business reporting information—most often, accounting information.

- *Taxonomy.* Broadly speaking, a taxonomy is a way to organize knowledge. The table of contents of a book is a taxonomy. If someone asked you about the information contained in a balance sheet, you would likely describe it as "assets, liabilities, and equity." Those three elements of financial statements are a taxonomy—they are a way of grouping items together for ease of presentation and discussion. XBRL is made up of several taxonomies, which, for the most part, are focused on specific industry groups. For example, the terminology that describes financial information in a manufacturing firm (such as material, labor, overhead, work in process) has some significant differences from financial terminology in a government entity (fund, encumbrance).

- *Namespace.* If you were reading and ran across a word you didn't know, where would you look to find its meaning? Probably a dictionary—online or in book form. A namespace is like an XBRL dictionary. Remember what the "X" stands for: *extensible.* So, if someone invents a new XBRL term (i.e., extends XBRL), he or she has to let others know what it means. The meaning (definition) of the new term would reside in a namespace. Namespaces have Internet addresses (URLs) just like Web pages. For example, the namespace for the 2012 US GAAP Financial Reporting Taxonomy is http://xbrl.fasb.org/us-gaap/2012/.

- *Instance document.* An instance document is a specific example of properly tagged XBRL information. For example, a publicly traded company like Microsoft might mark up its balance sheet with XBRL tags. The balance sheet, then, would be an instance document.

Those five terms will come up again as you read the chapter. You might find it helpful to mark these pages in some way in case you need to refer back to them later. Table 9.1 summarizes the five terms with some examples of each.

**TABLE 9.1**
**Basic XBRL Terminology**

| Term | Definition | Example |
|---|---|---|
| Extensible | The quality of XBRL that allows users to add tags | Components of the income statement item labeled "Other Revenue" |
| Specification | A specific example of a broader class of objects | XBRL is a specification of XML, the eXtensible Markup Language |
| Taxonomy | A way to organize knowledge | XBRL US GAAP Taxonomy 2009 |
| Namespace | The Internet location of an XBRL taxonomy | http://xbrl.us/us-gaap/2008-10-31 |
| Instance document | A document that includes data properly tagged with XBRL | Microsoft's income statement for the year ended 30 June 2013 |

# HISTORY AND STRUCTURE

Take a look at this number:

305.36.10

What do you suppose it means? If you're like most students, you're thinking "it could mean anything!" The problem is you don't have any *context* for interpreting the number. On the other hand, if I provide you the following facts, the number might make more sense:

- At my university, 305 is the course number for our Advanced AIS class.
- The section of Acc 305 I'm currently teaching has 36 students enrolled.
- The term is 10 weeks long.

Now, extrapolate the difficulty of interpreting a relatively simple number in a relatively easy-to-understand language to the complexity of an accounting information system.

- Organizations can have significantly different structures and titles in their chart of accounts. For example, one company's block coded chart of accounts might assign 110 as the account number for Supplies. But, a hierarchically coded chart of accounts might assign 13.110 as its account number for Supplies.
- Every account in the system has its own balance. Not only will the dollar amounts differ, but the "side" on which you find the balance will be different.
- The balances can be measured in hundreds of world currencies. As I'm working on this chapter, the exchange rate between the dollar and the Euro is 1 USD = 0.74 Euro.
- Some of the numbers in the system reflect results for a period of time, while others reflect position at a point in time. Sales and cost of goods sold, for example, reflect results for a period of time; cash and inventory reflect position at a point in time.
- The numbers in an accounting system can be produced with or without information technology. When information technology is used, the specific hardware and software variations are practically limitless. A small sole proprietorship might use Quickbooks, while a large multinational firm might use the SAP enterprise resource planning system.

## Reflection and Self-Assessment    9.1

Consider the list of complexities inherent in accounting information presented above. Suggest one or two more items that make it difficult to interpret accounting information without some context.

Suppose, for example, ASR Corporation has two divisions: RBE Division in the United States and CLG Division in Mexico. RBE collects and processes accounting information using an enterprise resource planning system; CLG is a much smaller division and keeps its accounting records in Peachtree. At the end of a recent accounting period, RBE sent the following accounting information to corporate headquarters:

| Account Number | Account Title | Balance |
|----------------|---------------|---------|
| 101 | Cash | $80,000 |
| 105 | Accounts receivable | 15,000 |
| 108 | Inventory | 7,000 |

At the same time, CLG sent this information:

| Account Number | Account Title | Balance (pesos) |
|---|---|---|
| 102 | Seguro | 10,000 |
| 107 | Seguridades comerciales | 9,000 |
| 109 | Fuentes | 5,000 |

How could ASR's corporate controller combine the information from RBE and CLG to produce corporate financial statements? One solution might be to reenter all the information into Excel or some other piece of software—but that would be time-consuming and inefficient. In addition, reentering the information creates the risk of making an error that could impact the corporate financial statements.

The need for XBRL arose out of situations like the one described above. XBRL is one application of XML, the eXtensible Markup Language. According to the XBRL Web site (www.xbrl.org), XML "is a standard for the electronic exchange of data between businesses and on the Internet. Under XML, identifying tags are applied to items of data so that they can be processed efficiently by computer software." Let's dissect the pieces of the name *XBRL* to understand it more clearly.

1. XBRL is *extensible*. In other words, users can "extend" the language beyond its original parameters based on their own needs. Certain terms are commonly used in accounting: assets, liabilities, revenue, gross profit, and the like. But suppose a company has its own unique labels for its financial information: revenue from the southern division, gross profit on products, gross profit on services, and similar terms. If XBRL wasn't extensible, users would be "stuck with" whatever labels its creators built into the language. As it stands, users can create their own unique tags for financial data as the need arises.

2. XBRL is for *business reporting*. It is specifically designed to tag and transmit financial information—the kind produced by an accounting information system. Other languages in the XML family include the Resource Description Framework (RDF), Rich Site Summary (RSS), Mathematical Markup Language (MathML), and Scalable Vector Graphics (SVG).

3. XBRL is a *language*. Just like English, French, or Visual Basic, XBRL has its own rules regarding things like syntax and punctuation. Here is an example of how the language looks:

```
<!--Row:10 Property, plant and equipment -->
<iascf-pfs:PropertyPlantEquipment numericContext="Current_AsOf">540000</iascf-pfs:PropertyPlantEquipment>
<iascf-pfs:PropertyPlantEquipment numericContext="Prior_AsOf">400000</iascf-pfs:PropertyPlantEquipment>

<!--Row:11 Investment property-->
<iascf-pfs:InvestmentProperty numericContext="Current_AsOf">150000</iascf-pfs:InvestmentProperty>
<iascf-pfs:InvestmentProperty numericContext="Prior_AsOf">150000</iascf-pfs:InvestmentProperty>

<!--Row:12 Goodwill-->
<iascf-pfs:Goodwill numericContext="Current_AsOf">140000</iascf-pfs:Goodwill>
<iascf-pfs:Goodwill numericContext="Prior_AsOf">150000</iascf-pfs:Goodwill>
```

Keep in mind that the preceding example of XBRL is designed to be read by computers, not people. In fact, the XBRL Web site says: "Ordinary users of XBRL may be largely or totally unaware of the technical infrastructure which underpins the language. However, software companies, such as accountancy software providers, need to take account of XBRL and its features when producing their products." We won't get further into the technical details of XBRL as a language in this text; we'll focus the rest of our discussion on XBRL at a conceptual level.

XBRL, then, is a **specification** of XML. XBRL itself is comprised of several **taxonomies;** taxonomies are developed by professional organizations and industry

## Reflection and Self-Assessment                                    9.2

Point your Web browser to http://www.xbrl.org/FRTaxonomies to see a list of currently approved XBRL taxonomies. Click the link for one of them and prepare a summary of what you find.

groups based on their unique accounting standards and needs. The XBRL Web site defines taxonomies as

> The dictionaries used by XBRL. They define the specific tags for individual items of data (such as "net profit"). Different taxonomies will be required for different financial reporting purposes. National jurisdictions may need their own financial reporting taxonomies to reflect their local accounting regulations. Many different organizations, including regulators, specific industries or even companies, may require taxonomies to cover their own business reporting needs.

Approved US taxonomies include:

- U.S. Accountants' Report Taxonomy 2009
- U.S. Country Taxonomy 2009
- U.S. Currency Taxonomy 2009
- U.S. GAAP Taxonomy 2009

Most current software, such as Microsoft Excel and Great Plains Dynamics, can interpret XBRL tags. Namespaces must be "declared" at the beginning of an XBRL document so the software knows where to look on the Internet for its interpretive rules.

Figure 9.1 shows the relationship between XML, XBRL, and the XBRL taxonomies. The rules and terminology associated with a specific taxonomy reside in a **namespace** on the Internet; that way, XBRL-enabled software can reference the taxonomy simply by locating its namespace.

The XBRL US consortium offers the following explanation of an **instance document** on its Web site (http://xbrl.us/preparersguide/pages/section7.aspx):

> An XBRL instance document is a file designed to be read only by computers. It contains business reporting information representing a collection of company, operating, and financial facts using tags from XBRL taxonomies. Instance documents in use around the world include annual financial statements, earnings releases, bank regulatory reports, and tax forms, all encoded in XBRL using different taxonomies.

Many types of softwares are able to interpret XBRL instance documents, including spreadsheet software and Web browsers.

**FIGURE 9.1**
**Basic XBRL**
**Concepts**

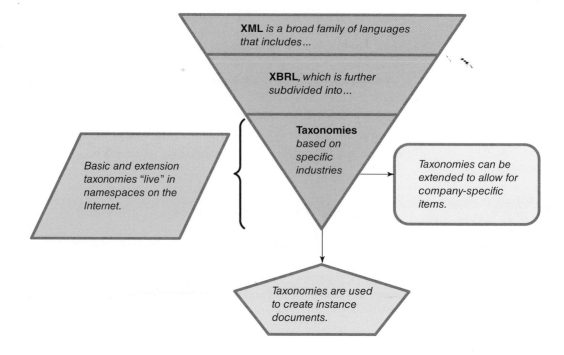

## GLOBAL TAXONOMIES AND TAGGING TOOLS

Many XBRL taxonomies are country-based; that is, approved taxonomies in the United States are different from approved taxonomies in, for example, China or Ireland. But two taxonomies cut across national borders: the International Financial Reporting Standards (IFRS) taxonomy and the Global Ledger (GL) taxonomy.

As stated on the IFRS Foundation Web site (www.ifrs.org):

> The IFRS Taxonomy is the XBRL representation of IFRSs, including international accounting standards (IASs), interpretations, and the IFRS for Small and Medium-Sized Entities (SMEs), issued by the IASB. The IFRS Taxonomy contains tags for all IFRS disclosures. By providing the IFRS Taxonomy, the IFRS Foundation seeks to address the demand for an electronic standard to transmit IFRS financial information. Like the IFRS Bound Volume, the IFRS Taxonomy is released once a year to incorporate new IFRSs, improvements to existing IFRSs, and also changes in XBRL technology.

Like all XBRL taxonomies, the IFRS Taxonomy can be extended as needed to create instance documents.

The Global Ledger taxonomy, commonly known as XBRL-GL, helps organizations manage internal information. According to the XBRL Web site discussion of XBRL-GL, "the XBRL Global Ledger taxonomy allows the representation of anything that is found in a chart of accounts, journal entries or historical transactions, financial and non-financial. It does not require a standardized chart of accounts to gather information, but it can be used to tie legacy charts of accounts and accounting detail to a standardized chart of accounts to improve communications within a business." Like other XBRL taxonomies, XBRL-GL cuts across organization types, hardware/software combinations, and languages. As stated earlier, all SEC filings, such as 10-Q and 10-K forms, must be done with XBRL; if you access the SEC's EDGAR database, XBRL-based filings will be marked "Interactive Data."

The process of creating XBRL instance documents is largely automated. You can check out http://www.xbrl.org/tools-and-services for examples of tagging software. The use of tagging software doesn't eliminate the need to understand the purpose, nature, and structure of XBRL, any more than the use of general ledger software eliminates the need to understand principles of debit and credit, the accounting cycle, and the purpose and structure of financial statements. Rather, tagging software is a tool that helps organizations tag their documents more efficiently than they could with manual coding.

## ORGANIZATIONAL BENEFITS

Fundamentally, XBRL helps organizations in two major ways. First, it allows for more efficient data collection and reporting. Consider, for example, a corporate controller in an international organization. The controller would be receiving reports from all over the world that are prepared using a multitude of software packages. If all the information came into the controller's office with appropriate XBRL tags, it could be collected and summarized quickly and easily, then reported to both internal and external stakeholders in a relatively short time.

Second, XBRL facilitates data consumption and analysis. Using XBRL, our corporate controller can collect data and report information much more quickly and easily—leaving more time for analysis and interpretation. Additionally, XBRL-tagged documents can be searched for specific kinds of information, such as sales revenue by geographic region.

The XBRL Web site lists 10 specific benefits organizations can derive from implementing this important new technology:

- Save costs by preparing data in one form and automatically generating many outputs. Companies will avoid re-keying of data and other manual tasks.
- Consolidate results across divisions and subsidiaries with much greater speed and reliability.
- Improve accuracy and reliability of financial data.
- Focus effort on analysis, forecasting, and decision making, rather than on laborious tasks in gathering, compiling, and preparing data.
- Achieve quicker and more efficient decisions.
- Make more effective use of the internet in communicating with investors. Companies will benefit from the growing importance of web sites as a means of communication.
- Improve investor relations through provision of more transparent and user-friendly information.
- Simplify the process and reduce the costs involved in regulatory reporting to tax and other authorities.
- Obtain quicker responses from counterparties, including banks and regulators.
- Free themselves from proprietary systems and software which are difficult and costly to replace.

As accountants, we can benefit from XBRL as well. Again, XBRL International cites the following advantages for accountants using XBRL:

- Obtain more rapid and reliable data on company financial performance.
- Greatly reduce effort and costs in gathering and analyzing data.
- Simplify and automate tasks.
- Focus effort on analysis and value-added work.
- Make better use of software to improve efficiency and speed.

Consider how general ledger software, such as Sage 50 Complete Accounting, automated many manual tasks commonly associated with the accounting cycle. XBRL accomplishes a similar goal, leaving accounting professionals free to participate more in planning and decision making. The XBRL Web site also identifies specific advantages for other kinds of organizations and groups of financial information professionals.

## INTERNAL CONTROL

First, a bit of review. In general, internal control has four main purposes: safeguard assets, ensure reliable financial statements, encourage adherence to management directives, and promote operating efficiency. COSO's Internal control—Integrated Framework comprises five parts: control environment, risk assessment, control activities, information and communication, and monitoring.

What risks, then, do organizations face when they use XBRL? Consider the list below:

- XBRL moves data between and within information systems electronically. Therefore, the data are subject to theft, loss, and manipulation in the same ways all electronic data are.
- XBRL tagging, while not complex, is detail oriented. So, the coding process is subject to the risk that humans will make errors in coding.
- Since XBRL is so technology dependent, we also must consider the risks of hardware and software failure in an XBRL environment.

Table 9.2 summarizes a few risks and related control activities associated with XBRL.

Does XBRL create new risks for organizations that adopt it? Yes. But, with strong internal controls (such as those listed below), the benefits of adopting XBRL far outweigh its associated costs and risks.

**TABLE 9.2**
**Risks and Control Activities Associated with XBRL**

| Risks | Potential Control Activities |
|---|---|
| Compromised data | Daily data backups, firewalls, mandatory password changes, "strong" password requirements, password-protected access, virus protection software |
| Tagging errors | Electronic tagging (rather than manual), independent review after tagging (e.g., by internal auditors), periodic user training |
| Hardware and software failure | Disaster recovery plans, physical security (e.g., locked doors, alarms), uninterruptible/backup power supplies |
| Inappropriate/missing authorizations | Internal audit review of selected transactions, periodic user training, up-to-date procedures manuals |
| Selection of an inappropriate taxonomy | Periodic review and approval of taxonomies used, centralized approval process for taxonomy extensions |

# CRITICAL THINKING

For this chapter's critical thinking exercise, let's consider the steps involved in creating an XBRL instance document. Many organizations use XBRL tagging software as an add-on to a spreadsheet, such as Microsoft Excel. Although the process might vary slightly across organizations, the basic steps are:

1. Download the data to Excel.
2. Download the relevant taxonomy.
3. Map the data to the taxonomy; that is, determine which tags are associated with which data.
4. Tag the data with appropriate tagging software.
5. Validate the document.
6. File the document appropriately (e.g., with the SEC).

A flowchart of those steps might look like Figure 9.2.

Notice that the accounting information system is represented as a database. Its data would be stored in several tables; you would use queries to calculate account balances. XBRL taxonomies are also databases—just more complex ones. The taxonomy database would likely have a table for each separate taxonomy, such as the XBRL US Currency Taxonomy 2009. (You'll find more taxonomies listed on XBRL International's Web page.) In each individual table, you might find two columns: one for the actual tag and one for the data associated with it.

**FIGURE 9.2**
**Systems Flowchart of XBRL Instance Document Creation Process**

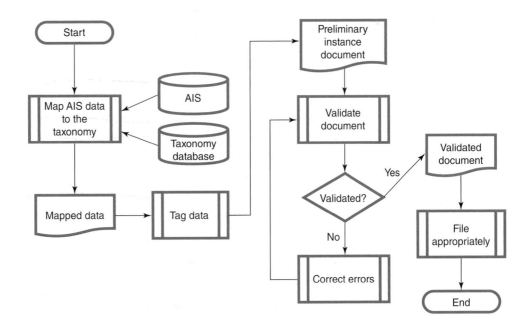

**Summary**

Here is a summary of the chapter's main points for your review:

1. *Define the following terms as they relate to XBRL:* extensible, specification, taxonomy, namespace, *and* instance document.
   a. *Extensible:* The characteristic of XBRL that allows users to create new tags as the need arises.
   b. *Specification:* Describes the relationship between XBRL and its parent language (XML). XBRL is a specification (example) of the eXtensible Markup Language.
   c. *Taxonomy:* The organizational unit of XBRL. Taxonomies typically are linked to industry groups, such as commercial and industrial or investment management.
   d. *Namespace:* An XBRL dictionary. This is an Internet location that defines some of the tags used in a taxonomy.
   e. *Instance document:* A specific example of properly tagged XBRL information.

2. *Explain the history and structure of XBRL.* The eXtensible Business Reporting Language grew out of a need for increased efficiency in collecting, analyzing, and reporting financial information. XBRL is one specification of XML, the eXtensible Markup Language. XBRL comprises several approved taxonomies that are used to create individual instance documents.

3. *Discuss ways XBRL can benefit organizations.* XBRL allows organizations to collect data from disparate accounting systems, combining it quickly and easily. It smoothes the data collection process and automates many tasks previously completed by hand. Just as general ledger software allowed accountants to automate many repetitive tasks, XBRL helps managers accomplish the same goal. Automating tedious tasks such as consolidating financial statements provides more time for analysis and decision making.

4. *Identify software tools for creating XBRL-tagged documents.* Accountants can avail themselves of a plethora of software tools for creating XBRL-tagged documents. Tagging software does not replace human judgment on preparing instance documents. Rather, it is a tool that makes such preparation more efficient and less tedious.

5. *Discuss internal control issues for XBRL.* XBRL exposes an organization to many risks commonly associated with any information technology. Internal controls to combat those risks include proper authorizations and approvals, periodic user training, virus protection software, password procedures, and up-to-date procedures manuals.

XBRL is here to stay. It provides a language for understanding financial information that transcends national borders, differences in GAAP, languages, currencies, and software packages.

**Key Terms**

| | | |
|---|---|---|
| benefits, *169* | namespace, *167* | taxonomies, *167* |
| instance document, *167* | specification, *167* | XBRL, *163* |

**Chapter References**

XBRL International, www.xbrl.org.
IFRS Foundation, www.ifrs.org
XBRL US, www.xbrl.us

## End-of-Chapter Activities

1. *Reading review questions.*

   a. What is XBRL? How is it related to XML?

   b. Define the following terms related to XBRL: *specification, taxonomy, instance document.*

   c. How can XBRL benefit organizations?

   d. Will most accountants need to learn to write "code" in XBRL? If not, how can they create XBRL-tagged documents?

   e. Respond to the questions for this chapter's "AIS in the Business World."

2. *Reading review problem.* Your old friend, Bumble Beasley, just completed his accounting degree at Dewey, Cheatham and Howe University. Although he studied XBRL in several of his accounting and information systems courses, he's not really sure he has mastered the topic. In talking with you, Bumble made the following statements:

   a. XBRL is a new set of accounting principles that everyone must use, similar to the International Financial Reporting Standards (IFRS).

   b. The Securities and Exchange Commission encourages companies to use XBRL when they file forms like 10-K and 10-Q.

   c. Different organizations may use different taxonomies depending on where they are located and what type of company they are.

   d. If a taxonomy does not include an appropriate tag for a specific company, the company cannot use XBRL.

   e. The risks associated with using XBRL must be mitigated with internal controls unique to XBRL; existing controls cannot be adapted for that purpose.

   f. Since the tagging process is automated, most accounting professionals will never prepare an instance document manually.

   g. XBRL should only be used by publicly traded corporations that must file with the SEC in its EDGAR database.

   h. In the EDGAR database, instance documents are labeled "interactive data."

   i. An XBRL namespace is a file on a company's main computer server; it cannot be accessed by people outside the company.

   j. No relationship exists between XBRL and relational database concepts.

   Consider each of Bumble's statements. Determine whether each one is true; for those that are not true, indicate why.

3. *Multiple choice review questions.* Please select the best answer for each question.

   1. XBRL is:

      a. A new GAAP standard that must be used for SEC filings.

      b. A tool for labeling financial information and providing context for it.

      c. Owned by the SEC.

      d. All of the above.

   2. As the term is used in XBRL, a namespace is:

      a. A URL created by a company that wants to extend XBRL.

      b. A dictionary for finding definitions of new XBRL terms.

      c. Both a and b.

      d. Neither a nor b.

   3. Tagging software:

      a. Is a requirement for using XBRL.

      b. Removes the need for human judgment from XBRL coding.

      c. Often functions as an add-on to other software.

      d. All of the above.

4. Implementing XBRL entails some risks for organizations; internal controls are needed to address those risks. Which of the following correctly pairs a risk with an internal control that addresses it?

   a. Hardware failure, disaster recovery plan.

   b. Compromised data, electronic tagging.

   c. Tagging errors, mandatory password changes.

   d. Software failure, internal audit review.

5. In the SEC's EDGAR database, documents that have been tagged with XBRL are labeled as:

   a. Tagged data.

   b. Contextualized data.

   c. Taxonomies.

   d. Interactive data.

4. *Making choices and exercising judgment.* Point your Web browser to www.xbrl .squarespace.com. Summarize the information you find there, and evaluate it using the UMUC criteria discussed in Chapter 1.

5. *Field work.*

   a. In the April 2013 issue of the *Journal of Accountancy*, read "A Tour of Five XBRL Tools" by Wenger, Elam and Williams. (You'll find a link to the article in the 4 February 2014 post on my AIS blog.) Choose two or three of the software packages discussed in the article; apply the software evaluation methodology discussed earlier in the text. As your evaluation criteria, use cost (weight = 5), ease of use (weight = 3), and support services (weight = 2).

   b. Consult the 4 February 2014 post on my AIS blog. Using the link provided, complete KPMG's free XBRL tutorial; prepare a summary of what you learned to discuss in class.

6. *Contextual categories of XBRL.* The purpose of XBRL is to provide a context for understanding financial information. Several contextual categories associated with financial information are listed below; for each category listed, give at least two examples of how it might vary across organizations and financial reporting systems. The first item is done as an example.

   a. Type of balance: debit, credit

   b. Time period

   c. Currency

   d. Account type

   e. Accounting rules (i.e., GAAP)

   f. Reporting language

   g. Preparation tools

7. *XBRL tagging.* Read "Six Steps to XBRL" by Phillips, Bahmanziari, and Colvard in the February 2008 issue of *Journal of Accountancy.*

   a. Is XBRL relevant to companies that don't file with the SEC? Justify your response.

   b. List the six steps the authors recommend for creating XBRL-tagged documents.

   c. How many XBRL-tagged filings did the SEC receive as part of its voluntary program?

8. *Benefits of XBRL.* Fill in the blanks below with terminology that describes the benefits of XBRL for organizations and accountants.

   a. Consolidate results across ___ with much greater speed and reliability.

   b. Focus effort on ___, rather than on laborious tasks in ___ data.

 c. Free themselves from ___ and software that are difficult and costly to replace.

 d. Greatly reduce ___ in ___.

 e. Improve ___ through provision of more ___ information.

 f. Make better use of ___ to improve ___.

 g. Make more effective use of the ___ in ___.

 h. Obtain ___ data on company financial performance.

 i. Save costs by ___ and automatically generating many ___.

 j. Simplify the process and reduce the costs involved in ___ to tax and other authorities.

9.  *Terminology.* Please match each item on the left with the most appropriate item on the right.

| | |
|---|---|
| 1. Context | a. The quality of XBRL that allows users to add tags as needed |
| 2. Cost savings and improved investor relations | b. The relationship between XBRL and the Extensible Markup Language |
| 3. Extensible | c. US GAAP 2009, for example |
| 4. IFRS taxonomy | d. www.xbrl.org/TaxonomyRecognition/MIX/2009.xsd, for example |
| 5. Instance document | e. Microsoft's balance sheet, labeled as "interactive data" in EDGAR |
| 6. Namespace | f. What XBRL provides for financial information |
| 7. Periodic review and approval of taxonomies used | g. An XBRL taxonomy focused on the chart of accounts, journal entries, and similar items |
| 8. Specification | h. Released annually with updates to XBRL and relevant accounting principles |
| 9. Taxonomy | i. Benefits of XBRL |
| 10. XBRL-GL | j. An internal control for XBRL |

10.  *Multiple choice questions.* This series of questions deals with XBRL's Global Ledger taxonomy. Before attempting to answer them, point your Web browser to the 4 February 2014 post in my AIS blog on XBRL. Use the link provided to access the presentation titled "Key Features of XBRL-GL." Reference those slides as you answer the following questions.

 1. XBRL-GL follows information:

  a. From an initial transaction directly to financial reporting.

  b. From operational systems to transaction recording.

  c. From initial transaction through operational systems to reporting.

  d. From a taxonomy to a namespace.

 2. How does XBRL-GL relate to tax filings?

  a. It provides supporting data to substantiate the filing.

  b. It eliminates the need for tax software like Turbo Tax.

  c. It ensures error-free tax reporting.

  d. All of the above.

 3. Operational systems that tie into an organization's general ledger include all of the following except:

  a. Project accounting.

  b. View-driven AIS.

  c. Accounts payable.

  d. Fixed assets.

4. The URL gl.iphix.net presents:

   a. The global ledger taxonomy specifications.

   b. Instructions for extending the global ledger taxonomy.

   c. A summary of how operational systems feed into the general ledger.

   d. Material to help people learn more about XBRL-GL.

5. Which of the following statements is most true?

   a. XBRL cannot be adapted for use in filing tax returns.

   b. XBRL without XBRL-GL does not go deep enough to support tax audit processes.

   c. XBRL-GL is unrelated to SOX and IFRS recordkeeping.

   d. All of the above statements are true.

11. *Statement evaluation.* Indicate whether each of the following statements is (i) always true, (ii) sometimes true, or (iii) never true. For those that are (ii) sometimes true; explain when the statement is true.

    a. All necessary XBRL tags were developed by the XBRL Consortium.

    b. Companies must use software to prepare XBRL instance documents.

    c. Companies that do business in a single country do not need XBRL.

    d. Diversified organizations should use XBRL.

    e. General ledger software can create XBRL tags.

    f. Organizations that adopt XBRL must create their own namespace.

    g. Publicly traded companies must use XBRL for SEC reporting.

    h. XBRL adopters must create specific internal controls for XBRL.

    i. XBRL is a nonproprietary system.

    j. Only general purpose financial statements can be formatted as XBRL instance documents.

12. *Prior material application.* You'll see a problem of this type in every chapter from here through the end of the text. In these problems, you'll be considering the relationship between the current chapter's material (XBRL in this case) and material discussed in earlier chapters (such as transaction processing, internal controls, and systems documentation). My goal in including problems like these is to encourage you not to do a "memory dump" as you finish each chapter. These problems should also help you develop your critical thinking skills.

    a. Earlier in the text, you learned that most AIS have five generic parts. The chapter talked about internal controls related to XBRL; give an example of each additional part related to XBRL. (For example, a 10-K report to the SEC would be an example of an AIS output.)

    b. When an organization incurs a cost, it can be recorded in one of two basic ways in the AIS: It can be debited to an asset (capitalized), as when a company buys a piece of equipment, or it could be debited to an expense (expensed), as with salaries. Suppose a company hired a consultant to help with XBRL implementation. If the company expects to use XBRL for at least five years, should the cost of the consultant be capitalized or expensed? Use the FASB conceptual framework to justify your response.

    c. In our discussion of management concepts, you read about Vroom's expectancy theory, which helps us understand and analyze motivation in organizations. With respect to an XBRL project, someone with low expectancy might say: "Why should I invest the time and energy to learn about XBRL? I'm lousy with computer stuff, and I probably can't learn it anyway." Create a similar statement for the other two elements of expectancy theory (instrumentality and valence). Then, explain how you would improve someone's motivation by addressing each objection.

d. The systems development life cycle comprises seven steps; the development and implementation of XBRL is a systems development project. Work with a group of students to develop a paper/presentation that explains how the SDLC would apply to an XBRL project. For example, the initiation/planning phase might begin when the CFO attends an XBRL workshop/presentation.

13. *Excel application.* Consider the following data from BNF Corporation's statement of cash flows for the quarter ended 31 March 2014:

| | |
|---|---|
| Cash received from issuance of capital stock | $ 9,499 |
| Cash received from customers | 9,215 |
| Cash received from sale of marketable securities | 7,448 |
| Cash loaned as notes receivable | (5,265) |
| Cash paid for inventory | (5,676) |
| Cash paid to retire long-term bonds | (8,427) |
| Cash paid to employees | (9,805) |

a. Group the cash flows listed into the three categories found on the statement of cash flows. Use a formula to calculate the total for each category. (Check figure: the last group total = $1,072)

b. Using the link in the 4 February 2014 post on my AIS blog, find the XBRL tags for the three categories on the statement of cash flows.

## Chapter Ten

# E-business and Enterprise Resource Planning Systems

## AIS in the Business World

### Amazon

If there's one company in the world known for its presence in the e-business industry, it's Amazon. From its founding by Jeff Bezos in 1994, when it sold books online, Amazon has burgeoned into a comprehensive "e-tailer," selling everything from books to automobile parts. And, the company must be doing something right; as I look up Amazon's stock price in February 2014, it's just over $360/share.

Amazon Cloud is one part of the company's overall operations. Cloud drives allow users to store virtually any file remotely, accessing it from almost anywhere on the planet with desktop computers, smart phones, tablets, and similar devices. Customers looking for an enterprise resource planning (ERP) system can access that service as part of Amazon Cloud. Doing so makes Amazon an application service provider—a company that "rents" software and other capabilities to its clients, as opposed to the client buying the software/capability outright.

In this chapter, we'll look at those three important and interrelated topics: e-business, ERP systems, and application service providers. We'll draw on what you've already learned about relational databases and internal control so you'll be able to see the connection between those topics and AIS.

### *Discussion Questions*

1. What are the defining features, advantages, and disadvantages of the e-business platform?
2. How does an ERP system provide better, more useful information for decision making in organizations?
3. How is the modular structure of most ERP systems similar to a relational database?
4. What internal control issues arise when an organization ventures into e-business? When it installs an ERP system? When it uses application service providers in its operations?
5. What is SSAE 16?

E-business systems have become a fact of life in most sectors of the economy; we truly live in a networked world. Think of all the ways information technology impacts your life today, from the hundreds of television and radio stations available via satellite, to the process of registering for classes and ordering textbooks at your university, to the ways you've done research and completed assignments for your AIS class.

When you've finished studying this chapter, you should be able to:

1. Explain the nature of e-business, comparing and contrasting it with traditional "brick-and-mortar" organizations.
2. Discuss major forms of e-business, including business-to-business, consumer-to-consumer, business-to-consumer, government-to-business, and government-to-consumer.
3. Describe the basic nature, purpose, and structure of enterprise resource planning systems.
4. Give examples and analyze the causes of ERP system failures.
5. List and discuss steps associated with successful ERP implementations.
6. Discuss the role of application service providers in e-business.

We'll relate some material in this chapter to your prior study of relational databases; in addition, some of the material "looks ahead" to our discussion of auditing. The topics in this chapter can also be considered in the context of the AICPA Core Competency Framework.

# E-BUSINESS

*We'll use the terms e-business and e-commerce interchangeably throughout this chapter.*

Encarta (www.encarta.msn.com) offers the following definition of e-business:

> **E-commerce** is the exchange of goods and services by means of the Internet or other computer networks. E-commerce follows the same basic principles as traditional commerce—that is, buyers and sellers come together to exchange goods for money. But rather than conducting business in the traditional way—in stores and other "brick-and-mortar" buildings or through mail order catalogs and telephone operators—in e-commerce buyers and sellers transact business over networked computers.

The central feature of e-business is business is transacted over computer networks. Completing business transactions over **computer networks** offers many costs and benefits, including those summarized in the following table. The next few paragraphs look at how Amazon has taken advantage of the benefits of e-business.

| Benefits of E-business | Costs of E-business |
|---|---|
| • Marketing: geographic market expansion, hard-to-reach markets, more targeted marketing | • Financial costs associated with setting up networks |
| • Reduced operating costs: marketing, telecommunications, transaction processing | • Need to develop different, better internal control systems |
| • Streamlined operations | • Potential for customer distrust |
| • Quicker, easier product and service delivery | • Severe consequences for technology breakdowns |

From a *marketing* point of view, e-business allows companies to reach customers they might never be able to contact in a traditional brick-and-mortar operation. According to MarketingPlan.net (2014), Amazon's marketing strategy is based on six pillars:

1. It freely proffers products and services.
2. It uses a customer-friendly interface.

3. It scales easily from small to large.

4. It exploits its affiliate's products and resources.

5. It uses existing communication systems.

6. It utilizes universal behaviors and mentalities.

By following those six principles, Amazon has been able to extend its marketing reach across the planet.

E-business also can help organizations *reduce their operating costs.* Think of all the costs Amazon avoids by not having traditional "brick-and-mortar" buildings like its competitors (e.g., Barnes & Noble): purchase price/lease payments, depreciation, utilities, and many others.

Companies also can *streamline their operations* using e-business. As noted by Mangalindan (2012):

> The Seattle-based online book store transformed itself into an e-commerce giant by developing a gospel of saving that informs everything from its operations to its brand identity and new products like the Kindle Fire tablet. "Cost-cutting is the corner-stone of Amazon," says RJ Hottovy, director of equity research at Morningstar. Because the firm doesn't suffer the costs of maintaining real-world stores, it has been able to charge consumers less.

And, much of the impact of Amazon's cost reductions are passed along to its customers in the form of lower prices.

Finally, e-business can promote *quicker, easier product and service delivery.* Amazon is able to deliver its products and services very quickly—often instantaneously, in the case of items like online books and music. Late in 2013, Amazon announced a somewhat controversial plan to explore the use of drones as product delivery mechanisms; if that venture is successful, Amazon may be able to accomplish that goal even more quickly.

Of course, almost everything in business that has a benefit also involves a cost. Organizations that are just starting their venture into e-business may experience *significant financial costs* associated with developing, purchasing, and configuring software and hardware to support the e-business operation. In addition, e-business systems necessarily require different kinds of *internal controls* than brick-and-mortar operations. Such controls would probably include customer identity authentication via usernames and passwords. Many e-business operations also require customers to input the "control number" from the back of a credit card. A control number is typically a three-digit number printed next to the card number itself, above the signature panel on the back of the card. Billing addresses must match the credit card company's records as a preventive internal control as well. Most companies engaged in e-business operations also process their transactions using a secure server dedicated to that purpose. You may have seen the VeriSign logo on Web pages, indicating an added layer of security for online transactions.

The AICPA's WebTrust and SysTrust projects also provide extra security. The AICPA Web site (http://infotech.aicpa.org) offers the following comments about trust services, WebTrust, and SysTrust:

You can get more information about both services at www.cpawebtrust.org.

> Trust Services (including WebTrust® and SysTrust®) are defined as a set of professional assurance and advisory services based on a common framework (that is, a core set of principles and criteria) to address the risks and opportunities of IT. Trust Services principles and criteria are issued by the Assurance Services Executive Committee of the AICPA.
>
> WebTrust is the accounting profession's answer to concerns relating to electronic commerce. WebTrust is based on Trust Services Principles and Criteria, which constitute professional guidance and serve as best practices for electronic commerce. Using these Principles and Criteria either separately or in combination, CPAs can offer a range of advisory and assurance services to help either clients or employers address security, online privacy, availability, and confidentiality needs.

SysTrust is the accounting profession's answer to concerns relating to system reliability. SysTrust is based on the Trust Services Principles and Criteria, which constitute professional guidance as well as serving as best practices for system reliability. Using these Principles and Criteria either separately or in combination, CPAs can offer a range of advisory and assurance services to help either clients or employers address their security, availability, processing integrity, and confidentiality needs.

Data encryption is another common internal control found in e-business systems. With data encryption, the party that receives data over the Internet must have a decryption key to make it understandable; without encryption, computer criminals can use high-tech techniques to intercept data as they are transmitted electronically. Finally, e-business systems also can incorporate their own form of segregation of duties. You may recall reading about segregation of duties earlier in the text; for any asset, three important responsibilities should be vested in three different people: physical custody, authorization for use, and recordkeeping. In e-business operations, designers can restrict access to various parts of the system based on organizational level and/or job function. For example, faculty members can access certain student information that is unavailable to others at a university.

Beyond the development and internal control costs of e-business, doing business online can create significant amounts of *customer distrust*—particularly for customers who are accustomed to doing business in a traditional brick-and-mortar context. Perhaps you know someone who simply refuses to buy things on the Internet because of concerns over data security and related issues. Finally, the effects of *technology breakdowns* can be severe in an e-business environment: Loss of customer confidence, lost sales, overloaded customer service phone lines, and generalized damage to a company's reputation are just a few.

## Reflection and Self-Assessment                                    10.1

How has Amazon experienced the costs of e-business in its own operations?

Business professionals and researchers have developed many taxonomies, or **e-business categories,** to describe e-business. I've generally found it helpful to classify e-businesses by the parties they connect, leading to a five-part classification system:

| Type | Abbreviation | Example |
|---|---|---|
| Business-to-consumer | B2C | Travelocity |
| Business-to-business | B2B | Dell Computers |
| Government-to-consumer | G2C | Internal Revenue Service |
| Government-to-business | G2B | EDGAR (SEC) |
| Consumer-to-consumer | C2C | eBay |

You may have experienced examples of one or more categories of e-business as a consumer. For example, if you've ever purchased anything online, you've been a part of a B2C transaction. C2C transactions are associated with organizations like eBay (www.ebay .com), where people deal with each other directly in selling goods and services. B2B transactions take place when two organizations do business over a computer network; for example, your university bookstore may use e-business techniques to order textbooks from publishers each semester.

Suggest one other specific example for each of the five categories presented in the table above.

Government at all levels is moving head on into the networked economy as well. For example, the Internal Revenue Service (www.irs.gov) provides a lot of information to taxpayers on its Web site; taxpayers also can file their taxes electronically there. And the U.S. Securities and Exchange Commission's EDGAR database (www.sec.gov/edgar.shtml) allows publicly traded companies to file their required SEC reports. Investors, researchers, and potential investors also can access companies' documents via EDGAR.

How would e-business impact the accounting information system? Let's go back to the basic model of AIS discussed earlier in the text: inputs, processing tools, storage media, outputs, and internal controls.

We've already discussed a few of the internal controls associated with an e-business environment (data encryption, segregation of duties, access restrictions). From an input perspective, e-business can cut down on the number of paper documents in an accounting information system; it also can shift data entry responsibilities from accounting clerks to customers, since transaction data can be captured directly from a Web site. Consider the process of buying a book from a retail bookstore such as Barnes & Noble. In a brick-and-mortar environment, the steps might include:

1. Customer locates book and brings it to a cash register.
2. Register clerk rings up the sale and provides the customer with a paper receipt.
3. At the end of the day, the register clerk retrieves data on the day's sales from the cash register and transmits them to a corporate office or an accounting department.
4. Clerks in the accounting department make journal entries to record the day's transactions.

Contrast those steps with purchasing a book online, whether from Barnes & Noble, Amazon, or some other company:

1. Customer identifies books and adds them to an electronic "shopping cart."
2. Customer provides billing and shipping information electronically.
3. E-business system creates and posts journal entries and related inventory information in the accounting information system.

The flowchart in Figure 10.1 depicts the brick-and-mortar process. Figure 10.2 shows what the process would look like in an e-business environment.

Purchasing airplane tickets is another business process that has been profoundly streamlined via e-business. In a brick-and-mortar environment, most people who wanted to purchase airline tickets would consult a travel agent. The travel agent would communicate with the airline, then present options to the client. The client would make a choice; the agent would buy the tickets from the airline, sometimes charging an additional fee for the service. The process could often take several days, and paper tickets were required in the overwhelming majority of transactions.

Consider the process you probably follow now if you want to fly. You log on to an airline or travel-related Web site (e.g., www.jetblue.com or www.travelocity.com). You put in the parameters of your travel; the computer searches for tickets and can even compare nearby airports. You submit your payment information on a secure server, and an e-mail arrives in your mailbox confirming the transaction. When you get to the airport, you don't need a paper ticket in most cases.

**FIGURE 10.1**
**Brick-and-Mortar Sales Process**

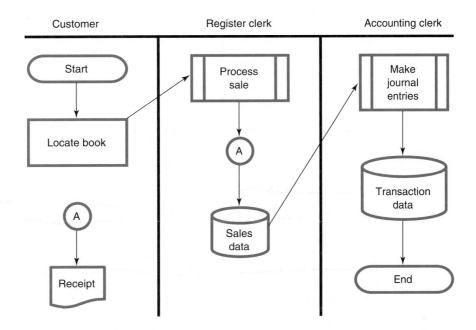

While e-business probably cannot remove the need for human intervention in an accounting information system, it can significantly reduce that need—and all the attendant problems that accompany it (e.g., data entry mistakes, billing problems, incorrect journal entries).

From an output perspective, e-business systems facilitate the preparation of general purpose financial statements and other reports. In an early job in my accounting career, I worked for a heavy-equipment manufacturer with consistently large amounts of outstanding accounts receivable. At the end of each business day, I manually prepared an accounts

**FIGURE 10.2**
**E-business Sales Process**

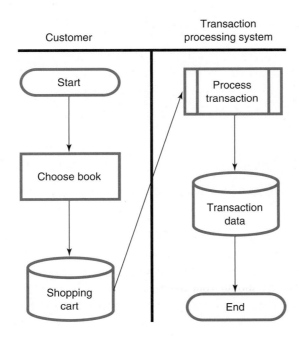

receivable aging, showing each customer's name, balance owed, and length of time the balance had been outstanding. In an e-business system, generating an accounts receivable aging is normally a matter of "pushing a button." The computer does the analysis and prints out the results with little or no human effort.

So, with that very brief overview of e-commerce as background, let's turn our attention to one of the most important, yet most controversial, technologies associated with the networked economy: enterprise resource planning systems.

# ERP SYSTEMS

An **enterprise resource planning system** (ERP) is, at its core, a relational database that provides comprehensive information for making decisions in organizations. Two well-known ERP systems are Oracle's PeopleSoft (www.oracle.com) and SAP (www.sap.com). If your university is part of the SAP University Alliance (scn.sap.com/community/uac), you may be using SAP in your AIS and other courses.

Virtually all ERP systems are organized in modules—separate parts of the program aligned with specific functions of/departments in the organization. Even though the modules are separate, the information they provide can easily be linked via queries and reports, thus allowing decision makers a more holistic view of the organization.

Table 10.1 lists some common ERP system modules, along with some of the components found in SAP.

As a relational database, each component of each module would include several tables, along with forms, queries, and reports. Review Table 10.2 below for some examples.

**TABLE 10.1**
**Modular Organization of ERP Systems**

| Generic Module Name | Primary Stakeholder Group | Module Components in SAP |
|---|---|---|
| Customer relationship management (CRM) | Customers | Sales and distribution |
| Human resource management (HRM) | Employees | Human resources |
| Supply chain management (SCM) | Vendors | Materials management |
| Financial management | Stockholders | Financial accounting |

**TABLE 10.2**
**Database Tables in ERP Systems**

| Generic Module Name | Table Names | Table Primary Key |
|---|---|---|
| Customer relationship management (CRM) | Customer, sales | Customer ID, sales transaction ID |
| Human resource management (HRM) | Employee, pay employees | Employee ID, payroll transaction ID |
| Supply chain management (SCM) | Vendor, inventory | Vendor ID, inventory ID |
| Financial management | Chart of accounts | Account number |

Many organizations have experienced significant difficulty in implementing ERP systems; consider the example below:

> [A major soft drink bottler], which implemented a major ERP system, completed the implementation, but not without losing significant personnel and system functionality. After committing millions of dollars to purchase an ERP software, the soft drink maker tried cutting corners during implementation. Relying too heavily on its own people instead of consultants, the bottler expected too much from its already-taxed employees. Trying to minimize setup costs and reduce expenses, the company overlooked many of the planning team's recommendations regarding the project. This ERP implementation created high turnover and communication problems, which led to the termination of key people and animosity among employees. All of these factors, in turn, led to a system that was grossly underused, and in the beginning, a hindrance to the overall business. (Barker and Frolick, 2003)

Umble and Umble (2002) identified 10 major **causes of ERP implementation failures:**

1. *Poor leadership from top management.* Selecting and installing an ERP system is an enormous undertaking in terms of time, money, and energy. Clear, strong leadership and support from top management are essential for a successful implementation—without them, employees are likely to view the ERP system as just another "initiative du jour."

2. *Automating existing redundant or non-value-added processes in the new system.* An ERP implementation project is a terrific time to reconsider the company's business processes. In other words, do policies, procedures, document flows, and internal controls make sense from a business point of view? Do the processes add value to organizational stakeholders? In most organizations, at least a few policies and processes will need to be changed to make the most of the ERP system. Otherwise, managers will be doing the same, ineffective things—only faster.

3. *Unrealistic expectations.* An ERP system is designed to collect, process, and report data and information for making management decisions more effectively. Systems are not a panacea for problems with organizational culture, poorly designed business processes, or inadequate internal controls. Expecting an ERP system to fix those kinds of problems is a forlorn hope and will seriously jeopardize the project's success.

4. *Poor project management.* ERP system selection, testing, and implementation are time-intensive, long-term projects. To be successful, managers have to apply solid project management techniques for selecting the right people, completing tasks in the right order, and staying on schedule.

5. *Inadequate education and training.* This failure cause is linked to many others in this list. Without good training and education, employees may have unrealistic expectations of what the ERP system can do; they also may see the ERP implementation as solely an information technology project, rather than as an opportunity to analyze business processes and make them better.

6. *Trying to maintain the status quo.* Since an ERP system is such a major undertaking, implementation will almost always create fear and uncertainty throughout an organization. When people are fearful about their job security and future in the firm, they will likely act in very dysfunctional ways, either intentionally or unintentionally. To avoid this problem, be upfront and honest from the start about the purpose and possible results of implementing the ERP system.

7. *A bad match between ERP software and organizational processes.* Every organization has its own ways of doing business. And, while ERP systems can be customized to a degree based on specific organizational contexts, such modifications are time-consuming and expensive. Managers would be well advised to consult with colleagues in the field about which ERP software has worked well, and which has worked poorly, in a specific industry.

8. *Inaccurate data in the system.* As the old saying goes: "garbage in, garbage out." The reports and information generated by an ERP system are only as valid and useful as the data that undergird them. Faulty or inaccurate data in the ERP system can be even worse than the same condition in less-integrated systems, since they will be used throughout the organization for decision making. Once inaccurate data have been discovered in a system, every other prior and future output are called into question until the situation has been resolved.

9. *ERP implementation viewed as an IT project.* As discussed above, implementing an ERP system goes far beyond the information technology requirements. Fundamentally, an ERP project needs to be viewed as holistic, touching not only information technology, but also business processes and organizational behavior issues.

10. *Significant technical difficulties.* Of course, even though an ERP project is not solely concerned with IT issues, some technical problems may arise. Bugs in the software, problems interfacing with existing information systems, and hardware difficulties are just three identified by Umble and Umble.

Similarly, Umble and Umble (2002) discussed six necessary **conditions for a successful ERP implementation:**

1. *Obtain organizational commitment.* This condition speaks most clearly to poor leadership from management and trying to maintain the status quo. The ERP project team needs to get a clear, strong commitment to the project throughout the organization, but especially from the top management. Without a psychological and financial commitment to see the project through to its completion, the project may "lose steam" when encountering difficult problems.

2. *Communicate strategic goals clearly.* This idea also relates to two of the common causes of ERP implementation failure: unrealistic expectations, and inadequate education and training. Employees in all functions at all levels of the organization need to understand the goals of the ERP project—typically, providing better information more quickly for decision making.

3. *View ERP as an enterprise-wide venture.* An ERP system will eventually touch every aspect of operations; therefore, it must be viewed as a company-wide project. If the project is viewed as "just another information technology initiative," managers will lose the opportunity to examine business processes thoughtfully and critically—possibly leading to automating redundant or non value-added processes.

4. *Select a compatible ERP system.* Here, we're talking about items 7 and 10 from the list of common causes of failure: a bad match between ERP software and organizational processes, and significant technical difficulties. The bottom line: Don't believe everything the software vendor or implementation consultants tell you! Do your own research; ask for other companies that have had successful (and unsuccessful) implementations.

5. *Resolve multisite issues.* ERP implementations are inherently complicated. But they become more complicated when an organization is geographically dispersed. The project management plan (see item 4 in the preceding list) must deal specifically with multisite issues.

6. *Ensure data accuracy.* The final key to success in ERP implementation is directly related to item 8 on the previous page. The project team needs to do significant employee education about the importance of accurate data entry; test runs with fictitious data before the system "goes live" also can help achieve this goal.

Many of those conditions were found at Marathon Oil, leading to a successful implementation of SAP ERP software (Stapleton and Rezak, 2004). Marathon used a change-management approach in implementing its ERP system, recognizing that the goal was "the transfer of ownership from the project team that designed and configured the new system and processes to the end users, the internal clients who would employ these tools and processes in their day-to-day operations." Other keys to Marathon's successful experience included constant communication via newsletters, workshops, and hands-on interaction to increase employees' comfort level with the software.

# APPLICATION SERVICE PROVIDERS

Organizations that want to move into an e-business environment have two basic choices for doing so: create applications "from scratch" or hire an **application service provider** (ASP). Jaruzelski, Ribeiro, and Lake (2014) define an ASP as "an organization that provides a contractual service to deploy, host and manage applications for customers remotely from a centralized location."

The ASP industry can be divided into five subcategories:

- Enterprise ASPs—deliver high-end business applications.
- Local/Regional ASPs—supply wide variety of application services for smaller businesses in a local area.
- Specialist ASPs—provide applications for a specific need, such as Web site services or human resources.
- Vertical Market ASPs—provide support to a specific industry such as healthcare.
- Volume Business ASPs—supply general small/medium-sized businesses with prepackaged application services in volume.

COSO's *Enterprise Risk Management—Integrated Framework* discusses ASPs as a form of risk sharing, one way of responding to risks in an organization's environment.
Organizations and individuals have used ASPs to

- Process insurance claims (www.processclaims.com).
- Complete the steps in the accounting cycle (http://www.online50.net/).
- Manage stock market transactions electronically (www.tradingtechnologies.com).
- Provide personal financial planning (www.zywave.com).
- Prepare income tax returns (www.taxslayer.com).

Just as with e-business in general, ASPs offer both benefits and risks to organizations. The table below summarizes a few:

| ASP Benefits | ASP Risks |
| --- | --- |
| Less costly than purchasing software outright | Psychological and behavioral factors |
| Increased flexibility | Service interruptions |
| Potentially improved customer service | Compromised data |
| Role in disaster recovery plans | Inability to pay monthly fees |

Internal controls like those listed below can help address some of those risks:

- Establishing a budget for the ASP project.
- Backing up data on a daily basis.
- Providing ongoing training for employees using the ASP.
- Creating firewalls and encryption protocols.

ASPs, while beneficial for many organizations, can increase the complexity of a financial statement audit. As a result, the American Institute of Certified Public Accountants issued its Statement on Standards for Attestation Engagements No. 16 in April 2010. Officially titled "Reporting on Controls at a Service Organization," SSAE 16 effectively replaced its predecessor, SAS 70.

As stated on the AICPA Web site (www.aicpa.org), "Service Organization Control Reports® are internal control reports on the services provided by a service organization providing valuable information that users need to assess and address the risks associated with an outsourced service."

According to Bourke (2012), SSAE 16 includes three broad types of SOC Reports. The AICPA (2014) differentiates the three as follows:

- SOC 1 reports on controls relevant to user entities internal control over financial reporting
- SOC 2 reports on controls over security, availability, processing integrity, confidentiality, or privacy
- SOC 3 reports, less-detailed but similar to SOC 2 reports

If you want to learn more about SSAE 16 and SOC reports, please check out the 9 February 2014 post on my AIS blog. You'll find links there to Bourke's paper and related resources.

## CRITICAL THINKING

As you may recall from our earlier discussions, a relational database can comprise at least four different types of objects: tables, queries, forms, and reports. And, as stated earlier in this chapter, an ERP system is essentially a very sophisticated relational database. So, for this chapter's critical thinking application, let's consider how a relational database would calculate account balances for the financial statements; we'll use the cash account as an example.

First, consider Figure 10.3. It shows the relationships between three tables with data about cash. The "cash table" has the beginning balance, while the other two have data about activity in the cash account. Notice that the cash table is linked to both the cash receipts and the cash payments table via the account number; the account number is the primary key of the cash table as well as a foreign key in the other two tables.

**FIGURE 10.3**
**Database Relationship Grid**

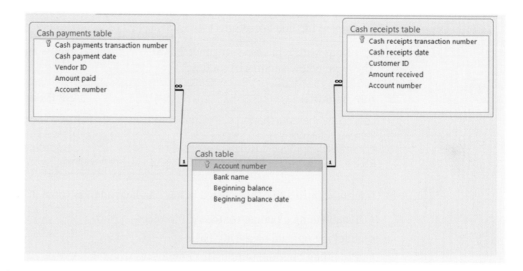

Next, consider Figure 10.4. It shows the design view of two queries that calculate, respectively, the total cash paid and the total cash received.

Finally, in Figure 10.5, we use another query to calculate the balance in cash.

(The spacing in Figure 10.5 simply makes it easier to read.) An ERP system would pull the beginning cash balance from the financial management module. The cash receipts data would likely come from the customer relationship management module, while the cash payments data would originate in the supply chain management module.

Thankfully, an ERP system would have all those queries and computations "built in," so that the end user would not have to construct them from scratch. Similar tools would be used to calculate the remaining account balances for the financial statements. In relational database parlance, each financial statement would be considered a report; the data entry screens, such as the one in Figure 10.6, would be considered forms.

As you work with ERP systems, either in school or in practice, keep in mind that they are essentially relational databases. By applying what you've learned about the latter, you'll have a much better understanding of what's going on "behind the scenes" with the former.

**FIGURE 10.4**
**Query Design Grids**

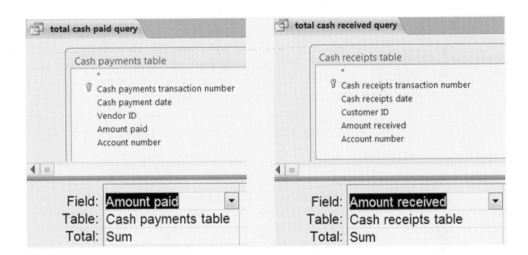

**FIGURE 10.5**
**Expression Builder**

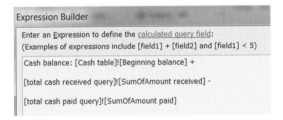

**FIGURE 10.6**
**Data Entry Form**

## Summary

After reading the chapter, I'm confident you can see that e-business and ERP systems, like most other aspects of AIS, are full of judgments—they are almost certainly a blend of "art" and "science," at the very least. Here's a summary of the chapter's main points in terms of its learning objectives:

1. *Explain the nature of e-business, comparing and contrasting it with traditional "brick-and-mortar" organizations.* The essential feature of e-business is the computer network. It is otherwise very similar to traditional businesses in terms of its stakeholder groups, information needs, and organizational structures.

2. *Discuss major forms of e-business, including business-to-business, consumer-to-consumer, business-to-consumer, government-to-business, and government-to-consumer.* E-businesses often are classified by the types of entities connected via computer networks. B2B arrangements partner organizations, such as when a company purchases inventory from a supplier. B2C transactions are characterized by operations such as Travelocity or Amazon. G2B partners government agencies with businesses, as with EDGAR. G2C operations allow consumers to obtain information from the government; consider the Web site of the Internal Revenue Service (www.irs.gov) in this category. C2C sites, like eBay, facilitate business between individuals.

3. *Describe the basic nature, purpose, and structure of enterprise resource planning systems.* An ERP system is a relational database designed to capture data and provide for reports and analyses via queries. Common modules include financial, human resources, vendors, and customer relationships. Popular ERP vendors include Oracle and SAP.

4. *Give examples and analyze the causes of ERP system failures.* ERP implementations fail for one or more of a few common reasons, including poor leadership from top management, failure to analyze business processes thoroughly, unrealistic expectations, poor project management, inadequate education and training, bad match between software and organization, technical problems, and inaccurate data.

5. *List and discuss steps associated with successful ERP implementations.* Successful ERP implementations commonly follow a six-step implementation process: (i) Obtain organizational commitment. (ii) Communicate strategic goals clearly. (iii) View ERP as an enterprisewide venture. (iv) Select a compatible ERP system. (v) Resolve multisite issues. (vi) Ensure data accuracy.

6. *Discuss the role of application service providers in e-business.* Application service providers can facilitate an organization's entry into the networked economy. ASPs deliver a wide range of applications on a subscription or rental basis: managing elements of the human resource function, preparing tax returns, and completing the steps in the accounting cycle. Organizations using ASPs must modify their internal control systems to address the risks they present. The AICPA's SSAE 16 (Statement on Standards for Attestation Engagements 16) explains three types of reports that should be applied when an audit client utilizes an ASP.

Now, please proceed to the end-of-chapter activities assigned by your instructor to get some practical applications of the concepts discussed in this chapter.

## Key Terms

application service provider, *187*
causes of ERP implementation failure, *185*

computer networks, *179*
conditions for a successful ERP implementation, *186*
e-business categories, *181*

e-commerce, *179*
enterprise resource planning system, *184*

## Chapter References

AICPA. 2012. "Service Organization Control Reports." Retrieved 9 February 2014 from www .cpa2biz.com/AST/Main/CPA2BIZ_Primary/AuditAttest/PRDOVR~PC-780281/PC-780281.jsp.

Barker, T., and M. Frolick. 2003. "ERP Implementation Failure: A Case Study." *Information Systems Management,* Fall, pp. 43–49.

Bourke, J. (2012) "Explaining SOC: Easy as 1-2-3." Retrieved 9 February 2014 from www .cpa2biz.com/Content/media/PRODUCER_CONTENT/Newsletters/Articles_2012/CPA/Jun/ Easy123.jsp.

Jaruzelski, B., F. Ribeiro and R. Lake. "ASP 101: Understanding the Application Service Provider Model." Retrieved 9 February 2014 from www.boozallen.com/media/file/ASP_Whitepaper.pdf.

Mangalindan, J.P. 2012. "Amazon's core? Frugality." Retrieved 9 February 2014 from tech.fortune .cnn.com.

MarketingPlan.net. 2014. "Marketing Strategies of Amazon.com." www.marketingplan.net/ amazon-com-marketing-strategies/ (February 9).

Stapleton, G., and C. Rezak. 2004. "Change Management Underpins a Successful ERP Implementation at Marathon Oil." *Journal of Organizational Excellence,* Autumn, pp. 15–22.

Umble, E., and M. Umble. 2002. "Avoiding ERP Implementation Failure." *Industrial Management,* January/February, pp. 25–34. Reprinted with the permission of the Institute of Industrial Engineers. 3577 Parkway Lane, Suite 200, Norcross, GA 30092, 770-449-0461. Copyright © 2002.

## End-of-Chapter Activities

1. *Reading review questions.*

   a. What is the distinguishing characteristic of e-business that makes it different from traditional brick-and-mortar businesses?

   b. The chapter discusses five basic types of e-business arrangements. Identify and describe each one; give an example for each type other than the example in the chapter.

   c. What is an enterprise resource planning system?

   d. What common problems cause ERP implementations to fail? What can managers do to promote successful ERP implementations?

   e. Prepare a response to the questions for this chapter's "AIS in the Business World."

2. *Reading review problem.* This chapter's AIS in the Business World focused on Amazon, but many other companies are also involved in e-business. Consider one of the following as the basis for answering the questions below: Google, Dell, Best Buy.

   a. What forms of e-business does your chosen company engage in?

   b. Which common ERP system modules would the company use to calculate the net sales reported on the income statement? How would they be used?

   c. Could the company you chose be considered an application service provider? Why, or why not?

3. *Multiple choice review.* Please select the best answer for each question.

   1. All of the following are costs associated with e-business except:

      a. Potential for customer distrust.

      b. Financial costs associated with setting up networks.

      c. Need to develop different internal control systems.

      d. REA modeling requirements.

   2. WebTrust and SysTrust are:

      a. Required for e-business.

      b. Always part of an SSAE 16 audit.

      c. Tools for providing security in an e-business environment.

      d. Federal government programs.

3. Which ERP module is most concerned with vendor relationships?

   a. Customer relationship management

   b. Supply chain management

   c. Financial management

   d. Human resource management

4. All of the following are conditions for a successful ERP implementation except:

   a. Thinking of the implementation as an IT project.

   b. Obtaining organizational commitment.

   c. Ensuring data accuracy.

   d. Communicating strategic goals clearly.

5. An application service provider provides HR services for the health care industry. It can be considered:

   a. A specialist, vertical market ASP.

   b. An enterprise, specialist ASP.

   c. A local, specialist ASP.

   d. An enterprise, vertical market ASP.

4. *Making choices and exercising judgment.*

   a. Point your Web browser to www.baselinemag.com. Locate and read "Hershey's Sweet Victory" by David F. Carr. In the blinding light of hindsight, which of the common causes of ERP failure did Hershey experience? What could management have done to avoid those problems?

   b. The e-business model can be applied very effectively in some industries, but not as effectively in others. You may remember early attempts to establish online grocery shopping with companies such as Web Grocer and Net Grocer. Think of another industry where the value of e-business might be considered questionable. Explain your reasoning.

5. *Field work.*

   a. Conduct research into WebTrust and/or SysTrust. Prepare an oral or written report summarizing at least the following items: historical development, nature and purpose of the system, financial and nonfinancial benefits, and costs and examples of companies using the technology. You can start your research at www.webtrust.org.

   b. Visit a company in your geographic area that uses an ERP system. Ask for a demonstration of the system (or at least one part of it) and prepare a brief oral or written presentation to the class on your findings.

   c. As stated in the chapter introduction, the three topics we've examined are related to many parts of the AICPA Core Competency Framework. Choose one of the three topics (e-business, ERP systems, application service providers), and identify at least two related AICPA competencies. Explain how the competencies are related to the area you chose.

6. *Internal controls in e-business.* The chapter mentioned three potential internal controls for an e-business environment: encryption, segregation of duties, and access restrictions. Consider your study of internal controls throughout this text; suggest five additional internal controls for e-business environments. Explain specifically how you would apply them.

7. *Types of computer networks.* As you read in the chapter, the presence of a computer network is the defining characteristic of e-business. Research the topic and define each of the following terms related to networks and networking.

   a. Local area network

   b. Network architecture

   c. Network protocol

   d. Network topology

   e. Node

    f. Server

    g. Wide area network

**8.** *Forms of e-business.* Which category of e-business (B2B, B2C, G2B, or G2C) best describes each of the following items?

    a. Buying materials for professional practice from www.aicpa.org

    b. Electronic reporting of state unemployment taxes

    c. Filing personal income taxes with TaxSlayer.com

    d. Getting medical advice from www.webmd.com

    e. Making appointments with the Department of Motor Vehicles

    f. Online banking

    g. Paying traffic citations online

    h. Purchases from Amazon.com

    i. Receiving the online newsletter from the Institute of Management Accountants

    j. Registration for seminars sponsored by the Association of Certified Fraud Examiners

**9.** *Promoting ERP success.* Choose one of the Fortune 100 companies; investigate it on the Internet and through your university's library. Work with a group of students to prepare a PowerPoint presentation to fulfill the first three of Umble and Umble's six conditions for promoting ERP success (obtain organizational commitment, communicate strategic goals, and view ERP as an enterprisewide venture).

**10.** *Application service providers.*

    a. Companies considering utilizing an ASP might start the process by identifying a need to lower costs and increase flexibility. What other steps would a manager likely take in selecting an ASP? Who should be involved in such a decision?

    b. Refer to www.ssae16.com. Determine which of the following statements are true based on the information provided there:

        i. SSAE 16 outlines four report types for service organization audits.

        ii. The standard is designed to bring the U.S. standard for service organization audits into alignment with the related international standard.

        iii. SSAE 16 superseded SAS 70.

        iv. A Service Auditor's Report can help an organization build trust with its stakeholders.

        v. An SSAE 16 audit is required if a company uses COSO's Internal Control—Integrated Framework.

    c. All professional accounting certifications and licenses (such as the CPA and CFE) require continuing professional education (CPE) on an annual basis. Suppose you and a group of friends started an ASP designed to track CPE requirements for accounting professionals. Design a database that would capture the required information about your clients. What internal controls would you implement to promote the integrity of those data?

**11.** *Terminology.* Please match each item on the left with the best item on the right.

| | | |
|---|---|---|
| 1. Brick-and-mortar | a. | A well-known ERP system |
| 2. Computer network | b. | Another name for "old economy" organizations |
| 3. Financial management | c. | Associated with G2C and G2B e-commerce |
| 4. Hershey | d. | B2C e-commerce example |
| 5. Human resource management | e. | ERP module associated with employees |
| 6. Internal Revenue Service | f. | Had a "not so sweet" experience with ERP |
| 7. Multisite issues | g. | Module in an ERP system associated with stockholders |
| 8. Online banking | h. | Need to be resolved for a successful ERP project |
| 9. PeopleSoft | i. | Technology underlying ERP |
| 10. Relational database | j. | The salient feature of e-business |

**12.** *Multiple choice questions.*

1. The Web site www.sco.ca.gov/upd.html is an example of which form of e-business?

    a. B2C

    b. G2C

    c. G2B

    d. C2C

2. WebTrust and SysTrust are forms of:

    a. Internal control.

    b. E-business.

    c. Systems documentation.

    d. Transaction processing software.

3. In February 2011, Pfizer Inc. authorized a $5 billion program to repurchase shares of its own common stock from investors. Which ERP system module is most likely to be involved in the transactions?

    a. Customer relationship management

    b. Financial management

    c. Supply chain management

    d. Human resource management

4. Which of the following can cause problems in ERP system implementation, internal control design, and enterprise risk management?

    a. Lack of strong positive signals from top management

    b. Assuming staff understand project goals and purposes

    c. Both a and b

    d. Neither a nor b

5. To calculate cost of goods sold for the income statement, an ERP system would access data from all of the following except:

    a. Financial management module

    b. Human resource management module

    c. Customer relationship management module

    d. Supply chain management module

**13.** *Statement evaluation.* Indicate whether each of the following statements is (i) always true, (ii) sometimes true, or (iii) never true. For those that are (ii) sometimes true, explain when the statement is true.

    a. Companies involved in e-business report higher profit margins than traditional companies.

    b. Computer networks are the defining feature of e-business.

    c. E-business expands an organization's geographic markets.

    d. E-business removes the need for human intervention in accounting information systems.

    e. An organization that adopts an ERP system will use that system's financial management module.

    f. Implementing an ERP system ensures that data will be accurate and accessible.

    g. Many enterprise resource planning systems are modular in nature.

    h. Organizations enter into relationships with stakeholders to get the resources they need to operate.

    i. Successful ERP implementations often require business process redesign.

    j. WebTrust and SysTrust can strengthen internal controls in e-business.

**14.** *Prior material application.*

  a. When an organization implements an ERP system or enters into the e-business arena, it is exposed to a variety of risks. Use the COSO ERM framework discussed in Chapter 4 to design a generic risk management plan for one of those two situations.

  b. A small bookstore wants to expand its operations to include e-business. Use the generalized model of business process management discussed in Chapter 4 to develop a plan for doing so.

  c. A business plan is essential for starting an e-business venture. Do some research on how to develop a business plan; you might start by consulting www.sba.gov or by asking a strategy/entrepreneurship professor at your university. Document the steps for developing a business plan using one of the formats discussed in Part Two of the book.

**15.** *Excel application.* Use the indicated Excel formulas to respond to the following independent situations.

  a. *Formula: PMT.* BBT Corporation wants to lease an ERP system for a period of three years. If the total lease price is $50,000, and the ERP vendor charges an interest rate of 3%, how much will BBT pay annually? (Check figure: annual payment should be between $17,000 and $18,000.)

  b. *Formula: RATE.* RDN Corporation wants to lease an ERP system for a period of four years. If the total lease price is $40,000, and RDN's monthly payment is $1,200, what annual interest rate is RDN paying? (Check figure: interest rate is between 15% and 20%.)

  c. *Formula: NPER.* JPD Corporation wants to lease an ERP system with a total lease price of $32,000. If the annual interest rate on the lease is 6% and JPD makes monthly payments of $1,500, how long is the lease? (Check figure: number of periods is between 20 and 25 months.)

# Chapter **Eleven**

# Computer Crime and Information Technology Security

## AIS in the Business World

### Target

In late 2013, Target Stores experienced a major security breach that left many customers vulnerable to identity theft and related crimes. The incident was widely reported in the media, as shown by the following quotes:

> Target says that its stores have been hit by a major credit-card attack involving up to 40 million accounts. Chief Executive Officer Greg Steinhafel confirmed Thursday morning earlier reports that a brazen data breach had taken place. In a statement, Steinhafel said: "Target is working closely with law enforcement and financial institutions, and has identified and resolved the issue." The retailer said that the unlawful access to customer information took place between Nov. 27 and Dec.15. (Eversley and Hjelmgaard, 2013)
>
> Over the past month, details about the breadth of the Target data breach have continued to emerge. It's not a pretty story. Bad enough when it appeared that through some means, hackers had gotten data all the way from credit card swipe machines out the other side of Target's systems, including encrypted pin numbers from debit cards. Then it was announced that other information was also stolen, specifically name, address, phone number and/or email address. (Rosenblum, 2014)

Later investigation revealed that the problem impacted at least 70 million Target customers. This chapter extends our earlier discussion of internal control into the realm of information technology. We'll look at various forms of computer crime, along with tools organizations can use to combat it.

### Discussion Questions

1. What type of computer crime did Target and its customers experience according to Carter's taxonomy?
2. What risk exposures did Target have that allowed the data breach to occur?
3. What principles guide the development and implementation of IT-related internal controls?
4. What role can/should CoBIT play in cases like the one described?

With individuals becoming more than simply computer literate and the emergence of the Internet as a tool for global information exchange, accounting information systems and the information they store and process will increasingly fall victim to computer crime and fraud. Computers also have become facilitators for criminals, providing them with new methods of perpetrating classic forms of crimes and creating many new "business opportunities" for these criminals. This chapter examines many facets of computer crime and fraud: associated risks and threats, the use of accounting information systems, and investigation of computer crime.

When you've finished studying this chapter, you should be able to:

1. Explain Carter's taxonomy of computer crime.
2. Identify and describe business risks and threats to information systems.
3. Discuss ways to prevent and detect computer crime.
4. Explain the main components of the CoBIT framework and their implications for IT security.

Understanding the various types of computer crime will allow you to understand more clearly how the AIS can be affected by common malicious acts. Carter (1995) suggested a four-part **taxonomy for computer crime:**

- *Target.* This category comprises of computer crimes where the criminal targets the system or its data. The objective of these crimes is to impact the confidentiality, availability, and/or integrity of data stored on the computer.
- *Instrumentality.* Computer as the instrumentality of the crime uses the computer to further a criminal end. In crimes *targeting* the computer, the data are the object of the crime; in this case, the computer is used to commit a crime.
- *Incidental.* This type of computer crime encompasses crimes where the computer is not required for the crime but is related to the criminal act. The use of the computer simplifies the criminal actions and may make the crime more difficult to trace.
- *Associated.* The simple presence of computers, and notably the growth of the Internet, has generated new versions of fairly traditional crimes. In these cases, technological growth essentially creates new crime targets and new ways of reaching victims.

The lines between each type of crime can be blurry at times and some criminal transactions may overlap the different types of crimes.

## BUSINESS RISKS AND THREATS TO INFORMATION SYSTEMS

Organizations, both large and small, have come to rely heavily on information systems to provide timely information used in making critical business decisions. As such reliance on information systems grows, so do the risks the organization faces. So, anyone involved in decision making should understand those risks and how they can impact the organization.

We'll discuss the following business **risks and threats:**

- Fraud
- Error
- Service interruption and delays
- Disclosure of confidential information
- Intrusions

- Information theft
- Information manipulation
- Malicious software
- Denial-of-service attacks
- Web site defacements
- Extortion

## Fraud

In 1989, the U.S. Department of Justice defined computer fraud as being any illegal act for which knowledge of computer technology is used to commit the offense. Fundamentally, computer fraud is people fraud; no computer system can perpetrate fraud without at least some human intervention.

Computer skills required will vary greatly depending on the type of fraud being perpetrated. Frauds such as data diddling—the intentional modification of information—require only basic skills; on the other hand, theft of information in a secure database will require more advanced computer skills from the fraudster.

Following a series of scandals and lapses in corporate governance, the Sarbanes-Oxley Act was introduced to restore customer confidence in the stock markets. It was introduced with the firm resolve to increase corporate responsibility and requires that companies establish extensive governance policies to prevent and respond to fraudulent activities. The act and the accompanying SEC regulations require that organizations produce a report of the internal controls it has in place to ensure compliance with the act itself.

## Error

Losses associated with errors can vary widely depending on where the error originated and the time it may take to identify and correct it. A single error when entering a product code will lead to the wrong item being shipped; a programming error in a financial institution's transaction system could lead to a loss of many millions and some very angry customers. Implementing preventive controls that will detect and correct errors before they occur can prevent financial losses and negative impacts to the organization's image.

## Service Interruption and Delays

A delay in processing information or a service interruption can bring an organization to a standstill; such delays can lead to missed deadlines for payables and receivables. Service interruptions can be due to many factors, but they all fall into three main categories: accidental, willful neglect, and malicious behavior. Accidental service interruption can be caused by someone shutting down the wrong machine. Willful neglect could be due to outdated antivirus software; a malicious service interruption could be caused by a hacker launching a denial of service attack against an organization's Web site.

## Disclosure of Confidential Information

The disclosure of sensitive information can have major impacts on an organization's financial health. No organization wishes to imagine its customer or employee data being made available to all on the Internet, but such disclosure has become an important risk for most organizations. Privacy laws have made managers and other stakeholders aware of the critical need to protect information assets.

## Intrusions

The main objective of an intrusion is to gain access to a network or a system by bypassing security controls or exploiting a lack of adequate controls. An intruder's motivations will vary widely: Some hack for profit while others hack for fun. Hackers for profit will often target specific organizations or specific information before beginning their attack; hackers looking for entertainment will often choose "low-hanging fruit": data and/or systems that are relatively unprotected and easy to access.

## Information Theft

This form of computer crime targets the organization's most precious asset: information. Trade secrets, marketing plans, advertising campaigns, research and development data for new products, and customer lists are just a few examples of data in this category. These assets, which are represented in a numeric format, often have a higher value than other traditionally targeted assets, resulting in potentially higher losses for the organizations.

## Information Manipulation

Information manipulation can occur at virtually any stage of information processing, from input to output. Input manipulation in computer systems is probably the most common form of fraud since it is easy to perform, requiring only basic computer skills. Furthermore, it is hard to detect, since the fraudulent input may look valid until an in-depth examination is performed. Such a situation could occur when an employee creates fake refunds in the payables system to benefit a family member.

Program manipulation is a complex task and is extremely difficult to detect as both the modification and detection require advanced computer programming knowledge. Manipulating computer programs involves the modification or insertion of specific functions in the computer information system.

Other forms of manipulation involve taking advantage of the automatic repetitions of a computer program. Such manipulation is characteristic of the "salami technique," where unnoticeable slices of a financial transaction are removed and transferred to another account. Under such a scenario, a computer programmer employed in a bank could redirect interest smaller then a penny to his own account. Over time, those fractional amounts can add up to a large sum.

## Malicious Software

Malicious software, or malware, can take many different forms: a virus infecting a system and modifying its data, a worm replicating over the network causing a bottleneck, or a Trojan horse allowing an unauthorized backdoor into a system that directly impacts the confidentiality of the files residing on the system.

Logic bombs are another example of malicious software. In a payroll system, for example, software validates whether a specific employee's number is present or not when paychecks are issued. If the employee was ever dismissed, his employee number would no longer be present and, upon execution of the payroll application, the logic bomb would detect the missing employee number and trigger the deletion of all employee records.

## Denial-of-Service Attacks

Denial-of-service (DOS) attacks prevent computer systems and networks from functioning in accordance with their intended purpose. These attacks cause loss of service to the users by consuming scarce resources such as bandwidth, memory, or processor cycles; they also can disrupt configuration information or physical components.

In a distributed denial-of-service attack, many compromised systems under the control of one or many attackers are used to multiply the impact by launching concurrent attacks against a determined target. These attacks can be devastating to an organization as they will bring computer operations to a complete standstill; in many cases, distributed DOS attacks are virtually impossible to block as they come from so many sources.

### Web Site Defacements

Web site defacements are a form of digital graffiti where intruders modify pages on the site in order to leave their mark, send a message, or mock the organization. Politically motivated defacement, often called hacktivism, attempts to send a message to the organization or some part of the online community.

### Extortion

Online extortion is often the result of the computer being the object of a crime; the extortionist contacts an organization after successfully stealing information or launching a DOS attack. The criminal then threatens either to reveal the information to the public or to launch a prolonged denial of service if demands are not met.

## Reflection and Self-Assessment                              11.1

Which types of computer crime apply to the Target data breach discussed in this chapter's AIS in the Business World?

Next, let's examine ways to reduce the risk of computer crime in organizations.

## INFORMATION SECURITY

The three principles are often referred to as the C-I-A triad.

Information security is defined as the protection of data in a system against unauthorized disclosure, modification, or destruction, and protection of the computer system itself against unauthorized use, modification, or denial of service. It is based on three fundamental principles: confidentiality, availability, and integrity. While the level of security varies from one organization to the next, controls are implemented to achieve one or more of these three **basic principles** (see Figure 11.1):

- *Confidentiality.* Condition that exists when data are held in confidence and are protected from unauthorized disclosure.
- *Data integrity.* State that exists when data stored in an information system are the same as those in the source documents or have been correctly processed from source data and have not been exposed to accidental or malicious alteration or destruction.
- *Availability.* Achieved when the required data can be obtained within the required time frame.

These three principles must be maintained throughout the information life cycle from creation to destruction.

**FIGURE 11.1**
**C-I-A Triad**

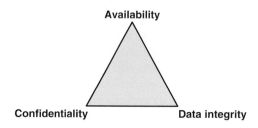

**FIGURE 11.2**
**Control Taxonomy**

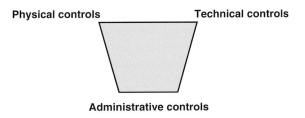

**Physical controls**    **Technical controls**

**Administrative controls**

Failure to protect the organization's information adequately could lead to financial losses, legal action, and loss of trust. Controls are thus implemented to protect the information. Much like the preventive/detective/corrective taxonomy we explored for internal controls, IT controls can be classified as physical, technical, or administrative (see Figure 11.2).

**Physical security controls** are required to protect computers, related equipment, and their contents from espionage, theft, and destruction or damage by accident, fire, or natural disasters (e.g., floods, earthquakes, and hurricanes). They involve the use of locks, security guards, badges, alarms, and similar measures to control access to computers, network equipment, and the processing facility. Other forms of controls such as smoke and fire detectors and generators are implemented to protect against threats such as fire and power outages.

Sometimes referred to as logical controls, **technical security controls** involve the use of safeguards incorporated in computer and telecommunication hardware and software. Firewalls, encryption, access control software, antivirus software, and intrusion detection systems fall into the category of technical security controls.

Firewalls are the first line of defense in protecting the corporate network from network-based threats. An access control policy determines which packets can flow between the network segments protected by firewalls; common techniques include examining packet information (such as source and destination address) and/or determining a message's transmission protocol. A firewall will only be as secure as the policy that it implements, the most effective being designed to restrict all traffic except that which is expressly permitted. You may be familiar with Windows Firewall or McAfee Security Suite, which incorporates firewall technology.

Intrusion detection systems and intrusion prevention systems detect potentially malicious data and access patterns. Both system types operate at both network and individual computer levels. Network-based systems examine network traffic; they look for specific patterns of anomalous behavior or deviations from the standard behavior of the network. Individual systems detect malicious activity by examining system calls, event logs, critical system files, and other valuable system information.

Access controls protect the confidentiality, integrity, and availability of information resources. Access control can usually be seen as a three-step process: identification (the user provides information in order for the system to recognize him or her), authentication (once identified, the user must prove his or her identity), and authorization (the user is granted the privileges associated with his or her profile). Fundamentally, access controls ensure that only the "right" people have access to specific types of information. For example, as a faculty advisor at my university, I can access the records of any student, but an individual student has access only to his or her own academic records.

Cryptography transforms data to (*i*) hide them, (*ii*) prevent them from being modified, and/or (*iii*) prevent unauthorized access to them. Most cryptography uses mathematical functions (algorithms) to turn ordinary data into an incomprehensible format.

Management constraints, as well as operational and accountability procedures, are known as **administrative security controls**. Examples include security policies and procedures, security awareness and training, adequate supervision of employees, and security reviews and audits.

A security policy is a clear and concise set of guiding statements supported by management; it provides a framework that ensures that information assets are secured. It is the key component to an organization's information security management system; without it, internal stakeholders have no specific guidance with respect to information system security issues.

Security awareness training is an often-overlooked part of a security management program. Communicating the roles and responsibilities of employees as they are defined in the security policy is the first line of defense in protecting critical computing infrastructures.

Organizations should conduct security reviews in which they monitor the program to ensure compliance, fine-tune the security policy and controls in accordance with the organization's goals, and ensure that any deficiencies are corrected. Security audits will examine whether the information systems operate in accordance with the security policy and ensure that the controls are effective in protecting these systems. The information system auditing process collects and examines evidence to determine whether the information system possesses controls that adequately protect the organization's informational assets in an effective way.

Administrative security controls are established for three main reasons: (i) to provide supplemental controls, (ii) to protect information processing resources, and (iii) to ensure that all employees have proper authorization to access computing resources.

Physical, technical, and administrative controls can further be classified as preventive, detective, or corrective controls. Preventive controls are implemented to keep unwanted events from occurring, detective controls attempt to identify anomalous and unwanted events once they have occurred, whereas corrective controls remedy problems discovered by detective controls.

# Reflection and Self-Assessment                      11.2

Under what circumstances could each of the preceding information systems controls be classified as preventive, detective, and/or corrective?

Let's conclude our discussion of computer crime with a look at an important set of internal control ideas: ISACA's Control Objectives for Information and Related Technology (CoBIT).

## CoBIT

You'll find ISACA's Web site at www.isaca. org.

ISACA is an acronym for the Information Systems Audit and Control Association, a professional group that bridges the gap between accounting and information technology. They offer the Certified Information Systems Auditor (CISA) credential along with other professional designations. ISACA's well-respected Control Objectives for Information and Related Technology framework gives accountants and other information systems professionals clear guidance in establishing strong internal controls, thereby deterring fraud.

Now in Version 5.0, the **CoBIT framework** acknowledges that information is the most important organizational "asset" in the 21st century—although no corporate balance sheet has a line item for it! As information expands rapidly, organizations need to manage it more effectively. So, the CoBIT framework lays out some fundamental, widely applicable concepts, and ideas to achieve that goal.

CoBIT 5.0 features five principles (Figure 11.3) that form the foundation of a strong IT governance and management. Let's take a closer look at each one.

1. *Meeting stakeholder needs.* A stakeholder is any person who has an interest in an organization's activities. So, stakeholders include groups like employees, stockholders, customers, vendors, and others. Different stakeholder groups have different information needs; for example, a stockholder might want information about dividends, while a customer might focus on prices and quality of goods sold. When an organization manages its IT well, the system will meet the legitimate information needs of all stakeholder groups.

2. *Covering the enterprise end-to-end.* All parts of the organization have information; therefore, all parts of the organization have to be part of the plan to manage it! Just as a well-designed relational database provides comprehensive inputs for decision making, a well-designed plan for managing information covers the whole entity—not just the IT function.

3. *Applying a single integrated framework.* We've talked about several different frameworks so far in the text: the FASB Conceptual Framework of Accounting, the AICPA Core Competencies Framework, the COSO frameworks for internal control and enterprise risk management. CoBIT's third principle incorporates and builds on other frameworks to produce a unified set of ideas.

4. *Enabling a holistic approach.* Because CoBIT 5 is so comprehensive, it allows stakeholders to look at the organization holistically—that is, in its totality. Rather than separating IT governance and management from the other essential functions of organizations, CoBIT 5 integrates them throughout the entity, whether its organizational structure is based on function (accounting, marketing, human resources), product (widgets, wadgets), or some other principles.

5. *Separating governance from management.* Although the two terms appear very similar, CoBIT makes an important distinction between them. Governance focuses on strategic decision making, goal setting, and prioritization; management focuses more on the day-to-day actions needed to achieve those goals. Many of the corporate scandals of the late 20th century occurred, in part, because governance and management were too comingled.

**FIGURE 11.3**
**CoBIT 5 Principles**

Source: CoBIT 5 © 2012 ISACA. All rights reserved. Used by permission.

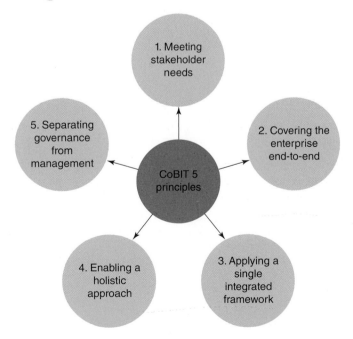

**FIGURE 11.4**
**CoBIT 5 Enablers**

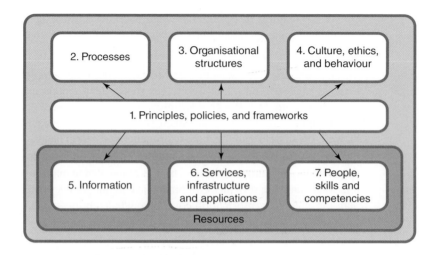

Along with the five principles, CoBIT suggests seven enablers—tools that make the best possible uses of information and information technology vis-à-vis the needs of organizational stakeholders. Figure 11.4 presents the seven enablers.

Table 11.1 explains each enabler.

We can only scratch the surface of CoBIT 5 here, but we'll look at it in more depth in this chapter's critical thinking application and end-of-chapter activities.

**TABLE 11.1**   **CoBIT 5.0 Enablers**

| Enabler | ISACA Explanation | Examples |
|---|---|---|
| Principles, policies, and frameworks | Vehicle to translate the desired behavior into practical guidance for day-to-day management | Enterprise risk management plan, internal control plan |
| Processes | Organized set of practices and activities to achieve certain objectives and produce a set of outputs in support of achieving overall IT-related goals | Sales/collection process, acquisition/payment process, conversion process, human resources process, financing process |
| Organizational structures | Key decision-making entities in an enterprise | C-suite executives |
| Culture, ethics, and behavior | Very often underestimated as a success factor in governance and management activities | Valuing open dialogue and cooperation |
| Information | Required for keeping the organization running and well governed, but at the operational level . . . very often, the key product of the enterprise itself | Product demand, employee satisfaction, vendor reliability |
| Services, infrastructure, and applications | Infrastructure, technology, and applications that provide the enterprise with information technology processing and services | Enterprise resource planning systems, relational databases, transaction processing software |
| People, skills, and competencies | Required for successful completion of all activities, and for making correct decisions, and taking corrective actions | Functional experts, cross-functional thinking |

# CRITICAL THINKING

We've looked at several topics related to computer crime and IT security in this chapter: Carter's taxonomy, risks and threats, internal controls, and CoBIT. In this section, I want to tie all of those together with an example.

Consider the following true account of a situation at Blue Security, an anti-spam firm that is now out of business (Lemos, 2006):

> Blue Security had created a small program called Blue Frog to turn a spam flood back on the advertiser, thus raising the cost of sending spam. The program would send a single opt-out request to the advertisers' Web sites for every registered user who received a spam message. Blue Security had about 500,000 subscribers to its service, so if a spam flood hit 20 percent of those users, then 100,000 opt-out requests would hit the advertisers who requested that the spam be sent. In revenge, one of the spammers—reportedly the one called PharmaMaster— attacked Blue Security and all Internet services associated with it for more than two weeks. The attack was so crippling that Blue Security was forced to close its doors.

How would the attack on Blue Security be classified using Carter's taxonomy of computer crime? As with many cases, it would fit in more than one category. We could think of it in Carter's *target* classification; the attack targeted Blue Security's information system, and its data to stop it from using Blue Frog. Since a computer was used to launch the attack, it also could be considered in the *instrumentality* classification. The incident wouldn't be appropriately classified as either incidental or associated; the computer was an integral part of the attack, but the attack was not simply a new version of an old crime.

The chapter discussed 11 business risks and threats associated with computer crime. The attack on Blue Security could be considered an example of any of the following:

- *Fraud.* According to the U.S. Department of Justice definition, the Blue Security case constitutes fraud. Knowledge of computer technology was critical in launching the attack.
- *Service interruption and delays.* During the attack, Blue Security's services were interrupted. If your campus has ever experienced a denial-of-service attack, as mine has, you know the kind of frustration those interruptions and delays can create.
- *Malicious software.* Attackers also sent incredible amounts of spam to Blue Security's customers. They were able to access customers' e-mail addresses by comparing e-mail lists based on responses to spam.
- *Denial-of-service attack.* The attack is a classic example of a distributed denial-of-service (DDOS) attack. SearchSecurity.com describes DDOS like this: "On the Internet, a distributed denial-of-service (DDOS) attack is one in which a multitude of compromised systems attack a single target, thereby causing denial of service for users of the targeted system. The flood of incoming messages to the target system essentially forces it to shut down, thereby denying service to the system to legitimate users."

Most experts agree that there is no 100 percent foolproof way to prevent situations like the one at Blue Security. But managers can still implement some internal controls to reduce their likelihood and lessen their effects on an information system. Here are some ideas:

- Develop a business continuity plan that lays out how the organization will respond to cyber-attacks.
- Ensure that the information system isn't stretched to its capacity limits. If a system has excess capacity, denial-of-service attacks may not be as severe.

- Purchase insurance to cover the costs associated with system attacks.
- Store data and Web pages on multiple servers so that attackers don't have a single focal point.
- Track activity on the system so that you can detect denial-of-service attacks and other forms of intrusion. By knowing what a system's traffic usually looks like, it's easier to determine when an attack has occurred.

How does the Blue Security case relate to the principles and enablers of CoBIT 5.0? Certainly, the Blue Frog program was designed to meet stakeholder needs (CoBIT principle 1). However, in meeting the needs of Blue Security's stakeholders, the program worked against the stakeholder needs of spammers—albeit in a way that most nonspammers would appreciate and value!

In terms of the seven enablers, the Blue Frog program was attempting to "weed out" nonvaluable information in the form of spam. The Blue Frog program itself was an example of an application, one element of services/infrastructure/applications. Finally, the program was likely a part of an overall enterprise risk management plan (principles/policies/frameworks) for organizations that adopted it.

While the preceding examples are by no means comprehensive, I hope they give you a sense of how the CoBIT framework applies to real cases in real organizations.

| | |
|---|---|
| **Summary** | Here is a summary of the chapter's important points based on its learning objectives: |

1. *Explain Carter's taxonomy of computer crime.* Carter identified four basic types of computer crime: target (where the object is to attack the computer itself, often with the intent of compromising its data), instrumentality (where the computer is used to commit the crime), incidental (where the computer is not necessarily required for the crime but is used to make it easier to complete and/or harder to detect), and associated (where the computer is used to commit old crimes in a new way).

2. *Identify and describe business risks and threats to information systems.* Computers expose businesses to at least four specific risks, some of which are also present in noncomputerized information systems. First is the risk of fraud; while not unique to a computerized environment, the risk of fraud is increased because of the unique ways computers can be used to commit crime (refer to Carter's taxonomy for specific examples). Error is also an information systems risk; people can make data entry errors or create inaccurate processing instructions, just as they can in noncomputerized systems. Service interruptions and delays are unique to information technology environments; for example, without adequate internal controls, power failures can cause service interruptions. Finally, companies must consider the risk of disclosing confidential information; while not unique to a computerized environment, that risk is enhanced when data are stored electronically.

   The chapter discussed seven specific threats associated with computerized information systems. Intrusions allow a computer criminal to bypass information security and internal controls. Information theft is self-evident; it involves stealing sensitive or proprietary information from the system. Information manipulation doesn't necessarily mean that the information is stolen outright; however, it changes information, often resulting in inaccurate reports or less-than-optimal decision making. Malicious software, for example, a logic bomb, can exist in an information system benignly until a date, event, or condition activates it. At that point, it may change or delete data or cut off access to the information system. In a denial-of-service attack, a computer criminal bombards the information system with requests for information, thus preventing it from fulfilling its legitimate purpose. Think of Web site defacement as digital "tagging" or graffiti. Finally, extortion involves threats from a computer criminal (such as disclosing confidential information) unless the organization meets the criminal's conditions (such as paying cash).

3. *Discuss ways to prevent and detect computer crime.* Internal control is at least as important in a computerized information system as it is in manual systems. Physical controls are perhaps the simplest type: locking doors, installing alarms, and requiring identification badges are some examples. Technical controls are part of the computer hardware and software themselves; think of firewalls, virus detection software, and access controls in this group. Finally, administrative controls refer to management policies and procedures designed to promote information security. For example, organizations may develop a clear information security policy and/or require periodic security training for employees.

4. *Explain the main components of the CoBIT framework and their implications for IT security.* As stated by ISACA: "CoBIT 5 provides a comprehensive framework that assists enterprises to achieve their goals and deliver value through effective governance and management of enterprise IT." The framework is built around five principles and seven enablers that, when present and functioning effectively, can help organizations maintain strong control and security over their information technology assets.

| Key Terms | administrative security controls, *201*<br>basic principles of information security, *200* | CoBIT framework, *202*<br>physical security controls, *201*<br>risks and threats, *197* | taxonomy for computer crime, *197*<br>technical security controls, *201* |
|---|---|---|---|

**Chapter References**

Carter, D. 1995. "Computer Crime Categories." *FBI Law Enforcement Bulletin,* pp. 21–28.

Eversley, M. and K. Hjelmgaard. "Target confirms massive credit-card data breach." *USA Today,* 19 December 2013.

Lemos, R. (2006, August). "Gangland Web Attacks; How Not to Get Whacked by the Botnet Mafia." *PC Magazine* 25(13), 116. ABI/INFORM Trade & Industry database (Document ID: 11070446111; February 1, 2009).

Rosenblum, P. "The Target data breach is becoming a nightmare." *Forbes*, 17 January 2014.

**End-of-Chapter Activities**

1. *Reading review questions.*

   a. What four common classifications are often associated with computer crime?

   b. What computer crime–related risks and threats are associated with information systems?

   c. What categories are commonly associated with computer criminals? Describe each category.

   d. How can organizations safeguard against computer crime? How can they detect it and recover from it if it happens? What role does CoBIT play in those tasks?

   e. What is CoBIT? What are the principles and enablers discussed in the CoBIT framework?

   f. Respond to the questions for this chapter's "AIS in the Business World."

2. *Reading review problem.* The Payment Card Industry Security Standards Council (PCI DSS) has suggested standards to address cases similar to the Target data breach discussed in this chapter's AIS in the Business World; the Council's Web site is www.pcisecuritystandards.org.

   a. Point your web browser to the Council's Web site. Access the "Payment Card Industry Data Security Standard Version 3.0," published in November 2013. In consultation with your instructor, choose one of the 12 requirements discussed in the standard.

   b. Explain how the requirement you selected, if violated, could lead to one type of computer crime identified in Carter's taxonomy. For example, failure to "regularly test security systems and processes" (Requirement 11) could allow a computer criminal to hack the organization's information system remotely (an example of instrumentality).

   c. Relate the same requirement and the same category from Carter's taxonomy to one or more of the business risks and threats discussed in the chapter. For example, a hacker could shut down the organization's information system for a period of time (an example of service interruption and delays).

   d. Considering all the three of the preceding items (requirement, Carter's taxonomy element, business risk/threat), explain how strengthening one of CoBIT's seven enablers could address the problem. For example, training all employees to recognize red flags for a hacked information system (people/skills/competencies) could lead to the organization becoming aware of a problem more quickly.

   e. Using the control taxonomy in Figure 11.2, classify the control you indicated in (d). (Training employees is an example of an administrative control.)

3. *Multiple choice review.*

   1. Carter suggested a four-part taxonomy of computer crime, comprising:
      a. Technical, physical, administrative, and software crime.
      b. Target, instrumentality, incidental, and associated.
      c. Preventive, detective, corrective, and coercive.
      d. Motivation, expectancy, valence, and instrumentality.

   2. According to the U.S. Department of Justice, which of the following is defined as any illegal act for which knowledge of computer technology is used to commit the offense?
      a. Fraud
      b. Intrusion
      c. Information theft
      d. Malicious software

   3. As a part of its five principles, CoBIT emphasizes the need to separate:
      a. Governance from management.
      b. Stakeholder needs from management.
      c. Governance from stakeholder needs.
      d. All of the above.

   4. All of the following are CoBIT enablers except:
      a. Services, infrastructure, and applications.
      b. Culture, ethics, and behavior.
      c. AICPA core competency framework.
      d. People, skills, and competencies.

   5. The three fundamental principles that guide the development and implementation of IT controls are:
      a. Physical, technical, and administrative.
      b. Effectiveness, efficiency, and compliance.

   c. Confidentiality, availability, and data integrity.

   d. Preventive, detective, and corrective.

**4.** *Making choices and exercising judgment.*

   a. What would motivate someone to engage in computer crime?

   b. Do a Google search for the most recent list of AICPA Top Ten Technologies. Choose one and explain how it might be used to engage in computer crime.

   c. Suggest at least three specific internal controls you'd employ to prevent, detect, or correct the computer crime you identified above.

**5.** *Field work.*

   a. Point your Web browser to www.cybercrime.gov, the Web site for the U.S. Justice Department's Computer Crime and Intellectual Property section. Based on criteria provided by your instructor, summarize one or more of the press releases on the site.

   b. Use a literature search to investigate one or more of the following computer criminals. Describe each one's crime; also compare and contrast them in terms of personal characteristics and motivations.

      i. Lewys Martin

      ii. James Jeffery

      iii. Jeremy Hammond

**6.** *Applying Carter's taxonomy.* Which element(s) of Carter's taxonomy apply to each of the following situations? If more than one category applies, explain why.

   a. A bookkeeper steals cash as it comes into the company. The bookkeeper later falsifies accounting entries using general ledger software to cover the trail.

   b. A bored teenager initiates a denial-of-service attack on his Internet service provider's information system.

   c. A disgruntled employee uses a previously installed "back door" into an information system to lock out other users by changing their passwords.

   d. A gang of criminals breaks into a local retail store. They steal all the store's computers and then later hack into them for the purpose of identity theft.

   e. A pair of computer criminals uses e-mail to contact victims for an illegal pyramid scheme. They use money from new investors, rather than profits, to pay off old investors, keeping most of the money themselves.

   f. A recently fired employee laid the groundwork for corporate espionage by installing spyware on the company's network.

   g. A student discovers the password to his university's information system. He then hacks the system to change grades for himself and his friends.

   h. A woman impersonates her wealthy employer, stealing personal information about the employer from her bank's information system.

**7.** *Identifying business risks and threats.* Which type(s) of business risks/threats described in the chapter best applies to each situation below? If more than one applies, explain why.

   a. Blackmail based on stolen information.

   b. Concurrent attacks against a determined target.

   c. Digital graffiti.

   d. Discovery of customer Social Security numbers by external parties.

   e. Hacking.

   f. Intentional modification of information.

   g. Mistakes in data entry.

   h. Power failure.

   i. Salami technique.

   j. Stealing research and development data for new products.

   k. Trojan horse.

8. *Classification of controls.* Classify each of the following controls as physical, technical, or administrative. Then, describe each control in your own words.

   a. Access control software

   b. Adequate supervision of employees

   c. Badges

   d. Encryption

   e. Firewalls

   f. Internal audits

   g. Intrusion detection systems

   h. Locks

   i. Ongoing training regarding security issues

   j. Security guards

   k. Security policy

   l. Smoke detectors

   m. Universal power supplies

9. *Terminology.* Please match each item on the right to the most appropriate item on the left.

   | | | |
   |---|---|---|
   | 1. Confidentiality | a. | Computers used to carry out a crime |
   | 2. Creating fake refunds to benefit a friend | b. | Crime classification that does not necessarily require a computer |
   | 3. Data diddling | c. | Data are protected from unauthorized disclosure |
   | 4. Human element | d. | Designed to help restore consumer confidence |
   | 5. Incidental | e. | Information manipulation |
   | 6. Instrumentality | f. | Intentionally changing information in a system |
   | 7. Logic bomb | g. | Interest of less than one cent diverted to computer criminal's account |
   | 8. Salami technique | h. | Most vulnerable part of an information system |
   | 9. Sarbanes-Oxley Act | i. | One type of service interruption/delay |
   | 10. Willful neglect | j. | Shuts down a payroll system if a specific employee number is deleted |

10. *Multiple choice questions.* Consider the following short case in responding to these questions:

    Tim was upset with his accounting instructor because of the grade he earned in her class. As an act of revenge, Tim used a computer program he downloaded from the Internet to discover the instructor's password for the university's information system. He used the password to infiltrate the system and introduced a program that would shut it down; he contacted his accounting instructor and threatened to activate the program if she did not change his grade.

1. Which elements of Carter's taxonomy apply?
   a. Target and instrumentality
   b. Target and incidental
   c. Instrumentality and incidental
   d. Target, instrumentality, and incidental

2. Which of the following are administrative controls the university should implement to prevent such situations in the future?
   a. Backup files, strong passwords
   b. Backup files, mandatory password rotation
   c. Strong passwords, mandatory password rotation
   d. Backup files, strong passwords, mandatory password rotation

3. Because Tim is threatening his instructor, his actions are best described as:
   a. Extortion.
   b. Malicious software.
   c. Information theft.
   d. Service interruption.

4. Which of the following statements is most true with respect to CoBIT's enablers?
   a. Since the university is not a business, the "process" enabler is irrelevant in the case.
   b. Tim's accounting instructor must be incompetent since she could neither prevent nor detect Tim's action until it was too late.
   c. If the university had an appropriate organizational structure in place, the problem would have been prevented.
   d. At the minimum, the university needs to consider two enablers: culture/ethics/behavior, and services/infrastructure/applications.

5. Consider CoBIT's five principles. The relevant stakeholders in this case include:
   a. Tim and his accounting instructor only.
   b. Tim and all instructors (including his accounting instructor) at the university.
   c. All students (including Tim) and Tim's accounting instructor only.
   d. All students (including Tim) and all instructors (including Tim's accounting instructor) at the university.

11. *Statement evaluation.* Indicate whether each of the following statements is (i) always true, (ii) sometimes true, or (iii) never true. For those that are (ii) sometimes true, explain when the statement is true.

   a. A specific instance of computer crime can involve multiple categories from Carter's taxonomy.
   b. Computer crime involves using a computer to commit a crime.
   c. Computer crime is perpetrated by organized crime groups.
   d. Confidentiality, availability, and data integrity comprise the C-I-A triad.
   e. Each element of the C-I-A triad is also mentioned in CoBIT's seven enablers.
   f. Although not an asset in the accounting sense, information is a resource according to CoBIT's seven enablers.
   g. Information technology controls can be physical, technical, or administrative.
   h. Organizations that implement CoBIT are immune to computer crime.
   i. Perpetrators of computer crime come from outside the organization.
   j. The "salami technique" is an example of information manipulation.

**12.** *Prior material application.*

   a. Consider the five generic elements of most accounting information systems. For each element, suggest one way it could be compromised via computer crime.

   b. Read "Protect Small Business" by Joseph T. Wells in the March 2003 issue of *Journal of Accountancy;* consider the case presented in the opening paragraphs of the article (Denise, a bookkeeper for a small trucking firm). Work with a group of students and/or interview a forensic accountant/certified fraud examiner to suggest a series of steps you could use to investigate the fraud. Document your steps using one of the techniques described in Part Two of the text.

   c. This chapter provided a three-part taxonomy for IT controls; earlier in the text, you learned that internal controls have four broad purposes. Fill in the table below with appropriate examples; be prepared to explain your reasoning.

| Internal Control Purpose | Physical Controls | Technical Controls | Administrative Controls |
|---|---|---|---|
| Safeguard assets | | | |
| Ensure financial statement reliability | | | |
| Promote operating efficiency | | | |
| Encourage compliance with management directives | | | |

**13.** *CoBIT 5.* This problem is structured in three main parts. The first two parts require less critical thinking, as they ask you simply to recall elements of the CoBIT 5 framework. The second part requires more critical thinking, as it asks you to apply those elements.

   a. Fill in the blanks according to CoBIT 5's principles.
      i. Applying a _____ framework.
      ii. Covering the enterprise _____.
      iii. Enabling a _____ approach.
      iv. Meeting _____ needs.
      v. Separating _____ from _____.

   b. Which of CoBIT 5's enablers is described by each of the following items?
      i. Key decision-making entities
      ii. Often underestimated as a success factor
      iii. Organized set of practices to achieve objectives
      iv. Provide the enterprise with IT processing
      v. Required for making correct decisions
      vi. Translates desired behavior into practical guidance
      vii. Very often the key product of the enterprise itself

   c. For each of the following independent cases, indicate at least one relevant CoBIT principle and at least one relevant CoBIT enabler. The first case is provided as an example.

| Case | Principle(s) | Enabler(s) |
|------|-------------|-----------|
| TSO Corporation provides all employees with an employee manual. In its section on IT security, the manual specifies required annual training to understand the company's enterprise risk management plan | Applying a single integrated framework (the ERM plan is part of the overall IT security plan)<br><br>Enabling a holistic approach (all employees must have the training) | Principles, policies and frameworks (the employee manual is a policy)<br><br>People, skills, and competencies (the annual training gives employees needed skills) |
| UPT Corporation surveys its stockholders and employees annually to determine their concerns about IT security; the corporation's chief executive officer and chief information officer address those concerns in its annual report | | |
| YWN Corporation has a seven-member board of directors. Every 5 years, the board develops a strategic plan, which YWN's employees implement. The strategic plan is structured, in part, according to the corporation's usual activities | | |

14. *Excel application.* Consider the following data set (available for download in the 3 February 2014 post on my AIS blog):

| Fraud Dollar Amount | Number of IT Employees | Number of Accounting Employees | Annual Sales |
|---------------------|------------------------|--------------------------------|--------------|
| $ 5,694 | 78 | 20 | $ 7,400 |
| 5,785 | 52 | 15 | 7,500 |
| 6,887 | 83 | 13 | 8,900 |
| 5,737 | 52 | 37 | 7,400 |
| 6,457 | 70 | 23 | 8,300 |
| 6,531 | 57 | 27 | 8,400 |
| 6,781 | 92 | 38 | 8,700 |
| 6,247 | 71 | 30 | 8,100 |
| 6,801 | 97 | 39 | 8,800 |
| 5,321 | 76 | 33 | 6,900 |

    a. Use Excel's regression function to analyze the data. Use "Fraud dollar amount" as the dependent variable, and the others as independent variables. (Check figure: regression statistics standard error = 23.97.)

  b. Interpret the results by answering the following questions:

   i. What percentage of the variance in "Fraud dollar amount" is explained by knowing the values of the other three variables?

   ii. Are any of the independent variables statistically significant in predicting the fraud dollar amount? If so, which?

   iii. If a company has 60 IT employees, 22 accounting employees and annual sales of $7,000, what fraud dollar amount does the regression equation predict?

## Comprehensive Problem

### Part 3 of 5

Each part of the comprehensive problem is based on Big Marker (www.bigmarker.com). Consider the narrative in Part 1 as you respond to the following questions on XBRL, e-business and ERP systems, and computer crime and IT security.

### Part Three Questions

1. Consider the following list of transactions Big Marker might record in its AIS. Indicate the journal entry required for each transaction, then use XBRL's Global Ledger taxonomy to find the correct tags for any five of the indicated accounts.

| Transaction Date | Transaction |
|---|---|
| 9 Feb 20x4 | Purchased a new computer server. List price, $7,700. Paid 30% down and financed the remainder with a 2%, 6-month note payable |
| 14 March 20x4 | Paid employees, $18,000 |
| 18 March 20x4 | Paid in advanced for six months' advertising that will start in April 20x4, $3,000 |
| 24 July 20x4 | Billed monthly communities for the 30 days ended 15 July 20x4, $25,000 |
| 23 Nov 20x4 | Received required portion of community dues, $8,000. (Community dues total was $80,000) |

2. Most observers would agree that Big Marker is engaged in e-business.

 a. Which e-business categories apply to Big Marker? (e.g., B2B)

 b. Which benefits of e-business does Big Marker provide to its customers? Which costs apply?

3. Could Big Marker be considered an application service provider? Justify your response. If Big Marker is an ASP, which category (e.g., enterprise, specialist) best describes it?

4. Consider the material in Chapter 11 on computer crime and information technology security.

 a. Which business risks/threats impact Big Marker? Explain your response.

 b. How does the narrative presented at the end of Part One demonstrate one or more of CoBIT's processes and enablers?

# Business Processes

**12.** Sales/Collection Process

**13.** Acquisition/Payment Process

**14.** Other Business Processes

Many AIS courses focus on business processes. In this section, we'll explore a fundamental, comprehensive set of business processes. In addition, we'll apply many of the topics from previous chapters (e.g., AIS structure, transaction processing and internal controls) within the context of those processes. The first two chapters in this section are devoted to processes that generalize easily across organizations; the third chapter discusses processes that often vary in detail (i.e., conversion, financing, human resources).

# Chapter **Twelve**

# Sales/Collection Process

## AIS in the Business World

### Krispy Kreme Doughnuts

For all three chapters in this part of the book, we'll use Krispy Kreme Doughnuts as the "AIS in the Business World" focus. According to the investor relations section of its Web site (www.investor.krispykreme.com), "Krispy Kreme is an international retailer of premium-quality sweet treats, including its signature hot . . . doughnut. Headquartered in Winston-Salem, NC, the company has offered the highest-quality doughnuts and great-tasting coffee since it was founded in 1937. Today, Krispy Kreme and its one-of-a-kind Hot Light can be found in approximately 812 locations around the world." The company trades its capital stock under the symbol KKD; as of mid-February 2014, their stock was trading at just under $20/share.

KKD has a sales/collection process like most other organizations. Customers enter a store, choose the doughnuts / beverages/other items they want to purchase, then pay at the cash register. Like most retail companies, KKD does not extend credit directly to its customers; rather, it relies on third-party entities, such as American Express and Visa, to verify customers' credit.

### *Discussion Questions*

1. Which elements of Porter's value chain are related to the sales/collection process?
2. How does Krispy Kreme's sales/collection process differ from the generic version described in the chapter? How are the two similar?
3. For each generic part of the AIS discussed in Chapter 1, give two examples in KKD's sales/collection process.

In AIS study, we combine sales and collection activities because of their logical relationship to one another. But, as you're probably aware, a "collection" does not necessarily constitute a "sale" according to GAAP. The rules of accrual-basis accounting still apply—we just organize the knowledge a little differently in AIS.

This chapter, and the two that follow, put together much of what you've already learned within the context of specific business processes. So what is a "business process"? At its most basic, a **business process** is a set of procedures and policies designed to create value for some organizational stakeholder. Those stakeholders might include customers, stockholders, employees or vendors.

Porter (1998) developed the **value chain** as a way to think about the processes organizations use to create value for their stakeholders. The value chain (shown in Figure 12.1) is organized into two parts: primary activities are directly involved in value creation, while support activities provide essential services to the organization.

Consider, for example, the value created by your university. If you were extraordinarily hardworking and diligent, you might be able to get the knowledge afforded by your degree on your own—but very few students have that kind of determination. So, instead, it's much more effective and efficient for you to gain that knowledge through an organization (your university) and its business processes.

While the details of processes can vary significantly from one organization to another, most of them share some common features. Those common features will be our focus in the next three chapters, starting here with the sales/collection process.

You might need to review some of the fundamental concepts from earlier chapters as you read and study this one.

When you finish studying this chapter, you should be able to complete the following tasks within the context of the sales/collection process:

1. Explain its role and purpose.
2. List and discuss, in order, the steps in the process.
3. Explain how the generic structure of most AIS applies to the process.

**FIGURE 12.1**
**Porter's Value Chain**

Primary activities

Inbound logistics: move raw materials

Operations: transform materials into finished products

Outbound logistics: move finished product

Marketing & sales: sell the product

Service: provide support as needed

Support activities

Procurement: purchasing function

Information technology: R & D, other forms of IT

Human resource management: personnel-related functions

Infrastructure: other aspects of the organization

4. Process common transactions.
5. Design and critique internal controls based on common risk exposures.
6. Develop and interpret process-related systems documentation.
7. Relate Porter's value chain to the process.

# PROCESS DESCRIPTION

The fundamental purpose of the sales/collection process is to provide goods and services to clients and to collect payment from them. Without an effective sales/collection process, an organization will soon cease to exist. Ineffective processes may arise from lack of demand for a company's product or service, inadequate exposure in the marketplace, and/or poor credit policies (with the attendant difficulty in cash collections).

So, what exactly are the **steps** involved in an effective sales/collection process? Consider the list below (Hollander, Denna, and Cherrington, 2000):

1. *Take a customer's order.* Sales staff can take a customer's order in a variety of ways: face-to-face, via the Internet, through the mail, over the phone, and others.
2. *Approve the customer's credit.* Once the customer's order is in hand, the organization often must approve his/her credit. When you shop in a store, credit approval comes from scanning your credit card. Organizations doing business with one another, though, often extend credit directly—without the use of a credit card.
3. *Fill the order based on approved credit.* If the customer's credit is approved, the warehouse staff can fill the order and prepare it for shipment.
4. *Ship the product (if necessary).* In the best-case scenario, a separate shipping department actually sends the product to the customer (we'll talk more about this idea when we consider internal controls later in the chapter). If a customer is paying cash, she might take the product on a cash-and-carry basis, rather than having it shipped. In some cases, a customer may be forced to pay cash for goods and services if his credit is insufficient or he has a poor payment history.
5. *Bill the customer.* When goods and services are sold on credit, the billing department will typically send an invoice or statement on a monthly basis. Your credit card company, for example, follows that process. They are a third-party intermediary between you and the company that sold the goods and services, but the process is basically the same.
6. *Collect payment.* In a perfect world, the client timely remits payment. The client may take advantage of cash discounts for early payment. Customers that fail to pay timely may undergo more extensive collection processes and/or be denied further credit. Systems for recording cash collections fall into two broad groups: open invoice and balance forward. In an open invoice system, a customer's remittance is tied to a specific invoice or set of invoices. While more complex to maintain, open invoice systems do provide more detail for decision making. In a balance forward system, remittances are not applied to a particular invoice; rather, they are simply applied to a customer's total outstanding balance.
7. *Process uncollectible receivables as necessary.* In a worst-case scenario, when all attempts to collect cash have failed, the organization may be forced to write off its bad debts using a method approved under GAAP.

Figure 12.2 presents a partial systems flowchart that captures the first two steps of the sales/collection process.

**FIGURE 12.2**
**Partial Systems Flowchart of the Sales/Collection Process**

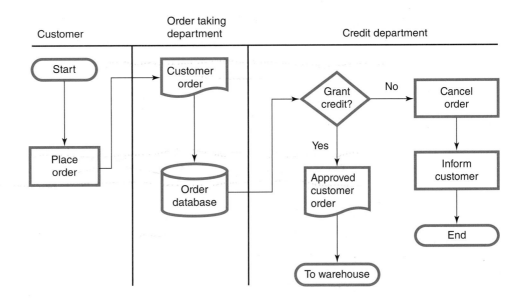

Keep in mind that the seven steps are very generic in nature. In your accounting career, you may be called upon to design an effective sales/collection process and/or to evaluate one as part of an audit. In either case, use the seven steps as a guide, but make allowances for individual company practices.

Next, let's consider how the five generic parts of an AIS (input, process, output, storage, internal control) are applied in the context of the sales/collection process.

# Reflection and Self-Assessment                                    12.1

Consider the way your campus bookstore or other source sold you your textbooks this term. How did the transaction, from the bookstore's point of view, exemplify the steps in the sales/collection process?

## AIS STRUCTURE

From an AIS perspective, inputs and outputs most often refer to documents. Documents in the sales/collection process can be paper-based, electronic, or some combination of the two. Table 12.1 summarizes the most commonly used documents in the sales/collection process; we'll take a look at each of them in more detail in the following paragraphs. Note that an output from one step in the sales/collection process often serves as an input to subsequent steps; likewise, an output from one organization can serve as an input to another.

As we discuss **documents** associated with the sales/collection process, keep in mind that we're examining them from the point of view of the *selling* organization. The customer will have its own names and formats for the same documents; we'll explore those in the next chapter.

**TABLE 12.1** **Documents Associated with the Sales/Collection Process**

| Document Name | Basic Purpose | Originator | Recipient |
|---|---|---|---|
| Customer order | To summarize items ordered and prices | Sales department | Warehouse |
| Picking list | To guide selection of items from warehouse | Warehouse | Shipping department |
| Packing list | To specify contents of shipment | Shipping department | Customer |
| Bill of lading | To specify freight terms | Shipping department | Common carrier |
| Customer invoice | To bill client | Billing department | Customer |
| Customer check | To remit payment | Customer | Cash receipts department |
| Remittance advice | To provide a source document for AIS | Customer | Accounting department |
| Deposit slip | To transmit cash receipts to bank | Cash receipts department | Bank |

In the first step of the sales/collection process (take customer order), a sales clerk (or someone with a similar title) notes the type and quantity of merchandise the customer is requesting. The customer's order, then, might be filled out by the sales staff or the customer him- or herself. In many cases, the customer may simply bring the needed merchandise to a cash register; in that situation, a formal "order" does not exist. See Figure 12.3 for an illustration of a customer order form. If the order taking process is electronic, the order form would likely be part of a relational database.

The picking list comes into play when an order is filled based on approved credit. A picking list typically tells warehouse or stockroom staff what products to take (pick) off the shelves to fill the customer's order. If you've ever ordered any merchandise from the Internet or a catalog, you've probably seen a packing list. It serves as a final check of what is actually loaded into the box before the goods are shipped to the customer.

A bill of lading is used when the goods are shipped to the customer. A bill of lading is a contract between the seller (such as Amazon.com) and a common carrier (such as Federal Express or United Parcel Service). The bill of lading tells the common carrier where to deliver the goods. It also explains the freight terms associated with the shipment. **Freight terms** identify two important items: who is responsible for the goods while they're in transit and who ends up paying the freight bill. When the selling organization bears the cost of freight, it is treated as an expense in their AIS. However, if the buyer bears the freight cost, the buyer capitalizes the amount to inventory.

Customer invoices vary as much as the companies that issue them. Typically, though, they will contain some key information: the customer's name and address, the mailing address for the company, the total amount due, and the due date. To foster good internal control (discussed later in the chapter), invoices should be prepared by a billing department once the goods have been received by the customer.

To motivate customers to pay as quickly as possible, a company may offer a cash discount. Cash discounts commonly look like this: 2/10, n/30. Read that notation as "two-ten, net thirty." In plain English, it says that the customer may take a 2 percent discount off the merchandise cost if the bill is paid within 10 days. Otherwise, the full (net)

## FIGURE 12.3 **Customer Order**

Your Name: _____

Shipping Address: _____
(No PO box, please)

City: _____ State: _____ ZIP code: _____

Phone (days): _____

Phone (eves): _____

Credit Card #: _____ Exp. Date: _____
**(MasterCard, Visa, or Discover only, please)**

Signature: _____
**Your Distributor's ID** #:           **Name:**
**(Check on the e-rep's page for this name & number.)**

**Please send a free Fuller Brush Master Catalog. ____Yes ____ No**

| Item Number | Qty: | Description: | Price each | Total |
|---|---|---|---|---|
| | | | | |
| | | | | |
| | | | | |

Handling Charge Chart:

| | | |
|---|---|---|
| $0 to | $24.99 | $3.95 |
| $25 to | $49.99 | $4.95 |
| $50.00 | and up | $5.95 |

Sales Tax Policy: Since we have a business presence in all states, we are required by law to collect sales tax for every state. Need help finding your area's sales tax? Just call us at: 1-800-522-0499.

| | |
|---|---|
| Merchandise total | |
| Handling from chart | |
| Merchandise subtotal | |
| Sales tax on subtotal | |
| Total amount due | |

**Make checks payable to: The Fuller Brush Company**
PO Box 420130
Great Bend, KS 67530-1247

amount of the invoice is payable within 30 days. The discount will not apply to any freight charges included on the invoice.

Suppose, for example, CLM Corporation sends an invoice dated February 2, 2014, to a customer that includes $6,200 for merchandise and $100 for freight. If the cash discount is 2/10, n/30, the customer may pay the bill on or before February 12. The total remitted will be 6,200 × 98% + $100 for freight = $6,176. Otherwise, the full invoice amount ($6,300) is due within 30 days of February 2.

Collecting payment from a customer on open account involves two documents: the customer check and the remittance advice. While I'm sure you know what a check is, you may not be familiar with the term *remittance advice*. Basically, the purpose of a remittance advice is to *advise* the company that you are *remitting* payment on an invoice. Consider, for example, your monthly credit card bill. When you receive it, you tear off a portion to send back with your check. The portion you tear off is the remittance advice. It becomes the source document for journal entries related to cash receipts. The check itself goes to the bank; the remittance advice goes to the accounting department for recordkeeping. You can see a generic remittance advice in Figure 12.4.

Ideally, all cash received by a company is deposited daily in the bank. A deposit slip typically lists each item to be deposited with some identifying information (such as an ABA or routing number for checks), the account holder's name and account number, and the date. The bank issues a receipt as evidence that the deposit has been accepted.

How do organizations process the input documents to create outputs for the sales/collection process? They use the seven steps discussed earlier in this chapter. In addition, transactions must be appropriately recorded in the AIS.

# Reflection and Self-Assessment                          12.2

What journal entries would you make for each of the following transactions? Which input/output documents would trigger each one?

- Sale of inventory on account
- Sale of inventory for cash

- Cash collections for sales on account
- Inventory returns
- Payment of freight charges
- Bad debt write-offs

**FIGURE 12.4**
**Remittance Advice**

Remittance Advice for CPD INC.
Check # 3225 - Check Date 04/14/14

| Invoice # | Inv Date | Orig Amt | Payment | Reference |
|-----------|----------|----------|---------|-----------|
| 145216 | 03/12/14 | $    40.00 | $    40.00 | Warranty Replacement |
| 144540 | 03/04/14 | 158.00 | 158.00 | SSI Stock |
| 146035 | 03/25/14 | 1,890.00 | 1,700.00 | Civic Plaza |
| Totals |  | $ 2,088.00 | $ 1,898.00 |  |

As you read in Chapter 1, "storage" in the AIS often happens in a computer database or other electronic medium. Even in the small number of cases where storage happens with paper files, though, the AIS still must capture certain basic information in master files and transaction files. Table 12.2 shows a list of the common files, along with the data they would contain.

In the next section, we'll turn our attention to the last generic AIS element: internal controls.

## INTERNAL CONTROLS

Organizations commonly encounter various kinds of risks in the sales/collection process. Accountants, therefore, must design internal controls to ameliorate those risks as efficiently and effectively as possible.

The numbered items below are common risks faced in the sales/collection process. The associated lettered items represent **internal controls** that might lessen those risks. Keep in mind that the list is illustrative, not definitive; that is, each organization's risks and controls must be assessed and developed individually, based on time, money, and human constraints.

1. Granting credit to customers who are not creditworthy.
   a. *Relying on third-party vendors to grant credit.* A company may choose not to extend credit itself. Rather, it may rely on third parties such as Visa, Discover, or American Express to approve customers' credit.

**TABLE 12.2  File Structures in the Sales/Collection Process**

| File Name | File Type | Primary Key | Other Data |
|---|---|---|---|
| Employee | Master | Employee ID | Last name, first name<br>Street address, city, state, ZIP code<br>Phone number<br>Emergency contact<br>Department<br>Hire date |
| Customer | Master | Customer ID | Customer company name<br>Street address, city, state, ZIP code<br>Phone number<br>Contact person name<br>Credit limit<br>Date of first sale |
| Inventory | Master | Product ID | Product name<br>Beginning balance date<br>Beginning balance quantity<br>Beginning balance cost per unit<br>Preferred supplier |
| Sales | Transaction | Transaction ID | Transaction date<br>Customer ID<br>Employee ID |
| Sales/inventory | Junction | Transaction ID | Product ID<br>Quantity sold<br>Selling price per unit |

b. *Establishing a formal credit-approval process, independent of the sales function.* In the best possible situations, salespeople will not have the authority to grant credit directly. If you've ever purchased a new car, for example, you may have observed that the salesperson does not handle the financing part of the transaction. Granting credit independently from sales is an example of separation of duties.

c. *Conducting a cash-only business.* Smaller organizations may opt not to grant credit or accept third-party credit cards at all. While they may lose some sales as a result, they do not run the risk of inappropriately granting credit.

2. "Selling" products that are not available.

a. *Checking stock-on-hand before completing a customer's order.* While salespeople should not grant credit, they should be able to check inventory levels directly or via an information system. Without that ability, customers may be frustrated and the organization may lose business. If the company maintains its records in a relational database/ERP system, a query would fulfill this control.

b. *Maintaining adequate inventory.* An organization must constantly balance the need to have sufficient inventory on hand with the costs of maintaining that inventory. Costs include tying up cash in inventory, insurance, maintenance (such as keeping perishable products cool), and supervision/security costs. Although beyond the scope of this text, you may be familiar with terms like just-in-time, economic order quantity, and reorder point as methods for maintaining adequate inventory.

3. Filling the customer's order incorrectly.

a. *Incorporating independent order checking.* Warehouse personnel may misread the picking slip, select the wrong inventory from the shelves, or put incorrect quantities in the customer's order. Ideally, the organization should find and correct those errors before turning the merchandise over to the customer. An independent check by another member of the warehouse staff, or a member of the shipping staff, can reduce the chances that the wrong goods are shipped to the customer. Auditors (either internal or financial statement) might select a sample of appropriate documents (order/picking slip/packing slip) to determine the extent of any errors.

b. *Using information technology to fill orders.* Computerized order-filling is becoming more and more common in some sectors of the economy. Many hospital pharmacies, for example, use computers to fill prescriptions. While the orders should still be checked by a pharmacist for accuracy, using IT first can be much more efficient.

4. Damaging goods in the delivery process.

a. *Packing merchandise adequately prior to shipment.* Whether handled by a common carrier or the organization's own shipping department, goods should be properly packaged prior to shipment. Omaha Steaks (www.omahasteaks.com), for example, ships its products in Styrofoam containers with dry ice. The food therefore arrives at the customer's location fresh.

b. *Insuring goods in transit.* If you have ever shipped anything valuable, you may have purchased insurance for it. While insurance cannot prevent damage to the goods, it can mitigate financial risk by providing the customer reimbursement for the insured value if the goods are damaged in transit.

5. Billing the customer incorrectly.

a. *Matching documents prior to billing.* The customer should only be billed for what has been ordered and shipped. So, the billing department should receive a copy of both the customer's order and the bill of lading. Once those documents are received, billing clerks can generate customer invoices from the accounting information system.

    b. *Using information technology to ensure numerical accuracy.* In most accounting information systems, computers generate invoices. Mathematical errors are thus avoided.

6. Mishandling cash receipts.

The three basic duties to be separated include custody of an asset, its recordkeeping, and authorization for its use.

    a. *Separating duties.* As you learned in Chapter 3, separation of duties is a basic internal control in most accounting information systems. When it comes to the sales/collection process, cash should be deposited daily in the bank (custody). Accountants should use remittance advices as the source documents for journal entries (recordkeeping). And signatories on the checking account should not be allowed to handle cash received from customers (authorization).

    b. *Restrictively endorsing checks when they are received.* When you deposit checks in your bank account, you have to sign the back first—that's an endorsement. A restrictive endorsement includes the phrase "for deposit only" before the signature. Many banks encourage or require customers also to include their account number as part of the endorsement. Although managers should take great care not to lose or misplace checks once they have been endorsed, a restrictive endorsement can ensure that misplaced or lost checks are not cashed.

    c. *Reconciling the bank statement at least monthly.* At the very least, an independent accountant or someone who does not handle cash receipts or payments should reconcile the bank statement when it is received. The Association of Certified Fraud Examiners (www.cfenet.com) recommends that checking accounts be reconciled at least weekly—a process that is now entirely achievable with online banking records. As you may know, reconciling the bank statement involves accounting for timing differences in what the bank knows versus what the depositor knows; it also helps correct errors made by either the depositor or the bank.

Those six risks, and the suggested internal controls that accompany them, are by no means exhaustive. In designing and evaluating internal controls for the sales/collection process, you must develop an intimate knowledge of an organization's processes and personnel. Use your own creativity and critical-thinking abilities, coupled with your sense of cost–benefit issues, when confronted with the important task of internal control assessment in practice.

## Reflection and Self-Assessment      12.3

Relate the six risks described above to Brown's taxonomy of risk. Explain whether each suggested control is primarily preventive/detective/corrective. Suggest one additional internal control for each risk.

## SYSTEMS DOCUMENTATION

In Part Two of the text, we looked at three major ways to document the accounting information system: flowcharts, data flow diagrams, and REA models. Figure 12.2 presented a partial systems flowchart of the sales/collection process. Please refer to Figures 12.5 and 12.6 at the end of this chapter for illustrations of a Level Zero data flow diagram and REA model of the sales/collection process.

# CRITICAL THINKING

The first three parts of this book laid a foundation in some fundamental AIS concepts, such as transaction processing, internal control, and systems documentation. In the three chapters that comprise Part Four, we focus on how those fundamental topics are applied within the context of common business processes. Here's a brief look at how Krispy Kreme Doughnuts would apply some of those topics in its sales/collection process.

*Transaction processing* (Chapter 2). A Krispy Kreme customer purchased a dozen chocolate iced glazed doughnuts for $6. If the cost to produce the doughnuts was $2, Krispy Kreme's journal entry would be:

| | | |
|---|---|---|
| Cash | $6 | |
| Cost of goods sold | 2 | |
| Inventory | | $2 |
| Sales | | 6 |

Assuming the customer came into the store to buy the doughnuts, the only document involved in the sale would be the cash register receipt.

*Internal control* (Chapter 3). Using a cash register and issuing cash receipts are important internal controls for Krispy Kreme. The cash register maintains an internal electronic record of each sale, thus ensuring financial statement reliability; the cash register also helps safeguard the store's cash. A Krispy Kreme retail store might also have video surveillance as part of safeguarding its inventory.

*Business process management* (Chapter 4). As with most (or all) franchised retail food chains, consistency is very important. (You'll remember a similar point about Papa John's Pizza in Chapter 4.) Krispy Kreme's process for selling doughnuts is well organized and established, having gone through the generalized model of BPM presented in Chapter 4.

*CoBIT* (Chapter 11). Krispy Kreme does an effective job separating governance from management, one of CoBIT's five principles. The investor relations section of their Web site has an entire page devoted to corporate governance, which states (**emphasis added**): "The Board of Directors of Krispy Kreme Doughnuts, Inc. (the 'Company') sets high standards for the Company's employees, officers and directors. Implicit in this philosophy is the importance of **sound corporate governance**. It is the duty of the Board of Directors to serve as a prudent fiduciary for shareholders and to **oversee the management** of the Company's business."

## Summary

This chapter began our discussion of business processes by looking at the sales/collection process. In addition to introducing new information about the process, we also saw how to apply other topics. Here's a summary of the chapter's main points, structured according to its learning objectives:

1. *Explain its role and purpose.* The sales/collection process helps accounting professionals track inventory sales and related cash collections. Because sales are the lifeblood of most business organizations, fair, accurate, and complete accounting is critical. In addition, assets associated with the sales/collection process, such as inventory and cash, are more subject to fraud than other types of assets.

2. *List and discuss, in order, the steps in the process.* The sales/collection process comprises seven steps: (i) Take a customer's order. (ii) Approve the customer's credit.

(iii) Fill the order based on approved credit. (iv) Ship the product. (v) Bill the customer. (vi) Collect payment. (vii) Process uncollectible receivables as necessary.

3. *Explain how the generic structure of most AIS applies to the process.* As described in Chapter 1, a generic accounting information system has five elements: inputs, processes, outputs, storage, and internal controls. Inputs and outputs most often come in the form of paper-based or electronic documents, such as the customer order, picking list, packing list, bill of lading, customer invoice, customer check, remittance advice, and deposit slip. For each document, accountants should understand its content and purpose, where it originates and where it terminates. The sales/collection process includes three major types of storage files: master (e.g., customers and inventory), transaction (e.g., sales), and junction (e.g., sales/inventory). Common transactions can be processed with paper-based journals and ledgers, or with the benefit of information technology (such as ERP systems and general ledger software). XBRL also includes a multitude of tags for information related to the process. Internal controls for the sales/collection process help fulfill the four purposes of internal control: safeguarding assets, ensuring financial statement reliability, promoting operating efficiency, and encouraging compliance with management directives.

4. *Process common transactions.* Common transactions associated with the sales/collection process include sales of goods and services for cash and on account, cash collections for sales on account, inventory returns, freight payments, and bad debt write-offs.

5. *Design and critique internal controls based on common risk exposures.* Most sales/collection processes have at least six major risk exposures. Table 12.3 summarizes the information discussed in the chapter.

6. *Develop and interpret process-related systems documentation.* Figures 12.2, 12.5, and 12.6 in the chapter present, respectively, a flowchart, data flow diagram, and REA model of the sales/collection process.

7. *Relate Porter's value chain to the process.* Considering the value chain's five primary activities, the sales/collection process has ties to "marketing and sales." It may also be connected to "service," to the extent that service is sold. For the support activities in the value chain, the process is connected to information technology, human resource management, and infrastructure.

**TABLE 12.3**
**Risks and Internal Controls in the Sales/Collection Process**

| Risk | Recommended Controls |
|---|---|
| Granting credit inappropriately | Third-party vendors<br>Formal credit approval process<br>Cash-only business |
| Selling unavailable products | Inventory verification<br>Maintaining adequate inventory |
| Filling the order incorrectly | Independent order checking<br>Information technology |
| Delivering damaged goods | Adequate packing<br>Insurance |
| Billing incorrectly | Document matching<br>Information technology |
| Mishandling cash receipts | Separation of duties<br>Restrictive check endorsements<br>Bank reconciliations |

**FIGURE 12.5**
**Partial Level Zero DFD of the Sales/ Collection Process**

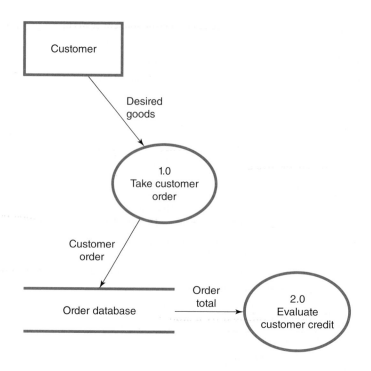

**FIGURE 12.6**
**Partial REA Model of the Sales/ Collection Process**

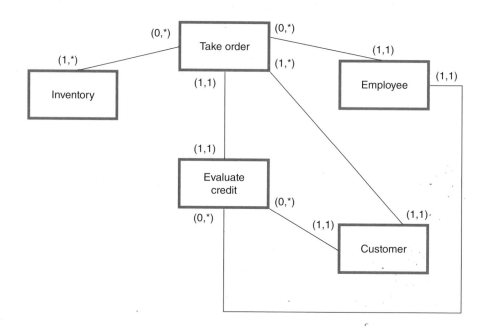

Key Terms

business process, *217*
common files, *223*
documents, *219*

freight terms, *220*
internal controls, *223*
steps, *218*

value chain, *217*

<table>
<tr><td>

Chapter
References

</td><td>

Hollander, A. S., E. L. Denna, and J. O. Cherrington. 2000. *Accounting, Information Technology and Business Solutions.* 2nd ed. New York: Irwin/McGraw-Hill.

Porter, M. 1998. *Competitive Advantage: Creating and Sustaining Superior Performance.* New York: Free Press.

</td></tr>
</table>

## End-of-Chapter Activities

1. *Reading review questions.*

    a. What activities are accounted for in the sales/collection process?

    b. What are the steps in the sales/collection process?

    c. How are the five generic elements of the AIS exemplified in the sales/collection process?

    d. What recordable transactions are commonly associated with the sales/collection process? How are they recorded in the AIS?

    e. What internal controls do organizations use in the sales/collection process? What risks do they address?

    f. Respond to the questions for this chapter's "AIS in the Business World."

2. *Reading review problem.* Krispy Kreme Doughnuts offers several ways community groups can use its products for fundraising; one such way is via fundraising certificates. Charitable groups fill out a fundraising application on KKD's Web site; the application is evaluated by a store manager, who verifies that the group's purpose is appropriate. The charitable group purchases the desired quantity of fundraising certificates from a local KKD store, then sells them at a higher price. For example, the charitable group might buy the certificates for $2 each and sell them for $5 each. More information about fundraising is available on the company's Web site (www .krispykreme.com) under the "fundraising" tab.

    a. What forms and documents would KKD use in the process described? Which generic step(s) in the sales/collection process would use each form?

    b. In a manner specified by your instructor (e.g., systems flowchart), document the process described from KKD's perspective.

    c. What risks do fundraising groups bear in the process? What internal controls would you recommend to a fundraising group to address those risks?

    d. Consider the following tables KKD might maintain for the process: fundraising group table, sell fundraising certificates table, redeem fundraising certificates table, redeem fundraising certificates/inventory table. What fields would you include in each table? Indicate primary keys by underlining and foreign keys with brackets.

    e. Based on the tables you laid out in (d), suggest one simple query and one complex query KKD might use. For each query, explain its purpose and indicate the fields you would incorporate.

3. *Multiple choice review*

    1. In a well-designed sales/collection process, the customer's credit should be evaluated:

        a. As the first step.

        b. Immediately after taking the customer's order.

        c. Immediately before billing the customer.

        d. By the salesperson taking the order.

    2. A remittance advice:

        a. Is the source document used to record cash receipts from a customer.

        b. Is the same as a sales invoice.

        c. Is not needed if payments are accepted only with checks.

        d. Is deposited in the bank.

3. Companies often rely on third-party vendors to avoid the risk of:

   a. Filling orders incorrectly.

   b. Selling products that are not available.

   c. Granting credit to customers who are not creditworthy.

   d. Billing the customer incorrectly.

4. A journal entry debits Cash and credits Accounts Receivable. Which of the following transactions is it recording?

   a. A cash sale

   b. Cash collected from a client

   c. Cash collected as deferred revenue

   d. Operating cash flow

5. All of the following are master files associated with the sales/collection process except:

   a. Employee.

   b. Customer.

   c. Inventory.

   d. Sales.

4. *Making choices and exercising judgment.* Rob, Teri, Kirk, and Peggy are students in the accounting program at Big State University. They have worked together on several projects throughout their classes and are considering starting a business together when they graduate. Their preliminary idea is a firm called Reliable Reminder Services (RRS). RRS would assist its clients in remembering important dates, purchasing and sending greeting cards, and providing specialized shopping services for important dates (birthdays, anniversaries, and the like). Using the seven generic sales/collection steps presented in the chapter, list and discuss the activities the students would likely incorporate in RRS's sales/collection process. Using one or more techniques specified by your instructor, create a document depicting the steps you develop.

5. *Field exercises.*

   a. Find examples of the documents discussed in the chapter. You may want to visit a local office supply store such as Office Depot or Staples or do an Internet search using the document names for your research.

   b. Contact a practicing accountant involved in auditing (either external or internal). Discuss the risks involved in the sales/collection process and internal controls he or she has observed in various organizations that address those risks.

6. *Modeling sales/collection processes.* In each of the following independent cases, use a systems documentation technique specified by your instructor to model the process.

   a. Dave's Pool Service is based in Upland, California; the firm offers a variety of pool- and spa-related services, including acid washing, routine maintenance, solar panel installation, and repair services. For regular customers, Dave prepares and mails paper invoices on a monthly basis; for one-time services, Dave leaves the invoice at the client's home. Dave accepts payment via check only; if a client fails to pay amounts billed within 30 days, Dave turns the case over to a collections firm. Dave deposits cash receipts in his personal checking account on a weekly basis; he does not maintain a separate business checking account.

   b. Steve and Mike Nauertz own an insurance agency with offices in Upland, Arcadia, and Pasadena, California; they offer several types of insurance, including automobile, motorcycle, homeowners, and whole life. When a client comes into one of the offices, one of the owners does a "needs assessment," which they record both on a paper form and in a relational database file. The client is then assigned to an office employee who presents the available options based on the needs assessment. Options include type of insurance, insurance providers, costs, and policy features. The client makes a choice; the employee writes the policy and collects the initial payment in cash or check. Thereafter, the insurance company bills the client directly; Nauertz Insurance collects a commission from the insurance company. Steve or Mike deposits client receipts in a business bank account daily; commissions are transmitted to the same account electronically.

c. Choose any organization where you do business regularly, such as a gas station, bookstore, or restaurant. Write a description of the sales/collection process, then document the process you described.

d. The chapter presented various diagrams of the first two steps in the sales/collection process. Extend those diagrams to cover Steps 3 through 6.

7. *Transaction processing.* BRN Corporation sells on credit with terms of 2/10, n/30. Freight charges are always paid by the customer when the goods are delivered by a common carrier. During the month of April 2011, BRN completed the following transactions:

| Date | Transaction |
| --- | --- |
| 2 | Sold inventory with a cost of $300 on account to TRB Corporation, $1,000. |
| 5 | Sold inventory with a cost of $200 for cash to FOF Corporation, $900. |
| 10 | Received cash from TRB Corporation for the sale on 2 April. |
| 15 | Wrote off uncollectible receivables, $500. |
| 19 | Sold inventory with a cost of $500 on account to TRB Corporation, $2,000. |
| 21 | Sold inventory with a cost of $300 for cash to FOF Corporation, $1,100. |
| 30 | Received cash from TRB Corporation for the sale on 19 April. |
| 30 | Estimated bad debts as 1% of total credit sales. |

a. Record the transactions in general journal form.
b. Compute BRN's gross profit for April.
c. Specify the source documents BRN would use for each transaction.
d. Create specifications for the following tables: customer, sell inventory, receive cash, inventory/sell inventory. Indicate primary and foreign keys in the usual ways.
e. Based on the table specifications in (d), suggest at least one complex query BRN might find useful. Which fields would you need to create the query?

8. *Internal controls.* Several potential problems in the sales/collection process are listed below. Indicate at least two internal controls that would address the problem. Also identify which of the four purposes of internal control it addresses.
a. A burglar takes cash while the office is closed.
b. A customer is unwilling to pay his bill.
c. A fire destroys inventory in the warehouse.
d. A sales clerk records incorrect items on a customer order.
e. An accounting clerk records cash received on account by debiting cash and accounts receivable.
f. Items ordered are missing from a shipment, although they appear on the packing list.
g. Merchandise is damaged during shipment.
h. Sales and warehouse clerks arrange to ship merchandise to their friends.
i. The cash receipts clerk steals money from incoming mail.
j. The customer invoice is sent before goods are shipped.

9. *Internal controls and risks.* Several risks are paired with potential internal controls in the list below. Place an "X" in the appropriate column to indicate if the internal control addresses the risk with which it is paired. Be prepared to explain your responses.

| Risk | Control | Does the Control Address the Risk? | |
| --- | --- | --- | --- |
| | | Yes | No |
| 1. Sales are lower than expected | Echo checks | | |
| 2. Salesperson extends credit limit | Separation of duties | | |
| 3. Customer exceeds credit limit | Employee background checks | | |
| 4. Order is filled incorrectly | Adequate supervision | | |
| 5. Merchandise is damaged during shipment | Sequentially numbered bill of lading | | |
| 6. Merchandise is shipped to the wrong address | Shipping via common carrier | | |
| 7. Customer is billed prematurely | Document matching | | |
| 8. Customer bill contains mathematical errors | Bank reconciliation | | |
| 9. Mailroom clerk steals cash from bank deposit | Employee bonding | | |
| 10. Uncollectable accounts exceed estimates | Video surveillance | | |

10. *Internal controls.* (CMA adapted, December 1993) Abid and Company manufactures a variety of pumps and valves that it distributes through several thousand plumbing supply houses as well as 100 manufacturer's representatives. As a result of the less-than-favorable business conditions that have existed over the last several years, Abid's cash flow situation has deteriorated. Accounts receivable have continually grown due to creeping extensions of time that Abid's customers have been taking in remitting payments for supplies. In addition, as Abid has been easing credit to its customers, bad debts have grown to 3 percent of sales.

Abid's president has hired Joe Jackler, an experienced cash manager, to improve Abid's liquidity position. Jackler met with Dora Mooney, Abid's controller, and ascertained that Abid's (i) product sales prices have a 20 percent margin over the sum of direct operating costs and all delivery and selling costs; (ii) production is currently slightly less than full capacity; (iii) current credit terms are 2/12, n/45, which is in line with industry practices; and (iv) dunning notices are sent monthly on all past due accounts with telephone follow-ups for delinquent accounts in excess of $8,000. On average, customers currently pay 35 days after the sale. Delinquent accounts are sent to collection agencies when they reach a past due status of 12 months.

From a review of credit records, Jackler was able to group Abid's customers into risk classes according to the probability of loss associated with sales to a customer, as follows:

| Risk Class | Probable Loss (%) |
|:----------:|-------------------|
| 1 | None |
| 2 | 0% to 0.5% |
| 3 | 0.6% to 1% |
| 4 | 2% to 3% |
| 5 | 4% to 6% |
| 6 | 7% to 12% |
| 7 | 13% to 20% |
| 8 | Over 20% |

After considering the available alternatives, Jackler has implemented the following changes to Abid's credit policies in order to improve cash flow:

- The credit terms extended to customers will change to 2/10, n/30. Jackler believes the current customers will accept this change as a sound business decision and, consequently, there will be minimal effect on sales. The overall effects of this change will be to improve accounts receivable turnover, reduce the opportunity costs of carrying receivables, and identify potentially troubled accounts sooner to minimize write-offs.

- Customers in risk groups 1 through 5 will continue to have the customary credit extended to them; selling to groups 6 and 7 will be under more stringent credit terms, such as cash on delivery; and sales to group 8 will require advance payments. Jackler believes this change will cause a reduction in sales; however, this reduction will come from the high-risk customer profile.

- Collection efforts will be increased to ensure better compliance with the new credit terms. Dunning notices will continue to be sent monthly; however, telephone follow-ups will be initiated for all delinquent accounts in excess of $2,000. Accounts outstanding nine months or more will be turned over to a collection agency. Jackler believes this action, coupled with the other changes in policy, will reduce bad debts to a level of 1 to 1.5 percent of sales.

Mooney is responsible for extending credit to customers who deal directly with the company and for establishing the guidelines under which manufacturer's representatives operate. Mooney has tailored credit to various customers to meet their needs and over time has developed a close relationship with a number of the larger customers. In view of the indicated impact the new policies will have on company sales and production, as well as on some of the larger customers, Mooney performed her own risk study. She concluded that some of Jackler's "risk classifications" were inappropriate and believes that some of the larger customers are better business risks than indicated in Jackler's analysis.

Mooney did not share her findings with Abid's president or with Jackler. She decided that to follow the policies in their entirety would reduce sales more than Jackler estimates and result in idle manufacturing capacity. Consequently, Mooney does not intend to totally comply with the new policies, particularly as they affect her larger customers.

What internal control strengths and weaknesses are indicated by the narrative? What additional internal controls would you recommend in this situation?

11. *Flowchart interpretation and internal controls analysis.* (CMA adapted, June 1994) The flowchart below depicts the sales/collection process for Richards Furniture Company, a mid-sized retailer of living room and bedroom furniture.

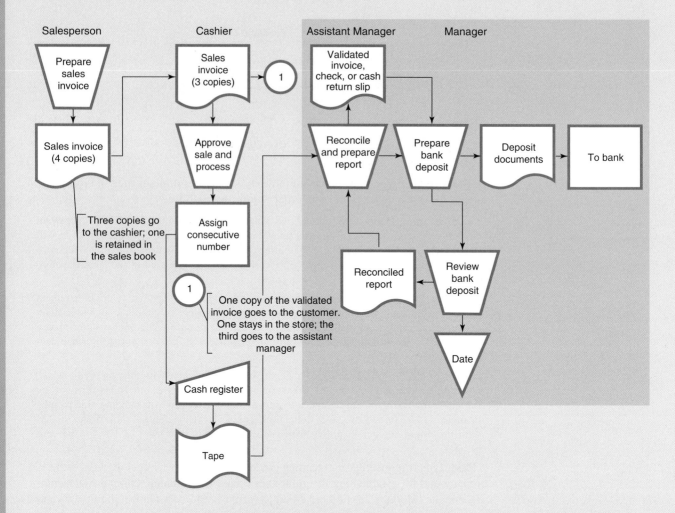

a. Identify and describe at least three weaknesses in the flowchart itself. For example, it does not have a "start" symbol.

b. What internal control weaknesses are evident based on the flowchart? Suggest controls that will address them.

c. List the steps Richards should complete as part of the process depicted. Then, redraw the flowchart based on them.

12. *Comprehensive problem.* Bonnie makes and sells her own jewelry over the Internet. A customer browses Bonnie's catalog online and fills out a sales order. The sales order is transmitted electronically to Bonnie, who checks her inventory for each item ordered. If the item is on hand, Bonnie packs it securely and ships it to the customer via a common carrier. If the item is not on hand, Bonnie e-mails the client with an expected shipment date; at that point, the customer must agree to wait until the expected shipment date or cancel the order. Bonnie encloses an invoice with all shipped merchandise; the client sends a check directly to Bonnie's bank for deposit. The bank reports all deposits to Bonnie on a weekly basis; Bonnie reconciles her bank account every day.

a. In a format specified by your instructor, document Bonnie's sales/collection process.

b. What are Bonnie's risk exposures? What internal controls does she have in place to address them? Which additional internal controls would you recommend?

c. Create database specifications for Bonnie's inventory and customer tables. Also create database specifications for any required junction tables.

d. Design a sales order form and a customer invoice for Bonnie.

13. *Terminology*. Match each item on the left with the most appropriate item on the right.

| | |
|---|---|
| 1. Bill of lading | a. Support activity |
| 2. Face-to-face, Internet, mail, phone | b. Specifies freight terms |
| 3. For deposit only | c. Restrictive endorsement |
| 4. Independent order checking | d. Primary activity |
| 5. Information technology | e. Order taking methods |
| 6. Outbound logistics | f. Junction file |
| 7. Picking list | g. Internal control |
| 8. Sales/inventory | h. Guides product selection from warehouse |
| 9. Sales department, credit department, warehouse | i. Flowchart column headings |
| 10. Value chain | j. Comprises primary and support activities |

14. *Multiple choice*. Please refer to the case in Problem 12 as you respond to these questions.

1. In a systems flowchart, which of the following is most likely to be depicted with a predefined process symbol?
   a. Browse catalog
   b. Make bank deposit
   c. E-mail client
   d. None of the above.

2. In a systems flowchart, which of the following is most likely to be depicted with a decision symbol?
   a. The customer's decision to order from Bonnie.
   b. Bonnie checking the inventory on hand.
   c. Bonnie's decision to reconcile her bank account.
   d. The client's decision to remit payment.

3. At what point will Bonnie make a journal entry that debits accounts receivable and credits sales?
   a. When the order is transmitted
   b. When the goods are shipped
   c. When the cash is deposited
   d. When Bonnie reconciles the bank statement

4. Which of the following internal controls should Bonnie implement in the first step of the sales/collection process?
   a. Data encryption
   b. Separation of duties
   c. Lockbox system
   d. Bank reconciliation

5. All of the following are likely to be tables in Bonnie's relational database except:
   a. Customer.
   b. Inventory.
   c. Employee.
   d. Order/inventory.

15. *Statement evaluation.* Indicate whether each of the following statements is (i) always true, (ii) sometimes true, or (iii) never true. For those that are (ii) sometimes true, explain when the statement is true.

a. A junction table would be required in a relational database for the sales/collection process.

b. Cash receipts clerks should reconcile a company's bank statement at least monthly.

c. Companies complete all activities in the value chain to serve their stakeholders.

d. Customers should borrow money to take advantage of cash discounts in paying their bills.

e. Documents in the sales/collection process can be paper or electronic.

f. In the sales/collection process, separation of duties can be applied to credit decisions.

g. Restrictive check endorsements eliminate the need for other internal controls over cash.

h. Separation of duties helps safeguard inventory in the sales/collection process.

i. Transactions in the sales/collection process require a bill of lading.

j. Web sites assist companies in the sales/collection process.

16. *Application of prior material.* Consider the following short case as you respond to the requirements for this problem:

The Institute for Computer Enthusiasts (ICE) sponsors four computer seminars each year: Access, Excel, PowerPoint, and QuickBooks. Participants can sign up for any or all of the seminars; pricing varies with the number of seminars and with the participant's membership and professional status as shown in the chart below:

| Classification | Single-Seminar Price | Four-Seminar Price |
| --- | --- | --- |
| Professional member | $40 | $120 |
| Student member | $30 | $100 |
| Non-member | $50 | $150 |

ICE has a four-member executive board: president, vice president, secretary, and treasurer. The vice president processes all registrations for each seminar; the treasurer collects payment at the beginning of each seminar.

a. Use COSO's enterprise risk management framework to develop an ERM plan for ICE's computer seminars.

b. How could ICE use the principles of business process management to improve its sales/collection process with respect to the seminars?

c. ICE's board of directors is interested in expanding their seminar offerings to other IT-related topics. Consider the other topics we've discussed in previous chapters. Work with a group of students to develop materials for a seminar based on one of them.

17. *Excel application.* Consider the data below and on the next page for DSC Corporation's recent sales. (The file is available on my AIS blog in the 3 February 2014 post.)

| Transaction Number | Sales Revenue | Cost of Goods Sold |
| --- | --- | --- |
| 1 | $ 4,818 | $ 973 |
| 2 | 1,070 | 411 |
| 3 | 3,783 | 817 |
| 4 | 4,862 | 979 |
| 5 | 1,510 | 477 |
| 6 | 4,419 | 913 |
| 7 | 3,269 | 740 |
| 8 | 2,477 | 622 |
| 9 | 2,409 | 611 |
| 10 | 3,643 | 796 |

| Transaction Number | Sales Revenue | Cost of Goods Sold |
|---|---|---|
| 11 | 4,163 | 874 |
| 12 | 1,926 | 539 |
| 13 | 4,659 | 949 |
| 14 | 4,421 | 913 |
| 15 | 1,120 | 418 |
| 16 | 1,107 | 416 |
| 17 | 3,320 | 748 |
| 18 | 4,955 | 993 |
| 19 | 3,568 | 785 |
| 20 | 2,315 | 597 |

a. Use appropriate formulas to calculate the following amounts in the columns indicated: gross profit (Column D), cost of goods sold divided by sales (Column E), gross profit divided by sales (Column F), and cost of goods sold divided by gross profit (Column G).

b. Use Excel's conditional formatting ability to format each added column as follows: Column D, Top 10%. Column E, Greater than 25%. Column F, Green solid fill data bar. Column G, Below average.

c. Explain how conditional formatting could be useful in the sales/collection process.

# Chapter **Thirteen**

# Acquisition/Payment Process

## AIS in the Business World

### Krispy Kreme Doughnuts

The acquisition/payment process can focus on virtually any asset, but most commonly focuses on inventory. Since Krispy Kreme makes its own doughnuts (in the conversion process, which we'll explore in the next chapter), "inventory" refers to the required raw materials—items like flour, yeast, and sugar.

To order raw materials, KKD would issue a purchase order to a vendor. The purchase order includes information like the vendor's identification data (name, address, and so on), the items KKD wants to purchase, the quantities of each item and the expected cost of each item. The purchase order can be electronic or paper-based.

In its relational database, KKD would include an "issue purchase order" table like the one shown below:

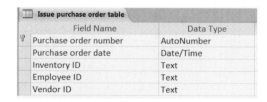

| Issue purchase order table | |
| --- | --- |
| Field Name | Data Type |
| Purchase order number | AutoNumber |
| Purchase order date | Date/Time |
| Inventory ID | Text |
| Employee ID | Text |
| Vendor ID | Text |

Allowing only employees in the purchasing department to issue purchase orders is a form of internal control—specifically, separation of duties.

### Discussion Questions

1. What steps, other than "issue purchase order," are included in the acquisition/payment process?
2. How is the acquisition/payment process related to Porter's value chain?
3. List and discuss, within the context of the acquisition/payment process, examples of each generic element of the AIS.

The acquisition/payment process is the flip side of the sales/collection process. Like the sales/collection process, it follows a fairly common set of steps and uses some consistent documents and internal controls across a wide range of companies and industries.

The chapter follows the same structure as Chapter 12. When you finish studying this chapter, you should be able to complete the following tasks within the context of the acquisition/payment process:

1. Explain its role and purpose.
2. List and discuss, in order, the steps in the process.
3. Explain how the generic structure of most AIS applies to the process.
4. Process common transactions.
5. Design and critique internal controls based on common risk exposures.
6. Develop and interpret process-related systems documentation.
7. Explain how the process relates to Porter's value chain.

Although it can be applied to virtually anything an organization needs to acquire, our discussion of the acquisition/payment process will focus on inventory. In addition, the acquisition/payment process can incorporate noninventory purchases such as fixed assets (equipment, furniture, and similar items) and other current assets (such as supplies).

## PROCESS DESCRIPTION

The primary purpose of the acquisition/payment process is to obtain the resources the organization needs and to pay for them. Fundamentally, organizations exist to create value for their stakeholders; the acquisition/payment process is one element of that basic purpose. In the last chapter, we looked at Porter's value chain as a way to think about business processes; the acquisition/payment process is principally related to procurement and inbound logistics. Procurement is a synonym for purchasing; inbound logistics refers to the process of getting resources from "where they are" to "where they are needed." For example, McGraw-Hill might use air and ground transportation to ship books to university bookstores.

# Reflection and Self-Assessment                    13.1

Other than inventory, what resources would an organization commonly need to create value for its stakeholders?

Although an acquisition/payment process can have slight differences across organizations and industries, its basic **steps** include (Hollander, Denna, and Cherrington, 2000)

1. *Request goods and services based on monitored need.* Organizations use all sorts of tools and techniques to establish the need for a good or service. Inventory levels, for example, might be monitored with a reorder point; orders could be based on an economic order quantity formula. Other resources may be time-sensitive; for example, your car insurance bill may be paid monthly or semiannually. A special project, such as the design and implementation of an accounting information system, may lead to a request for goods or services on a more episodic basis. In many organizations, requests for inventory, supplies, and services are coordinated through a central purchasing department, thus creating economies of scale and discounted purchase prices.

In many organizations, employees can use a departmental credit card to purchase small items quickly. But, those purchases must be monitored as a form of internal control.

2. *Authorize a purchase.* This step, illustrated in this chapter's AIS in the Business World, promotes strong internal control (discussed in greater depth later in the chapter). For example, your AIS instructor may be authorized to select her own textbook for the course. Or the decision may be a collaborative one, with a department chair or course coordinator having the final authorization for placing a textbook order with your university bookstore. Even in the bookstore, not every employee is authorized to deal with publishers and other suppliers; rather, that right is probably vested in one employee or a small group of employees.

3. *Purchase goods/services.* Once a purchase has been authorized, the appropriate documentation (purchase order) must be submitted to the vendor/supplier.

4. *Receive goods and services.* Major purchases of goods, particularly inventory, are received through a dedicated receiving department for stronger internal control. The receiving department should get a "blind copy" of the purchase order. A "blind copy" indicates what items are expected from what vendor, but not the item quantities. Thus, the receiving department employees must count the items to verify the quantity.

An audit trail consists of source documents, journal entries, and ledger postings; it also may involve electronic data in a computer-based accounting information system.

5. *Disburse cash.* Once the goods have been properly purchased and received, accounting personnel generate payment to the vendor. Keeping a solid audit trail is very important here, as it is in the other steps and in the sales/collection process. Document matching is an important form of internal control at this step. Before issuing a check, the accounting department should have the purchase order (to show what was purchased), the receiving report (to show what was received), and the vendor invoice (to show the amount due). All three documents should agree before payment is issued.

6. *When necessary, process purchase returns.* If received goods are defective, do not meet quality standards, or are otherwise unacceptable to the buyer, they may need to be returned to the vendor.

As with our discussion of the sales/collection process, keep in mind that those six steps are very generic. Each organization will have its own modifications to the basic steps; the fundamental idea is purchasing the goods and services you need, when you need them, and paying for them timely. Figure 13.1 shows a partial systems flowchart depicting some of the basic steps in the acquisition/payment process (later in the chapter, you'll find a Level Zero DFD and a REA model encompassing the same steps).

**FIGURE 13.1**
**Partial Systems Flowchart of the Acquisition/Payment Process**

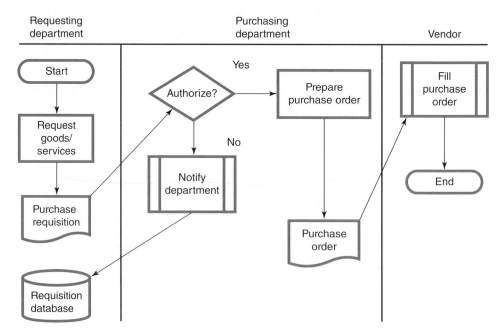

The steps in the sales/collection process are related to those in the acquisition/payment process as shown in the table below:

| Sales/Collection | Acquisition/Payment |
|---|---|
| Take customer order | Purchase goods and services |
| Ship the product | Receive goods and services |
| Collect payment | Disburse cash |

As we did in Chapter 12, let's take a look at how the five generic parts of an AIS are applied to the acquisition/payment process.

# AIS STRUCTURE

**Documents** in the acquisition/payment process, as in the sales/collection process, can be paper-based, electronic, or some combination of the two. Table 13.1 summarizes the most commonly used documents in the acquisition/payment process; we'll take a look at each of them in more detail in the following paragraphs. Note that an output from one step in the acquisition/payment process often serves as an input to subsequent steps; likewise, an output from one organization can serve as an input to another.

Once an operating department establishes the need for a good or service, its personnel generate a purchase requisition. The purchase requisition, like all forms, should have a clear title and plenty of white space for easy reading. Information should be complete and logically laid out. In most cases, the operating department keeps a copy of the purchase requisition for its own files and sends a copy to the purchasing department; in Figure 13.1, the requesting department stores the requisition electronically, then sends the paper copy to the purchasing department. Figure 13.2 shows an example of a purchase requisition.

The purchasing department, then, will consolidate various purchase requisitions into a single purchase order. Consolidating purchase requisitions may allow the company to take advantage of quantity discounts. Creating a separate purchasing department also facilitates strong internal control through the separation of duties. Purchasing agents may be in charge of dealing with a specific set of vendors, a certain group of parts or supplies, or the purchase requisitions from one or more operating departments. While the purchase requisition generated by the operating department is an informal, internal document, the signed purchase order functions as a "contract" between the company and the vendor. The purchase requisition will normally include the goods and quantities requested; the purchase order will

**TABLE 13.1**
**Documents Used in the Acquisition/Payment Process**

| Document Name | Basic Purpose | Originator | Recipient |
|---|---|---|---|
| Purchase requisition | To request that the purchasing department order goods or services from a vendor | Operating department | Purchasing department |
| Purchase order | To specify the items to be ordered, freight terms, shipping address, and other information for the vendor | Purchasing department | Vendor |
| Receiving report | To ensure that goods have been ordered and received in good condition | Receiving department | Various departments |
| Vendor invoice | To request payment from a customer | Vendor | Accounting department |
| Check | To pay the vendor | Accounting department | Vendor |

**FIGURE 13.2**   **Purchase Requisition**

# George Mason University

**PURCHASE REQUISITION**

Sample   Sample

**835457**

| SUGGESTED VENDOR | DELIVERY INSTRUCTIONS | DEPARTMENTAL APPROVAL |
|---|---|---|
| | DELIVER TO: | DATE NEEDED: |
| | DEPARTMENT: | FUND CODE: |
| | TELEPHONE: | APPROVAL SIGNATURE: |
| | BUILDING: | |
| | ROOM NUMBER: | TITLE: |
| | | DATE APPROVED: |

| ITEM NUMBER | DESCRIPTION OF ITEM/SERVICE DESIRED | | QUANTITY | UNIT | UNIT PRICE | EXTENSION |
|---|---|---|---|---|---|---|
| | | | | | | |
| | | | | | | |
| | | | | | | |
| | | | | | | |
| | | | | | | |
| | | | | | | |
| | | | | | | |
| | | | | | | |
| | | | | | | |
| | | | | | | |
| | | | TOTAL AMOUNT OF REQUISITION: | | | |

+++ FOR BUYER'S USE ONLY +++

| VENDOR ADDRESS: | CONTRACT NO: |
|---|---|
| | FOB: |
| | DELIVERY: |
| CONTACT: | BUYER: |
| PHONE: | REMARKS |
| EIN/SSN: | |

specify the vendor, the expected price, the freight terms, and other important data for the transaction. In most cases, the purchasing department keeps a copy on file; it also sends copies to the receiving department and the accounting department. Figure 13.3 shows an example of a purchase order. From a database perspective, purchase requisitions and purchase orders may have a many-to-many relationship. Similarly, each will have a many-to-many relationship with inventory.

When the goods arrive from the vendor, the receiving department prepares a receiving report. The goods should be matched and verified against an existing purchase order so that the company does not receive goods that were not properly ordered; remember that the receiving department gets a "blind copy" of the purchase order. The receiving personnel also may verify the quality and condition of the goods before accepting delivery. Commonly, the receiving department copies the accounting department and purchasing department as well.

**FIGURE 13.3**
**Purchase Order**

# Purchase Order

Purchase Order No.:_____

Requisition No.:_____

Vendor Code:_____

Vendor Name:_____

Vendor Address:_____

Vendor Contact:   Vendor Phone: (_____) _____-_____

Order Description

| Product Item No. | Product Description | Quantity | Estimated Cost | Tax | Total |
|---|---|---|---|---|---|
|  |  |  |  |  |  |
|  |  |  |  |  |  |
|  |  |  |  |  |  |
|  |  |  |  |  |  |
|  |  |  |  |  |  |
|  |  |  |  |  |  |
|  |  |  |  |  |  |
|  |  |  |  |  |  |

Notice that the accounting department receives both a copy of the purchase order and a copy of the receiving report. When the vendor mails an invoice for payment, then, accounting personnel use those documents to ensure that the invoice reflects goods that were properly ordered and received before generating payment. The department then issues a check in payment of the invoice, taking advantage of any discounts offered.

How do organizations process the input documents to create outputs for the acquisition/payment process? They use the seven steps discussed earlier in this chapter. In addition, transactions must be appropriately recorded in the AIS.

# Reflection and Self-Assessment                                     13.2

What journal entries would you make for each of the following transactions? Which input/output documents would trigger each one?

- Purchase of inventory on account
- Purchase of inventory for cash
- Cash payments for payments on account
- Inventory returns

As you read in Chapter 1, "storage" in the AIS often happens in a computer database or other electronic medium. Even in the small number of cases where storage happens with paper files, though, the AIS still must capture certain basic information in master files and transaction files. Table 13.2 shows a list of the **common files,** along with the data they would contain.

**TABLE 13.2**    **File Structures in the Acquisition/Payment Process**

| File Name | File Type | Primary Key | Other Data |
|---|---|---|---|
| Employee | Master | Employee ID | Last name, first name<br>Street address, city, state, ZIP code<br>Phone number<br>Emergency contact<br>Department<br>Hire date |
| Vendor | Master | Vendor ID | Vendor company name<br>Street address, city, state, ZIP code<br>Phone number<br>Contact person name<br>Credit limit<br>Date of first purchase |
| Inventory | Master | Product ID | Product name<br>Beginning balance date<br>Beginning balance quantity<br>Beginning balance cost per unit<br>Preferred supplier |
| Purchases | Transaction | Transaction ID | Transaction date<br>Vendor ID<br>Employee ID |
| Purchases/inventory | Junction | Transaction ID | Product ID<br>Quantity purchased<br>Purchase price per unit |

Notice that both the sales/collection and acquisition/payment processes need data from the employee table. Although conceptually possible to create a separate employee table for each process/department, most organizations find it simpler to use a single employee table—that's why you need a field titled "department." The purchases/inventory table is needed because each inventory item can be involved in multiple purchase transactions, and each purchase transaction can include multiple inventory items.

In the next section, we'll turn our attention to the last generic AIS element: internal controls.

## INTERNAL CONTROLS

As with the sales/collection process, our discussion is centered on the various risks managers confront in the acquisition/payment process. Many of the controls discussed in the last chapter also apply here, so don't consider the list that follows comprehensive or exhaustive. Remember: The idea is to implement internal controls that provide *reasonable* assurance—not *absolute* assurance. Even if the latter were possible, it almost certainly would not be cost-effective in most organizations.

As in the previous chapter, the numbered items below suggest risks to be addressed; the lettered items beneath them discuss possible **internal controls.**

1. Ordering unneeded goods.
   a. *Institute a system for monitoring inventory levels.* In addition to traditional systems like EOQ, many organizations use information technology to monitor inventory levels. Jonietz (2001) reported on the use of wireless systems in a Tulsa-based retail warehouse for inventory control.
   b. *Require justification for unusual orders or orders over a specified dollar amount.* If an employee is ordering goods unnecessarily, or is attempting to defraud the organization by ordering goods for personal benefits, an additional authorizing signature or approval process can be effective in detecting the problem.
   c. *Specify the business purpose for ordered goods.* This control is connected to the previous one. Consider, for example, a company with unusually high travel expenses; employees should be required to justify the business purpose of a trip before taking it.

2. Purchasing goods from inappropriate vendors.
   a. *Develop and enforce a conflict-of-interest policy.* Such policies make clear the actions that constitute a conflict of interest, as well as the consequences for engaging in those actions. The World Wide Web Consortium (www.w3.org) established a detailed policy in 2003; you may view it at their Web site: www.w3.org/2000/09/06-conflictpolicy.html.
   b. *Establish criteria for supplier reliability and quality of goods.* Managers may establish standards for delivery time, product quality, and availability for their suppliers. Home Depot (www.homedepot.com), for example, requires its vendors to maintain adequate inventory levels in their own operations so that they can fill Home Depot's inventory needs. Many organizations use a "preferred vendor list" for that purpose.

The value chain consists of four support activities (infrastructure, human resource management, technology development, and procurement) and five primary activities (inbound logistics, operations, outbound logistics, marketing and sales, and service).

   c. *Create strategic alliances with preferred vendors.* Porter (1985, p. 33) conceptualized the value chain as a way of "examining all the activities a firm performs and how they interact. . . . The value chain disaggregates a firm into its strategically relevant activities in order to understand the behavior of costs and the existing and potential sources of differentiation." When an organization is particularly expert at one or more value chain activities, it may form a strategic alliance with organizations that are more adept at other value chain components. For example, an outstanding manufacturer may establish a strategic alliance with a particular common carrier, thus creating value for both organizations.

3. Receiving unordered or defective goods.

a. *Match receiving reports with approved purchase orders.* Document matching is a fundamental internal control found in many organizations. In the acquisition/payment process, the receiving clerk should verify that goods have been ordered by an authorized company representative before accepting them. Goods received without a purchase order are suspicious; such receipts should either be refused outright or investigated more carefully to ensure that no fraud is involved.

b. *Inspect goods before accepting a shipment.* This control is especially applicable when dealing with very specialized goods. Receiving clerks should have a clear grasp of acceptable quality standards and verify that (at least) a sampling of products meets those standards.

c. *Insure products en route.* Purchasing transit insurance cannot necessarily prevent damage, but it can help organizations recover financially if goods are damaged in transit.

4. Experiencing theft of inventory and/or cash.

a. *Establish an internal audit function.* The Sarbanes-Oxley Act of 2002 has done a lot to establish the importance of internal audits in organizations. Your university may have a separate class on internal auditing; you also can get more information about the field from the Institute of Internal Auditors (www.theiia.org/).

b. *Reconcile bank statements promptly.* Consider the case of Wholelife Counseling Center (Hurt, 1994). In that organization, failure to reconcile bank statements promptly led to a major loss of cash due to embezzlement.

c. *Separate authorization, custody, and usage functions for both inventory and cash.* Separation of duties is another common, and essential, internal control procedure. Three important duties should always be separated to foster good internal control: physical custody of an asset, authorization for its use, and recordkeeping associated with it.

d. *Install employee monitoring systems.* Systems like these are controversial and may involve ethical and legal issues. Consider, for example, one company that put detection sensors in its employees' identification badges. The sensors allowed management to track employee movements inside the corporate headquarters.

e. *Bond employees who handle high-value goods.* Fidelity bonding is a form of insurance focused on employee behavior. According to Kishel and Kishel (1993), three types of fidelity bonds are common. "Individual bonds cover theft by a specific named individual. Schedule bonds list every name or position to be covered. Blanket bonds, the most encompassing of the three, cover all employees without reference to individual names or positions."

5. Making errors in paying invoices.

a. *Require document matching (purchase order, receiving report, invoice) before issuing a check.* This control technique is especially effective when incorporated with good separation of duties. When the accountant/cash payments clerk has all three documents in hand, he or she will know that goods were properly ordered and received. The invoice will show the amount due, and the accountant/cash payments clerk will cut a check for the vendor. Notice how, in a relational database or ERP system, a cash payments clerk could create a query to match the documents.

b. *Employ information technology to take advantage of available discounts.* Most general ledger software packages, such as QuickBooks or Great Plains Dynamics, can prompt users to pay invoices before cash discounts expire.

c. *Stamp documents "paid" to avoid duplicate payments.* This control seems simple (and it is!), but it is very effective in avoiding duplicate payments. Whether documents are stamped electronically or physically, they should be somehow marked so they are not paid more than once.

Those risks, and the suggested internal controls that accompany them, are by no means exhaustive. In designing and evaluating internal controls for the acquisition/payment process, you must develop an intimate knowledge of an organization's processes and personnel. Use your own creativity and critical thinking abilities, coupled with your sense of cost–benefit issues, when confronted with the important task of internal control assessment in practice.

## Reflection and Self-Assessment                    13.3

Relate the six risks described above to Brown's taxonomy of risk. Explain whether each suggested control is primarily preventive/detective/corrective. Suggest one additional internal control for each risk.

## SYSTEMS DOCUMENTATION

Figure 13.1 showed a partial flowchart of the steps in the acquisition/payment process. Figures 13.5 and 13.6 at the end of the chapter show, respectively, a Level Zero DFD and a REA model of the same steps.

## CRITICAL THINKING

The chapter discussed several common documents associated with the acquisition/payment process, providing examples of two (purchase requisition and purchase order). A sample receiving report is shown in Figure 13.4.

The relational database form would be based on the receiving report/inventory table; a junction table is required because each receiving report can include many inventory items, and each inventory item can be included on many receiving reports. In the junction table, Employee ID and Vendor ID are foreign keys. Figure 13.4 also includes a subform comprising two fields: Inventory ID and Quantity received.

**FIGURE 13.4**
**Receiving Report Form**

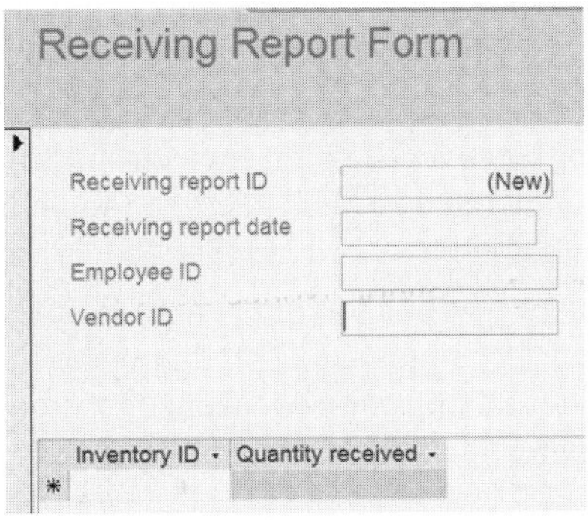

Receiving Report Form

Receiving report ID          (New)
Receiving report date
Employee ID
Vendor ID

Inventory ID · Quantity received ·

When a shipment arrives at the receiving department, an employee would query the database/ERP system to ensure that it is related to a valid purchase order. Provided it is, the receiving department employee would access the receiving report form, count the items received and record the relevant data.

Handling receiving transactions in that way promotes strong internal control by:

1. Matching the shipment with an existing purchase order.
2. Requiring the receiving department to count the items received.
3. Establishing responsibility for the receiving transaction by including the Employee ID in the form.
4. Having one centralized location for receiving all shipments.

The Accounting department would be able to **view** (not edit) both the purchase order and the receiving report as an additional internal control (document matching) before issuing a check to pay the vendor's invoice.

## BUSINESS PROCESS RELATIONSHIPS

So, now we've looked at both the sales/collection process and the acquisition/payment process. Keeping in mind that the two complement one another in two different organizations, here's a comprehensive view of both processes:

1. An operating department in the buying organization requests goods and services. For example, the production department might need additional raw materials. Or the accounting department might need new computers. A purchase requisition is the relevant document in this step. The purchase requisition serves as an important internal control by allowing the organization to respond to legitimate needs, take advantage of quantity discounts, and establish relationships with suppliers based on objective criteria. A purchase requisition would indicate the items needed and their quantities; one copy would typically remain with the requisitioning department, while another copy would go to purchasing.

2. The purchasing department in the buying organization authorizes the purchase. Having a central location that handles all purchasing for an organization is an important element of internal control. It promotes adequate supervision, helping ensure that the organization is only buying things that are legitimately needed; in addition, it promotes operating efficiency through coordination. A purchasing agent would complete a serially numbered purchase order based on one or more requisitions; the purchase order would be transmitted to the supplier electronically and/or in paper form. One copy of the purchase order, without the quantities of items ordered, would be sent to the receiving department; a second copy would go to the accounting department.

3. The sales department in the selling organization takes the customer's order. Taking a customer order can refer to receiving a purchase order; on the other hand, the selling organization can receive orders over the phone, electronically (such as through a Web site), or via electronic data interchange. The sales staff member would fill out an order form based on the data in the purchase order.

4. The credit department in the selling organization approves the customer's credit. Having a credit department promotes good separation of duties. If the sales staff is allowed to grant credit, internal control is weakened; customers might be allowed to purchase items on credit when they are not creditworthy, which can lead to collection problems later.

5. The warehouse in the selling organization fills the order based on approved credit. Again, we see good separation of duties here—physical custody of inventory is separated from its recordkeeping (handled in the accounting department) and from authorization for its use (which comes from the sales and credit departments). The warehouse employee would complete a picking slip to show what merchandise he or she took off the shelves.

6. The selling organization's shipping department ships the product. The shipping department would verify the customer's name and address; shipping also would fill out a packing slip to enclose with the goods, showing what was shipped. If the seller uses a common carrier such as UPS to ship the goods, a bill of lading also would be required. Insurance could be an important internal control here as well. The shipping department would send a copy of the shipping documents to the accounting department, as the shipment would trigger a journal entry recording the sale.

7. The buying organization's receiving department receives the goods. The receiving department would have a "blind copy" of the related purchase order(s). A blind copy contains all the usual information but not the quantities ordered. Thus, the receiving department can verify that the goods really were ordered (an important element of internal control) but would have to count the merchandise received physically, rather than simply verifying quantities against the purchase order. Receiving would send a copy of the receiving report to accounting and the merchandise itself to the warehouse or the location where it is needed.

8. The billing department in the selling organization bills the client. Document matching is an important internal control in this step and the ones that follow. Before issuing a bill, the selling organization needs to ensure that the client has indeed ordered the goods *and* that the goods have actually been shipped. Separation of duties also comes into play here, as the authorization to bill is separated from the physical custody of the inventory. The invoice (bill) could be mailed, faxed, and/or transmitted electronically; it would normally include the payment terms (e.g., 2/10, n/30) and the seller's address.

9. The cash disbursements department in the buying organization disburses cash. The cash disbursements department needs to ensure that the goods really were ordered (purchase order), that they were received (receiving report), and that the company is being billed for the correct amount (invoice). If all three documents match, the company could issue a check and/or an electronic funds transfer in payment of the invoice. The cash disbursements clerk would typically not be a signatory on the company's checking account; rather, the clerk would prepare the check and send it to an authorized signer—once again promoting good internal control through separation of duties. Checks would be sequentially numbered; they should ideally be kept in a locked filing cabinet until needed.

10. The cash receipts department in the selling organization collects payment. If the payment is mailed, it would be received in the selling organization's mailroom. Adequate supervision in the mailroom is an important internal control, as it is throughout most business processes. Most companies will not accept currency and coin through the mail, as it weakens internal control. The mail clerk would separate the check from the remittance advice; the check would be endorsed restrictively and prepared for deposit. The remittance advice would go to the accounting department to serve as a source document for the related journal entry.

So, that's a comprehensive picture of both the acquisition/payment and sales/collection business processes. I've described an "ideal" situation here; as an accounting professional, you might be called upon to audit or recommend improvements to similar systems in practice.

## Summary

This chapter continued our discussion of business processes by looking at the acquisition/ payment process. In addition to introducing new information about the process, we also saw how to apply other topics. Here's a summary of the chapter's main points, structured according to its learning objectives:

1. *Explain its role and purpose.* The acquisition/payment process is all about an organization acquiring the resources it needs to create value for its stakeholders. It's most often applied to inventory, but can be applied to virtually any resource.

2. *List and discuss, in order, the steps in the process.* The acquisition/payment process comprises six steps: (i) request goods and services based on monitored need; (ii) authorize a purchase; (iii) purchase goods/services; (iv) receive goods and services; (v) disburse cash; and (vi) when necessary, process purchase returns.

3. *Explain how the generic structure of most AIS applies to the process.* Inputs and outputs most often come in the form of paper-based or electronic documents, such as the purchase requisition, purchase order, receiving report, vendor invoice, and check. For each document, accountants should understand its content and purpose, where it originates, and where it terminates. The acquisition/payment process includes three major types of storage files: master (e.g., vendors and inventory), transaction (e.g., purchases), and junction (e.g., purchases/inventory). Common transactions can be processed with paper-based journals and ledgers or with the benefit of information technology (such as ERP systems and general ledger software). XBRL also includes a multitude of tags for information related to the process. Internal controls for the acquisition/payment process help fulfill the four purposes of internal control: safeguarding assets, ensuring financial statement reliability, promoting operating efficiency, and encouraging compliance with management directives.

4. *Process common transactions.* Common transactions associated with the acquisition/ payment process include purchases of goods and services for cash and on account, cash payments for purchases on account, and inventory returns.

5. *Design and critique internal controls based on common risk exposures.* Most acquisition/ payment processes have at least five major risk exposures. Table 13.3 summarizes the information discussed in the chapter.

**TABLE 13.3**
**Risks and Internal Controls in the Acquisition/Payment Process**

| Risk | Recommended Controls |
|------|----------------------|
| Ordering unneeded goods | Inventory monitoring system<br>Order justification<br>Business purpose specification |
| Using inappropriate vendors | Conflict of interest policy<br>Supplier criteria<br>Strategic alliances |
| Receiving unordered/defective goods | Document matching<br>Inspection<br>Insurance |
| Theft of inventory/cash | Internal audit<br>Bank reconciliations<br>Separation of duties<br>Employee monitoring systems<br>Employee bonding |
| Payment errors | Document matching<br>Information technology<br>"Paid" stamp |

6. *Develop and interpret process-related systems documentation.* Figures 13.1, 13.5, and 13.6 present, depictions of portions of the acquisition/payment process

7. *Explain how the process is related to Porter's value chain.* The acquisition/payment process has several links to Porter's value chain. "Procurement" (a support activity) is another name for the purchasing department—a key component in this process. Once goods are purchased, they must be moved from the vendor to the buyer, a description of inbound logistics. Information technology is important in all business processes; specific to the acquisition/payment process are things like RFID, UPC codes, and bar code scanners.

**FIGURE 13.5**
**Partial Level Zero DFD of the Acquisition/ Payment Process**

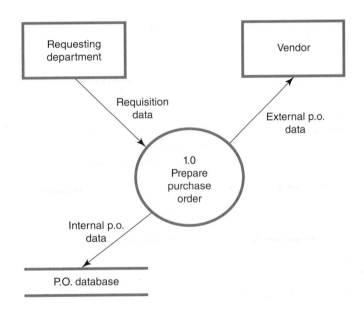

**FIGURE 13.6**
**Partial REA Model of the Acquisition/ Payment Process**

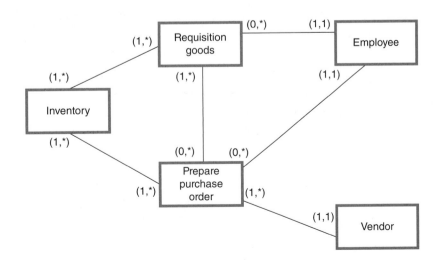

## Key Terms

common files, *244*          internal controls, *245*          steps, *239*

documents, *241*

## Chapter References

Hollander, A. S., E. L. Denna, and J. O. Cherrington. 2000. *Accounting, Information Technology, and Business Solutions.* 2nd ed. New York: Irwin/McGraw-Hill.

Hurt, R. 1994. "Wholelife Counseling Center." *Journal of Accounting Case Research,* pp. 97–98.

Jonietz, E. 2001. "Wireless Stockroom." *Technology Review,* July/August, p. 32.

Kishel, G., and P. Kishel. 1993. "Safeguarding Your Business." *Black Enterprise,* July, pp. 98–104.

Porter, M. 1985. *Competitive Advantage: Creating and Sustaining Superior Performance.* New York: Free Press.

## End-of-Chapter Activities

1. *Reading review questions.*

   a. What is the basic purpose of the acquisition/payment process?

   b. What steps do companies commonly complete as part of the acquisition/payment process?

   c. How are the generic elements of the AIS exemplified in the acquisition/payment process?

   d. What risks do managers face as part of the acquisition/payment process? What internal controls help reduce exposure to those risks?

   e. Prepare a response to the questions for this chapter's "AIS in the Business World."

2. *Reading review problem.* The chapter discussed how the acquisition/payment process functions for inventory, but it can also apply to virtually any asset on an organization's balance sheet. In responding to the following questions, consider KKD's capital assets, such as buildings and equipment.

   a. If a KKD franchise location wants to purchase equipment through the KKD corporate office, what document would the franchise use? What document would the corporate office use to buy the equipment from a vendor?

   b. What documents would the franchise location need before issuing a check to pay for the equipment?

   c. Suppose a franchise location purchased a piece of equipment with a list price of $25,000; transportation and testing costs totaled $5,000, and sales tax of 5% was levied on the list price alone. Create the required journal entry if the franchise location paid 30% of the list price, all the sales tax and all the transportation and testing costs in cash and financed the remainder with a 10-month, 6% note payable.

   d. Other than document matching prior to issuing a check, what internal controls should the franchise location have in place with respect to the equipment?

   e. Each purchase transaction can involve multiple pieces of equipment, but each piece of equipment is only purchased one time. What tables should the franchise location maintain in its relational database for the purchase transaction and the equipment itself? What fields would each table contain? Indicate primary and foreign keys in the usual way.

3. *Multiple choice review.*

   1. The acquisition/payment process can involve an organization buying:

      a. Inventory.

      b. Plant assets.

      c. Supplies.

      d. All of the above.

   2. All of the following are methods for monitoring inventory levels except:

      a. Reorder point.

      b. FIFO and LIFO.

c. Time.

d. RFID.

3. Which of the following documents specifies items to be ordered, freight terms, shipping address, and other information for a vendor?

a. Purchase requisition

b. Purchase order

c. Receiving report

d. Bill of lading

4. Internal controls that address the risk of purchasing goods from inappropriate vendors include:

a. Strategic alliances.

b. RFID technology.

c. Sequentially numbered purchase orders.

d. Order justification.

5. The primary key for the inventory master file is most likely to be:

a. Product name.

b. Product description.

c. Product ID.

d. Quantity on hand.

4. *Making choices and exercising judgment.* Consider the following short case:

FMD Corporation is a multinational corporation, with corporate headquarters in Colorado. The corporate headquarters comprises the following divisions: marketing, finance, operations, information systems, and human resources. The information systems division provides IT support and training to the remaining corporate divisions.

a. FMD has asked you to design a process by which the other divisions request work from the IT division. How would you adapt the generic steps in the acquisition/payment process to that situation?

b. Once you have designed the process, use one of the techniques discussed in Part Two of this book (flowchart/DFD/REA model) to document it.

c. Create database specifications for the process you describe.

5. *Field exercises.*

a. Contact a practicing accountant involved in auditing (either external or internal). Discuss the risks involved in the acquisition/payment process and internal controls he or she has observed in various organizations that address those risks.

b. Contact a practicing accountant in a corporate environment. Ask about forms of information technology the company employs in its acquisition/payment process. Also find out how various functional managers use the AIS data from the process for making decisions.

6. *Modeling acquisition/payment processes.*

a. The library at Big State University routes all purchase requests through its requisitions department. Faculty, staff, and students can suggest titles for books, periodicals, electronic media, and other items via e-mail or by using a paper form sent to the requisitions librarian. The requisitions librarian tracks the various requests in a database; once at least 10 requests for the same item have come in, the requisitions librarian orders it from an appropriate vendor using a standard purchase order. The requisitions librarian e-mails the requestors to tell them the item has been ordered and files a copy of the purchase order by title. When the item is received, the receiving clerk matches it against the purchase order supplied by the requisitions librarian; if it matches, the item moves out of the receiving department into the library, where it is filed. A copy of the receiving report goes to the requisitions librarian and to the financial services department; financial services clerks match the invoice against the receiving report and purchase order. They also reconcile any differences between them with the vendor. Invoices are paid on a monthly basis according to the company name of the vendor; for example, vendors starting with A through C are paid the first five days of the month. The financial services clerk creates a payment packet of all relevant documents, stamps "Paid" on the top, and files it alphabetically by vendor name, and by date within vendor name. Create a flowchart or data flow diagram that depicts the preceding process.

b.  Goodkind Corporation replaces one-third of its desktop computers every year, so that every employee has a new computer every three years. In January of each year, Goodkind's information technology division accesses the corporate database to determine which computers are eligible for replacement. The information technology division manager consults with the chief financial officer to determine the budget for computer replacement, then asks each employee whose computer is eligible to be replaced for a list of three "must have" features and three "wish list" features for his or her new computer. A committee comprised of the information technology manager, the chief financial officer, and three employees prepares a request for proposal (RFP) to send to various computer vendors; vendors typically have about 30 days to respond to the RFP. At the end of the RFP period, the committee ranks the proposals based a on standard set of criteria. After discussion, they select the best proposal and contact the vendor. Goodkind's purchasing department issues a purchase order; the original goes to the vendor, while Goodkind's accounting department receives a copy. The receiving department gets a "blind copy" of the purchase order. When the computers arrive, the receiving department inspects them for quality; any computers that do not meet quality specifications are returned to the vendor. The receiving department prepares a receiving report for all good computers received. The computers are transferred to the information technology department; IT staff install them for the employees, typically in April of each year.

c.  Visit my AIS blog at http://bobhurtais.blogspot.com/. Access the entry titled "Acquisition/Payment Process: Buying a Home," posted on 16 April 2011. Watch the video, then write a short description of the home buying process. In a format specified by your instructor, document the written description you prepared.

d.  Brooks Corporation strives to keep a minimum cash balance of $10,000 for its operating needs. When its actual cash exceeds that threshold by at least $5,000, Brooks' management frequently invests the excess cash by purchasing marketable securities. The board of directors' finance committee consults preestablished criteria for such investments, then conducts a search to identify potential investments. From the list of potential investments, the finance committee chooses the top three to present to the full board of directors. After discussion, the board approves up to two of the investments; Brooks' chief financial officer purchases the securities through the corporation's broker. Brooks maintains an electronic database of its short-term investments, liquidating them as necessary to meet the corporation's cash needs.

e.  Complete Figures 13.1, 13.5, and/or 13.6 based on the generic steps in the acquisition/payment process.

7.  *Acquisition/payment transactions.* As of 30 April 2011, PLR Corporation's accounts payable subsidiary ledger included the following information:

| Vendor | Invoice Number | Invoice Date | Invoice Amount | Terms |
|---|---|---|---|---|
| HRP Corp. | 1398 | 15 April 2011 | $12,890 | n/30 |
| VLD Corp. | 432 | 10 April 2011 | $ 5,780 | 2/10, n/30 |
| RGN Corp. | 848 | 21 April 2011 | $ 4,500 | 1/15, n/45 |

PLR completed the following transactions in May 2011:

| Date | Transaction |
|------|-------------|
| 1 | Paid half the amount due to HRP Corp. |
| 3 | Purchased inventory on account form VLD Corp., $1,220. |
| 6 | Paid the amount due to RGN Corp. |
| 12 | Purchased inventory on account form HRP Corp., $3,555. |
| 14 | Paid the total amount due to HRP Corp. |
| 18 | Purchased supplies on account from QOC Corp., $600. Terms: 2/10, n/30. |
| 21 | Issued a check to VLD Corp. in payment of Invoice 432, including the applicable discount. |
| 24 | Purchased inventory on account form RGN Corp., $1,500. |
| 25 | Paid the total amount due to RGN Corp. |
| 27 | Purchased factory equipment, $20,000. Paid 20% down and financed the rest with a 6-month, 12% note payable. |

a. Record the May transactions in general journal format.

b. Prepare a schedule of accounts payable as of 31 May 2011.

c. Beyond the information in the journal entries, what information about the transactions would you include in a relational database?

8. *Document information.* The documents discussed in this chapter are listed below on the right. Various information items that might appear in them are listed on the left. For each information item listed on the left, indicate the document(s) in which it would most likely appear with the appropriate letter(s).

| | |
|---|---|
| __ 1. Vendor name | a. Purchase requisition |
| __ 2. Items needed | b. Purchase order |
| __ 3. Vendor address | c. Receiving report |
| __ 4. Purchasing agent's name | d. Vendor invoice |
| __ 5. Operating manager's name | e. Check |
| __ 6. Transaction date | |
| __ 7. Cost per unit | |
| __ 8. Total cost of all items | |
| __ 9. P.O. number | |
| __10. ABA routing number | |

9. *Internal controls.* (CMA adapted, June 1991) Brock Company is a manufacturer of children's toys and games. The company has been experiencing declining profit margins and is looking for ways to increase operating income. Because of the competitive nature of the industry, Brock is unable to raise its selling prices and must either cut costs or increase productivity.

As the company purchases a variety of raw materials, the volume of paperwork in the Accounts Payable Department is very large, and there are several accounting clerks involved in processing and paying the invoices. The repetitive nature of this work leads to errors because of inattention to details such as part numbers and unit prices. These errors have led to double payments, payments for goods not yet received, and delays in the receipt of raw materials because suppliers that should have been paid have not been paid. These situations often require a great deal of supervisory time to resolve.

The department manager has recommended that increased emphasis be placed on quality control. This would be achieved by increased monitoring of daily output, curtailing talking among staff members, and strict adherence to work hours. All errors would be discussed with the employee, and the staff would be informed that performance evaluations will be negative if errors are not reduced.

Comment on the costs and benefits of Brock's proposed new internal control system in Accounts Payable. Suggest an alternative system that would achieve the same results.

**10.** *Internal control analysis.* (CMA adapted, December 1992) LCK Corporation manufactures small tools such as hammers and screwdrivers. Many of LCK's employees pocket some of the firm's manufactured tools for their personal use. Since the quantities taken by any one employee were typically immaterial, the individual employees did not consider their actions detrimental to LCK. As the company grew larger, management instituted an internal audit department. The internal auditor charted gross profit percentages for particular tools and discovered higher gross profit rates for tools related to industrial use than for personal use. Subsequent investigation uncovered the fraudulent acts.

As an internal auditor, what steps would you take to uncover the fraud? What additional internal controls should LCK Corporation institute to prevent this problem from occurring in the future?

**11.** *Terminology.* Please match each item on the left with the most appropriate item on the right.

| | |
|---|---|
| 1. Authorize a purchase | a. A way to monitor inventory needs |
| 2. Bank reconciliation | b. Audit trail components |
| 3. Purchase order | c. Internal control to manage the risk of embezzlement |
| 4. Purchase requisition | d. One reason for consolidating purchase requisitions |
| 5. Quantity discounts | e. Possible internal control for purchasing from inappropriate vendors |
| 6. Receiving report | f. Prepared by purchasing department |
| 7. Reorder point | g. Promotes separation of duties |
| 8. Source documents, journal entries, ledger postings | h. Requests customer payment |
| 9. Strategic alliance | i. Several can be combined on one purchase order |
| 10. Vendor invoice | j. Step in the acquisition/payment process |

**12.** *Multiple choice questions.*

1. PLP Corporation maintains an electronic database file for all its vendors and purchases. Which of the following amounts would you be least likely to find in the "vendor" table?

   a. Total amount owed

   b. Vendor name

   c. Part numbers commonly purchased

   d. All of the above would be included in the vendor table.

2. An accounting clerk debited inventory and credited accounts payable for $500. Which of the following is the most likely source document for that transaction?

   a. Purchase order

   b. Receiving report

   c. Vendor invoice

   d. Purchase requisition

3. In the context of an acquisition/payment process, the three-way match concept applies to which of the following sets of documents?

   a. Purchase requisition, vendor invoice, and remittance advice

   b. Vendor invoice, receiving report, and purchase requisition

   c. Receiving report, purchase order, and vendor invoice

   d. Remittance advice, purchase order, and receiving report

4. The difference between a purchase requisition and a purchase order is

   a. Purchase orders are paper, while requisitions are electronic.

   b. Purchase requisitions are electronic, while purchase orders are paper.

   c. Purchase requisitions are purely internal documents; purchase orders leave the company.

   d. Purchase requisitions often have different prices than purchase orders.

  5. Which of the following is the best example of a conflict of interest?

   a. RKH Corporation established a list of preferred vendors.

   b. RKH's conflict-of-interest policy was developed by their auditors.

   c. RKH purchases 80 percent of its inventory from a firm where its purchasing agent is a stockholder.

   d. All of the above constitute conflicts of interest.

**13.** *Statement evaluation.* Indicate whether each statement below is (i) always true, (ii) sometimes true, or (iii) never true. For any statements that are (ii) sometimes true, explain when the statement is true.

  a. A bill of lading is required in the acquisition/payment process.

  b. A data flow diagram of the acquisition/payment process has six numbered circles.

  c. A vendor invoice triggers a cash disbursement event in a well-organized acquisition/payment process.

  d. Companies without a conflict-of-interest policy have weak internal control over the acquisition/payment process.

  e. Daily bank reconciliations eliminate the need for other forms of internal control over cash.

  f. Most of the documents in the acquisition/payment process are paper-based, rather than electronic.

  g. Purchase orders are binding contracts between a customer and a vendor.

  h. The passage of time triggers events in the acquisition/payment process.

  i. The receiving department should have a blind copy of the purchase order.

  j. When two signatures are required, blank checks should be signed by one person to promote operating efficiency.

**14.** *Process relationships.* The steps in the sales/collection and acquisition/payment processes are listed below, but they are out of order. Put the statements in the proper order based on how they occur in organizations.

  a. An operating department in the buying organization requests goods and services.

  b. The billing department in the selling organization bills the client.

  c. The buying organization's receiving department receives the goods.

  d. The cash disbursements department in the buying organization disburses cash.

  e. The cash receipts department in the selling organization collects payment.

  f. The credit department in the selling organization approves the customer's credit.

  g. The purchasing department in the buying organization authorizes the purchase.

  h. The sales department in the selling organization takes the customer's order.

  i. The selling organization's shipping department ships the product.

  j. The warehouse in the selling organization fills the order based on approved credit.

**15.** *Prior material application.*

  a. Point your Web browser to www.download.com, and search for inventory management software packages, such as inFlow Inventory Software and Inventoria Stock Manager. Choose two or three such packages, and use the weighted rating technique discussed in Chapter 5 to evaluate them for use in a small business.

  b. Point your Web browser to www.acfe.com, the Web site for the Association of Certified Fraud Examiners. Look for the June 2001 article by Joseph T. Wells titled "Ghost Goods: How to Spot Phantom Inventory." Use expectancy theory to analyze what might motivate someone to commit inventory fraud.

16. *Relational database design.* In many business processes, resources and agents have no relationship outside the context of a specific event. For example, a customer has no relationship with an inventory item unless the customer buys the item. A REA model of that scenario appears below:

However, in some situations, an agent has a relationship with a resource outside the context of a specific event. Consider, for example, the relationship authors have with books: a single book can have many authors, and a single author can have many books; whether the books are sold is another matter. Here is a REA model of that scenario:

   a. How many tables would be required in a relational database of the second REA model? Justify your response.

   b. For each table indicated by the second REA model, indicate: its name, its primary key, and at least two additional fields.

   c. Update the second REA model by adding the event "revise book." Create appropriate cardinalities. Indicate any additional table(s) that would be required; specify needed primary and foreign keys for any additional tables.

17. *Excel application.* Consider the data array below (also available in the 3 February 2014 post in my AIS blog):

| | A | B | C |
|---|---|---|---|
| | Transaction Number | Units Purchased | Cost per Unit |
| 1 | | | |
| 2 | 1 | 212 | $25 |
| 3 | 2 | 226 | 12 |
| 4 | 3 | 200 | 13 |
| 5 | 4 | 256 | 14 |
| 6 | 5 | 219 | 15 |
| 7 | 6 | 250 | 18 |
| 8 | 7 | 292 | 19 |
| 9 | 8 | 262 | 21 |
| 10 | 9 | 214 | 17 |
| 11 | 10 | 213 | 23 |

a.  Use Excel's "SumProduct" function to calculate the total cost of all units purchased in Transactions 1 through 10. (Check figure: $41,568)

b.  In Column D, using Excel's "If" function, create a formula that will calculate the total transaction cost for any transaction with fewer than 250 units. For transactions with 250 units or more, the output should be the phrase "250 units or more."

c.  In Column E, using Excel's "If" function, create a formula that will output the phrase "cost less than $15" where applicable. For transactions where the cost is at least $15, the formula should calculate the total transaction cost.

# Chapter **Fourteen**

# Other Business Processes

## AIS in the Business World

### Krispy Kreme Doughnuts

Although the sales/collection and acquisition/payment processes are vitally important for KKD, its overall operation encompasses many other processes.

When KKD combines raw materials, direct labor and overhead to make doughnuts and other finished goods, it is engaged in the conversion process. If you've taken a cost or introductory management accounting class, you may recall that those three items are first combined in a work in process account; when the doughnuts are ready to sell, they are moved from work in process to finished goods.

KKD also needs people to work in both its corporate office and in the retail locations; all activities related to personnel are accounted for in the human resources process. Those activities include: interviewing, hiring, evaluating performance, paying, and managing separation from KKD, whether an employee quits, retires, or is fired. The human resource process is heavily regulated by both Federal and State laws.

Finally, KKD (like most organizations) has a financing process. The financing process includes activities like issuing capital stock, paying dividends, borrowing money through short- or long-term debt, making principal and interest payments on borrowed money, purchasing treasury shares, and many others.

Those three activities are all included in one chapter because their details can vary significantly across organizations. As a publicly-traded, multinational manufacturing organization with thousands of employees around the globe, KKD's processes are likely to be much more complex and sophisticated than a sole proprietorship CPA firm.

### Discussion Questions

1. How are the preceding business processes aligned with Porter's value chain?
2. What documents, journal entries, and internal controls are associated with each process?
3. How should a relational database for each process be designed?

In the last two chapters, we've examined business processes that are very similar even in diverse organizations. In this last chapter on business processes, we turn our attention to three others that can vary greatly in their detail, depending on the kind of organization you're considering: conversion, financing, and human resources.

When you finish studying this chapter, you should be able to complete the following tasks for each process listed above:

1. Explain its role and purpose.
2. Explain how the generic structure of most AIS applies.
3. Identify and process common transactions.
4. Design and critique internal controls based on common risk exposures.
5. Develop and interpret process-related systems documentation.
6. Appropriately use terminology common to each process.
7. Explain how each process is related to Porter's value chain.

We'll be taking a "big picture" look at each process in the next few pages—not because these processes are less important or less interesting than those we've already examined, but because it's more difficult to talk about them in a generic way. The end-of-chapter exercises will give you plenty of opportunity to apply the concepts in specific situations.

## CONVERSION PROCESS

*Your study of cost accounting elsewhere in your accounting curriculum will discuss the conversion process in much greater depth.*

Organizations can be classified in several ways in today's economy; one such way is by the basic nature of their operations: service, merchandising/retail, and manufacturing. The **conversion process** is typically associated with manufacturing enterprises; its basic purpose is to convert direct material, direct labor, and manufacturing overhead into a finished product. Collectively, direct material, direct labor, and manufacturing overhead are often referred to as "factors of production." Direct material refers to the major kinds of materials in a product—those you can easily "see" when you look at it. Direct labor refers to the salaries, wages, and benefits of assembly-line workers—people who are directly involved in the manufacture of the product. Manufacturing overhead, sometimes referred to as factory overhead, comprises everything else in the production operation. Items such as factory equipment depreciation, salaries of factory supervisors, factory utilities, and custodial costs are typically included in manufacturing overhead.

Manufacturing companies typically organize their conversion processes in one of three major ways: job costing, process costing, or a hybrid system that combines elements from both. Understanding the kind of production system a manufacturing firm uses is important because it helps us design the right kind of AIS.

In **job costing,** units of product are differentiated from one another; that is, you can tell them apart simply by looking at them. Custom-built homes or commissioned works of art fall into that category. At Krispy Kreme doughnuts, the different doughnut types are differentiated; it's easy to distinguish between a plain glazed doughnut and an apple fritter.

**Process costing** systems produced undifferentiated goods; in other words, you cannot tell them apart simply by looking at them. Think about mass-produced furniture, like the chairs in a university classroom, or office supplies, like three-ring binders, as examples of process costing. At KKD, within each type of doughnut, the units are undifferentiated. In other words, it's virtually impossible to distinguish one glazed doughnut from another glazed doughnut.

Hybrid systems combine some elements of both job and process costing systems. They often take a base product (accounted for in a process costing model) and customize it (accounted for in a job costing model). A computer manufacturer, for example, might produce a base unit that can be customized with additional memory, different kinds of ports, and optical drives. Since KKD's operations have characteristics of both job and process costing, it has a hybrid system.

# Reflection and Self-Assessment     14.1

Give examples of two products that would be accounted for in a job costing system. Also give two examples for a process costing system.

## AIS Elements

Although the specifics of every conversion process are different, certain tasks are common in nearly every one. And, as with the other business processes we've considered, we use conversion process documents as inputs and outputs of the AIS to track and report on those common activities. Consider Table 14.1, which summarizes some of the input and output documents for the conversion process.

As you can imagine, the processes associated with conversion can be radically different, depending on the finished product. Nevertheless, there are some common conversion process journal entries needed in the accounting information system. In a job costing system, those include:

- Purchasing raw materials
  - Debit raw material inventory
  - Credit accounts payable
- Accumulating costs by job
  - Debit "job account" (e.g., Job 123A)
  - Credit raw materials inventory
  - Credit wages payable (for direct labor costs)
  - Credit manufacturing overhead (for applied overhead)

**TABLE 14.1**    **Conversion Process Documents**

| Form Name | Purpose | Originator | Recipient |
|---|---|---|---|
| Materials requisition | Requests raw material from the warehouse for production | Production | Warehouse |
| Job cost sheet | Summarizes the material, labor, and overhead costs in a job costing system | Production | Accounting |
| Labor time ticket | Accumulates labor data (time, pay rate, total labor cost) | Production | Accounting |
| Production cost report | Summarizes cost and quantity information in a process costing system | Production | Accounting |
| Materials move ticket | Documents the movement of materials from the warehouse into production | Warehouse | Production |

- Selling finished goods
  - Debit accounts receivable
  - Debit cost of goods sold
  - Credit sales
  - Credit "job account"

In a process costing system, things are a bit more complex. Costs have to be moved from one process to another; they also have to be transferred to finished goods when units are completed and awaiting sale.

- Transferring costs from Process A to Process B
  - Debit Work in Process—Process B
  - Credit Work in Process—Process A
- Transferring costs of completed units to finished goods
  - Debit Finished Goods
  - Credit Work in Process—Process B

Data from the conversion process can be stored electronically or with paper. You would use file structures similar to those we examined in Chapters 12 and 13 for that purpose.

What risks need to be addressed in the conversion process? And what internal controls could organizations use to address them? Consider Table 14.2 as a starting point.

Consider the process of writing a textbook like this one. Authors and publishers typically go through a set of steps such as those listed below:

1. *Author.* Develop a textbook proposal. The proposal includes a general overview of the book and a sample first chapter. The author sends the materials to the publisher for review.
2. *Publisher.* Accept or reject the proposal. If accepted, prepare standard contracts governing the development and publication process.
3. *Author.* Write chapter drafts based on the proposal. Submit the drafts to the publisher in batches.
4. *Publisher.* Solicit professors in the field to review the chapters as they are submitted. Reviews consist of responses to a common set of questions.
5. *Publisher.* Summarize and analyze the reviewers' responses. Send them to the author.
6. *Author.* Revise chapters as necessary based on reviewer feedback. Submit revised chapters to publisher.
7. *Publisher.* Publish and print the text.

Figure 14.1 shows a flowchart depicting those steps.

**TABLE 14.2**
**Risks and Controls in the Conversion Process**

| Risk | Control |
| --- | --- |
| Damage to raw materials | Special storage conditions<br>Backup power supplies for heating and cooling |
| Loss/theft of raw materials | Secured storage areas<br>Adequate documentation<br>Separation of duties |
| Worker injuries | Workers' compensation insurance<br>Safety training<br>Protective clothing |

**FIGURE 14.1   Conversion Process Flowchart**

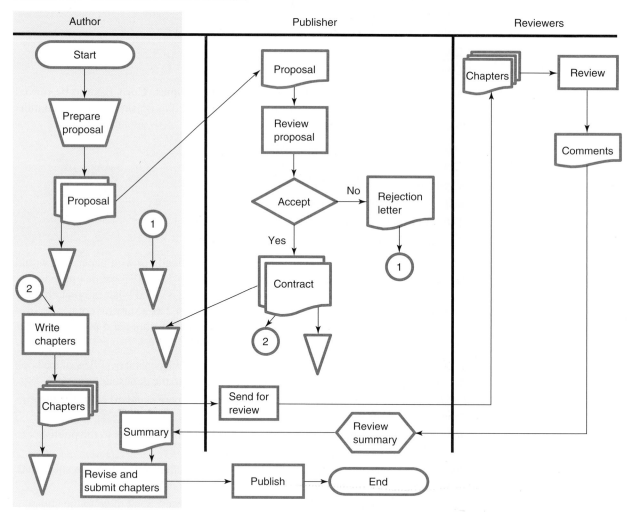

The key in understanding the conversion process is to understand the company's operations. AIS designers and auditors can gather data via direct observation, interview, and/or survey, then prepare a flowchart to ensure that they understand the process thoroughly.

# Reflection and Self-Assessment                    14.2

Draw a flowchart to depict the conversion process at KKD. Use the following steps as the basis for the flowchart: (i) Assemble the required raw materials. (ii) Make the dough. (iii) Complete any additional steps before frying. (iv) Fry the doughnuts. (v) Complete additional steps to finish the doughnut (e.g., glazing). (vi) Store the doughnuts appropriately.

As you learned in our previous discussion of internal controls, the idea in risk assessment and internal control design is to understand the overall operation. Then, you can think of the most likely problems and create controls to mitigate those problems.

# FINANCING PROCESS

## Role and Purpose

Courses in intermediate accounting cover the technical aspects of these transactions, while finance courses explore them from a conceptual perspective with discussions of optimal capital structure and weighted average cost of capital.

In our discussion of the acquisition/payment process, we looked at how an organization acquires and pays for many of the physical assets it needs for operations, with a particular emphasis on inventory. But, organizations also need money to operate. While some money comes from the successful operation of the business, some funds have to come from outside; that's where the **financing process** comes into play.

In general, organizations have two choices about acquiring external financing: debt or equity. As you may recall from your introductory financial accounting course, debt financing has the following characteristics:

- Amounts borrowed must be repaid, usually with interest.
- Interest is, in most cases, a tax deduction.
- It does not dilute ownership of the business, but can throw a firm into bankruptcy if not repaid on time.

Treasury shares can be accounted for at par, but most organizations use the cost method.

You'll commonly see debt financing in the long-term liabilities section of a balance sheet.

Equity financing, on the other hand, is seen in the equity section of the balance sheet. Its characteristics include:

- Amounts do not have to be repaid.
- Dividends are optional, but are not a tax-deductible expense in most cases.
- Equity investors become owners of the organization.

Which is better, you might ask. The answer: it depends. The "best mix" of debt and equity financing is sometimes called the "optimal capital structure." You'll learn more about that topic in an introductory finance course.

## AIS Elements

The recordkeeping is more involved in an IPO than in subsequent securities transactions; for more information, point your Web browser to www.entrepreneur.com or do a Google search.

The input and output documents associated with the financing process include shares of capital stock, various forms of notes payable (including mortgages and bonds), and checks (for paying dividends, interest, and principal). Under certain circumstances, the SEC also requires registration forms before a publicly traded corporation can sell its securities in U.S. capital markets.

The process of issuing debt and/or equity securities is highly regulated and very detailed. So, we won't go into a lot of depth on it here. The very first time a corporation offers its stock for sale is called an initial public offering (IPO). KKD's initial public offering took place on 5 April 2000. The steps in an IPO are:

1. Choose an investment bank, an accounting firm, and a lawyer.
2. Develop a prospectus.
3. File the prospectus with the SEC and wait for approval.
4. Do a "road show" to solicit investors.
5. Distribute a final prospectus.
6. Determine the initial offering price and size of the IPO.
7. Sell the shares of stock.

In the accounting information system, we have to be concerned about how to record various **financing process transactions.** Some of those transactions include issuance of capital stock, purchase of treasury shares, issuance and repayment of long-term debt, and dividend distributions.

# Reflection and Self-Assessment                                                          14.3

Issuance of capital stock is recorded in the AIS by debiting cash for the total market price, crediting capital stock for the par value, and crediting additional paid-in capital for the difference. How are the other transactions listed above recorded?

Storing information about financing process transactions is particularly important. If a company misses a principal or interest payment or if it fails to issue a dividend check to the right stockholder, the consequences can be severe. The AIS therefore needs to capture at least the following information for financing process transactions:

- Equity financing transactions
  - Number of shares
  - Par value per share
  - Market value per share
  - Shareholder identification data
  - Dividend type
  - Dividend per share
  - Dividend dates (declaration, record, payment)
- Debt financing transactions
  - Principal
  - Coupon interest rate (the rate of interest paid in cash)
  - Market interest rate (the rate prevailing in the market for investments of similar risk)
  - Issue date
  - Time to repayment
  - Frequency of payments
  - Lender identification data

One of the most anticipated, best known IPOs of the early 21st century was Facebook; its IPO took place on 18 May 2012. All the hype drove up both the expected price and the number of shares to be offered. As you may be aware, the IPO did not live up to most expectations. For the year ended 20 February 2014, Facebook's stock price fluctuated between a low of $22.67 to a high of $70.11 per share. As of that date, Facebook had declared no dividends, so the only way investors could make money with the company's stock was to sell it for a higher price than their cost.

Clearly, the biggest risk associated with the financing business process is the misappropriation of cash, either through skimming or larceny. The internal controls over cash discussed in the previous chapters are at least as applicable to the financing business process: separation of duties, bank reconciliations, and adequate documentation, to name a few. Other risks here include missing payment deadlines and insufficient cash to repay principal. Missing payment deadlines can be addressed via automatic electronic funds transfers or simple scheduling software installed on accounting department computers. A sinking fund can be used to mitigate the risk of insufficient cash to repay principal. As you may know, a sinking fund is a pool of money restricted to just one purpose: debt repayment. Because of the time value of money, a borrower can put small amounts of cash into a sinking fund throughout the life of the debt; when it matures, then, the sinking fund has sufficient cash to handle the transaction. Finally, a lender also may institute a debt covenant as an internal control. Debt covenants may restrict the borrower's ability to pay dividends to shareholders, specify a minimum current ratio level throughout the life of the debt, or hold the borrowing organization accountable for its overall financial leverage.

# HUMAN RESOURCE PROCESS

## Role and Purpose

The **human resource process** may be the most complex of all business processes today. Whole textbooks, courses, and fields of study have been devoted to its objectives, which include

- Hiring employees.
- Paying them.
- Coordinating employee benefits (insurance, pensions, and the like).
- Evaluating their performance.
- Managing their departures from the firm via termination, quitting, or retirement.

The Web site of the Professionals in Human Resources Association (www.pihra.org) lists many similar organizations involved in virtually all facets of the human resource process.

Consider the systems flowchart in Figure 14.2, which illustrates some of the preceding steps in the human resource process.

Because of its complexity and legal implications, many organizations outsource their human resource functions to organizations such as ADP.

## AIS Elements

From an AIS point of view, a main concern of the human resource process is the payroll function. It must be managed carefully and diligently to ensure accuracy and integrity. The **payroll forms** listed in Table 14.3 are commonly used as input and output documents in the payroll function.

Non-payroll forms associated with the human resource process would include completed job applications, interview notes, written performance reviews, and termination documents. As you can imagine, each of those can vary radically among firms.

---

# Reflection and Self-Assessment 14.4

Suggest two or three information items you would want to include in a termination letter.

**FIGURE 14.2**
**Partial Systems Flowchart of the Human Resources Process**

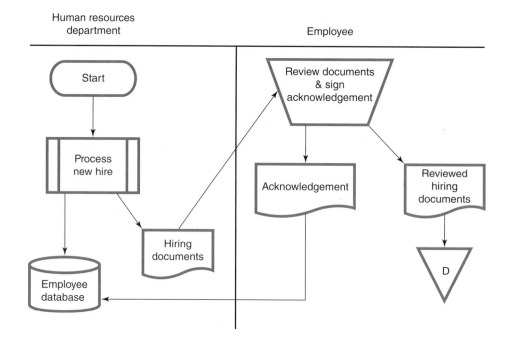

The risks associated with the human resource process fall into two major groups: financial and human. Financially, managers must ensure that they have sufficient cash on hand to meet payroll obligations; for that reason, companies often maintain a payroll checking account separate from their regular operating accounts. In addition, companies that pay employees by the hour typically need a way of tracking hours worked; Internet time-tracking systems or even simple time clocks mitigate the risk that hours will be recorded and reported inaccurately. When employees depart the company, whether through quitting, termination, or retirement, their access to organizational information systems (e.g., intranet accounts, passwords) should be eliminated to mitigate the risks of hacking, sabotage, and other forms of fraud.

Human risks in this business process are equally significant; some might say the human risks are weightier than the financial risks because of their long-term nature and potential for costly litigation. Human risks associated with the HR business process include hiring unqualified workers, failing to follow applicable laws (such as the Americans with Disabilities Act), engaging in acts of sexual harassment, and illegal or inappropriate employee terminations. Perhaps the best internal control for all those risks is a well-informed, educated human resources staff. Seeking the advice of legal counsel also may be appropriate in some cases; adequate documentation of human resource processes is essential, regardless of the type of organization under consideration.

Fraud is also a significant risk associated with employees. Internal controls that can help prevent and detect fraud include

- *Thorough background checks.* Several years ago, one of my students applied for a job with the federal government. The agency sent a representative to my home to ask me about the student, who had listed me as a reference.
- *Forced vacations.* You may be thinking, "Why would anyone need to be forced to take a vacation?" Consider the case of accounts receivable lapping. A/R lapping occurs

**TABLE 14.3   Payroll Forms**

| Form Name | Purpose | Data Included |
|---|---|---|
| Form W-4 | Establishes payroll withholding status | Employee identification data<br>Withholding status<br>Number of withholding allowances |
| Form W-2 | Reports year-end information for tax purposes | Employee identification data<br>Employer identification data<br>Gross pay and tax withholdings<br>401(k) contributions |
| Payroll register | Computes payroll data for all employees for a given pay period | Employee identification data<br>Hours worked<br>Pay rate<br>Total gross pay<br>Tax and benefit withholdings<br>Net pay |
| Employee earnings record | Summarizes payroll data for a single employee for multiple pay periods | Virtually the same as the payroll register |
| Form 1099 | Reports amounts paid to an independent contractor (I.C.) | I.C. identification data<br>Payer's identification data<br>Total amount paid |
| Form 940 | Reports employer's federal unemployment taxes | Company name<br>Amount paid |
| Form 941 | Reports amounts withheld by employer to IRS | Company name<br>Employee identification data<br>Amounts withheld |

# Reflection and Self-Assessment                     14.5

Visit the Web site of the Internal Revenue Service (www.irs.gov) and find examples of all the following forms: W-2, W-4, 1099, 940, 941. List two or three information items you find in each.

when a clerk steals money sent by one client, then uses money from another client to cover up the theft. For example, a clerk might steal money from Smith; then, when Jones pays her bill, the clerk would credit Jones's cash to Smith's account. Maintaining a lapping system requires an ongoing fraud; so, if an employee is forced to take a vacation, there's a greater chance of detecting the fraud than if vacations are not mandatory.

- *Adequate training and supervision.* We've looked at this control in connection with other business processes, but it's worth repeating here. Training can help promote effective and efficient operations, while adequate supervision can help safeguard assets.

While those controls will not prevent problems completely, they will be very effective in limiting opportunities to commit fraud.

## CRITICAL THINKING

Dividend payments are part of the financing process; they are nearly always entirely voluntary for the paying corporation. Although KKD has not paid a dividend as of February 2014, the process it would use might look like the one pictured in Figure 14.3 below.

KKD's related database would include, at minimum, a shareholder table and a "prepare check" table. The primary key of the shareholder table would be Shareholder ID, while the "prepare check" table's primary key would be an auto-numbered transaction number—perhaps the actual check number itself. Since each shareholder can receive many checks, but each check goes to just one shareholder, the primary key from the shareholder table would be included as a foreign key in the "prepare check" table.

Internal controls over the dividend payment process include:

1. Verifying that the organization has sufficient cash to pay a dividend, perhaps via a cash budget.
2. Requiring adequate documentation before preparing dividend checks.
3. Sequentially numbering the dividend checks.
4. Transmitting the dividend payments electronically.

We'll conclude this chapter by considering how all five business processes are related to one another.

**FIGURE 14.3**
**Systems Flowchart of the Dividend Payment Process**

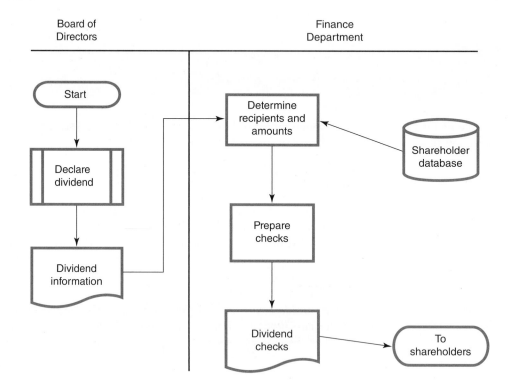

# PROCESS RELATIONSHIPS

This chapter concludes our examination of business processes. In total, we've looked at five: sales/collection, acquisition/payment, conversion, financing, and human resources. We studied the business processes separately to focus attention on the issues for each one, but, in real organizations, the processes are interrelated and highly dependent on one another.

Organizations typically need three kinds of resources to function effectively: people, money, and other assets (such as supplies, inventory, and equipment). The *human resource* process is concerned with people—how do organizations find them, train them, compensate them, and manage their separation from the company (e.g., through retirement or termination)? The *financing* process is associated with money—in particular, funds obtained from outside the company. Those funds typically come in the form of debt and equity financing. The *acquisition/payment* process is concerned with other kinds of assets: inventory, office equipment, factory machinery, supplies, and furniture, for example. The *conversion* process is particularly applicable to manufacturers, but also has implications for other types of organizations. In the conversion process, manufacturing companies combine raw material, direct labor, and manufacturing overhead to create a finished product. Finally, then, the company sells its product (or service) through the *sales/collection* process.

## Summary

This chapter concludes our discussion of business processes. We've looked at the conversion, financing, and human resource processes, briefly examining the same issues we considered for sales/collection and acquisition/payment. Table 14.4 summarizes those issues.

**TABLE 14.4**
**Chapter Summary**

|  | Conversion | Financing | Human Resource |
|---|---|---|---|
| Role and purpose | Transform material, labor, and overhead into finished products | Obtain external funding from debt and equity securities | Manage employees from initial hiring to termination, including payroll and performance evaluation |
| AIS structure |  |  |  |
| Input and output forms | Materials requisition, job cost sheet, labor time ticket, production cost report, materials move ticket | Shares of capital stock, various forms of notes payable, checks, SEC forms | W-2, W-4, 1099, 940, 941, payroll register, employee earnings record |
| Common transactions | Purchasing raw materials, accumulating and transferring costs, selling finished goods | Capital stock issuance, treasury shares purchase, dividend distributions, issuance and repayment of debt | Wage payments, tax deposits |
| Storage | Raw material data and transactions, cost accumulation data, and transactions | Capital stock files, shareholder data files, debtholder data files | Applicant database, employee database, payroll database |
| Internal controls | Adequate raw material storage, procedures manuals, separation of duties, insurance, training | Separation of duties, electronic funds transfers, sinking funds, debt covenants | Separate payroll checking account, time clocks, employee database update procedures, adequate training, background checks |

Regarding Objective 6, important terms in the conversion process include: job costing, process costing, hybrid costing, raw material, direct labor, overhead, and the various documents outlined in Table 14.1. In the financing process, important terms include: debt financing, equity financing, principal, interest, capital stock, dividends, treasury stock, initial public offering, and prospectus. In the human resource process, important terms include the forms discussed in Table 14.3, including all the terminology used within them.

Finally, with respect to Porter's value chain (Objective 7), the conversion process most closely aligns with operations (a primary activity). The support activity, human resource management, encompasses the activities of the human resource process. Since accounting and finance are commonly viewed as part of an organization's infrastructure, the financing process is found there in the value chain.

## Key Terms

conversion process, *261*

financing process, *265*

financing process transactions, *266*

human resource process, *267*

job costing, *261*

payroll forms, *267*

process costing, *261*

## End-of-Chapter Activities

1. *Reading review questions.*

   a. What is the basic purpose of each business process discussed in this chapter (conversion, financing, human resources)?

   b. What are the similarities and differences between job costing and process costing systems? How is each system reflected in the organization of the accounting information system?

   c. What are the four common transactions associated with the financing business process? What information must be tracked for each transaction?

   d. What forms are commonly used in processing payroll transactions?

   e. How are the purposes of internal control fulfilled in each business process discussed in the chapter?

   f. Respond to the questions for this chapter's "AIS in the Business World."

2. *Reading review problem.* Throughout the text so far, we've examined the following companies in the various chapter openers: Starbucks, Amazon, Papa John's, Google, Barnes & Noble, Microsoft, and Target. Choose one of those companies as the basis for responding to the following questions:

   a. Does the organization have a conversion process? If so, what is its primary product? Which type of costing system does it use? If the organization does not have a conversion process, suggest a product it might use to start one. Which type of costing system would that product use?

   b. Figure 14.2 shows a systems flowchart of the employee hiring process. Choose another task associated with the human resources process, such as paying employees, evaluating their performance or terminating them. Draw a systems flowchart of the task, then suggest at least three internal controls you would implement for it.

   c. Do some research on your chosen company to determine: its IPO date, its current stock price, its last dividend payment date and amount, its total market capitalization. Explain how each of those items relates to the financing process.

3. *Multiple choice review.*

   1. In which type of costing system are goods undifferentiated?
      a. Job order
      b. Process

    c. Both a and b

    d. Neither a nor b

2. Which type of costing system combines characteristics from both job order and process systems?

    a. Activity-based costing

    b. Value chain costing

    c. Hybrid costing

    d. Just-in-time costing

3. Which of the following steps in an IPO typically occurs first?

    a. Determine the initial offering price.

    b. Develop a prospectus.

    c. Determine the size of the IPO.

    d. Sell shares of stock.

4. All of the following are typical database files in a human resource process except:

    a. Applicant.

    b. Employee.

    c. Payroll.

    d. Performance evaluation.

5. Which of the following payroll forms is most closely associated with independent contractors?

    a. Form W-2

    b. Form W-4

    c. Form 940

    d. Form 1099

**4.** *Making choices and exercising judgment.*

    a. In the last three chapters, you've learned about five different business processes: sales/collection, acquisition/payment, conversion, financing, and human resources. Draw a diagram or write a paper that explains the connections between the five.

    b. Phil and Lil are the owners of Planters for All, a company that makes small decorative planters for homes and offices. Their planters come in various shapes, including a well with a bucket, a telephone, a wheelbarrow, and others. Each shape can be made in two sizes: large and small. If you were advising Phil and Lil about setting up their production process, would you recommend a job costing system or a process costing system? Why?

    c. PKT Corporation has annual sales of $1,600,000 and a profit margin averaging 8 percent. The corporation employs 40 people and currently does its payroll processing internally. Typically, the two accounting staff spend one day every two weeks calculating and processing payroll; each accounting staff member's annual salary is $48,000. The president of PKT has asked your advice regarding outsourcing payroll processing. List and discuss at least three factors you would tell the president to consider in making this decision. Based on the data provided, should PKT outsource its payroll or keep doing it internally?

**5.** *Field exercises.*

    a. Look online or in your local Yellow Pages for a company that manufactures a product. Arrange an interview with a member of the company's accounting staff and a tour of its production facilities. Prepare a brief presentation or paper discussing the results of your research.

    b. Contact a local human resources professional or an attorney that specializes in labor law. Ask about legislation that impacts the human resource function in organizations, such as the Americans with Disabilities Act, the Family and Medical Leave Act, the Occupational

Safety and Health Act, or the Immigration Reform and Control Act, or about the company's policies with regard to sexual harassment, substance abuse testing, or use of information technology. Prepare a brief presentation or paper discussing the results of your research.

6. *Costing systems.* Indicate whether each of the following types of businesses would be more likely to use a job or process costing system. Justify your choices.

   a. Architect
   b. Attorney
   c. Dentist
   d. Heavy-equipment manufacturer
   e. House painter
   f. Landscaper
   g. Magazine publisher
   h. Management consultant
   i. Pet groomer
   j. Tax preparer

7. *Transaction and business processes.* Which business process (conversion, financing, or human resources) is most closely associated with each transaction listed below?

   a. Payroll taxes expense
       Cash
   b. Manufacturing overhead
       Accumulated depreciation
   c. Treasury stock
       Cash
   d. Cash
       Capital stock
       Additional paid-in capital
   e. Payroll expense
       Wages payable
       Withholding taxes payable
   f. Retained earnings
       Capital stock
   g. Work in process
       Manufacturing overhead
   h. Interest expense
       Premium on bonds payable
       Interest payable
   i. Cash
       Discount on bonds payable
       Bonds payable
   j. Cost of goods sold
       Finished goods

8. *Transaction explanations.* Explain what is happening in each transaction presented in the previous exercise. For example, in transaction (*a*), the company is paying its share of payroll taxes.

9. *Payroll forms data.* Several data items that might be included on a payroll form are listed below on the left. The standard payroll forms discussed in the chapter are listed below on the right. For each data item, indicate the form(s) on which you'd find it.

   a. Address of employee
   b. Employee name
   c. Employer identification number
   d. Federal income tax withheld
   e. Location of employer
   f. Marital status
   g. Number of withholding allowances
   h. Social Security number
   i. State income tax withheld
   j. Unemployment tax paid—federal

   1. Form 940
   2. Form 941
   3. Form 1099
   4. Form W-2
   5. Form W-4

10. *Risk analysis and internal controls.* In each independent situation below, identify and describe at least three risks. For each risk, suggest two internal controls to address it.

    a. (CMA adapted, June 1992) Midwest Electronics Corp. manufactures computers. Recently, its products have met stiff competition from lower-priced imports, and the firm is seeking ways to improve its workers' productivity in order to maintain its market share. Over lunch in the company cafeteria, Alice Kumar (manager of the Accounting Department) and Greg Mossman (manager of the Sales Department) recently discussed a presentation made to the management of Midwest by a consultant on employee motivation. In the course of the conversation, Kumar recalled what happened at Spokane Computer Associates, her former employer. A national labor union had sought repeatedly to unionize the workers at the plant but had never succeeded. There was very little turnover among the workers, and the plant was considered a safe and pleasant place to work. Salaries were relatively high, and workers earned not only a base salary but incentive bonuses based on their individual output and company profits.

b. (CMA adapted, June 1992) Alaire Corporation manufactures several different types of printed circuit boards; however, two of the boards account for the majority of the company's sales. The first of these boards, a television circuit board, has been a standard in the industry for several years. The market for this type of board is competitive and, therefore, price sensitive. Alaire plans to sell 65,000 television circuit boards next year at a price of $150 each. The second high-volume product, a personal computer circuit board, is a recent addition to the company's product line. Because it incorporates the latest technology, it can be sold at a premium price; next year's budget calls for the sale of 40,000 personal computer boards at a price of $300 each.

c. (CMA adapted, December 1991) Microtronics Inc. is a private company involved in genetic engineering. The company was started several years ago by Joseph Graham, a scientist, and is financed by a group of venture capitalists. Microtronics has had some successful research, and one of its products recently received approval from the Federal Drug Administration (FDA). Two other products have been submitted to the FDA and are awaiting approval. Because of these successes, the investors believe the time is right for preparing the company for a public stock offering.

d. (CMA adapted, December 1991) Princess Corporation grows, processes, packages, and sells three apple products: sliced apples used in frozen pies, applesauce, and apple juice. The outside skin of the apple, which is removed in the Cutting Department and processed as animal feed, is treated as a by-product. In the company's conversion process, the Cutting Department washes the apples and removes the outside skin. The apples are then cored and trimmed for slicing; the three main products and the by-product are recognizable after processing in the Cutting Department. Each product is then transferred to a separate department for final processing. The trimmed apples are forwarded to the Slicing Department, where they are sliced and frozen. Any juice generated during the slicing operation is frozen with the slices. The pieces of apple trimmed from the fruit are processed into applesauce in the Crushing Department. Again, the juice generated during this operation is used in the applesauce. The core and any surplus apple generated from the Cutting Department are pulverized into a liquid in the Juicing Department. The outside skin is chopped into animal feed and packaged in the Feed Department.

e. (CMA adapted, June 1994) Damian Information Inc. is a four-year-old information processing and software development company serving a number of small clients in the midwestern United States. As its customer base has grown, DII has increased its staff to 30 employees. The company has been considering an arrangement whereby they would lease employees. Currently, there are in excess of 400 employee leasing companies in the United States representing nearly one million workers. The major users of this service are companies that need fewer than 100 workers. If DII were to enter into an employee-leasing arrangement, all of DII's current employees would become employees of the leasing company and then leased back to DII.

f. (CMA adapted, June 1994) Richmond Inc. operates a chain of department stores located in the northwest. The first store began operations in 1965 and the company has steadily grown to its present size of 44 stores. Two years ago, the board of directors of Richmond approved a large-scale remodeling of its stores to attract a more upscale clientele. Before finalizing these plans, two stores were remodeled as a test. Linda Perlman, assistant controller, was asked to oversee the financial reporting for these test stores, and she and other management personnel were offered bonuses based on the sales growth and profitability of these stores. Based on the apparent success of the test (sales growth for the two stores was reported at

11 percent and profitability showed a 14 percent increase), the board is now considering two alternatives for financing the balance of the remodeling effort. Alternative one involves pure debt financing. The company would make a public offering of bonds with a face value of $30 million and a stated interest rate of 11 percent. Alternative two is a combination alternative. It would involve $12 million in 9 percent bonds, common stock of $14.5 million, and retained earnings of $4.5 million. The current market value of Richmond's common stock is $30 per share; the dividends per share have held steady at $3.00 per share for the last year, but investors are expecting growth of 6 percent in the dividend.

11. *Systems documentation.* In each of the following independent cases, document the system using whatever technique(s) your instructor specifies.

   a. Dreambox Creations (www.dreamboxcreations.com/) in Diamond Bar, California, partners with Automatic Data Processing Inc. (ADP) for its payroll processing. Dreambox employs Internet-based time tracking. Employees log in and out based on the client for whom they're working; in that way, the company can track billable hours, which feed into the sales/collection process. (The concept of billable hours is also important in other professional organizations such as law firms and CPA firms.) Dan, in charge of operations and information technology, summarizes each employee's hours on a biweekly basis. He transmits them to ADP electronically or via telephone; ADP then processes the payroll, including all tax withholdings and deposits. ADP also handles Dreambox's year-end reporting via W-2 forms. Dreambox maintains a payroll account separate from its regular operating cash account for internal control purposes. ADP sends paper checks drawn on the payroll account back to Dan, who distributes them to the employees. The checks lag the pay period by one week; for example, checks for the pay period January 10 to January 21 are distributed on January 28.

   b. Point your Web browser to www.sba.gov, the Web site for the Small Business Administration. The SBA is a federal organization that helps entrepreneurs start and manage businesses. Click the link for "Financing Your Business." Browse the topics under "Financing Eligibility Topics" as the basis for documenting the system.

   c. Hiring new faculty is one of the most important human resource processes for universities. The department chair requests funding for a new full-time position and sends it to the dean, who approves or rejects the request. If approved, the department selects a faculty hiring committee. Their first task is to prepare a position description, which must be approved by the university's human resource office. The position description is submitted by the search committee to various Web sites, professional organizations, and periodicals; candidates submit required documentation for consideration. The committee reviews the required documentation and selects a small number of candidates for phone interviews. Based on the phone interviews, a few candidates (perhaps three to five) are invited to an on-campus interview. Based on feedback from references and on-campus interviews, the hiring committee forwards names to the dean, who makes the final selection. The dean's office sends out offer letters, which are either accepted or rejected by the applicant.

   d. Geoff is a Registered Tax Preparer in the State of California. Each year, he renews his registration on the Web site of the California Tax Education Council (www.ctec.org/). Geoff then makes his advertising plans for the year, which usually include direct mail flyers and classified ads in local newspapers. He also sends out appointment cards to his clients from the previous year; about 80 percent of them hire Geoff again. Clients call Geoff to make an appointment; Geoff maintains his appointment schedule in an online calendar. He uses commercial software to prepare and e-file each client's return.

   e. As part of discussing the financing process, the chapter laid out the seven steps associated with an IPO. Use those steps as the basis for documenting the IPO process.

12. *Database design.* In each of the following independent cases, indicate primary and foreign keys in the usual way.

   a. Consider the Dreambox Creations case presented in the preceding problem. Create specifications for the following tables: employee, report hours. Suggest at least two queries

Dreambox could run based on one or both of those tables; for each query, indicate how it would be useful in decision making and the fields it would include.

b. Consider the "hiring new faculty" case presented in the preceding problem. Create specifications for the following tables: request funding, advertise position/advertisers, candidate. Suggest at least two queries the hiring committee could run based on one or more of those tables; for each query, indicate how it would be useful in decision making and the fields it would include.

c. Consider the case involving Geoff from the preceding problem. Create specifications for the following tables: client, schedule appointment, prepare tax return/client. Suggest at least two queries Geoff could run based on one or more of those tables; for each query, indicate how it would be useful in decision making and the fields it would include.

d. Accounting information systems configured as relational databases would include at least the following tables with the indicated primary keys: chart of accounts (account number), make journal entries (journal entry ID), make journal entries/chart of accounts (account number and journal entry ID). What other fields would be included in each of those tables? How would you use the tables to determine account balances for the general purpose financial statements?

13. *Terminology.* Please match each item on the left with the most appropriate item on the right.

| | | | |
|---|---|---|---|
| 1. | Custom-made bicycles | a. | Associated with dividend payments |
| 2. | Date of record | b. | Human resource process internal control |
| 3. | Direct material | c. | Internal control for missed payments |
| 4. | Electronic funds transfer | d. | Job costing product |
| 5. | Factory supplies | e. | Method for gathering data |
| 6. | Number of interest payments | f. | Needed for stock issuance transaction |
| 7. | Observation | g. | Overhead |
| 8. | Par value of a share | h. | Process costing product |
| 9. | Pencils | i. | Required data for long-term debt transactions |
| 10. | Time clock | j. | Steel, for an automobile |

14. *Multiple choice questions.*

1. A company that reproduces fine works of art, such as the Mona Lisa, would most likely use what kind of production process?

   a. Hybrid

   b. Conversion

   c. Job

   d. Process

2. A journal entry in a company's accounting information system debited retained earnings. The purpose of the journal entry is most likely

   a. To record the declaration of a cash dividend.

   b. To account for the sale of finished goods inventory.

   c. To apply manufacturing overhead.

   d. To account for an employee leasing arrangement.

3. TRN Corporation produces a product that is highly perishable. Which of the following internal controls is the best alternative for controlling the risk of product spoilage?

   a. Separation of duties

   b. Adequate documentation

   c. Employee training

   d. Specialized storage containers

4. In a DFD of the human resources business process, "evaluate employees" would be represented with a

   a. Line.

   b. Circle.

   c. Rectangle.

   d. Triangle.

5. RKH Corporation maintains its job costing system using a relational database. Which of the following pieces of information would not be stored in a table in their system?

   a. Total cost of Job A244

   b. Manufacturing employee names

   c. Department affiliations of each employee

   d. Location of manufacturing equipment

15. *Statement evaluation.* Indicate whether each statement below is (i) always true, (ii) sometimes true, or (iii) never true. For statements that are (ii) sometimes true, explain when the statement is true.

   a. All five business processes discussed in the text are required to create value for stakeholders.

   b. Companies with long-term debt establish sinking funds.

   c. Conversion process forms are paper-based.

   d. Individual units of product in a process costing system are homogeneous.

   e. Information technology eliminates the problem of accounts receivable lapping.

   f. Separation of duties can be applied to fixed assets used in the conversion process.

   g. The "date of record" determines who receives dividends on capital stock.

   h. The par value of a share of capital stock is determined by the stock market.

   i. The total cost of a batch of units should be calculated and stored in a relational database table.

   j. With respect to long-term debt, the "coupon interest rate" and the "market interest rate" are two ways of referring to the same thing.

16. *Prior material application.*

   a. You read a bit about Porter's value chain at the beginning of Chapter 12. The value chain links together most, if not all, of the business processes we've examined in the last three chapters. To illustrate how, point your Web browser to www.heatercraft.com, a small manufacturer of marine accessories and other products in northern Idaho. List the primary and support activities in Porter's value chain, and give an example of each activity for Heater Craft. For example, the Web site itself is an example of "marketing and sales" in the value chain.

   b. Use COSO's enterprise risk management framework to develop a risk management plan for Heater Craft (or some other organization that focuses on one of the business processes discussed in the chapter).

   c. Most of today's college and university students have never known a world without information technology; MP3 players, digital video recorders, and laptop computers are commonplace tools in the 21st century. Work with a group of students to "invent" some new IT tool that will improve one or more of the business processes discussed in this chapter; for example, a voice-activated system for accessing employees' human resource records. Then, use the systems development life cycle to explain how you would develop and implement your idea.

17. *Excel application.* RVO Corporation makes and sells decorative picture frames and scenic photographs. Each unit is sold for $32 and incurs $17 variable cost per unit. RVO's total fixed costs are $18,000 annually.

   a. Use the preceding data to create a cost-volume-profit graph for RVO. Use absolute and relative cell referencing where appropriate. Here's an illustration of how it should look:

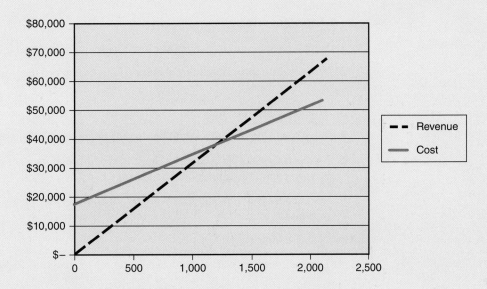

b. If the selling price per unit increases to $40, what happens to the graph? (All other factors remain the same as in the original data set.)

c. If the variable cost per unit decreases to $15, what happens to the graph? (All other factors remain the same as in the original data set.)

d. If the total annual fixed cost increases by 30%, what happens to the graph? (All other factors remain the same as in the original data set.)

e. If the selling price per unit decreases to $35, the variable cost per unit decreases to $12 and the total annual fixed cost increases by 10%, what happens to the graph?

## Comprehensive Problem Part 4 of 5

Each part of the comprehensive problem is based on Big Marker (www.bigmarker.com). Consider the narrative in Part 1 as necessary in responding to the following questions on business processes.

Consider the following transactions from Big Marker's accounting information system.

a. Accrued one month's interest on an existing note payable, $300.

b. Billed 30 communities for monthly dues of $600.

c. Borrowed $10,000 from First National Bank with a 6-month, 4% note payable.

d. Created a Chief Financial Officer position and established a support team for that function. The CFO's annual salary will be $150,000; each support team member will earn $60,000 annually.

e. Depreciated computer servers, $8,000.

f. Hired a new employee for the Development Team. The new employee's salary will be $45,000 annually.

g. Paid six months' rent in advance, $12,000.

h. Purchased new computer servers from Dell, $40,000.

i. Reimbursed employees for business expenses: Supplies, $500. Travel, $1,500.

j. Took an inventory of supplies on hand, which revealed $450 supplies used.

## Part Four Questions

1. Which business process is most closely associated with each transaction?

2. What is the appropriate journal entry (if any) to record the transaction in Big Marker's AIS?

3. Which elements of financial statements are represented in the journal entry?

4. What forms/documents would be used to process each transaction?

5. For each transaction, suggest at least two additional pieces of information you would want to capture in a relational database.

6. For each transaction, suggest two internal controls you would implement. Justify your response.

Here's an example to guide you:

- Transaction: Big Marker purchased supplies on account, $100.

- Business process: Acquisition/payment

- Journal entry: Debit Supplies $100. Credit Accounts Payable $100.

- Elements: Supplies is an asset; accounts payable, a liability.

- Forms: Purchase requisition and purchase order.

- Additional information: name of the primary contact person at the vendor, specific type and quantity of supplies purchased (e.g., 10 boxes of paper clips)

- Internal controls: Transaction authorizations would ensure that only the Purchasing department can issue purchase orders. Sending a blind copy of the purchase order to the Receiving department would aid in the segregation of duties.

# Other Topics in AIS

This last section of the book comprises three chapters:

**15.** Decision-Making Models and Knowledge Management

**16.** Professionalism, Ethics, and Career Planning

**17.** Auditing and Evaluating the AIS

The chapters in this section build on what you already know; they also connect AIS to other areas of accounting and business. In Chapter 15, you'll learn about Steps for Better Thinking, a structured way to make decisions. You'll also learn about knowledge management, another application of relational database technology. We'll also explore the ideas of "big data" and "cloud computing" in a new section of Chapter 15.

Chapter 16 considers the critically important topic of ethics. Historic and recent ethics scandals (such as Enron and Bernie Madoff) have rocked the accounting profession, calling into question the ethics and professionalism of accountants in virtually every employment sector. In this chapter, you'll learn what it means to be "a professional." You'll also be exposed to fundamental ideas about ethics and the ethics codes of several professional organizations. The chapter ends by offering some suggestions for planning your career in accounting.

The last chapter of the text provides an introduction to auditing. It discusses various kinds of audits you're likely to encounter in your career and focuses on the financial statement audit. You'll likely have at least one course in financial statement auditing as part of your accounting degree; this chapter will show you how that important area of practice is related to all you've learned about AIS.

# Chapter **Fifteen**

# Decision-Making Models and Knowledge Management

## AIS in the Business World

### Netflix

According to the investor relations section of its Web site (www.ir.netflix.com), "Netflix is the world's leading Internet television network with over 44 million members in 41 countries enjoying more than one billion hours of TV shows and movies per month, including original series."

New subscribers open an account, and then add programming to their list. Subscribers are invited to rate programming after watching it so that Netflix can recommend future selections. Netflix bills subscribers monthly; the exact rate depends on the subscription type (online only, DVD only, or a combination of the two).

Netflix would maintain a relational database that includes at least the following tables: subscriber, programming, subscriber/programming. With all the available programming choices, Netflix subscribers may experience information overload when trying to select items to view.

The Netflix system is an example of a knowledge management system (KMS) from at least two perspectives. From a customer's perspective, the current list of programming choices is a KMS. From Netflix's own perspective, data they gather about their customers that is later used for decision making is a KMS.

### *Discussion Questions*

1. What are the causes of information overload? What techniques and strategies can Netflix users employ to manage it?
2. What is a knowledge management system? How and why is Netflix an example of one?
3. How could Netflix management use Steps for Better Thinking in decision making?

Accounting is all about decision making—whether you're making decisions about the design and implementation of an accounting information system or using accounting information as the basis for decision making or in some other context. But, at the same time, the information available to business professionals for those decisions is increasing exponentially. So, how do accounting professionals manage all that information? And how do they make decisions based on it? We'll explore those two questions in this chapter.

When you've finished studying it, you should be able to:

1. Discuss and give examples of the concept of information overload, including causes, symptoms, and countermeasures.
2. Explain the nature of decision models and knowledge management.
3. Explain why those two topics are important in the study of accounting information systems.
4. Describe and apply Wolcott and Lynch's Steps for Better Thinking.
5. Explain fundamental concepts associated with Big Data, data analytics, and cloud computing.

The principles and ideas we'll discuss in this chapter have broad application across a wide range of business and nonbusiness disciplines. We'll keep our focus, though, on their application and meaning in the context of accounting information systems.

## INFORMATION OVERLOAD AND OTHER BARRIERS TO GOOD DECISIONS

The idea that managers can be receiving "too much information" goes back to at least the 1960s, according to Eppler and Mengis (2004). They provide several definitions of **information overload,** including (p. 328):

> The decision maker is considered to have experienced information overload at the point where the amount of information actually integrated into the decision begins to decline. Beyond this point, the individual's decisions reflect a lesser utilization of the available information.

> Information overload occurs when the volume of the information supply exceeds the limited human information processing capacity. Dysfunctional effects such as stress and confusion are the result.

> Information overload occurs when the information-processing requirements (information needed to complete a task) exceed the information-processing capacity (the quantity of information one can integrate into the decision-making process).

> Information overload occurs when the decision maker estimates he or she has to handle more information than he or she can efficiently use.

Notice what all those definitions have in common: our brains have a limited capacity for processing information. When too much information starts coming in, or information comes in faster than we can process it, information overload is the result.

So what are the **causes of information overload?** Eppler and Mengis distilled the writing of more than a dozen authors spanning over 30 years of research in this area. They suggest five fundamental causes of information overload (2004, p. 332), as shown in Figure 15.1.

*Personal factors* refer to everyone's individual limitations to process information. For example, I process information much better in the afternoon and evening than I do in the morning—something my own students can easily verify! If you've ever stayed up all night finishing a school project, you may have noticed your own ability to process information erodes. But, on the positive side, you can probably process more information today than you could 10 years ago, simply because you have more life experience and skills to help you manage information.

**FIGURE 15.1**
**Causes of**
**Information**
**Overload**

Source: Eppler and Mengis,
2004, p. 332.

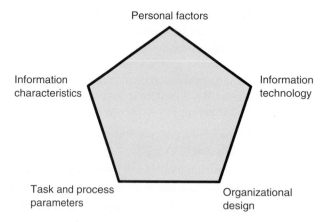

Readability indexes,
such as the Gunning
Fog index, can give an
objective measure of a
text's difficulty. A Web
search on readability
indexes or the Gunning
Fog index will return a
lot of information,
including how to calcu-
late a readability level.

*Information characteristics* also play an important part in triggering information overload. Information can be uncertain, ambiguous, complex, and intense—all of which create
a greater opportunity for decision makers to become overloaded. Consider, for example,
the complexity of information you read in an accounting text compared to the information
complexity in a newspaper or novel. Newspapers and novels are likely to be much easier to
"digest" than an accounting book, simply because of the nature of the information they
contain.

*Task and process parameters* are the third cause of information overload identified by
Eppler and Mengis. Have you ever had to make a decision under significant time pressure?
If you're like most accounting students, the answer is a resounding "Yes!" Time pressure is
one process parameter than can contribute to information overload. If you've taken any
intermediate accounting courses, or perhaps a course or two in taxation, you may have
found the rules and standards in one or both areas both numerous and incredibly detailed.
Other causes of information overload in this area include nonroutine tasks, task complexity
and interdependencies, and interruptions.

Fourth, Eppler and Mengis discuss *organizational design.* You've probably experienced
this cause of information overload if you've ever worked on a group project in school or in
practice. People in groups have differing ideas and approaches for problem solving and
decision making; integrating all those different points of view can easily lead to information overload.

The final cause of information overload, according to Eppler and Mengis, is *information technology.* Think of all the ways IT provides you with information: e-mail, instant
messaging, cell phones, the Internet, increased numbers of television channels. Every
day, people are bombarded with information—much more so than in the past. Having all
that information coming at you virtually all the time is bound to create some information overload.

# Reflection and Self-Assessment                    15.1

Think of a recent experience you had with information overload. What caused it? Can you classify the causes according to the five items in Figure 15.1?

Since you've probably experienced information overload at one time or another, you probably have at least some idea of its symptoms and effects. Eppler and Mengis grouped the symptoms and effects into four categories and provided several examples of each (2004, p. 333):

- Limited information search and retrieval strategies (information overload causes people to be less effective when looking for information).
  - Less systematic searching.
  - Increased problems differentiating relevant and irrelevant information.
- Arbitrary information analysis and organization (too much information coming in too fast impairs a person's ability to organize and classify information).
  - Overlapping and inconsistent categories.
  - Difficulty seeing "the big picture."
- Suboptimal decisions (decision making is weakened, producing poor results).
  - Inefficient work.
  - Reduced quality and accuracy of decisions.
- Strenuous personal situations (information overload takes its toll on people physically, psychologically, mentally, and spiritually).
  - Stress, confusion, and cognitive strain.
  - Overconfidence.

Of course, the examples given above are but a few of many ways people respond to information overload.

So, since information overload is such a widespread problem, and since its impacts can be diverse and severe, how can managers deal with it? Returning to the five-part framework suggested in Figure 15.1, Eppler and Mengis examined the literature and noted the following **countermeasures** for information overload (2004, pp. 335–336):

- Allow more time to complete important tasks.
- Compress, aggregate, categorize, and structure information.
- Create small, self-contained tasks rather than trying to do everything at once.
- Define decision models and rules for common decision contexts.
- Focus on creating value-added information.
- Formalize the language used to describe information.
- Handle information as it comes to you—don't put it off!
- Improve personal information management.
- Improve personal time management skills and techniques.
- Use graphs and other visual aids.

The list could go on for another page or two, but I don't want you to experience information overload from reading it!

# Reflection and Self-Assessment                              15.2

Choose one of the five causes of information overload identified in Figure 15.1. Explain how you would use one of the countermeasures to address it. For example, allowing more time to complete important tasks is a good way to address significant task and process parameters. More specifically, if your AIS instructor gave you an assignment four weeks before it was due, you would structure your time to complete the assignment gradually over those four weeks—rather than waiting until a few days before the due date.

Simon (1997) talked about two additional reasons people don't always make the "best" decisions: **satisficing** and **bounded rationality.** *Satisficing* refers to people's tendency to stop looking for solutions to a problem when they find a solution that works—whether that decision is the "best" or not. For example, an accountant trying to choose a piece of general ledger software might "settle" for the first package that came along, rather than continuing to search for software that might meet his or her needs even better.

*Bounded rationality* is a separate, but related, idea; it means that people will inherently avoid uncertainty and rely on proven "rules" for problem solving whenever they can. Suppose your friend rides with you to school one day and later tells you that there's a better route to take than the way you usually go. The concept of bounded rationality would predict that you'll keep going the same way as always, avoiding the uncertain (and perhaps better) alternative. In our example above, bounded rationality might cause a decision maker to reject hiring a consultant if he or she has had poor experience with consultants in the past.

Betsch et al. (2004) talked about the idea of **relapse errors** in decision making. Their research revealed that people will follow a familiar routine, even if the routine is ineffective and even if they have a positive intention to change. Perhaps you know a student who spends most weekends partying instead of studying. That student may say to him/herself: "I really need to stop partying so much on the weekends. It's starting to impact my grades, and I don't like that." The idea of relapse errors indicates that, even with the positive intention to change, the student is likely to continue repeating the same behavior over and over again. And, in the AIS example, relapse errors might cause a decision maker just to adopt a newer version of an old piece of software, without considering a broad range of choices.

Do the ideas of satisficing, bounded rationality, and relapse errors mean that people are doomed to make bad decisions? Of course not! But it takes tremendous effort to change ineffective decision-making processes, and being aware of those three important ideas may help.

## Reflection and Self-Assessment                                    15.3

Kathy has just started her own business after graduating from college. She is a management consultant, specializing in the development of business plans. She comes to you, a recent accounting graduate, for help in setting up her accounting information system. How would the ideas of satisficing and bounded rationality affect your advice to Kathy?

If you'd like to know more about the ideas in this section of the chapter, use your school's library to locate and read the Eppler and Mengis article. They do an excellent job of distilling and synthesizing the work of many other authors on this important topic.

## DECISION MODELS AND KNOWLEDGE MANAGEMENT

One of the ways to combat information overload is to apply effective models for making decisions and managing knowledge. A "model" in this context refers to a generalized set of processes employed to accomplish a specific task. For example, you may have a model for how you get ready to go to school; it is probably significantly different from the model you use when you get ready to go out with friends.

Within the context of an organization, the generalized set of processes people use to gather, organize, and retain information has become known as *knowledge management,* defined as "the organization of intellectual resources and information systems within a business environment" (MSN Encarta dictionary). Santosus and Surmacz (2005) defined **knowledge management** as "the process through which organizations generate value from their intellectual and knowledge-based assets. Most often, generating value from such assets involves sharing them among employees, departments and even with other companies in an effort to devise best practices. It's important to note that the definition says nothing about technology; while [knowledge management] is often facilitated by IT, technology by itself is not [knowledge management]." In today's world, knowledge is power. Organizations no longer derive most of their wealth from physical assets such as cash in the bank or property, plant, and equipment. Information drives the 21st century economy, and business professionals need strategies for capturing and organizing information, as well as for using that information for making decisions.

Rowley (1999) identified four objectives of knowledge management:

1. *To create knowledge repositories.* Think of this objective as developing a "library" for your organization. Knowledge here can refer to information on the competitive landscape, results of internal research, and the experiences of others in the organization.

2. *To improve knowledge access.* Here, we're talking about making knowledge more available throughout an organization. The most competitive organizations today share knowledge among individuals and responsibility centers. In fact, Drucker (1993) pointed out that knowledge may be the only genuinely sustainable economic resource in the modern economy.

3. *To enhance the knowledge environment.* This objective means stakeholders have a responsibility to create conditions that facilitate knowledge creation and sharing. Techniques that fall into this category include participative management, 360-degree performance evaluation, and decentralized management structures. Fundamentally, creating an environment of knowledge sharing is an issue of organizational culture.

4. *To manage knowledge as an asset.* The strict accounting definition of an asset is a probable future economic benefit obtained or controlled by a particular entity as a result of past transactions or events. While "knowledge" probably falls within that definition, we simply don't know how to measure its economic value for financial-reporting purposes. But, even though you won't see "knowledge" listed as an asset on organizational balance sheets, it must be managed for organizational benefit.

Call (2005) pointed out that "effective knowledge management changes the way organizations and individuals function." Building on the ideas of Nesbitt (2002), Call advocated seven **steps to create a knowledge management system.** Those steps are listed below; the text that follows each step explains how Netflix management might create a knowledge management system about its customers.

1. *Create an organizational culture that supports the ideas of knowledge sharing and development.* According to Schein (2010), organizational culture comprises three elements: artifacts (behaviors), values, and assumptions. Behaviors are driven by values, which are driven by assumptions. Developing a KMS is a behavior; its related value is the importance of knowledge sharing. For Netflix employees to value knowledge sharing, they must assume at least one of the following: (i) knowledge sharing is good for the company, (ii) sharing knowledge will not result in punishment, and (iii) knowledge sharing will be rewarded in some way. Creating an organizational culture

comprising those assumptions/values/behaviors is a daunting task, but not impossible. Top management must support, through words, actions, and policies, such a culture as a first step.

2. *Define the business goals the knowledge management system will address.* Companies should not create a KMS without understanding how it will help the organization; otherwise, it becomes just "another exercise" to occupy employees' time. Netflix management might determine that the KMS' goal should be to increase customer satisfaction and its subscriber base.

3. *Perform a knowledge audit to identify any duplication, gaps, and overlaps in an organization's knowledge base.* A knowledge audit could be as simple as a series of employee focus groups or as complex as a formal research project. Netflix would want to ask employees in various departments what they know about customers and their preferences, then determine what gaps exist in that knowledge.

4. *Create a visual map that describes units of knowledge and the relationships between them.* Figure 15.2 shows a sample visual map, often referred to as a knowledge map, which might grow out of the knowledge audit at Netflix.

5. *Develop a knowledge management strategy based on the content management, integration, search mechanisms, information delivery, and collaboration.* A knowledge management strategy comprises three main elements: purpose, policies, and procedures. For Netflix, the purpose of the strategy is to enhance the company's ability to compete in its markets. A related policy might be to complete a quarterly survey of customers who discontinued their Netflix subscriptions. The procedure for carrying out the survey would include deciding who should do it, how the customers should be identified and what questions should be asked.

**FIGURE 15.2**
**Netflix Knowledge Map**

6. *Purchase or build appropriate tools for capturing, analyzing, categorizing, and distributing knowledge.* Netflix would create a relational database to capture the knowledge it gathers through the KMS. It would use quantitative techniques, such as multiple regression, and qualitative techniques, such as text analysis, to draw conclusions from the captured data. Distributing that knowledge could happen through employee meetings, newsletters, and other formats.

7. *Periodically reassess the value of the knowledge management system and make necessary adjustments.* You may recall, from our earlier discussions of the COSO internal control and enterprise risk management frameworks, the importance of monitoring; the last step in Call's KMS creation process is a monitoring function.

# Reflection and Self-Assessment 15.4

If you've taken any intermediate accounting courses, you may be familiar with the FASB Accounting Standards Codification. Point your Web browser to http://aaahq .org/FASB/Access.cfm, where accounting students can get free access to the codification system. Explain why the codification is a knowledge management system.

The idea that accounting involves complex, open-ended problems may come as a surprise to you. In many accounting texts, the focus is on presenting problems with single correct responses. They form the foundation of the Steps for Better Thinking process but are not completely representative of the kinds of problems you'll have to solve in practice.

Business problems today require creative, critical thinking—bringing us to a discussion of Wolcott and Lynch's Steps for Better Thinking (2005). **Steps for Better Thinking** (SBT) is a developmental problem-solving and decision-making process. It is especially relevant to the kinds of problems we face in business today—complex and open-ended, without single, "correct," deterministic responses.

SBT starts with a foundation level, and proceeds through four problem-solving processes. Each process is more complex than the one before it. Wolcott (2005) presented the steps as shown in Figure 15.3. Let's look at how SBT could have helped Netflix deal with an issue they encountered with their pricing a few years ago.

Prior to 2011, Netflix customers paid a single price for access to both DVD and streaming programming. In 2011, however, Netflix changed its pricing significantly and separated the two options. Customers could still subscribe to both, but they paid a much higher fee each month for that option. Netflix suffered a serious loss of customers and its stock price decreased very quickly. In determining how to respond to those events, Netflix management could have used SBT like this:

1. *Identifying*
   a. *Problem.* Loss of customers
   b. *Relevant information.* Number and percentage of customers lost, reasons they canceled their subscription
   c. *Uncertainties.* Relationship between cancellations and pricing changes, other reasons customers may have canceled

The steps are presented in a very linear way in this example. In "real life," decision makers might move back and forth between the steps as new information comes to light.

2. *Exploring*
   a. *Biases.* "Rightness" of management's decision. Embarrassment resulting from changing back.
   b. *Assumptions.* New customers and higher fees to offset cancellations
   c. *Qualitative interpretation from various points of view.* (i) Customers: Price hikes were too extreme and too sudden. Alternatives to Netflix are abundant. (ii) Stockholders: Actions

**FIGURE 15.3**
**Steps for Better Thinking**

Source: Adapted with permission; Copyright 2005 by Susan K. Wolcott. Steps for Better Thinking and related materials can be accessed at www.wolcottlynch.com.

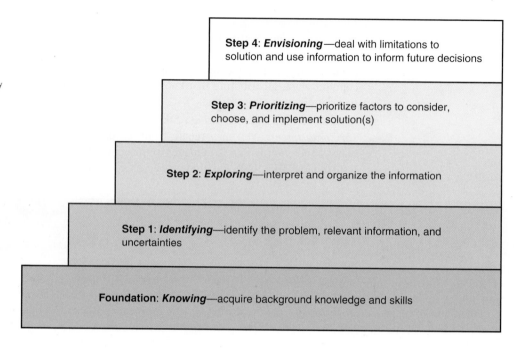

**Step 4:** *Envisioning*—deal with limitations to solution and use information to inform future decisions

**Step 3:** *Prioritizing*—prioritize factors to consider, choose, and implement solution(s)

**Step 2:** *Exploring*—interpret and organize the information

**Step 1:** *Identifying*—identify the problem, relevant information, and uncertainties

**Foundation:** *Knowing*—acquire background knowledge and skills

that reduce the stock price so dramatically and suddenly should be subject to change. Perhaps management should be replaced. (iii) Management: In the long run, things will "return to normal."

d. *Information organization.* **Customer** information: demographics, reasons for cancelling, intention to resubscribe. **Financial** information: stock price movement, profitability, P/E ratio, stock beta. **Market** information: alternatives to Netflix, cost of each alternative.

3. *Prioritizing*

a. *Ranked list of factors to consider.* **Very** important: impact of policy on profitability, market share, and share price. Ways to motivate subscribers who canceled to resubscribe. **Somewhat** important: Ways to avoid future loss of customers. (**Note:** The rankings and factors are highly subjective, and would likely differ across decision makers.)

b. *Conclusion.* Management made a poor decision. Netflix should offer subscribers who canceled one or more free months.

4. *Envisioning*

a. *Solution limitations.* How to determine the number of free months for each subscriber. Financial impact on Netflix. Potential resentment from customers who did not cancel.

b. *Information use for future decisions.* Conduct more extensive market research before making similar changes again.

# Reflection and Self-Assessment                                    15.5

Consider the case of Kathy presented in Reflection and Self-Assessment 15.3. Use the Steps for Better Thinking model to prepare your advice to Kathy.

As you can see, using the Steps for Better Thinking to reach a decision is a detailed process. As noted above, the ability to use the steps must be deliberately, consistently, and continually developed over time; a decision maker's comfort level with the steps will increase with practice, though, and careful application of SBT will typically result in high-quality decisions.

# CRITICAL THINKING

Now that we've discussed knowledge management systems and Steps for Better Thinking, let's take a look at some relatively new, yet highly related, concepts that impact both knowledge management and decision making. In this section, we'll examine the ideas of **Big Data, data analytics,** and **cloud computing.**

According to Arthur (2013), "Big data is a collection of data from traditional and digital sources inside and outside your company that represents a source for ongoing discovery and analysis." Notice the following elements of that definition:

- *Collection of data.* Many folks erroneously believe that "Big Data" constitutes nothing more than large quantities of data. But, most authorities in the field agree that it's not the volume of data that matters—it's the diversity of the data. Arthur's definition doesn't mention the *size* of the collection—only that Big Data *is* a collection.

- *Inside and outside the company.* Big Data arises, in part, from an organization's information systems, including its AIS. But, Big Data also comes from sources outside the company, such as social media. We'll look at the five types of Big Data shortly.

- *Ongoing discovery and analysis.* One of the main issues surrounding Big Data is how to analyze it. Since much of it is nontraditional in format, and since collecting it is a continuous process, Big Data requires ongoing analysis.

Soares (2012) discussed five types of Big Data:

1. **Web and social media data** includes . . . data from social media such as Facebook, Twitter, LinkedIn, and blogs.
2. **Machine-to-machine data** includes readings from sensors, meters, and other devices as part of the so-called "Internet of things."
3. **Big transaction data** includes healthcare claims . . . and utility billing records that are increasingly available in semi-structured and unstructured formats.
4. **Biometric data** includes fingerprints, genetics, handwriting, retinal scans, and similar types of data.
5. **Human-generated data** includes vast quantities of unstructured and semi-structured data such as call center agents' notes, voice recordings, email, paper documents, surveys, and electronic medical records.

How does Big Data relate to the ideas of knowledge management systems and decision making? By expanding the reach of KMS and by suggesting that decisions must sometimes be informed by new data types.

"Data analytics" refers to the tools decision makers can use to analyze Big Data. Many experts in the field divide those tools into three big groups: descriptive, predictive, and prescriptive. Bertolucci (2013) differentiated them as follows:

- **Descriptive** analytics "summarize what happened." Examples of descriptive analytics include things like average customer satisfaction rating (human-generated data) and number of households whose electricity usage exceeds the baseline (big transaction data).

- **Predictive** analytics "utilizes a variety of . . . techniques to study recent and historical data, thereby allowing analysts to make predictions about the future." Predictive techniques include all sorts of statistical models, such as multiple regression and analysis of variance.

- **Prescriptive** analytics "goes beyond descriptive and predictive models by recommending one or more courses of action—and showing the likely outcome of each decision." Prescriptive techniques include things like linear programming and time-series forecasting.

How do data analytics tools fit into the broader ideas of KMS and decision making? Clearly, they provide tools that allow decision makers to analyze the data in a KMS and use it to inform decisions.

Finally, let's consider the idea of cloud computing. According to Rouse (2010):

> Cloud computing is a general term for anything that involves delivering hosted services over the Internet. The name cloud computing was inspired by the cloud symbol that's often used to represent the Internet in flowcharts and diagrams.

If you've ever used tools like Google Drive, you've done cloud computing. Cloud computing has an important relationship to the topics discussed in this chapter. Specifically, cloud computing allows decision makers to access data (Big or otherwise) from virtually anywhere at virtually any time. The data can then be analyzed (using data analytics tools), organized into a KMS and used to make decisions.

## Summary

Here's a brief synopsis of this chapter's main points:

1. *Discuss and give examples of the concept of information overload, including causes, symptoms, and countermeasures.* Information overload occurs when people have information coming in faster than they can process that information. Information technology has definitely contributed to information overload in modern organizations; other factors include human, task, process, and information characteristics. Symptoms and responses include suboptimal decisions and arbitrary analysis. Managers can effectively combat information overload with good time management, personal discipline, and knowledge management systems.

2. *Explain the nature of decision models and knowledge management.* A model is a generalized framework for completing a task. Knowledge management systems achieve four important objectives: create knowledge repositories, improve knowledge access, enhance the knowledge environment, and manage knowledge as an asset.

3. *Explain why those two topics are important in the study of accounting information systems.* The essence of accounting is decision making. As accountants, we need to collect information that is relevant and helpful in specific decision contexts.

4. *Describe and apply Wolcott and Lynch's Steps for Better Thinking.* The Steps for Better Thinking is an example of a decision-making model; it involves four levels of increasing complexity: identifying, exploring, prioritizing, and envisioning.

5. *Explain fundamental concepts associated with Big Data, data analytics and cloud computing.* "Big Data" refers to the diverse types of data decision makers have available in modern systems. The process of data analytics allows organizations to examine that data and draw insights from it. Many organizations are moving to cloud computing models that store data remotely so it can be accessed from virtually anywhere.

You make personal and professional decisions every day. Some of them are more mundane (what to wear to school, what to eat for lunch), while others are of vital long-term importance (how to allocate your time, which job offer to accept at graduation). The information presented in this chapter will assist you in developing your own decision-making style and process.

## Key Terms

Big Data, *291*
bounded rationality, *286*
causes of information overload, *283*
cloud computing, *291*

countermeasures, *285*
data analytics, *291*
information overload, *283*
knowledge management, *287*
relapse errors, *286*

satisficing, *286*
Steps for Better Thinking, *289*
steps to create a knowledge management system, *287*

## Chapter References

Arthur, L. 2013. "What Is Big Data?" Retrieved 1 March 2014 from www.forbes.com.

Bertolucci, J. 2013. "Big Data Analytics: Descriptive Vs. Predictive Vs. Prescriptive." Retrieved 1 March 2014 from www.informationweek.com.

Betsch, T., S. Haberstroh, B. Molter, and A. Glockner. 2004. "Oops, I Did It Again—Relapse Errors in Routinized Decision Making." *Organizational Behavior and Human Decision Processes* 93, no. 1, pp. 62–74.

Call, D. 2005. "Knowledge Management—Not Rocket Science." *Journal of Knowledge Management* 9, no. 2, pp. 19–30.

Drucker, P. 1993. *Post-Capitalist Society.* New York: Harper Row Publishing.

Eppler, M., and J. Mengis. 2004. "The Concept of Information Overload: A Review of Literature from Organization Science, Accounting, Marketing, MIS and Related Disciplines." *Information Society,* pp. 325–44.

Nesbitt, K. 2002, February 8. "Designing a Knowledge Management System." http://academic.edu.2081/products/faulknerlibrary/00018382.htm (May 2, 2005).

Rouse, M. (2010) "Cloud Computing Essential Guide." Retrieved 1 March 2014 from searchcloudcomputing.techtarget.com/definition/cloud-computing.

Rowley, J. 1999. "What Is Knowledge Management?" *Library Management,* pp. 416–19.

Santosus, M., and J. Surmacz. 2005. "The ABCs of Knowledge Management." www.cio.com (April 28).

Schein, E. 2010. *Organizational Culture and Leadership.* 4th ed. Jossey-Bass.

Simon, H. 1997. *Administrative Behavior.* 4th ed. New York: Free Press.

Soares, S. 2012. "A Framework that Focuses on the 'Data' in Big Data Governance." Retrieved 1 March 2014 from www.ibmdatamag.com.

Wolcott, S., and C. Lynch. 2005. "Steps for Better Thinking." www.wolcottlynch.com (April 29).

## End-of-Chapter Activities

1. *Reading review questions.*

   a. What is information overload? What causes it? What are its effects? How can decision makers deal with information overload in their professional lives?

   b. Explain the idea of knowledge management. Why is it important? What are some techniques you can use to manage knowledge now and in the future?

   c. Summarize the ideas and steps associated with Wolcott and Lynch's Steps for Better Thinking.

   d. Prepare a response to the questions for this chapter's "AIS in the Business World."

2. *Reading review problem.* American Express (www.americanexpress.com) offers four broad types of credit cards: personal, small business, corporate, and prepaid. Each card type is tailored to a specific group of customers. A knowledge management system would help American Express develop new cards within those four types.

   a. What is a knowledge management system? What steps would American Express use to develop one?

   b. Bumble Beasley was considering applying for an American Express card, but had a difficult time deciding which card was right for him. Suggest why Bumble was experiencing difficulty; frame your answer using the causes of information overload discussed in the chapter. For each cause you identify, suggest at least one countermeasure Bumble could use.

c. Shawn has had a personal American Express card for many years. He recently started a business and has considered changing to a small business American Express card. Use Steps for Better Thinking to explain how Shawn should decide whether to follow through with his idea.

d. What types of Big Data would American Express use to make decisions about developing new card types? How would it use descriptive/predictive/prescriptive analytics in that process?

3. *Multiple choice review.*

1. When a decision maker estimates he or she has to handle more information than he or she can efficiently use, the decision maker is experiencing:
   a. Knowledge mismanagement.
   b. Information overload.
   c. Satisficing.
   d. Bounded rationality.

2. All of the following are objectives of knowledge management except:
   a. Recording knowledge as an asset in the AIS.
   b. Creating knowledge repositories.
   c. Enhancing the knowledge environment.
   d. Improving knowledge access.

3. In Steps for Better Thinking, which step is concerned with interpreting and organizing information?
   a. Identifying
   b. Exploring
   c. Prioritizing
   d. Interpreting

4. In the first of the Steps for Better Thinking, decision makers should identify: (i) the problem, (ii) relevant information, (iii) limitations.
   a. i and ii only
   b. ii and iii only
   c. i and iii only
   d. i, ii, and iii

5. Which of the following steps for creating a knowledge management system should occur first?
   a. Adopt Steps for Better Thinking.
   b. Normalize database tables.
   c. Define business goals the system should address.
   d. Build appropriate tools.

4. *Making choices and exercising judgment.* Parmeet is currently pursuing a degree in accounting because she heard that jobs are plentiful in the field. However, she is not doing well in her accounting courses and is considering changing her major to some form of engineering. Use Steps for Better Thinking to analyze her choice.

5. *Field work.* Do a Google search for "The NIST Definition of Cloud Computing" by Mell and Grance. In a format specified by your instructor, summarize one or more of the following: (i) the five essential characteristics of cloud computing, (ii) the three service models of cloud computing, and (iii) the four deployment models of cloud computing.

6. *Analyzing current issues in accounting.* Consider the list of current and classic issues in accounting presented below (or others specified by your instructor). With your instructor's help and guidance, form a team of students to investigate one of the issues. Use the Steps for Better Thinking to analyze the issue and prepare a short oral report for the class.

   a. What are the obstacles associated with adopting International Financial Reporting Standards?

   b. Should the provisions of the Sarbanes-Oxley Act be extended to nonpublic corporations?

   c. Will principles-based accounting become the norm for U.S. GAAP?

   d. Has the 150-hour requirement for becoming a CPA been a success?

   e. What systems documentation techniques should be taught in AIS courses?

   f. Has the conceptual framework of accounting fulfilled its purpose?

   g. What issues should managers consider with regard to corporate governance?

   h. Should social and environmental reporting be mandatory?

   i. How, if at all, should fair-value accounting be implemented?

7. *Software acquisition decision using SBT.*

   a. Critter Sitters (www.stlouiscrittersitters.com/) is an in-home pet care company based in St. Louis, Missouri. Their Web site lists several services available to pet owners, including mid-day dog walking, puppy care, and in-home dog training. Suppose Critter Sitters is considering three general ledger packages for its accounting information system: Sage 50 Complete Accounting, Quickbooks, and Microsoft Dynamics. Use the Steps for Better Thinking to help the company's president make a choice.

   b. According to its Web site (www.40debts.org/counseling/default.asp), Harbour Credit Management "provides credit management services to families and individuals experiencing financial stress." Suppose the firm is searching for software that will help manage spam on its information system. Point your Web browser to www.download.com, and investigate three different software packages that fulfill that purpose. Make a recommendation to Harbour's management using the Steps for Better Thinking to inform your decision.

8. *Types of Big Data.* The chapter discussed five types of Big Data. Indicate which category best fits each of the following examples; if an example fits more than one category, explain why.

   a. Airline ticket reservations

   b. Blood type

   c. Cell phone tower usage

   d. Daily credit card transactions

   e. Fax transmissions

   f. Journal articles

   g. Pinterest posts

   h. Voice print analysis

   i. X-rays

   j. YouTube videos

9. *Creating knowledge management systems.*

   a. Viola completed her accounting degree in 2000; she has had three professional positions since that time. She summarized information about each position as indicated below. Organize the information into a knowledge management system.

   Dewey, Cheatam and Howe, CPAs (2000 to 2001)

   Responsibilities: Small-business auditing

   Salary: $40,000 annually

Comments: I like working with small-business clients, but it's tough getting to know them.

ENZ Corporation (2001 to 2003)

Responsibilities: AIS design, accounts receivable management

Salary: $45,000 annually

Comments: More stable hours, interesting work—but not really diverse.

FNN Corporation (2003 to present)

Responsibilities: Divisional controller

Salary: $50,000 annually

Comments: Plenty of responsibility; interesting corporate culture.

b.  Most university accounting curricula cover a fairly standard range of topics: financial accounting, cost accounting, taxation, systems, and auditing. Think about the classes you've taken so far within your accounting program; develop a list of at least five topics for each class. Also, develop a list of other abilities (like writing, speaking, and use of information technology) that cut across the accounting classes you've had. Using a software tool of your choice (or one specified by your instructor), develop a system to organize and manage the items in the lists.

c.  Sebastian is a self-employed AIS consultant. He has several books on the subject in his library, as shown in Table 15.1, covering a variety of topics. Develop a knowledge management system based on the information provided. (Your instructor may ask you to use a relational database such as Microsoft Access to complete this task.)

**TABLE 15.1   Table of Books for Activity 9(c)**

| | Books | | | | | |
|---|---|---|---|---|---|---|
| **Title** | *Accounting Information Systems* | *Adventures in AIS* | *Basic AIS Concepts* | *Auditing AIS* | *The Role of AIS in Organizations* | *Safeguarding the AIS* |
| **Author** | Brady | Legault | Ogan | Barbagallo | James | Burkett |
| **Publisher** | Prentice Hall | Thomson | McGraw-Hill | Thomson | McGraw-Hill | McGraw-Hill |
| **Copyright** | 2010 | 2010 | 2012 | 2013 | 2014 | 2011 |
| **Strengths** | Easy to read; lots of illustrations | Real-world examples | Real-world examples; Sarbanes-Oxley | Topic breadth; checklists | End-of-chapter materials; independent organization | Small-business focus; easy to read |
| **Weaknesses** | Cost | Difficult to read | End-of-chapter materials | Sarbanes-Oxley | Difficult to read | Web materials |
| **Number of Pages** | 300 | 150 | 275 | 300 | 185 | 210 |
| **Topics** | • Information technology<br>• Internal controls<br>• Data modeling | • Accounting cycle<br>• Fraud detection<br>• Information technology<br>• Data modeling | • Accounting cycle<br>• Internal controls<br>• Data modeling<br>• Information technology | • Fraud detection<br>• Internal controls<br>• Accounting cycle<br>• Data modeling<br>• Information technology | • Information technology<br>• Internal controls | • Internal controls<br>• Fraud detection<br>• Information technology |

10. *Terminology.* Please match each item on the left with the most appropriate item on the right.

| | |
|---|---|
| 1. Behaviors, values, and assumptions | a. Type of Big Data |
| 2. Biometric | b. Parts of "identifying" in Steps for Better Thinking |
| 3. Dealing with solution limitations | c. Information overload countermeasure |
| 4. Formalizing language | d. Goal of knowledge management |
| 5. Linear programming | e. Form of prescriptive analytics |
| 6. Managing knowledge as an asset | f. Examples of descriptive analytics |
| 7. Mean, median, and mode | g. Elements of organizational culture |
| 8. Relevant information and uncertainties | h. Element of "envisioning" in Steps for Better Thinking |
| 9. Stress and confusion | i. Dysfunctional effects of information overload |
| 10. Task and process parameters | j. A cause of information overload |

11. *Multiple choice.* Please refer to the following short case as you answer these questions:

After earning both her accounting degree and her CPA license, Barb opened her own public accounting practice. One of her clients was looking for a way to make transaction processing more efficient; Barb immediately knew the client needed to invest in general ledger software. She assumed price and ease of use were the most important factors, so she identified three software packages that were both inexpensive and easy to use. The client chose one of the three for installation; a few months later, Barb conducted a follow-up interview to determine how the software was working.

1. "Identifying" is one of the levels in Steps for Better Thinking. Which element of "identifying" did Barb neglect most seriously?
   a. The problem.
   b. Relevant information.
   c. Uncertainties.
   d. Barb did not neglect any element of "identifying."

2. Gathering information on cost and ease of use for each software package is an element of ___ in Steps for Better Thinking.
   a. Identifying
   b. Exploring
   c. Prioritizing
   d. Envisioning

3. "Prioritizing" is one of the levels in Steps for Better Thinking. Who participated in the prioritizing process?
   a. Barb only.
   b. The client only.
   c. Neither Barb nor the client.
   d. Both Barb and the client.

4. Which of the following phrases is most indicative of the "foundation" level of Steps for Better Thinking?
   a. After earning both her accounting degree and her CPA license.
   b. Barb opened her own public accounting practice.
   c. The client needed to invest in general ledger software.
   d. Make transaction processing more efficient.

5. The follow-up interview is most directly associated with the ___ process in Steps for Better Thinking.

   a. Identifying

   b. Exploring

   c. Prioritizing

   d. Envisioning

12. *Statement evaluation.* Indicate whether each of the following statements is (i) always true, (ii) sometimes true, or (iii) never true. For those that are (ii) sometimes true, explain when the statement is true.

    a. An organizational culture comprises three parts: assumptions, principles, and constraints.

    b. Big Data refers to the volume of data an organization needs to manage.

    c. Decision makers should acquire background knowledge and skills before attempting to identify problems and relevant information.

    d. Descriptive analytics are less useful than predictive and prescriptive analytics.

    e. Improving personal time management skills can help information overload caused by personal factors.

    f. In a group setting, organizational design may cause information overload.

    g. In the "exploring" phase of Steps for Better Thinking, information should never be organized based on when it was received.

    h. Information technology always increases information overload.

    i. Using graphs and other visual aids is less helpful than structuring information when managing information overload.

    j. Using Steps for Better Thinking will always lead to solutions without limitations.

13. *Prior material application.*

    a. This chapter outlined seven steps for creating a knowledge management system, using Netflix as an example. Think about the steps in the broader context of a functionally organized corporation; who should complete each of the steps for creating the system? In a format specified by your instructor, document the steps based on the parties you believe should complete them.

    b. This chapter suggested five major causes of information overload. Think about one of the business processes discussed in Part Four. For the business process you choose, suggest one specific example for each major cause of information overload.

    c. When an organization incurs a cost, it has two basic choices for how to record it in the AIS: capitalizing or expensing. Suppose a corporation develops its own knowledge management system using a standard relational database like Access. How should it account for the development cost? Justify your response.

    d. This chapter's "Critical Thinking" section outlined three broad types of data analytics: descriptive, predictive, and prescriptive. Consider the Excel applications in Chapters 1 through 14. Which of them involve data analytics techniques? For those that do, classify the techniques as descriptive/predictive/prescriptive.

14. *Excel application.* This exercise will show you one way to generate a random sample using Excel.

    a. Consult the 3 February 2014 post on my AIS blog; download the Chapter 15 data file you'll find there.

    b. In Column B of the data file, use Excel's = RAND function to generate a random number for each record number in the file (100 records total).

    c. Use the "Copy" and "Paste Values" commands to replace the RAND function with the values it generated for each record.

d.  Sort both columns (the record numbers and the random numbers) in ascending order based on the random numbers. Notice that the original record numbers are now in random order. Here's an example of how it might look:

| Record Number | Random Number |
|---------------|---------------|
| 1542          | 0.18          |
| 1780          | 0.23          |
| 1164          | 0.35          |
| 1648          | 0.36          |
| 1023          | 0.55          |

e.  Using the first ten records as a random sample, calculate the following descriptive statistics: mean, median, and standard deviation.

f.  How might a random sample be used in accounting?

# Chapter **Sixteen**

# Professionalism, Ethics, and Career Planning

## AIS in the Business World

### HP and Autonomy

In 2012, HP (www.hp.com) paid $10.3 billion to acquire Autonomy (www.autonomy .com). Autonomy's business is creating tools organizations can use to search and analyze databases—similar to the data analytics tools we discussed in the previous chapter. Not long after, however, HP took a "write down" of $8.8 billion on the acquisition. HP claimed that it was a victim of fraud, alleging that Autonomy's accounting was deliberately manipulated to increase the firm's value in light of the impending acquisition. After the write down was announced, HP's stock price rapidly declined, but has since recovered somewhat.

Whether the HP/Autonomy transaction constituted fraud remains to be seen. Minimally, though, it raises serious questions about ethics—one of the main topics of this chapter.

### Discussion Questions

1. Define "ethics." Discuss four schools of ethical thought, indicating how each would respond to the ethics issues in the HP/Autonomy case.
2. What are the characteristics of a professional? Did everyone behave professionally in this case?
3. How should the CEO of HP resolve the ethical issues created by the merger?

Most accounting majors, arguably, are studying the subject because they intend to pursue a career in the accounting profession. In this chapter, we'll take a look at three topics closely related to that goal: professionalism, ethics, and career planning.

Professionalism and ethics are not skills that magically descend upon you once you earn your accounting degree; furthermore, planning your career is something that needs to begin now—not when you're ready to graduate. Indeed, developing a sense of professionalism, the habit of behaving ethically, and a plan for your career is at least as important as learning software applications, FASB pronouncements, and other technical areas of accounting. In this chapter, we'll consider what it means to be a professional, specifically within the context of accounting.

When you complete your study of this chapter, you should be able to:

1. List and discuss characteristics of a professional.
2. Explain how those characteristics apply to the accounting profession.
3. Define *ethics*.
4. Discuss various models/schools of ethical decision making.
5. Explain how to resolve ethical dilemmas.

Although this chapter may mark your first exposure to these issues, it almost certainly will not constitute your last.

# PROFESSIONALISM

You probably have heard many people talk about the "accounting profession." And you've probably noticed that people consistently refer to some careers as "professional," but not others. Have you considered what constitutes a "profession"? What is it about accounting that qualifies it as a profession, whereas other valuable and important careers are not labeled as such?

Dr. Nancy Bell (2004) suggests seven **characteristics of a professional.** Although her list is given in the context of insurance and risk management, its elements can be applied equally to accounting. In Dr. Bell's view, a professional

- Communicates effectively.
- Thinks rationally, logically, and coherently.
- Appropriately uses technical knowledge.
- Integrates knowledge from many disciplines.
- Exhibits ethical professional behavior.
- Recognizes the influence of political, social, economic, legal, and regulatory forces.
- Actively seeks additional knowledge.

Consider the idea that a professional communicates effectively. Good communication skills are fundamental in accounting. Our profession uses specialized, technical vocabulary that is not shared by the general population. For example, to the average person on the street, *depreciation* refers to an asset's loss in value over time. In accounting, however, *depreciation* is the periodic allocation of an asset's cost to the periods that benefit from its use—accounting depreciation is unrelated to changes in market value. So, as professionals, part of our job is to explain the differences between accounting depreciation and economic depreciation to those who are outside our profession. The same could be said for a variety of other terms: stock, capital, revenue, expense, and others.

As another example, think about the second characteristic in Dr. Bell's list: a professional thinks rationally, logically, and coherently. I often tell my students that the purpose of earning an accounting degree isn't to prepare to take the CPA exam—or any other accounting professional exam. Rather, the purpose of earning an accounting degree is to teach you how to think like an accountant: rationally, logically, and coherently. One of the most important skills you'll bring to your career is that ability. Being able to think that way develops over time and with practice, through a process of questioning and dialogue. I know some of my students are sometimes reticent to share their thoughts and opinions, out of concern that they'll say something "wrong." But I always try to challenge and encourage them so they can develop their thinking skills. I'm sure your AIS and other accounting professors feel the same way.

# Reflection and Self-Assessment   16.1

Choose three of the remaining characteristics in Dr. Bell's list. For each one, give a specific example of how an accounting professional might display it.

McDonald (2001) identified four criteria to be considered a professional:

- *Specialized knowledge base.* Accounting certainly has a specialized knowledge base. Whether we're talking about financial reporting rules, standards for conducting audits, tax research and planning skills, or activity-based accounting processes, the knowledge we share is not part of society's general body of knowledge.
- *Complex skills.* Accounting also involves complex skills. It requires the use of judgment, and also relies on fairly complex computations in some areas (such as pension accounting). Although some accounting software is straightforward and easy to use, some of our IT tools are reasonably sophisticated as well.
- *Autonomy of practice.* Autonomy refers to independence or self-sufficiency. As you'll learn in your later study of auditing, "independence of mind" is an important characteristic for accounting professionals. Historically, the accounting profession was almost completely independent and self-regulating. But ethical scandals, such as Enron, led to the creation of the Public Companies Accounting Oversight Board. The PCAOB "is a private-sector, non-profit corporation, created by the Sarbanes-Oxley Act of 2002, to oversee the auditors of public companies in order to protect the interests of investors and further the public interest in the preparation of informative, fair, and independent audit reports." Although the PCAOB has given less autonomy to auditors, the profession as a whole remains relatively self-sufficient.
- *Adherence to a code of ethical behavior.* Accountants also adhere to codes of ethical behavior. In the exercises at the end of this chapter, you'll have the opportunity to examine the ethical codes of three important organizations: the American Institute of Certified Public Accountants, the Institute of Management Accountants, and the Association of Certified Fraud Examiners.

You can find more information about the PCAOB at www .pcaobus.org/.

Notice how McDonald's four characteristics connect to the list of seven provided by Dr. Bell. For example, both lists include a component regarding ethical behavior.

One common element in almost all definitions of professionalism is the emphasis on professional ethics. Next, we'll turn our attention to that important topic.

## ETHICS

Boss (2014) offered the following thoughts on the nature of ethics:

1. Ethics is a set of standards that:
   a. Differentiates "right" from "wrong."
   b. Is established by a particular group.
   c. Is imposed on members of the group to regulate behavior.
2. Ethics is a discipline that:
   a. Studies values and guidelines for living.
   b. Considers the justification (or lack of it) for those values.

Thinking about ethics in the context of the accounting profession, items 1b and 1c from that list are the most relevant. As a student, you face ethics issues every day; consider, for example, group assignments in your accounting (or other) courses. When a professor assigns group work, the professor's intention is that students work collaboratively on the assignment; however, you may have been in/known of groups where the "heavy lifting" is done by just one or two students.

Professionally, accountants confront ethics issues like the one described in this chapter's AIS in the Business World. Other areas where ethics issues arise in the profession include revenue recognition, earnings smoothing, asset valuation and fair-value accounting. Table 16.1 summarizes some of the ethics questions associated with these topics.

In addition to her comments on the nature of ethics, Boss (2014) also described four schools of ethical thought—points of view that help decision makers determine what is ethical. Those schools are: ethical egoism, utilitarianism, deontology, and virtue ethics. These four are not the only schools of ethical thought, but they do provide a good background for accounting professionals. Each school has a slightly different way of

**TABLE 16.1  Ethics Issues in Accounting**

| Area | Ethical Questions |
| --- | --- |
| Revenue recognition | Is it ethical to boost revenue at the end of the year by shipping unordered goods to customers, telling them that they can send them back after the new fiscal year starts? |
| Earnings smoothing | Is it ethical to use accounting policies (such as depreciation methods) to ensure that earnings do not fluctuate much from one year to the next? |
| Asset valuation | Is it ethical to raise/lower an estimated discount rate to change the price of an acquired asset? |
| Fair value accounting | How much discretion should managers have in determining an asset's fair value for accounting purposes? |

One rule/standard that guides ethical decision making in accounting is objectivity. As professional accountants, we have the responsibility to present information as fairly and objectively as possible. Suggest two other rules or standards accountants should observe as part of making ethical decisions.

determining what constitutes ethical behavior. The following paragraphs provide a brief overview of each school's fundamental tenets, along with an application based on the HP/Autonomy case.

**Ethical egoism** teaches that people are fundamentally solitary creatures, each pursuing their own best interest. In the view of an ethical egoist, everyone has an ethical obligation to pursue their own best interest. An ethical egoist would look at the HP/Autonomy case and conclude that Autonomy executives behaved ethically; they were considering their own well-being in taking actions associated with the merger.

**Utilitarianism** teaches that the most ethical decision is the one that promotes the greatest good for the greatest number of stakeholders; in other words, the "needs of the many" are placed before the "needs of the few." An HP stockholder who followed utilitarian ethics would likely conclude that Autonomy behaved unethically; their actions caused harm to HP stockholders, a much larger group than Autonomy owners.

**Deontology** is sometimes referred to as the "rights and duties" school of ethical thought. Deontologists believe that individuals have rights, and that ethical principles are developed through reasoning. From a deontological point of view, people should never be used as a "means to an end." Ethical decisions are based on a universal moral code, not on the outcome of a particular decision. How would a deontologist respond to the HP/Autonomy case? As you can probably tell, the answer is not entirely "cut and dried." To the extent that Autonomy used accounting (and other) means to inflate its own worth, a deontologist would likely conclude that Autonomy behaved unethically, but not for the same reason a utilitarian would draw the same conclusion.

In **virtue ethics,** decision makers are more concerned about the "ethical character" of a decision maker. From that point of view, ethical actions are a natural outgrowth of being a fundamentally ethical person. Virtue ethicists are motivated by internal, not external, rewards; in other words, being a good person is more important than a particular outcome of a particular decision. Once again, how a virtue ethicist would respond to the HP/Autonomy case depends on their point of view. Wisdom and justice are considered important virtues; emphasizing those, a virtue ethicist might conclude that Autonomy behaved unethically since their actions may have been less than completely honest.

Table 16.2 summarizes the fundamental principles of each school of ethical thought. Next, let's consider how accountants should make ethical decisions.

**TABLE 16.2  Schools of Ethical Thought**

| School | Principles |
| --- | --- |
| Ethical egoism | People have an ethical obligation to behave in their own self-interest. |
| Utilitarianism | Ethical actions are those that result in the greatest good for the greatest number. |
| Deontology | Individuals have rights; ethical norms are "universal truths" that consider those rights. |
| Virtues | Ethical behavior is a natural product of being fundamentally ethical and virtuous. |

Langenderfer and Rockness (1989) proposed an **eight-step model** for dealing with ethical dilemmas:

1. Identify the facts.
2. Identify the ethics issues and the stakeholders involved.
3. Define the norms, principles, and values related to the situation.
4. Identify the alternative courses of action.
5. Evaluate the consequences of each possible course of action.
6. Decide the best course of action consistent with the norms, principles, and values.
7. If appropriate, discuss the alternative with a trusted person to help gain greater perspective regarding the alternatives.
8. Reach a decision as to the appropriate course of action.

Many companies will have an established practice for resolving ethical issues. They might include discussions with a neutral party (such as an ombuds or ethics officer) or reporting ethical violations anonymously. If a company you work for has an established policy for resolving ethical dilemmas, you should generally follow that policy first. As with many issues in accounting practice, there is no "one right way" to resolve an ethical problem.

If, though, your company has no established policy for dealing with ethics issues, try talking to your supervisor. If your supervisor is involved in unethical conduct, talk to his/her supervisor. After talking with your supervisor, the issue may be resolved. If not, though, take the problem to the next highest level of authority in the organization—with your supervisor's full knowledge. Don't do an "end run" around your boss, unless you suspect his/her involvement in the problem. Continue up the organizational hierarchy until the problem is resolved. In extreme cases, you may need to consider resigning your position with the organization if the issue is egregious and cannot be resolved internally.

## ETHICS CASES

Unfortunately, the unethical and unprofessional actions of a small group of accountants have tarnished the profession's reputation in the eyes of the public. To conclude this chapter, let's take a look at a few "infamous" cases of unethical behavior in the profession.

In the early 20th century, **Charles Ponzi** committed a multimillion-dollar fraud with international postal reply coupons. Ponzi collected money from investors but never purchased the international postal reply coupons. Basically, he was using new investors' money to pay off old investors. This practice has continued to the present day; you may have heard frauds like this one referred to as "pyramid" or "multilevel marketing" schemes. When such a fraud involves the use of securities or financial instruments, we often refer to it as a Ponzi scheme. Ponzi eventually was sentenced to five years in federal prison for mail fraud, followed by an additional seven-to-nine-year sentence in Massachusetts.

In 1952, John Rigas purchased a Pennsylvania cable company for $300. Twenty years later, he and his brother, Gus, created the **Adelphia Communications Corporation.** Adelphia was a family-run business; indeed, *Adelphia* is Greek for "brothers." In the late 1990s, Adelphia purchased Century Communications for $5.2 billion, making it the sixth largest cable company in the United States. John loved the limelight and was quite the philanthropist. But he also had a huge ego. For example, he bought homes for people and also was known to fly people on private planes for medical treatment; at the same time, he personally had to approve every business transaction for Adelphia. Adelphia's fraud was multifaceted. The company funded more than $2 billion in personal loans to the Rigas family. Adelphia management engaged in deceptive accounting practices to meet analysts' expectations for profitability; the company also commingled its assets with the Rigas family's personal assets. Ultimately, Adelphia filed for bankruptcy in June 2002 and was delisted from NASDAQ.

The **Enron/Arthur Andersen** debacle may be the best-known accounting fraud in recent history. Enron filed for bankruptcy in December 2001; at that time, it was the largest bankruptcy filing ever. Enron was created in 1985 from the merger of two other companies in the natural gas and pipeline industries. After a few years, though, Enron found itself with mounting liabilities and loss of exclusive control over its pipelines. Based on the recommendation of consultant Jeffrey Skilling, Enron embarked on a new business strategy by creating a "bank" to buy and sell gas. In 1990, Enron created a financial subsidiary and hired Skilling to run it. The financial subsidiary hired the "best and brightest" but subjected them to a brutal performance evaluation system. Eventually, most of Enron's business came from its financial division, rather than from its original gas pipeline activities. Earnings, but not cash flows, continued increasing, and its stock price went up as well for 20 quarters in a row. Meanwhile, Enron's employees continued making deals of increasing risk, unbeknownst to Enron's investors. The company's accounting information system became rife with earnings management, off balance-sheet debt, and related-party transactions. The company also failed to disclose key facts in the notes to its financial statements. Ultimately, Enron's ethical breaches led to its bankruptcy filing; the downfall of Arthur Andersen, one of the then "Big Five" CPA firms, also was closely related to its activities in auditing Enron.

The preceding cases are just three among many in the accounting profession. By applying the principles of professionalism and ethics discussed in this chapter, you will hopefully be able to avoid such situations and help our profession become more respected in the business world.

# CAREER PLANNING

Believe it or not, you've already started planning your career. You may not have been consciously aware of that fact up until now, but making the choice to pursue a degree in accounting is an important first step. In this section, we'll take a look at some additional things you should do to think more concretely about your career.

While your **career plan** will almost certainly change as your career progresses, consider the steps listed here as you develop your initial ideas:

1. *Determine your strengths, aptitudes, and abilities.* You can complete this important step in many ways, one of which is with assessment tools likely available in your campus career center. The Discover Inventory (http://webapps01.act.org/eDISCOVER/) will give you a three-letter code that denotes the kinds of working environments in which you're most comfortable. The code is based on Holland's Hexagon (www .learning4liferesources.com/holland_codes.html), which classifies working environments into six broad categories: enterprising, conventional, realistic, social, artistic, and investigative. Another good instrument for completing this step is the Gallup Organization's StrengthsFinder (www.strengthsquest.com/). StrengthsFinder identifies your five top "themes" based on your responses to a series of objective questions. The themes were developed from extensive research and statistical analyses of hundreds of individuals and can be used to help you find a career that builds on those innate abilities.

2. *Create a career mission statement.* You may have run across the idea of organizational mission statements in your management coursework. Basically, an organizational mission statement explains its reason for being—the way(s) it expects to achieve a

competitive advantage in its markets. Your career mission statement can work the same way. It gives you a goal to work toward—one that will not absolutely dictate your educational and professional choices, but will provide some direction as you enter the accounting profession.

3. *Research employment opportunities related to the first two items.* This research might involve conducting informational interviews with practicing accountants, attending student organization events related to career opportunities on your campus, or finding an internship in an environment where you think you might eventually like to work. The earlier you can start that research, the better off you'll be; that way, if you discover you don't have the interest, aptitude, or ability to sustain a particular career, you can change your career plan accordingly. In a very fundamental sense, your career planning process began the day you started college; too many students wait until the year they expect to graduate to think about their career. I encourage you to start the process early, so you can make more informed choices when you graduate.

4. *Build your résumé.* Your campus career center can give you clear, specific guidance about how to create a strong résumé. Too many students wait until they're ready to graduate to visit the career center. I encourage you to visit it early in your academic career. You'll find your job search process goes a lot more smoothly if you take advantage of the career center's services regularly.

5. *Practice your interviewing skills.* Most career centers offer practice (mock) interviews; if your school has an accounting society, an IMA student chapter, and/or a chapter of Beta Alpha Psi, they also may host mock interview events throughout the year. Practicing your interviewing skills in those settings will make you a lot more comfortable when you're ready for the "real thing." While you'll always be somewhat nervous during an interview situation, practicing in advance can significantly reduce those feelings, allowing you to put your best foot forward with potential employers.

These five steps certainly aren't the sum total of career planning efforts, but they are a good beginning. The earlier you begin developing a plan, the more time you'll have to explore it.

## CRITICAL THINKING

One of the most publicized ethics cases of the last decade involved **Bernie Madoff.** Through his firm, Bernard L. Madoff Investment Securities (BMIS), Madoff perpetrated an elaborate Ponzi scheme on his investors. When Harry Markopolos, a certified fraud examiner and certified financial analyst, succeeded in bringing the case to light, Madoff was arrested, tried, and convicted on several fraud-related counts, including securities fraud, mail fraud, and wire fraud. Madoff was eventually sentenced to 150 years in prison.

Let's consider the Madoff case through the lens of some of this chapter's topics.

1. *Professionalism.* Most people would agree that Madoff exhibited very few (if any) characteristics of a professional. Apart from his unethical behavior, he inappropriately used his technical knowledge of securities and investments; he also ignored important laws such as the Bank Secrecy Act and wire fraud statutes. Markopolos, on the other hand, behaved professionally. He communicated effectively, brought to bear his skills both as a financial analyst and fraud examiner and thought rationally, logically, and coherently about the case.

2. *Schools of ethical thought.* Madoff is best described as an ethical egoist; he considered his own interests above all others. Markopolos, on the other hand, represents deontology; his ethical values are derived from universal standards, such as "lying is wrong."

3. *Ethical decision making.* Madoff's scheme started to unravel when he confessed what he had been doing to his sons, Andrew and Mark. At that point, the two were faced with an ethics decision. Let's consider how they might have used the Langenderfer and Rockness model to determine their course of action.

   a. *Identify the facts.* Madoff had confessed to the Ponzi scheme he had been conducting for many years.

   b. *Identify the ethics issues and stakeholders involved.* The main ethics issue confronting Madoff's sons was what to do about their father's confession. The stakeholders were wide ranging, including Madoff himself, the rest of his family, and the defrauded investors.

   c. *Define the norms, principles, and values related to the situation.* At this point, we consider the ethical school of thought that guided Andrew and Mark. Based on their actions, we can conclude that they were probably deontologists, subscribing to the point of view that lying/cheating/stealing is wrong. (Note that Madoff himself was likely an ethical egoist.)

   d. *Identify the alternative courses of action.* Madoff's sons had a few choices. They could do nothing, turn Madoff in or encourage him to turn himself in.

   e. *Evaluate the consequences of each alternative.* By doing nothing, the Ponzi scheme would likely have continued—at least until someone else (like Markopolos) discovered it. Turning Madoff in would, the sons may have reasoned, resulted in his conviction and imprisonment; in turn, those consequences would have additional consequences (some positive, some negative) for Madoff's wife, his investors, and other parties. The two could probably not predict what would happen if they merely encouraged Madoff to turn himself in; he may or may not have done so depending on his own ethical point of view.

   f. *Decide the best course of action.* Madoff's sons eventually turned him in; Madoff was arrested in late 2008.

We may never know if Madoff's sons discussed their choices with other trusted individuals, but we know the decision they eventually made and its consequences.

---

## Summary

Here is a summary of the chapter's main points based on its learning outcomes:

1. *List and discuss characteristics of a professional.* A professional communicates effectively; thinks rationally, logically, and coherently; appropriately uses technical knowledge; integrates knowledge from many disciplines; exhibits ethical professional behavior; recognizes the influence of political, social, economic, legal, and regulatory forces; and actively seeks additional knowledge.

2. *Explain how those characteristics apply to the accounting profession.* As professionals, accountants have a responsibility to exhibit all seven of the preceding characteristics. Failing to do so violates the public trust.

3. *Define ethics.* The field of ethics has been subdivided into three parts: metaethics, normative ethics, and applied ethics. Each part concerns the ways people make choices between "right" and "wrong."

4. *Discuss various models/schools of ethical decision making.* The four schools of ethical thought discussed in the chapter are: ethical egoism, utilitarianism, deontology and virtues.

5. *Explain how to resolve ethical dilemmas.* If a company policy on resolving ethical dilemmas exists, accountants should follow it. However, if no such guidelines are in place, one good model, proposed by Langenderfer and Rockness, for making ethical decisions involves eight steps: identify the facts; identify the ethics issues and the stakeholders involved; define the norms, principles, and values related to the situation; identify the alternative courses of action; evaluate the consequences of each possible course of action; decide the best course of action consistent with the norms, principles, and values; if appropriate, discuss the alternative with a trusted person to help gain greater perspective regarding the alternatives; and reach a decision as to the appropriate course of action.

Although this chapter comes near the end of the text, I hope you now recognize the importance of its three topics.

| | |
|---|---|
| **Key Terms** | Adelphia Communications Corporation, *305*     Charles Ponzi, *305*     Utilitarianism, *304* <br> Bernie Madoff, *307*     deontology, *304*     virtue ethics, *304* <br> career plan, *306*     eight-step model, *305* <br> characteristics of a professional, *301*     Enron/Arthur Andersen, *306* <br> ethical egoism, *304* |

**Chapter References**

Bell, N. 2004. "Characteristics of a Risk Management and Insurance Professional." www.wsu.edu/belln/ (October 4, 2004).

Boss, J. 2014. *Ethics for Life: A Text with Readings*. 6th ed. McGraw-Hill Education.

Dictionary.com. 2004. "Ethics." http://dictionary.reference.com/search?q=ethics (October 4).

Internet Encyclopedia of Philosophy. 2004. "Ethics." www.utm.edu/research/iep/e/ethics.htm (October 4).

Langenderfer, H., and J. Rockness. 1989. "Integrating Ethics into the Accounting Curriculum: Issues, Problems, and Solutions." *Journal of Accounting Education,* Spring, pp. 58–69.

McDonald, C. 2001. "A Review of Continuing Professional Education." *Journal of Continuing Higher Education,* Winter, pp. 29–40.

**End-of-Chapter Activities**

1. *Reading review questions.*

   a. List and discuss at least five characteristics of a professional and/or professional behavior. Where possible, include a specific example of each characteristic from your own experience as a student.

   b. Define *ethics.* Explain why ethics is so important in the accounting profession.

   c. What basic schools of thought exist regarding ethical behavior? What are the strengths and weaknesses of each one?

   d. Explain the basic facts of fraud schemes associated with Ponzi, Adelphia, and Enron.

   e. In a manner specified by your instructor, respond to the questions for this chapter's "AIS in the Business World."

2. *Reading review problem.*

   Olympus Corporation (www.olympus-global.com) is a Japan-based company that makes digital cameras, accessories, and other devices. In April 2011, Michael Woodford was appointed president of the corporation; he was the first non-Japanese president of Olympus in the firm's history. In July 2011, some of the corporation's actions surrounding merger and acquisition activity were called into question by the press. Woodford asked for information about the activity, but was denied access to it. He wrote a series of letters to the press and other parties to establish his own views and actions, and was fired from his position in October 2011.

    a. Which characteristics of a professional did Woodford demonstrate?

    b. Which school of ethical thought best explains Woodford's actions? The actions of Olympus staff?

    c. Suppose you were an Olympus employee that Woodford asked for information. Outline a process you would use to decide whether to provide it.

    d. Do a Google search to learn more about the Olympus case and its aftermath. What similarities and differences do you see between it and the Madoff case?

3. *Multiple choice review.*

    1. A professional exhibits all the following characteristics except:

      a. Always following the deontology school of ethical thought.

      b. Communicating effectively.

      c. Appropriately using technical knowledge.

      d. Incorporating knowledge from many disciplines.

    2. According to McDonald, four criteria define a professional. They include:

      a. Specialized knowledge base and complex skills.

      b. Autonomy of practice and ethical behavior.

      c. Both a and b.

      d. Neither a nor b.

    3. _____ is a set of standards that differentiates right from wrong.

      a. The FASB Conceptual Framework

      b. Ethics

      c. The AICPA Core Competency Framework

      d. All of the above

    4. Which school of ethical thought teaches that people should behave in their own best interest?

      a. Ethical egoism

      b. Utilitarianism

      c. Deontology

      d. Virtues

    5. Langenderfer and Rockness suggested a 10-step model for resolving ethical dilemmas. Which of the following steps comes first in their model?

      a. Identify the ethics issues.

      b. Define the relevant norms and principles.

      c. Identify alternative courses of action.

      d. Reach a decision.

4. *Making choices and exercising judgment.*

Federico Buenrostro was the CEO of the California Public Employees' Retirement System (CalPERS) from 2002 to 2008; Alfred Villalobos was a CalPERS board member from 1993 to 1995. Buenrostro created false documents that enabled Villalobos to make money as a placement agent between CalPERS and Apollo Global Management, a pension fund investment firm. The two were indicted in March 2013 for conspiracy to commit mail and wire fraud (among other charges). The CalPERS Web site is www.calpers.ca.gov.

    a.  Which school of ethical thought guided Buenrostro and Villalobos? Justify your response.

    b.  How would proponents of the other schools discussed in the chapter evaluate the ethics of their actions? Justify your response.

5.  *Field exercises.*

    a.  Research one or more of the following accounting frauds. Report the results of your research in a two- to three-page paper and/or an oral presentation to the class.

- Tenet Healthcare
- Tyco International
- Worldcom

    b.  Through interviews or other research, find a company's code of ethics. Summarize it and discuss how it is similar to and different from one of the codes of ethics discussed in the chapter.

    c.  Point your Web browser to www.cfenet.com. Click the "local chapters" link and find a CFE chapter near you. Attend a meeting, interview a member, or, in cooperation with your instructor, ask a CFE to come and speak to your class.

    d.  Visit your campus career center; talk with a career counselor about your future career plans. Take an aptitude or interest assessment, such as the Discover Inventory or StrengthsQuest; what does the assessment tell you about yourself?

6.  Describe your personal philosophy for making ethical decisions. Your philosophy may be based on one or more of the schools of thought discussed in the chapter; it also may be completely original. Meet with a group of your classmates to discuss your ethical philosophies. Describe a time when you had to make a personal ethical choice; explain the choice you made and its consequences. If confronted with the same decision again, would you make the same choice? Why, or why not?

7.  Which school of ethical thought is described in each of the following independent scenarios? Justify your choices. Reword each scenario so that it reflects a different school of ethical thought.

    a.  Sean was working with a group of three other students on a financial statement analysis project for his introductory financial accounting course. He told the other group members that he would do the entire project with minimal input from them to ensure the whole group got a good grade.

    b.  Lydia downloaded a solution to a graded homework problem in her AIS course from the Internet. She reasoned that doing so was ethical since it would give her a better grade when she presented the problem in class.

    c.  Nicole's friend offered to share her intermediate accounting term paper with her; the paper had received an A when Nicole's friend took the course. Nicole refused her friend's offer, saying that cheating in any form is unethical.

    d.  Ruben felt that using his class notes for a closed-book exam contradicted the values he had grown up with, so he decided not to do so.

8.  *Professional certification and licensure.* In my view, the purpose of an accounting degree is not to prepare you to take any particular certification/license exam; the purpose of an accounting degree is to teach you to think like an accountant. But, many accounting professionals enjoy both the challenge and recognition associated with obtaining a professional license or certification. Many such certifications are available, including Certified Public Accountant, Certified Management Accountant, Certified Fraud Examiner, Certified Internal Auditor, Certified Information Systems

Auditor, Enrolled Agent, Certified Government Financial Manager. In consultation with your AIS professor, choose one or more of those credentials; respond to the following questions about it.

a. Is the credential a license or a certificate?

b. What are the steps associated with obtaining the credential?

c. What topics are included in the credential's professional exam? How do those topics align with your university studies?

d. What organization sponsors/offers the credential?

e. Does the sponsoring organization have a local chapter in your area? If so, arrange to attend one of its meetings.

f. Summarize the sponsoring organization's code of ethics, if it has one.

g. Look online or in a newspaper for job listings that seem related to the credential. Make a list of the companies, job titles, responsibilities, and (if available) salaries for each position you locate.

9. *Terminology.* Please match each item on the left with the most appropriate item on the right.

| | |
|---|---|
| 1. Autonomy of practice | a. Virtue ethics viewpoint |
| 2. Considering audience characteristics | b. Principle of utilitarian ethics |
| 3. Determining whether goodwill has been impaired | c. Ponzi scheme |
| 4. Finance, management, information systems | d. One tool for identifying strengths, aptitudes, and abilities |
| 5. Holland's Hexagon | e. One element of communicating effectively |
| 6. Off balance sheet debt and related party transactions | f. Issues at Enron |
| 7. People "do good" when they "are good." | g. Disciplines that should be integrated with AIS |
| 8. Professional codes of ethics | h. Characteristic of a professional reduced by SOX |
| 9. The most ethical decision is the one that benefits the most people. | i. Associated with the third step of the Langenderfer and Rockness model |
| 10. Using money from new investors to pay off old investors | j. A complex skill in accounting |

10. *Multiple choice questions.* Consider the following case as you respond to the questions below:

Alberto and Cristina were partners in a travel agency that specialized in arranging corporate travel. Because the partnership was on the verge of bankruptcy, they invited Alberto's cousin, Mark, to become a "limited partner" by investing $500,000 in the agency. At the end of the year, Alberto and Cristina submitted their financial records to Mel, a local CPA who had been doing their taxes for many years. Mel completed the tax return and sent it to the partners for review. A few days later, Mark called Mel. "I invested $500,000 in the company. Why didn't I get a $500,000 tax write off?" Mel explained the relevant tax rules to Mark, who then insisted he redo the return using falsified information. When Mel refused, Mark hired a different tax preparer.

1. Which of Bell's characteristics best explains Mel's actions?

   a. Appropriately uses technical knowledge

   b. Recognizes the influence of political forces

   c. Actively seeks additional knowledge

   d. Engages in autonomy of practice

2. Which school of ethical thought best describes Mark?
    a. Ethical egoism
    b. Utilitarianism
    c. Deontology
    d. Virtue

3. Which school of ethical thought best describes Mel?
    a. Ethical egoism
    b. Utilitarianism
    c. Deontology
    d. Virtue

4. Suppose Mel followed the Langenderfer and Rockness model in deciding how to respond to Mark. If he consulted the AICPA Code of Professional Conduct as one of the steps, which of the following would he do next?
    a. Establish his ethical point of view.
    b. Consider who would be affected by his decision.
    c. List his options for responding to Mark.
    d. Discuss the situation with Alberto and Cristina.

5. Suppose Mel had complied with Mark's request. His action would be least similar to the _____ case.
    a. Enron
    b. Adelphia Communications
    c. Charles Ponzi
    d. HP/Autonomy

11. *Statement evaluation.* Please indicate whether each of the following statements is (i) always true, (ii) sometimes true, or (iii) never true. For those that are (ii) sometimes true, explain when the statement is true.

    a. As part of their commitment to professionalism, accounting professionals should communicate effectively.
    b. Continuing professional education is part of an accountant's professional responsibilities only if the accountant is a licensed CPA.
    c. Following the Langenderfer and Rockness model will always lead different decision makers to the same decision.
    d. Following the requirements of SOX ensures that accountants will behave ethically.
    e. From an ethical egoism point of view, acting in one's self-interest is always the same as acting selfishly.
    f. In completing the seventh step of the Langenderfer and Rockness model, a decision maker may consult a non-accountant.
    g. Professionalism in accounting requires adherence to the principles of virtue ethics.
    h. Since most important ideas in accounting have not changed in many years, professionalism does not require any education beyond a bachelor's degree.
    i. Two different decision makers may reach different conclusions, even if both follow the Langenderfer and Rockness model.
    j. Whether a person considers an action ethical or unethical depends on the person's ethical point of view.

12. *Prior material application.*

    a. Check out the post titled "AIS coverage in professional exams" on my AIS blog (http://bobhurtais.blogspot.com/). It spells out the topics you've studied in your AIS course relative to the CPA exam. Choose another professional certification exam, such as the CMA or CFE. Map the content of the exam to your AIS study, similar to what you'll find in the blog post.

b. One of Bell's seven characteristics of a professional is integrating knowledge from many disciplines. Look back over the topics we've examined in earlier parts of the book; explain how they fulfill that characteristic. For example, business process management (Chapter 4) is a topic commonly associated with operations management.

c. McDonald's four criteria for being a professional include a specialized knowledge base and complex skills. Consider the topics you've studied in AIS this quarter; which of them constitute specialized knowledge? Which involve complex skills?

d. Ethics issues can arise in virtually any business process. Consider the steps in either the sales/collection or acquisition/payment process; suggest an ethical dilemma that could arise in one or more of those steps. For example, in the sales/collection process, an employee could knowingly ship extra units of product in an effort to boost company revenue.

e. Explain how each school of ethical thought discussed in this chapter would respond to the ethical dilemma you identified in part (d) of this problem. For example, the virtues school of ethics might consider shipping extra units of product unethical because it is not moral/virtuous.

13. *Excel application.* Consider the data set below, which you'll also find in the 3 February 2014 post on my AIS blog.

| Firm ID | Annual Sales | Number of Ethics Code Violations |
|---------|-------------|----------------------------------|
| A | $ 5,461 | 7 |
| B | 5,390 | 6 |
| C | 7,540 | 12 |
| D | 7,568 | 15 |
| E | 9,249 | 13 |
| F | 9,457 | 5 |
| G | 7,239 | 7 |
| H | 6,443 | 8 |
| I | 7,570 | 12 |
| J | 5,507 | 9 |
| K | 5,149 | 13 |
| L | 5,530 | 10 |
| M | 8,616 | 9 |
| N | 9,738 | 7 |
| O | 8,325 | 13 |

a. Use Excel's correlation function to calculate the correlation between annual sales and number of ethics code violations. (Check figure: 0.03.)

b. Sort the data based on annual sales. Then, arrange the number of ethics code violations in three groups (small, medium, and large) based on annual sales. Here's an illustration of how the grouped data should look:

| Small | Medium | Large |
|-------|--------|-------|
| 13 | 8 | 13 |
| 6 | 7 | 9 |
| 7 | 12 | 13 |
| 9 | 15 | 5 |
| 10 | 12 | 7 |

c. Use Excel's ANOVA function to perform a single-factor ANOVA. Is there a relationship between firm size (as measured by annual sales) and the number of ethics code violations? (Check figure: $p$-value $= 0.66$.)

## Chapter Seventeen

# Auditing and Evaluating the AIS

## AIS in the Business World

### Bitcoin

Bitcoin is a decentralized, peer-to-peer, and completely digital currency. Developed in the early 2000s by a person/group of people named Satoshi Nakamoto, Bitcoin has had frequent media mentions that both criticize and applaud its existence. As a completely digital currency, Bitcoin has no "backing" in any other world currency, making it significantly different from services like PayPal. On PayPal, for example, users can complete digital transactions, but the currency amounts represent real world currencies like the U.S. dollar or the Euro.

At present, very few companies accept Bitcoins as payment, so most people who hold them convert them into a physical currency at some point. (You can find real-time information about Bitcoin trading at www.blockchain.info.) Mt. Gox was the world's largest Bitcoin exchange until it shut its doors and filed for bankruptcy in February 2014.

For more information on Bitcoin, check out the February 2014 podcast of the Association of Certified Fraud Examiners (www.acfe.com/podcast), the FBI report, "Bitcoin Virtual Currency: Unique Features Present Distinct Challenges for Deterring Illicit Activity" and/or "A Fistful of Bitcoins: Characterizing Payments among Men with No Names" by Meiklejohn et al. (The simplest way to find the two papers is via Google search.)

### *Discussion Questions*

1. What types of audits would benefit Bitcoin users and related parties?
2. What steps are involved in a financial statement audit?
3. What is the Audit Clarity Project? Why is it important?
4. How are auditing and accounting information systems related?

**Auditing** is the area of accounting associated with AIS evaluation. The corporate scandals of the late 20th and early 21st centuries such as Parmalat, Global Crossing, and Enron point to the need for regular, thorough AIS evaluation as part of accountants' professional responsibility and fiduciary duties to shareholders and the public.

When you finish studying this chapter, you should be able to:

1. Describe the various kinds of audits you might encounter in your accounting career.
2. Explain the purpose of the Audit Clarity Project and summarize its essential components.
3. Explain 10 generally accepted auditing standards (GAAS) and their role in a financial statement audit.
4. Discuss the basic steps associated with a financial statement audit.
5. Explain the connection between auditing and accounting information systems.

Your accounting curriculum probably includes at least one course in auditing, so this chapter certainly will not make you an expert in the field, but it will give you an introduction to this important area of professional practice.

## TYPES OF AUDITS

The AICPA's Audit Clarity Project (discussed later in the chapter) made significant changes to audit reports. Formerly, for example, a clean report was called "unqualified." Under the new standards, it is "unmodified."

Dictionary.com lists several definitions for *audit,* but the one that seems most appropriate here is "a methodical examination or review of a condition or situation." There are seven basic kinds of audits you might be involved in as your career progresses:

1. *Financial audit.* A financial audit involves the examination of a company's accounting information system and financial statements. Auditors issue one of four types of audit reports on the company's financial statements. An unmodified report (also known as a *clean* report) says that the company's statements are prepared in accordance with generally accepted accounting principles (GAAP). Auditors issue a *qualified* report when one or more items don't conform to GAAP—but not so many items as to compromise the overall fairness of the statements. An *adverse* report means the statements are not prepared in accordance with GAAP, while a *disclaimer* denotes that the auditors could not tell if they were. Adverse reports and disclaimers are hard to find—most companies would change auditors (or the auditors would resign) before such an opinion was issued.

2. *Operational audit.* In an operational audit, auditors examine a company's rules and procedures for conducting business. They're asking if a company's rules make sense, and if they're followed. Systems documentation techniques such as flowcharting are particularly important in operational audits; for example, a flowchart of the purchasing process would give the operational auditor a standard for comparison against a company's actual practice in the same area. Internal auditors often are involved in operational auditing.

3. *Systems audit.* As we've discussed before, information technology is an integral part of most accounting information systems today. A systems audit determines whether the various forms of information technology in an AIS are producing expected results. It also examines the issue of systems security very closely, making sure the data are safe within the system. Basically, a systems audit looks "inside the box," rather than treating the computer as an unknown quantity in an audit. One important issue in systems auditing is the *service organization* audit discussed in SSAE 16 (Statement on Standards for Attestation Engagements 16). You may recall reading about SSAE 16 in Chapter 10. Many organizations outsource certain duties and responsibilities to external parties; for example, a corporation might hire ADP to do its payroll processing. Auditors need to

know that those service organizations are maintaining adequate internal controls for their client; SSAE 16 provides guidance in those situations.

4. *Compliance audit.* Governmental and not-for-profit organizations (GNFPs) are subject to compliance audits. Although almost every audit involves some sort of judgment on the part of the auditor, compliance audits are virtually devoid of judgment. GNFPs are subject to very strict government rules and regulations, many of which are contained in the **Yellow Book** published by the Government Accountability Office (GAO). You can learn a lot more about the Yellow Book and compliance auditing on the GAO's Web site: www.gao.gov. A compliance audit determines whether or not a GNFP is following the rules and regulations in the Yellow Book.

5. *Management audit.* Of all the kinds of auditing discussed here, the management audit may involve the greatest degree of judgment. A management audit determines the degree to which the assumptions underlying decisions are valid; it also examines the ways in which management decisions are supported. In the chapter on decision-making models, you read about the Steps for Better Thinking; a management audit would be looking for that type of support for major decisions.

6. *Investigative audit.* Also known as a *fraud audit,* it is associated with the broader field of forensic accounting. The recent ethics scandals at Enron, WorldCom, Global Crossing, and other firms have raised awareness of the costs of occupational fraud and abuse in organizations. An investigative audit, which may be conducted by a Certified Fraud Examiner, may be triggered by observation of unusual behavior or discrepancies in the accounting information system. Figure 17.1 lays out a common order for gathering evidence in an investigative audit (www.cfenet.com).

   Most investigative audits start with reviewing pertinent *documents;* for example, the auditor might examine physical or electronic copies of checks in cases where embezzlement is suspected. Interviews of *neutral third-party witnesses* often come next. For example, an employee might have observed a coworker taking computer equipment out of the office; the employee might have assumed a perfectly innocent, legitimate reason/motivation, even if fraud was involved. *Corroborative witnesses* can lend additional information to the investigation by (for example) confirming information collected in the first two stages—or even in subsequent stages. *Coconspirators* are involved in the fraud, but often not as deeply or as seriously as the target of the investigation. For example,

**FIGURE 17.1**
**Investigative Audit Tools**

Source: Wells, 2004.

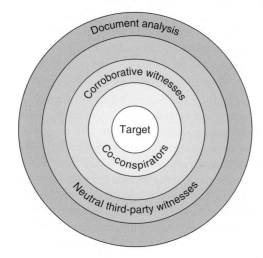

a purchasing agent might collude with a receiving department employee to steal merchandise; the receiving department employee would be considered a co-conspirator. Finally, the investigative auditor interviews the *target.* By that time, the auditor has a clear idea of how the fraud occurred—an idea supported by evidence from the other steps.

7. *International audit.* This type of audit is really a "basket" of the other types. It can be conducted in a U.S.-based firm with international operations or a non-U.S.-based firm. International auditing is exceptionally challenging. It requires the auditor to understand the accounting rules in another country, but it also necessitates an intimate understanding of national culture, laws, religion, and other nonaccounting issues.

While the degree, role, and type of **professional judgment** vary among the seven types of audits discussed here, all of them incorporate judgment to some degree. Other commonalities between the seven types of audits include

- Checking existing conditions against some predetermined standard.
- Questioning, firmly but professionally, managers and employees of the organization being audited.
- Maintaining an independent attitude and appropriate professional "distance" from the client.

## Reflection and Self-Assessment 17.1

What type of audit is indicated by each of the following descriptions? Justify your choices, particularly if more than one type of audit seems applicable.

1. Ray and Gary, partners in a psychotherapy practice, hire Rob to determine if their secretary has been embezzling cash.
2. An internal auditor works with managers in the purchasing department to determine a more efficient way to handle inventory transactions.
3. An audit client uses Peachtree for transaction processing. An auditor examines the system to ensure

that the software is processing the transactions correctly.

4. A German-based organization hires a U.S. firm to check out its accounting information system. The overall objective is enabling the German firm to list its securities on the NYSE.
5. A CPA firm conducts its annual evaluation of CHC Corporation's accounting information system. After the evaluation, the CPA firm issues an unqualified opinion.

The AICPA's Audit Clarity Project (ACP) made significant changes to virtually every aspect of the audit process. The next section discusses some of the basics of the ACP.

## AUDIT CLARITY PROJECT

According to Skinner (2012), the **Audit Clarity Project** "had two main objectives: (i) to make auditing standards easier to read, understand and apply, and (ii) to converge the U.S. Auditing Standards with International Auditing Standards." Think of the ACP as similar to the FASB Codification you may have learned about in intermediate accounting.

The ACP involved four groups of changes to the standards that guide financial statement audits: format, terminology, additional requirements, and the audit report.

The standards issued as part of the ACP all follow the same format, illustrated in Figure 17.2.

**FIGURE 17.2**
**Format of Audit
Clarity Project
Standards**

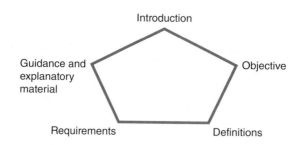

Each standard's introduction explains when the standard applies in an audit engagement. The objective section discusses the overall goal of the standard; it specifies what the auditor is trying to achieve in the audit with respect to the standard. The definitions section, as you might expect, identifies key terms related to the standard and explains their meanings. Requirements explain what the auditor needs to do to fulfill that standard; it can serve as a guide for designing specific procedures as part of a financial statement audit. The last section of each standard, guidance, and explanatory material, gives additional information about the requirements and related matters.

The clarity standards also introduce some new terminology, such as "applicable financial reporting framework" and "emphasis-of-matter paragraph." Auditors need to understand the financial reporting framework a company used in preparing its financial statements; for example, the company might use the International Financial Reporting Standards or U.S. Generally Accepted Accounting Principles (US GAAP). An emphasis-of-matter paragraph is used when the auditor wants to call attention to something in the financial statements themselves and/or in the related footnote disclosures.

The third element of the ACP requires financial statement auditors to do several things, including: (i) ensure that the "applicable financial reporting framework," if other than US GAAP, is appropriate, (ii) obtain agreement from management as to their responsibility for the financial statements and internal control, and (iii) adhere to quality control standards as they conduct the audit.

The ACP also made changes to the standard format of the auditor's report (sometimes referred to as the audit "opinion"). Under the ACP standards, the report must include the items indicated in Table 17.1. Additionally, the report must include subheadings for each paragraph to focus the reader's attention.

If the auditor's report contains a qualified/adverse/disclaimer of opinion, it must specify the basis for the opinion in an "emphasis-of-matter" paragraph.

**TABLE 17.1  Elements of the Unmodified Auditor's Report**

| Element | Explanation |
| --- | --- |
| Title | Must include the phrase "independent auditor's report" |
| Addressee | May be the board of directors, management, or other parties |
| Introductory paragraph | Must identify the organization, the financial statements audited, and related information |
| Management's responsibilities | Financial statements and internal controls |
| Auditor's responsibilities | Performing an audit according to generally accepted auditing standards (GAAS) |
| Auditor's opinion | States that, in the auditor's opinion, the statements are fairly presented |
| Signature, address, and date | Audit firm's information |

# GENERALLY ACCEPTED AUDITING STANDARDS

Prior to the Audit Clarity Project, audits were guided (in part) by ten **auditing standards.** The ACP did not eliminate the standards completely; rather, it incorporated them. Nevertheless, they are still widely referenced both in actual audits and auditing textbooks; I'm therefore including them here for your review. Please refer to Figure 17.3 for an overview of the standards.

The three *general standards* focus on the auditor's background and approach to the audit. First and foremost, an auditor must be well-trained in auditing before an engagement commences. Generalized knowledge of accounting principles and information systems is important, but specific *training* related to auditing is essential. Auditing is an important element of professional practice in accounting; without good auditing, decision makers cannot rely on the financial statements to be fair. *Independence* speaks to the auditor's mental attitude; that is, the auditor must always remain independent from the client. While some have questioned how independent an auditor can be from the organization signing his or her paychecks, maintaining a professional distance and appropriate professional skepticism are key to the conduct of a successful audit. Finally (in this group), the auditor must exercise due *professional care* in preparing for and completing the audit. The engagement must be properly planned in terms of personnel on the audit team and specific audit procedures. The duty of professional care also extends to preparing the audit report.

The second group of standards focuses on *field work;* in other words, they set out important ideas for conducting the audit itself. The audit is to be properly planned, and all staff members must be adequately *supervised.* Most audit teams comprise

**FIGURE 17.3**
**Generally Accepted Auditing Standards**

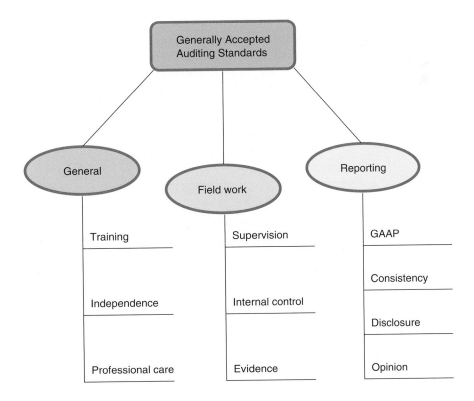

professionals at various stages of their careers, with varying levels of experience in auditing. As a team member's experience increases, the need for supervision may decrease. A thorough assessment of *internal controls* is a critical step early in the audit process. While such an assessment has always been critical, the Sarbanes-Oxley Act of 2002 has placed even greater emphasis on internal control issues. Auditors must assess an organization's risk exposures and determine the degree to which the organization's internal controls ameliorate those risks. The *evidence* standard speaks to the importance of having an objective, reasonable basis for expressing an opinion on the company's financial statements. Evidence can be obtained in many different ways, including observing organizational processes, inspecting documents, and obtaining external confirmations of account balances.

GAAS also contains four *reporting standards,* which speak to the ultimate opinion the auditors express on the financial statements. First, the opinion must state whether or not the statements are presented in accordance with *generally accepted accounting principles* (GAAP). The language of an audit opinion is very specific; unqualified opinions always include such a statement. You may recall that *consistency* is one of the qualitative characteristics of accounting information in the conceptual framework; it is also one of the reporting standards. The audit report must explain any inconsistencies between the current period's application of GAAP and the prior period's application. Full *disclosure* is another commonality between GAAS and the conceptual framework. Financial statement users can assume the disclosures in the financial statements are appropriate unless the audit opinion specifically states they are not. Finally, the audit report must clearly state the auditor's *opinion* on the financial statements. The auditor also must explain the reason(s) for the opinion.

## GENERIC AUDIT STEPS

Although professional judgment is an important aspect of auditing, auditors commonly follow a generalized set of steps when conducting an audit. Figure 17.4 outlines the generic steps often involved in a financial statement audit.

Ultimately, and particularly since Sarbanes-Oxley, management is responsible for the content of the organization's financial statements. So, assessing management's integrity is a necessary first step in the audit process. Dictionary.com defines "integrity" as "steadfast adherence to a strict moral or ethical code." Managers have a **fiduciary duty** to

**FIGURE 17.4**
**Audit Steps**

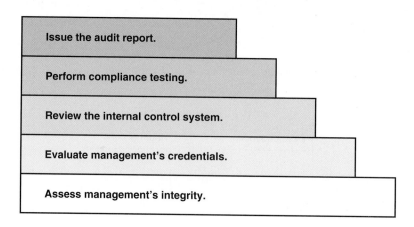

Issue the audit report.

Perform compliance testing.

Review the internal control system.

Evaluate management's credentials.

Assess management's integrity.

their employees and stockholders to act in the best interests of the organization—even when those interests may conflict with their own. COSO's *Internal Control—Integrated Framework* (Committee of Sponsoring Organizations, 2002) alludes to this step in its discussion of an organization's control environment:

> The control environment sets the tone of an organization, influencing the control consciousness of its people. It is the foundation for all other components of internal control, providing discipline and structure. Control environment factors include the integrity, ethical values and competence of the entity's people; management's philosophy and operating style; the way management assigns authority and responsibility, and organizes and develops its people; and the attention and direction provided by the board of directors.

Management must set the example by demonstrating integrity and ethical behavior; otherwise, employees throughout the organization are likely to feel justified in engaging in unethical actions.

## Reflection and Self-Assessment                                    17.2

What tools and techniques would you use to assess management's integrity?

After evaluating management's integrity, the auditor should consider management's credentials. This evaluation focuses on two questions: (*i*) Is management technically competent? (*ii*) Is management financially competent? Notice that the evaluation of management's competence comes *after* the evaluation of integrity. Managers can understand the organization at a deep and fundamental level; they can even comprehend clearly the role, purpose, and importance of accounting as a reporting mechanism. But those credentials mean very little without a generalized disposition toward ethical behavior. Managers can develop technical and financial competence via formal education and/or experience.

The next step is evaluating the organization's internal control system. The auditor must assess the organization's risk exposures and then determine whether the controls are in place to address those risks successfully. Remember: the goal is not to eliminate risk—that's impossible anyway. Rather, the goal is to address, manage, and/or reduce risk. Common controls you'd expect to find include

- Adequate documentation of business processes.
- Background checks for prospective employees.
- Comprehensive employee training.
- Document matching.
- Multiple signatures for checks over a specified threshold.
- Physical safeguards for assets.
- Regular bank reconciliations.
- Separation of duties.

Computerized AIS environments often require unique internal controls. Louwers et al. (2005, p. 732) listed the following examples:

| Administrative Controls | Physical Controls | Technical Controls |
|---|---|---|
| Security checks on personnel | Controlled access | Data encryption |
| Segregation of duties | Computer room entry log record | Access control software and passwords |
| Program testing after modification | Data backup storage | Transaction logging reports |
| Rotation of computer duties | Preprinted limits on documents (e.g., checks) | Range and reasonableness checks on transaction amounts |
| Transaction limit amounts | Inconspicuous location | Control totals |

The auditor's confidence in an organization's internal control system dictates the extent and character of compliance testing conducted in the next phase. Compliance testing involves examining a sample of transactions and verifying that they have been recorded in accordance with GAAP, thus leading to fair account balances on the financial statements. For example, an auditor might conduct a physical count of the inventory. Independent verification of major accounts receivable and accounts payable balances are also common compliance tests at this stage of an audit.

A company's financial statements implicitly involve several assertions by management that must be evaluated as part of auditing. Those assertions are commonly organized into five groups (Louwers et al., 2005, p. 9):

- *Existence or occurrence.* Did the recorded sales transactions really occur? Do the assets listed on the balance sheet really exist?
- *Rights and obligations.* Does the company really own the assets? Are related legal responsibilities identified?
- *Valuation and allocation.* Are the accounts valued correctly? Are expenses allocated to the period(s) benefited?
- *Completeness.* Are the financial statements (including footnotes) complete? Were all the transactions recorded in the right period?
- *Presentation and disclosure.* Were all the transactions recorded in the correct accounts? Are the disclosures understandable to users?

You may recall that a risk-control matrix can include an area for these assertions.

Note that the questions listed above are illustrative, not comprehensive. A well-designed accounting information system that incorporates strong internal controls and appropriate forms of information technology can assist auditors in verifying the five assertions related to financial statements.

The audit culminates with the issuance of the audit report, or opinion. As stated earlier, audit opinions fall into four broad categories: unmodified, qualified, disclaimer, or adverse.

The Sarbanes-Oxley Act has increased the role of judgment and the responsibility of management for financial statements. In addition, SOX requires its own compliance audit, conducted by a different firm, in addition to the financial audit. SOX is divided into 11 titles (similar to chapters in a book), which are further subdivided into sections. Some of the most important sections that relate to auditing and the accounting information system include

- *Section 302.* This section relates to the evaluation of internal controls in an audit. Specifically, it obligates the chief executive officer and chief financial officer to attest that they have personally reviewed internal controls within the preceding 90 days.

The CEO and CFO also acknowledge that they are responsible for the financial statements and the internal controls that promote their reliability and integrity. The responsibilities outlined in this section of SOX cannot be delegated, even via a power of attorney.

- *Section 401.* This section is titled "Disclosures in Periodic Reports." The financial statements must be "accurate and presented in a manner that does not contain incorrect statements or admit to state material information. These financial statements shall also include all material off-balance-sheet liabilities, obligations or transactions" (www.soxlaw.com). If you've made any study of the Enron debacle in this or another course, you may recall that off-balance-sheet transactions were one of the corporation's primary problems. Enron accountants structured transactions to conform to the "letter" of accounting rules and regulations while disregarding the "spirit" of those regulations.

- *Section 404.* Entitled "Management Assessment of Internal Controls," this section reemphasizes the importance of a sound internal control system as part of maintaining AIS integrity and reliability. As part of their annual reports, SOX-compliant organizations must discuss the scope and adequacy of internal controls. Independent auditors also must comment on the opinion expressed by the organization's management. In practice, you may hear this practice referred to as a "404 audit."

- *Section 409.* Real-time reporting is the primary issue in this section. If an organization experiences a material change in its financial condition or operations, it is required to disclose that change "on an urgent basis." In other words, the company cannot wait until its quarterly or annual SEC filings to communicate the change; it must be disclosed as quickly as possible. Additionally, section 409 requires that the disclosure be made in nontechnical, easy-to-understand terms. The disclosures should be supported by qualitative information as well.

- *Section 802.* This section spells out the penalties for noncompliance with the Sarbanes-Oxley Act. According to www.soxlaw.com, "This section imposes penalties of fines and/or up to 20 years imprisonment for altering, destroying, mutilating, concealing, falsifying records, documents or tangible objects with the intent to obstruct, impede or influence a legal investigation. This section also imposes penalties of fines and/or imprisonment up to 10 years on any accountant who knowingly and willfully violates the requirements of maintenance of all audit or review papers for a period of 5 years."

With my own students, I've often referred to SOX as the "full employment act for accountants." So long as SOX remains in effect, accountants will have jobs because of the responsibilities the act imposes on organizations.

## ACCOUNTING INFORMATION SYSTEMS AND AUDITING

So how does this discussion of auditing relate to your study of accounting information systems? Many of the topics we've discussed in this text, as well as many of the skills you have developed in your study of AIS, have direct relevance when it comes to auditing.

First, this text has emphasized the importance of critical thinking in the design and implementation of accounting information systems. Developing and exercising your professional judgment have been consistent themes in this book—whether they relate to selecting information technology tools, evaluating internal controls, documenting accounting information systems with flowcharts, or making recommendations for improving business processes. Decision-making models such as Wolcott and Lynch's Steps for Better

Thinking (www.wolcottlynch.com) provide a rational, systematic approach for making complex decisions. Professional judgment is critically important in the auditing process. It is an integral component of the general standards of independence and professional care; critical thinking also comes into play in maintaining appropriate levels of professional skepticism in the audit process.

Second, the discussion of internal controls throughout the text has an important relationship to auditing. Understanding the four broad purposes of internal control, the risk exposures for a specific organization, and the types of controls that can reduce those risk exposures are key elements of the third step in an audit: reviewing internal controls. Because no two organizations are likely to have identical sets of risk exposures and internal controls, accounting professionals must consistently return to the bedrock principles and ideas of this important area in their examination and evaluation of accounting information systems.

Third, in our examination of business processes, we talked about the importance of understanding an organization's environment as part of understanding its accounting information system. Understanding the organization's internal and external environment is also an important skill for the auditor. Specialization in specific industries is therefore a somewhat common practice among auditing firms. For example, Vicenti, Lloyd and Stutzman (www.vlsllp.com) in southern California maintains a strong practice in the government and not-for-profit sector.

Finally, information technology skills link accounting information systems and auditing in very important ways. Familiarity and skill with common forms of IT, such as spreadsheets and databases, can enable an auditor to examine the accounting information system much more effectively and efficiently. Auditors with backgrounds in both accounting and information systems may conduct information technology audits. As more and more large organizations move to enterprise systems and the utilization of enterprise resource planning software, this connection will only become more important.

## CRITICAL THINKING

I'm using the fraud audit as an example in this section because most of my students find discussions of fraud and forensic accounting really interesting. Also, as a certified fraud examiner, I like to use any opportunity I can to educate people about fraud detection and prevention.

Like accounting information systems, auditing is a multidisciplinary field. Of course, it requires an in-depth knowledge of accounting; but auditors also need to master various aspects of information technology, business law, and human behavior. Let's look at how each of those topics might impact one of the seven types of audits listed at the beginning of this chapter: the fraud audit.

Information technology can certainly be used to commit fraud; the good news is, information technology also can be used to detect fraud. IT allows auditors to examine transaction databases quickly and efficiently; here are some tasks auditors can complete more easily using information technology when conducting a fraud audit:

- *Graphical trend analysis.* Consider the data below, which shows total cash disbursements by week for two years:

| Week | 20x2 | 20x1 |
|---|---|---|
| 1 | $2,245 | $2,720 |
| 2 | 1,557 | 1,886 |
| 3 | 3,710 | 4,494 |
| 4 | 4,792 | 2,441 |
| 5 | 1,657 | 2,008 |

If you were looking for anomalies between the two years, a graphical representation of the data would be a lot easier to evaluate than a table of numbers. Here's that same data in graphic form:

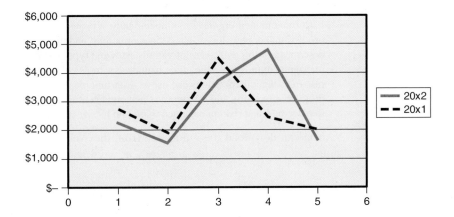

- *Statistical tests.* You've probably completed at least one statistics course by this time in your education. You may recall some of the tests that can be used to analyze differences between two samples, such as a *t*-tests. While *t*-tests can be performed without the use of information technology, they are much easier and quicker when IT is used—whether the IT is a simple spreadsheet or some more complex statistics software like SPSS.

- *Database queries.* A "find unmatched" query could be used to generate a list of unpaid purchase invoices or uncollected receivables. If a fraud auditor finds significant numbers of those transactions associated with a particular manager, department, or location, additional investigation is probably a good idea. A "just under limit" query can be used to locate suspicious amounts. For example, if an organization requires two signatures on purchase orders over $10,000, a "just under limit" query could identify purchase orders that are more than $9,000 but less than the $10,000 limit. Too many of those transactions may indicate that someone is trying to circumvent internal controls.

We've talked a lot about the Sarbanes-Oxley Act and its impact on accounting and auditing, but forensic auditors need to be aware of many other laws and legal issues, too. The Bank Secrecy Act, for example, requires banks to file a Currency Transaction Report for cash transactions that exceed $10,000 in a single day—whether from a single transaction or a series of transactions. The act also requires banks to keep a Monetary Instrument Log that records cash purchases between $3,000 and $10,000 of money orders, cashier's checks, traveler's checks, and other monetary instruments; finally, banks must file a Suspicious Activity Report for any transaction where it seems the customer is trying to avoid other reporting requirements, launder money, or engage in other potentially illegal activity.

While no single behavior provides conclusive evidence of fraud, there are some behavioral indications that a person may be lying or otherwise distorting the truth during a fraud audit. Some of them include nervous gestures (like tapping a pencil on the table), answering a question with a question (What possible motivation would I have for stealing money?), trying to cast suspicion on someone else in the organization, or an employee obviously living beyond his/her means (e.g., an employee who makes $20,000 a year driving an expensive new sports car to work).

If you'd like to know more about fraud auditing, check out *Managing the Business Risk of Fraud: A Practical Guide,* published by the Institute of Internal Auditors, the American Institute of CPAs, and the Association of Certified Fraud Examiners. According to its introduction (pp. 5–6):

> This guide recommends ways in which boards, senior management, and internal auditors can fight fraud in their organization. Specifically, it provides credible guidance from leading professional organizations that defines principles and theories for fraud risk management and describes how organizations of various sizes and types can establish their own fraud risk management program. The guide includes examples of key program components and resources that organizations can use as a starting place to develop a fraud risk management program effectively and efficiently. Each organization needs to assess the degree of emphasis to place on fraud risk management based on its size and circumstances.

You can download the guide free from the Web site of any one of the three organizations: www.theiia.org, www.aicpa.org, or www.acfe.com.

## Summary

In this chapter, then, you've had the briefest introduction to auditing—the evaluation of an accounting information system. Here is a summary of the chapter in terms of its learning objectives:

1. *Describe the various kinds of audits you might encounter in your accounting career.*
   a. Financial. In a financial statement audit, a team of CPAs examines the AIS and expresses an opinion on the organization's financial statements.
   b. Operational. Operational audits consider whether an organization's business processes are functioning as intended.
   c. Systems. In a systems audit, we consider whether the organization's information technology tools are producing expected results.
   d. Compliance. Compliance audits focus on governmental and not-for-profit entities.
   e. Management. Management audits consider the integrity and reliability of decision making processes.
   f. Investigative. Often referred to as a "fraud audit," the investigative audit helps to determine whether fraud has occurred.
   g. International. An international audit can comprise any/all of the preceding types; its defining feature is the setting.

2. *Explain the purpose of the Audit Clarity Project and summarize its essential components.* The Audit Clarity Project (ACP) was implemented to make auditing standards easier to comprehend. It made four broad types of changes in the financial statement audit process: format, terminology, additional requirements, and the audit report.

3. *Explain the 10 generally accepted auditing standards (GAAS) and their role in a financial statement audit.*
   a. The general standards (training, independence, and due professional care) focus on the auditor's overall attitude and approach.
   b. The field work standards (supervision, internal control, and evidence) relate more specifically to how the audit is carried out.
   c. The reporting standards (GAAP, consistency, disclosure, and opinion) provide information on the audit opinion.

4. *Discuss the basic steps associated with a financial statement audit.* Financial statement auditors commonly use five steps in the process: (i) assess management's integrity, (ii) evaluate management's credentials, (iii) review the internal control system, (iv) perform compliance testing, and (v) issue the audit report.

5. *Explain the connection between auditing and accounting information systems.* Auditing and AIS are linked via at least four important skill areas: critical thinking, internal controls analysis, understanding of business processes, and effective use of information technology.

Recent financial scandals have shaken public confidence in financial reporting and the accounting profession in general. Therefore, conducting audits with diligence and integrity is even more important today than in the past.

## Key Terms

| | | |
|---|---|---|
| Audit Clarity Project, *319* | auditing standards, *321* | professional judgment, *319* |
| auditing, *317* | fiduciary duty, *322* | Yellow Book, *318* |

## Chapter References

Committee of Sponsoring Organizations of the Treadway Commission. 2002. *Internal Control—Integrated Framework.* New York: AICPA.

Louwers, T., R. Ramsay, D. Sinason, and J. Strawser. 2005. *Auditing and Assurance Services.* 1st ed. New York: McGraw-Hill/Irwin.

Skinner, R. 2012. "The New Clarity Standards and What You Should Know about Their Effect on Your Next Audit." Retrieved 3 March 2014 from www.dhgllp.com.

Wells, J. 2004. *Principles of Fraud Examination.* 1st ed. New York: John Wiley & Sons.

## End-of-Chapter Activities

1. *Reading review questions.*
   a. List and discuss the seven types of audits described in the chapter.
   b. Explain the 10 generally accepted auditing standards that guide financial audits.
   c. Describe the common steps associated with an audit.
   d. Prepare a response to the questions for this chapter's "AIS in the Business World."

2. *Reading review problem.* John C. Beale was a senior policy advisor with the U.S. Environmental Protection Agency. In late 2013, however, he was sentenced to prison for stealing close to $900,000 in taxpayer funds. According to Marimow and Bernstein (2013):

   > Beale had skipped out on work for years by telling a series of supervisors . . . that he was doing top-secret work for the CIA. He was paid for a total of 2½ years of work he did not perform since early 2000 and received about $500,000 in bonuses he did not deserve, according to his plea agreement. He lied about contracting malaria to obtain a reserved parking space that cost the EPA $8,000 over three years. He took trips to visit his family in Los Angeles for which he charged the government more than $57,000.

   He had retired from the EPA in April after learning he was under investigation.

   *Source:* A. Marimow and L. Bernstein, "EPA Official, Who Pretended to Work for the CIA, Sentenced to 32 Months," *Washington Post,* December 2013.

a. Which type(s) of audits discussed in the chapter are relevant to this situation? Why?

b. The Audit Clarity Project standards apply to financial statement audits. Using Table 17.1 as a guide, prepare a memo that summarizes Beale's case.

c. How is the Beale case related to other topics you've discussed in your AIS course?

3. *Multiple choice review.*

1. The Yellow Book published by the GAO is most closely associated with ___ audits.

   a. operational
   b. compliance
   c. investigative
   d. international

2. The purpose of the Audit Clarity Project includes:

   a. eliminating all types of audits except the financial statement audit.
   b. revising US GAAP to make it easier to understand.
   c. making audit standards easier to apply.
   d. reorganizing the structure and content of audit opinions.

3. As specified in the Audit Clarity Project, which of the following elements of an unmodified audit report comes first?

   a. Auditor's opinion
   b. Auditor's responsibilities
   c. Addressee
   d. Management's responsibilities

4. Which of the following belong to the same group of generally accepted auditing standards?

   a. training and independence
   b. training and internal control
   c. internal control and disclosure
   d. evidence and opinion

5. In conducting a financial statement audit, which of the following immediately follows "evaluate management's credentials?"

   a. Review the internal control system.
   b. Assess management's integrity.
   c. Perform compliance testing.
   d. Issue the audit report.

4. *Making choices and exercising judgment.* Barb is an auditor for Vicenti, Lloyd and Stutzman (VLS), a regional CPA firm; she earned her CPA license three years ago and is supervising the audit team for CDR Corporation, a company that manufactures blank CDs. Last year's audit resulted in a qualified opinion, and both Barb and CDR's management are highly motivated to achieve a clean opinion this year. The audit team comprises four individuals (including Barb):

- Richard has been with VLS a little over two years. He has passed three parts of the CPA exam and is currently working on the fourth part. He graduated with a 3.8 GPA from a prestigious local university and is working on CDR's audit for the first time. In previous audits, Richard has been in charge of inventory observation and bank reconciliations.

- Laura joined VLS at the same time as Barb. She was licensed as a CPA one year ago. Laura has a master's degree in accounting from a local university and is an experienced auditor. In previous audits, she has taken the lead in evaluating internal controls and discussing audit matters with company management. This audit is her first for CDR Corporation.

- Albert came to work for VLS from one of the Big Four CPA firms about six months before the CDR audit started. He is an experienced CPA and made the move to get better working hours and a better chance at becoming a partner. The CDR audit will be Albert's first for VLS.

What responsibilities should Barb assign to each member of the audit team for the CDR audit? Explain your choices.

5. *Field work.*

   a. Contact an experienced auditor in your area for an interview about common audit procedures. Compare the process with the generic one presented in Figure 17.4. Prepare a short report or presentation comparing and contrasting the two.

   b. Reviewing internal controls is an important part of any AIS evaluation. Visit a local business such as a restaurant, movie theater, bank, or amusement park; observe one or more common transactions and assess the strength of internal control over those transactions. Classify the internal controls as preventive, detective, or corrective. If you wanted to circumvent the internal control system, how would you do it?

   c. Point your Web browser to www.soxtoolkit.com. Review and summarize the tools available for accountants and managers seeking to comply with the Sarbanes-Oxley Act of 2002.

6. *Audit types.* What type of audit is indicated in each of the following situations?

   a. Checking internal controls over the sales/collection process.

   b. Determining how an employee embezzled cash.

   c. Establishing whether an audit conformed to all provisions of Sarbanes-Oxley.

   d. Evaluating the accounting policy choices management made for conformity with GAAP.

   e. Expressing an opinion on the fairness of a company's financial statements.

   f. Inputting sample transactions and verifying the output from Peachtree.

   g. Observing internal controls over inventory to improve process effectiveness.

   h. Performing a comprehensive analysis of an Italian firm's accounting information system.

   i. Using test data to determine how QuickBooks processes transactions.

   j. Validating the assumptions made for a major capital investment.

7. *Audit Clarity Project.* Fill in the blanks below based on the ideas in the Audit Clarity Project.

   a. As structured under the ACP, each standard concludes with ___.

   b. Audit reports prepared under the ACP must have a ___ at the start of each paragraph.

   c. Auditors must obtain management's acknowledgement that they are responsible for ___ and ___.

   d. If an auditor expresses an adverse opinion, they must indicate the reason in a(n) ___.

   e. In an unmodified audit report, the opinion states that the financial statements are ___.

   f. In each audit standard, the requirements section can guide the auditor in ___.

   g. In terms of purpose, the ACP is similar to the FASB ___.

   h. One goal of the ACP is to converge ___ with ___.

   i. Specifying when an audit standard should be applied is part of the standard's ___.

   j. US GAAP and IFRS are examples of ___.

8. *Violations of GAAS.* Which of the 10 standards is violated in each of the following independent situations? Some situations may violate more than one.

   a. A team of auditors, each with varying levels of experience, divided up the audit tasks and completed them independently before expressing an opinion on the statements.

   b. An audit client changed its inventory cost flow assumption from LIFO to FIFO in the last year. The audit opinion makes no mention of the change.

   c. Auditors relied solely on the client's assertions in evaluating account balances.

   d. Austin supervised the audit team for a company in which he has an investment.

   e. Chip relied solely on the client's assessment of its AIS integrity in determining compliance tests for an audit.

   f. Sebastian conducted his first audit during his last semester of college. He audited the accounting information system of a nonprofit organization where he volunteers.

9. *Investigative audit.* For each independent case presented below, use Figure 17.1 as a guide in explaining the steps you would take to uncover fraud. Also suggest at least two internal controls that could have prevented the fraud described.

   a. KC Group is basically a high-integrity company with sound approaches to financial reporting. Associates involved in financial reporting are of high competence and ethical values. KC Group has grown in recent years. There are new systems, sometimes administered by those who do not fully understand them. KC Group is performance driven, and managers are under tremendous pressure to make their goals. KC Group has acquired several new companies. Some of the associates in the acquired companies do not share certain values inherent in the KG culture. Consequently, reporting and integrity in some of these subsidiaries have proven to be a problem. At an acquired subsidiary, certain executives who never traveled had traditionally been allowed $2,000 to $25,000 in travel advances. These permanent travel advances were essentially noninterest-bearing loans. The subsidiary had been told to stop the practice. Instead, the subsidiary's controller obtained repayment checks from the executives and credited the travel advance account. Rather than actually depositing the checks at the bank before year-end, he held them until after the end of the year. He then issued company checks to the executives to replace the travel advances purportedly repaid. The executives thus could cover their own checks by depositing company checks before their checks cleared. The controller back-dated the deposit slip reflecting the repayments from the executives and a fictitious deposit in transit. Although the amount was minor, the controller was knowingly and intentionally making false entries in the company records. (*Source:* C. Thompson, "The Reporting Challenge,"*Internal Auditor,* December 2002.)

   b. During a routine audit of your client, you discover the price the company pays for widgets has doubled in the past year. Moreover, you notice all of the business is going to a new vendor. You check further and find the price of widgets on the open market is half what your client is currently paying. Maybe there is a legitimate reason for this anomaly. Or maybe it's a fraud. (*Source:* J. Wells, "Sherlock Holmes, CPA—Part 1," *Journal of Accountancy,* August 2003.)

10. *Terminology.* Match each item on the left with the most appropriate item on the right.

| | |
|---|---|
| 1. Assesses whether a company's processes and procedures are followed | a. Systems audit |
| 2. Compliance testing | b. SOX Section 802 |
| 3. Consistency and disclosure | c. Reporting standards |
| 4. Designed to make audit standards easier to read | d. Professional care |
| 5. Determines whether IT assets are generating expected results | e. Operational audit |
| 6. Must be exercised in planning and conducting a financial statement audit | f. International audit |
| 7. Requires an understanding of culture, law, and religion | g. Field work standards |
| 8. Rights and obligations | h. Checking account balances prior to issuing an audit report |
| 9. Spells out penalties for noncompliance | i. Audit Clarity Project |
| 10. Supervision and evidence | j. Audit assertions associated with asset ownership |

11. *Multiple choice.* Please select the best answer for each of the following questions.

   1. An ERP system could be associated with ___ audits.

     a. Systems
     b. Financial
     c. Investigative
     d. All of the above.

   2. In an investigative audit, coconspirators are interviewed before the target

     a. Because the information they can provide is more important.
     b. So the investigative auditor will be certain to get a confession from the target.
     c. Because they can be offered a "deal" that will help prove the fraud.
     d. Because they are younger.

   3. Which type of audit opinion ensures that financial statements are true and correct?

     a. Unmodified
     b. Qualified
     c. Both of the above.
     d. None of the above.

   4. An auditor is dating an accounting manager in a firm he is auditing. His behavior is most likely in violation of a ___ standard.

     a. General
     b. Field work
     c. Reporting
     d. Forensic

   5. A client refuses to let a financial statement auditor examine certain documents. The auditor is most likely to issue a(n) ___ opinion.

     a. Unmodified
     b. Qualified
     c. Disclaimer
     d. Adverse

12. *Statement evaluation.* Determine whether each of the following statements is (i) always true, (ii) sometimes true, or (iii) never true. For those that are (ii) sometimes true, explain when the statement is true.

   a. A disclaimed audit opinion means the financial statements contain errors.
   b. Audits focus on a company's financial statements.
   c. Field work standards contain guidelines for conducting an audit.
   d. Financial statement audits result in an unmodified opinion.
   e. Following the provisions of Sarbanes-Oxley, CEOs can delegate their responsibility to examine internal controls.
   f. In an investigative audit, the target should be interviewed first.
   g. Independent auditors in the United States help determine whether financial statements are true.
   h. Investigative audits examine five main assertions about financial statements.
   i. U.S. companies need to undergo annual financial statement audits.
   j. Weak internal controls lead to qualified audit opinions.

13. *Prior material application.*

   a. Consider the five generic AIS elements discussed in Chapter 1. A financial statement auditor might examine input documents like purchase orders for mathematical accuracy, complete information, and proper recording in the AIS. How might a financial statement auditor examine the other four generic elements of the AIS?

b. Many organizations process thousands of transactions every year. An auditor, therefore, cannot possibly examine all of them in the course of an investigative audit. How would an investigative auditor determine which transactions to examine more closely?

c. WHM Corporation recently established an internal audit function. The chief internal auditor has developed a plan for conducting operational audits throughout the organization but has not shared the plan with anyone else at WHM. How would you classify the plan based on the capability maturity model? Suggest some signs that would indicate the internal audit plan is moving up the model's hierarchy.

14. *Excel application.* In this exercise, we'll use Excel's "sampling" function to create a random sample. Random samples of transactions are often used in financial statement audits.

a. Access the Excel data file in the 3 February 2014 post on my AIS blog. An excerpt of the file appears below:

| Transaction # | Transaction Amount |
|:---:|:---:|
| 1 | $ 645 |
| 2 | 350 |
| 3 | 630 |
| 4 | 432 |
| 5 | 333 |

b. Use Excel's sampling function (part of the data analysis tools) to select a sample of five transaction numbers. Sort the five transaction numbers from smallest to largest.

c. Use Excel's VLOOKUP function to find the associated transaction amounts. Here's an example of how it might look; your transaction numbers will likely be different.

| Transaction # | Transaction Amount |
|:---:|:---:|
| 11 | $ 523 |
| 22 | 464 |
| 28 | 370 |
| 29 | 327 |
| 48 | 361 |

d. Use appropriate Excel formulas to calculate the mean and standard deviation of the transaction amounts.

## Comprehensive Problem
### Part 5 of 5

Each part of the comprehensive problem is based on Big Marker (www.bigmarker.com). Consider the narrative in Part 1 as necessary in responding to the following questions on decision making models, knowledge management, ethics, and auditing.

Alex is a community organizer at Big Marker, specializing in topics related to cost and management accounting; she is considering organizing a Big Marker webinar on zero-based budgeting. Investopedia (www.investopedia.com) defines zero-based budgeting as "a method of budgeting in which all expenses must be justified for each new period. Zero-based budgeting starts from a 'zero base' and every function within an organization is analyzed for its needs and costs."

**Part Five Questions**

1. In preparing for the webinar, what causes of information overload is Alex likely to experience? Why? For each cause, discuss at least one countermeasure Alex can use.

2. Complete the partial knowledge map below by suggesting connections between the four elements.

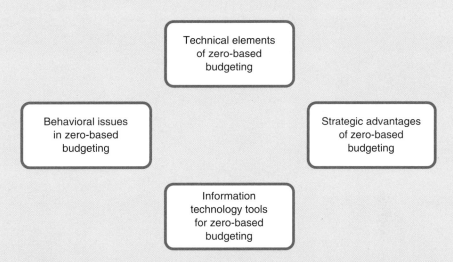

3. Use Steps for Better Thinking to help Alex decide whether to present the webinar.

4. Which characteristics of a professional is Alex demonstrating by preparing for and presenting the webinar?

5. One ethical issue related to budgeting is "padding" the budget; that is, deliberately overstating resources needed. How would an ethical egoist, a utilitarian, a deontologist, and a virtue ethicist view the practice of padding the budget respectively?

6. One of the steps in a financial statement audit is to review the company's internal control system. What internal controls would you recommend for a zero-based budgeting process?

# Answers for Multiple Choice Review Questions

## Part One

| | Chapter 1 | Chapter 2 | Chapter 3 | Chapter 4 | Chapter 5 |
|---|---|---|---|---|---|
| Question 1 | A | A | D | A | B |
| Question 2 | D | C | A | C | A |
| Question 3 | C | A | B | D | C |
| Question 4 | B | C | D | D | B |
| Question 5 | A | D | A | C | D |

## Part Two

| | Chapter 6 | Chapter 7 | Chapter 8 |
|---|---|---|---|
| Question 1 | C | B | A |
| Question 2 | D | A | D |
| Question 3 | A | D | B |
| Question 4 | C | C | C |
| Question 5 | D | A | B |

## Part Three

| | Chapter 9 | Chapter 10 | Chapter 11 |
|---|---|---|---|
| Question 1 | B | D | B |
| Question 2 | C | C | A |
| Question 3 | C | B | A |
| Question 4 | A | A | C |
| Question 5 | D | A | C |

## Part Four

| | Chapter 12 | Chapter 13 | Chapter 14 |
|---|---|---|---|
| Question 1 | B | D | B |
| Question 2 | A | B | C |
| Question 3 | C | D | B |
| Question 4 | B | A | C |
| Question 5 | D | C | D |

## Part Five

| | Chapter 15 | Chapter 16 | Chapter 17 |
|---|---|---|---|
| Question 1 | B | A | B |
| Question 2 | A | C | C |
| Question 3 | B | B | C |
| Question 4 | A | A | A |
| Question 5 | C | A | A |

# Glossary

## A

**accounting**   Accounting is the process of identifying, measuring, and communicating economic information to permit informed judgments and decisions by users of the information. (Ch. 2)

**accounting cycle**   The set of repetitive activities used to prepare general purpose financial statements. Although many parts of the accounting cycle can be completed more easily with information technology, some parts require significant human judgment and decision making. (Ch. 2)

**accounting information system**   A collection of interrelated processes, technologies, and documents designed to capture primarily financial data and process them into information for making decisions. (Ch. 1)

**accounting information system (AIS) structure**   Most accounting information systems comprise five parts: inputs (such as source documents), processing tools (such as general ledger software), outputs (such as the general purpose financial statements), storage (such as computer disks), and internal controls (such as separation of duties). (Ch. 1)

**Adelphia Communications Corporation**   Well-known fraud case involving a cable company. Key figure was John Rigas. (Ch. 16)

**adjusting entries**   Journal entries made at the end of an accounting period to account for timing differences between cash flow and accrual basis revenues and expenses. Types include accrued revenue, accrued expense, deferred revenue, prepaid assets, uncollectible receivables, and depreciation. (Ch. 2)

**administrative security controls**   One of three internal control types necessary to protect data integrity in a computerized information system. (Ch. 11)

**agents**   One element of an REA model. Agents can be internal (such as a sales clerk) or external (such as a customer). In laying out an REA model, agents should be in the third column from the left. (Ch. 8)

**AICPA core competency framework**   A three-part framework that outlines skills needed for success in the accounting profession. The three parts include broad business perspective competencies, functional competencies, and personal competencies. (Ch. 1)

**application service providers**   Companies that deliver software on an as-needed basis to their clients. (Ch. 10)

**audit clarity project**   An AICPA project designed to make audit standards easier to understand and follow, as well as to align US and international standards. (Ch. 17)

**auditing**   A systematic review of an organization's accounting information system, often for the purpose of expressing an opinion on the financial statements. (Ch. 17)

**auditing standards**   The rules auditors use to promote integrity and consistency in the audit process. Often referred to collectively as GAAS (generally accepted auditing standards). (Ch. 17)

## B

**balanced**   Characteristic of a set of data flow diagrams. Balanced diagrams do not allow symbols to disappear between levels. (Ch. 7)

**basic principles of business process management**   The text discusses seven principles suggested by Eppele. The seven principles focus on the relationship between BPM and strategy, attitude toward change, top management support, focusing on people, external consultants, task definition, and communication. (Ch. 4)

**basic principles of information security**   Confidentiality, availability, and data integrity are the three basic principles of information security. They are often referred to as the C-I-A triad. (Ch. 11)

**benefits of XBRL**   XBRL facilitates information exchange regardless of hardware or software platform. In addition, XBRL is flexible, allowing users to create their own tags when the need arises. (Ch. 9)

**Bernie Madoff**   Perpetrator of a massive Ponzi scheme, convicted and sentenced to 150 years in prison. (Ch. 16)

**Big Data**   Diverse data types available in organizations. The five types include: Web and social media data, machine-to-machine data, big transaction data, biometric data, and human-generated data. (Ch. 15)

**bookkeeping**   The process of recording transactions in a journal, posting them to ledger accounts, and preparing basic financial statements. Though often confused with accounting, bookkeeping is distinct; it focuses on the mechanical aspects and rules of accounting and often can be completed more easily with the aid of information technology. (Ch. 2)

**bounded rationality**   The idea that most decision makers will avoid uncertainty; rather, they will depend on a set of rules for making decisions. (Ch. 15)

**Brown's taxonomy of risk**   A way of looking at and categorizing risk. Four broad categories include financial, operational, strategic, and hazard. (Ch. 3)

**business process**   The set of steps associated with an activity; one way an organization creates value.

The processes discussed in the text include sales/collection, acquisition/payment, conversion, financing, and human resources. (Ch. 12 through 14)

**business process management**    Analyzing business processes with a view toward making them more efficient and/or effective. (Ch. 4)

# C

**capability maturity model**    A five-stage model developed by Humphrey, used to categorize and improve business processes. (Ch. 5)

**cardinalities**    Relationships between elements of an REA model. Cardinalities are set up in pairs, with each element of the pair having a minimum value and a maximum value. Proper design of cardinalities facilitates the development of a relational database. (Ch. 8)

**career plan**    The plans an accountant makes for his/her career in the profession. (Ch. 16)

**causes of ERP implementation failure**    ERP systems most often fail because of poor planning and lack of strategic vision. The chapter discusses other causes of ERP failure. (Ch. 10)

**causes of information overload**    As discussed in the chapter, at least five things can cause information overload: personal factors, information technology, information characteristics, organizational design, and task and process parameters. (Ch. 15)

**characteristics of a professional**    Bell's list includes seven components: communicates effectively; thinks rationally, logically, and coherently; appropriately uses technical knowledge; integrates knowledge from many disciplines; exhibits ethical professional behavior; recognizes the influence of political, social, economic, legal, and regulatory forces; and actively seeks additional knowledge. (Ch. 16)

**Charles Ponzi**    Originator of the fraud, now labeled a "Ponzi scheme," that involves paying off old investors with money from new investors, rather than money generated by an investment itself. (Ch. 16)

**cloud computing**    A general term for delivering data and applications over the Internet. (Ch. 15)

**CoBIT framework**    The CoBIT framework (Control Objectives for Information and Related Technology) was developed by the Information Systems Audit and Control Association (ISACA) to provide guidance for information systems internal controls. (Ch. 11)

**common files**    AIS include three major types of files: master, transaction, and junction. Every business process has specific examples of them. (Chs. 12, 13 and 14)

**compound primary key**    A primary key that comprises at least two fields in a relational database table. Junction files require compound primary keys, commonly including the primary keys of the tables they join. (Ch. 7)

**computer networks**    The defining feature of e-commerce. Computers can be networked via hardware or software, in the same physical location or different physical locations. (Ch. 10)

**conceptual framework of accounting**    A document produced by the Financial Accounting Standards Board in 1977, intended to guide the development of future accounting principles. The framework was updated in 2010. (Ch. 1)

**conditions for a successful ERP implementation**    Conditions include organizational commitment, clearly communicated strategic goals for the project, and involvement of the entire organization. (Ch. 10)

**context diagram**    Highest-level data flow diagram. Contains the least detail. Depicts a business process in a single circle, showing its interaction with external entities. (Ch. 7)

**conversion process**    The process of combining raw material, labor, and overhead in the production of finished goods. (Ch. 14)

**Cost-benefit analysis**    The process of analyzing an alternative's costs and benefits, not all of which are expressed in dollar terms. Should be utilized when designing internal controls and other elements of the AIS to ensure that benefits outweigh costs. (Ch. 4)

**COSO**    Committee of Sponsoring Organizations of the Treadway Commission. Includes five organizations: the Institute of Management Accountants, the American Institute of Certified Public Accountants, the American Accounting Association, the Institute of Internal Auditors, and the Financial Executives Institute. Created two important documents (integrated frameworks) related to internal control and risk management. (Ch. 3)

**countermeasures**    Actions people can take to avoid, or reduce the effects of, information overload. Examples include allowing additional time to complete important tasks and using graphs or other visual aids. (Ch. 15)

# D

**data analytics**    Descriptive, predictive, and prescriptive tools used to analyze data, including Big Data. (Ch. 15)

**data flow**    One of four elements of a data flow diagram. Depicted with an arrow. Always contains a noun phrase as a label, such as "purchase order information." (Ch. 7)

**data store**    One of four elements of a data flow diagram. Depicted with two parallel lines containing a noun phrase label, such as "employee database." (Ch. 7)

**database tables**    Primary organizational element of a relational database. Composed of fields and records. Each record must contain a primary key that uniquely identifies it. (Ch. 7)

**deontology** A school of ethical thought that emphasizes the rights of individuals. Teaches that people should never be used as a means to achieve a goal. (Ch. 16)

**document flowcharts** One of four flowchart types discussed in the chapter. Follows the flow of one or more documents through an information system. (Ch. 6)

**documents** Hard copy or electronic forms, often used as the basis for data entry in an accounting information system. For the sales/collection process, they may include remittance advices and customer invoices; in the acquisition/payment process, they may include purchase orders and receiving reports. (Chs. 12, 13)

# E

**e-business categories** Most taxonomies in this area identify five categories: business-to-business, business-to-consumer, government-to-consumer, government-to-business, and consumer-to-consumer. (Ch. 10)

**e-commerce** The process of conducting business using computer networks. (Ch. 10)

**eight-step model** Generic process for responding to ethical problems developed by Langenderfer and Rockness. (Ch. 16)

**Enron/Arthur Andersen** At the time, the largest bankruptcy in U.S. history. Issues of organizational culture and reward systems contributed to financial statement fraud through the use of special-purpose entities and non-GAAP revenue recognition policies. Andersen served as Enron's independent auditor; the scandal led to the demise of both firms. (Ch. 16)

**enterprise resource planning system** A very large relational database, designed to capture data for use in decision making. Most ERP systems are organized into modules such as human resource management and supply chain management. (Ch. 10)

*Enterprise Risk Management: Integrated Framework* One of two COSO documents. Contains eight elements to help professionals think about managing risk: internal environment, objective setting, event identification, risk assessment, risk response, control activities, information and communication, and monitoring. (Ch. 4)

**ethical egoism** A school of ethical thought that emphasizes self-interest above all others. Recognizes that, in some cases, acting in one's self-interest is not the same as acting selfishly. (Ch. 16)

**events** One element of an REA model. Events typically fall into one of three categories: operating, information, and decision/management. Only strategically significant operating events appear in an REA model; examples include selling services to a client or paying employees. Information events, such as updating ledger account balances, focus on recording and maintaining data, as well as reporting information. Decision/management events involve human decision making, such as changing compensation packages. (Ch. 8)

**expectancy theory** Motivation = Expectancy $\times$ Instrumentality $\times$ Valence. Suggested by Vroom. (Ch. 4)

**external entity** One of the four elements of a data flow diagram. Depicted with a rectangle. Represents an entity outside the boundary of an information system, such as a vendor. (Ch. 7)

**external transactions** Transactions that involve parties external to the organization. Typically do not require adjusting entries at the end of a period. Examples include selling inventory, purchasing plant assets, and paying vendors. (Ch. 2)

# F

**fiduciary duty** The responsibility of an accountant to act in the best interests of others, such as stockholders. (Ch. 17)

**financing process** The process of acquiring external funding, most commonly through debt or equity. (Ch. 14)

**financing process transactions** Issuance of capital stock, purchase of treasury shares, issuance, and repayment of long-term debt, and dividend distributions. (Ch. 14)

**flat file** Information not structured in relational database tables, such as a spreadsheet. Through the process of normalization, flat files can be converted to relational database tables. (Ch. 7)

**Foreign Corrupt Practices Act** One of the earliest laws focused on business ethics. Passed in 1977. Prohibits conduct that would be considered illegal in the United States, even if that conduct is acceptable in foreign countries. (Ch. 3)

**foreign keys** A field in a database table that is a primary key in another table. For example, a customer identification number would be a primary key in the customer table and a foreign key in a sales transaction table. (Ch. 7)

**form** A relational database object used to look up data and/or populate tables. (Ch. 7)

**freight terms** Terms that govern when title to merchandise passes from the seller to the buyer (destination or shipping point) and who is responsible for the cost of freight (collect or prepaid). (Ch. 12)

# G

**general purpose financial statements** Collective term referring to the balance sheet, income statement, statement of changes in equity, and statement of cash flows. Must be prepared in accordance with generally accepted accounting principles. (Ch. 2)

**generalized model of BPM** Seven generic steps associated with many business process management initiatives. (Ch. 4)

# H

**hardware flowcharts** One of four flowchart types discussed in the chapter. Depicts the hardware layout of an information system. (Ch. 6)

**human judgment**    A critical element of accounting and accounting information systems. For example, accountants exercise judgment in deciding which transactions are recordable in the AIS and in making decisions based on financial information. (Ch. 2)

**human resource process**    Associated with personnel activities in an organization, from the time of hiring to the time of discharge via retirement, termination, or quitting. (Ch. 14)

# I

**information competence**    The ability to formulate research questions, locate the information to answer the questions, evaluate information quality, and use it for decision making. (Ch. 1)

**information overload**    One factor that negatively impacts decision making. Symptoms and effects include limited information retrieval strategies, increased stress, arbitrary analysis, and suboptimal decisions. (Ch. 15)

**information technology**    Computer hardware and software, often employed in accounting information systems to make routine tasks more efficient. Examples include general ledger packages and enterprise resource planning software. (Ch. 2)

**instance document**    As applied in XBRL, an instance document refers to properly tagged information. For example, a balance sheet with XBRL tags would be an instance document. (Ch. 9)

**internal control**    One element of an accounting information system. Policies and procedures designed to achieve four objectives: safeguarding assets, ensuring financial statement reliability, promoting operational efficiency, and encouraging compliance with management's directives. (Chs. 3, 12, 13)

*Internal Control: Integrated Framework*    One of two COSO documents. Contains five elements to help professionals think about internal control: control environment, risk assessment, control activities, information and communication, and monitoring. (Ch. 3)

**internal transactions**    Transactions that do not involve parties external to the organization. Typically require adjusting entries at the end of an accounting period. Examples include depreciation of fixed assets and the use of prepaid assets such as supplies. (Ch. 2)

**iterative**    In the context of accounting information systems, iterative refers to the idea that steps don't always proceed in a linear fashion and/or that the development of systems documentation, internal controls, and other AIS elements is rarely accomplished in a single attempt. (Ch. 5)

# J

**job costing**    A production operation typically associated with unique, customized, or made-to-order goods. Examples include consulting assignments and custom-built homes. (Ch. 14)

**junction table**    Type of relational database table used to capture cardinalities where the maximum is many on both ends. For example, consider this cardinality: Sales (0,*)—(1,*) Inventory. That cardinality indicates that each sale involves one to many items of inventory; each item of inventory can be included in zero to many sales transactions. A junction table would be required in this situation. It would capture data such as the sales transaction number and inventory item numbers for each transaction. (Ch. 8)

# K

**knowledge management**    The way(s) managers and other decision makers organize knowledge to facilitate decision making. (Ch. 15)

# L

**Level Zero diagram**    One element of a leveled set of data flow diagrams. The next level down from a context diagram. Shows the processes, data flows, data stores, and external entities of an information system at a high level, but with more detail than a context diagram. (Ch. 7)

**leveled sets**    Applied to data flow diagrams. Refers to the idea that business processes are decomposed into greater levels of detail until they cannot be decomposed any more. Leveled sets of data flow diagrams must be balanced. (Ch. 7)

# M

**macro-level issues**    The "big picture" issues to be considered in adopting a specific form of information technology. The chapter discusses need, strategic fit, personnel involvement, and financing. (Ch. 5)

**McCarthy**    Professor credited with the development of REA modeling techniques and their application to accounting information systems. (Ch. 8)

**micro-level issues**    The more focused issues to be considered in adopting a specific form of information technology. The chapter discusses cost, adaptability, training, and vendor reliability. (Ch. 5)

**Microsoft Visio**    Software that can be used to create flowcharts and other forms of systems documentation. (Ch. 6)

# N

**namespace**    Related to XBRL. A place on the Internet that defines tags used for coding. Users can use an existing namespace and/or create one of their own. (Ch. 9)

**normalization**    The process of making relational database tables as efficient and effective as possible. Steps include first normal form, second normal form, and third normal form. (Ch. 7)

# P

**payroll forms**    The forms commonly used to process payroll transactions. Examples include Form W-4, Form W-2, payroll register, employee earnings record, Form 1099, Form 940, and Form 941. (Ch. 14)

**physical security controls**    One of the three internal control types necessary to protect data integrity in a computerized information system. (Ch. 11)

**primary key**    The field in a database table that uniquely identifies each record in the table. For example, a product identification code in an inventory table. (Ch. 7)

**primitive**    The lowest level of decomposition for processes in a data flow diagram. Systems analysts and designers use judgment in selecting/establishing primitive processes. (Ch. 7)

**principles of debit and credit**    The rules used to record transactions in a journal. Assets and expenses increase with debits and decrease with credits; liabilities, equity, and revenue follow the opposite rules. (Ch. 2)

**process**    Any set of procedures an organization uses to gather data, change the data into information, or report the information to system users. Depicted in data flow diagrams with circles, each of which has both a number and a name. (Ch. 7)

**process costing**    A production operation typically associated with mass-produced, undifferentiated goods such as flash drives. (Ch. 14)

**professional judgment**    A key element of the audit process and accounting information systems design and implementation. (Ch. 17)

**program flowcharts**    One of the four flowchart types discussed in the chapter. Illustrates the logic of a computer program and the steps required to complete it. (Ch. 6)

# Q

**query**    One object in relational databases. Allow the user to ask questions of the database based on specific conditions. For example, what are the names of all customers with credit limits exceeding $10,000? (Ch. 7)

# R

**relapse errors**    The human tendency to make the same mistakes repeatedly, even when determined not to. (Ch. 15)

**relational database**    A type of software that allows users to enter data, ask questions about the data, and create reports in response to those questions. Microsoft Access is an example of relational database software, which forms the basis for event-driven accounting systems. Enterprise resource planning systems are a sophisticated form of relational databases. (Ch. 8)

**report**    A relational database object used to display information from tables and/or queries.

**resources**    One element of an REA model. Resources refer to items such as inventory, cash, and supplies, which are required to carry out the events in an REA model. In a properly constructed REA model, all resources appear in the leftmost column. (Ch. 8)

**risks and threats**    Potential hazards for information systems. The development of internal controls often begins by identifying risks and threats. (Ch. 11)

**rules/conventions**    The rules associated with creating data flow diagrams. (Ch. 7)

# S

**Sarbanes-Oxley Act of 2002**    Federal legislative response to the corporate scandals of the late 20th century. Imposes specific duties on managers and auditors for the review of internal controls, disclosures, and related issues. Specifies fines and penalties for noncompliance. (Ch. 3)

**satisficing**    The idea that decision makers will not necessarily look for the best solution to a problem—just a solution that solves the problem. (Ch. 15)

**six-step process**    The steps AIS designers take to develop an REA model. (Ch. 8)

**SmartDraw**    Software that can be used to create flowcharts and other forms of systems documentation. www.smartdraw .com. (Ch. 6)

**source documents**    Paper-based or electronic documents often used as the basis for journal entries in an accounting information system. Examples include remittance advices, purchase orders, and check stubs. (Ch. 2)

**specification**    A specific example of a larger group. For example, "California" is a specification of "U.S. states." XBRL is a specification of a larger family of languages called XML (eXtensible Markup Language). (Ch. 9)

**steps**    The common activities associated with a business process. Although the steps may vary slightly for some processes between organizations, certain common elements are nearly always present. (Chs. 12, 13)

**Steps for Better Thinking**    A decision-making model developed by Wolcott and Lynch. The model is organized in five levels: knowing, identifying, exploring, prioritizing, and envisioning. (Ch. 15)

**steps to create a knowledge management system**    The seven-step process for creating a knowledge management system (recommended by Call) begins with developing an organizational culture that supports knowledge sharing and concludes with periodically reevaluating the system's value and making needed adjustments. (Ch. 15)

**strategically significant operating activities**    The subset of operating activities depicted in an REA model. AIS designers use judgment to identify strategically significant operating activities, which may include things such as purchasing inventory and paying vendors. (Ch. 8)

**symbols**    Elements of a flowchart and other forms of systems documentation. (Ch. 6)

**systems development life cycle**    Generic set of steps used to develop, implement, and maintain information systems. Four iterative phases include analysis, logical design, physical design, and implementation and maintenance. (Ch. 5)

**systems flowcharts**    One of the four flowchart types discussed in the chapter. Shows the components of an information system. Of the four types, this one is used most often in accounting information systems work. (Ch. 6)

# T

**taxonomies**    In general, a taxonomy is a way of organizing knowledge. In XBRL, a taxonomy refers to a specific set of tags, most often associated with an industry group. For example, XBRL contains government accounting taxonomies and manufacturing industry taxonomies. (Ch. 9)

**taxonomy for computer crime**    A classification system for computer crime. Carter's taxonomy has four parts: target, instrumentality, incidental, and associated. (Ch. 11)

**technical security controls**    One of three internal control types necessary to protect data integrity in a computerized information system. (Ch. 11)

**three-stage process**    Framework proposed by Sylla and Wen regarding the adoption of information technology. Stages include intangible benefits evaluation, IT investment risk analysis, and tangible benefits evaluation. (Ch. 5)

# U

**unstructured problems**    Frequently encountered in the study of accounting information systems and the practice of accounting. Refers to problems without single, correct responses/solutions that require creativity and judgment. Unstructured problems may have more than one acceptable answer, although some responses to them may clearly be incorrect or inappropriate. (Ch. 1)

**utilitarian model of ethics**    One of four schools of ethical thought discussed in the chapter. Relies on the idea that the "end justifies the means." (Ch. 16)

# V

**value chain**    Model suggested by Porter that describes how organizations create value. Activities are in two groups: primary and support. (Ch. 12)

**virtues model**    One of four schools of ethical thought discussed in the chapter. Relies on the idea that people should do what is right/moral/virtuous. (Ch. 16)

# W

**Watts Humphrey**    First suggested the capability maturity model. (Ch. 5)

**weighted-rating technique**    System for comparing specific software packages. The user selects a list of criteria, such as cost and ease of use, and assigns each criterion a weight. Then, each software package is rated on each criterion. The rating is multiplied by the weighting to arrive at an overall weighted score, which informs (but does not dictate) the choice. (Ch. 5)

# X

**XBRL**    The eXtensible Business Reporting Language. A software- and hardware-independent way of coding financial data. According to www.xbrl.org, it is "a language for the electronic communication of business and financial data which is set to revolutionize business reporting around the world." (Ch. 9)

# Y

**Yellow Book**    A document published by the Government Accountability Office (GAO) that explains the rules for conducting a compliance audit. (Ch. 17)

# Comprehensive Chapter References

AICPA. 2012. "Service Organization Control Reports." Retrieved 9 February 2014 from www.cpa2biz.com/AST/Main/CPA2BIZ_Primary/AuditAttest/PRDOVR~PC-780281/PC-780281.jsp.

AICPA. 2013. *Core Competency Framework and Educational Competency Assessment.* http://www.aicpa.org/interestareas/accountingeducation/resources/pages/corecompetency.aspx (December 7, 2013).

Arthur, L. 2013. "What Is Big Data?" Retrieved 1 March 2014 from www.forbes.com.

Barker, T., and M. Frolick. 2003. "ERP Implementation Failure: A Case Study." *Information Systems Management,* Fall, pp. 43–49.

Bell, N. 2004. "Characteristics of a Risk Management and Insurance Professional." www.wsu.edu/~belln/ (October 4, 2004).

Bertolucci, J. 2013. "Big Data Analytics: Descriptive Vs. Predictive Vs. Prescriptive." Retrieved 1 March 2014 from www.informationweek.com.

Betsch, T., S. Haberstroh, B. Molter, and A. Glockner. 2004. "Oops, I Did It Again—Relapse Errors in Routinized Decision Making." *Organizational Behavior and Human Decision Processes* 93, no. 1, pp. 62–74.

Boss, J. 2014. *Ethics for Life: A Text with Readings.* 6th ed. McGraw-Hill Education. Dictionary.com. 2004. "Ethics." http://dictionary.reference.com/search?q=ethics (October 4).

Bourke, J. (2012) "Explaining SOC: Easy as 1-2-3." Retrieved 9 February 2014 from www.cpa2biz.com/Content/media/PRODUCER_CONTENT/Newsletters/Articles_2012/CPA/Jun/Easy123.jsp.

Bradford, M., S. Richtermeyer, and D. Roberts. 2007. "System Diagramming Techniques: An Analysis of Methods Used in Accounting Education and Practice." *Journal of Information Systems,* Spring, pp. 173–212.

Brown, B. 2001. "Step-by-Step Enterprise Risk Management." *Risk Management,* September, pp. 43–49.

Call, D. 2005. "Knowledge Management—Not Rocket Science." *Journal of Knowledge Management* 9, no. 2, pp. 19–30.

Carter, D. 1995. "Computer Crime Categories." *FBI Law Enforcement Bulletin,* pp. 21–28.

Committee of Sponsoring Organizations of the Treadway Commission. 2002. *Internal Control—Integrated Framework.* New York: AICPA.

Committee of Sponsoring Organizations of the Treadway Commission. 2013. *Internal Control—Integrated Framework.* New York: Committee of Sponsoring Organizations of the Treadway Commission.

Curzon, S. 1995. *Information Competence in the CSU.* www.calstate.edu/LS/Archive/info_comp_report.shtml (May 25, 2005).

DeMarco, T. 1979. *Structured Analysis and Systems Specifications.* Englewood Cliffs, NJ: Prentice Hall.

Drucker, P. 1993. *Post-Capitalist Society.* New York: Harper Row Publishing.

Egerdahl, R. 1995. "A Risk Matrix Approach to Data Processing Facility Audits." *Internal Auditor,* June, pp. 34–40.

Eppler, M., and J. Mengis. 2004. "The Concept of Information Overload: A Review of Literature from Organization Science, Accounting, Marketing, MIS and Related Disciplines." *Information Society,* pp. 325–44.

Eversley, M., and K. Hjelmgaard. "Target confirms massive credit-card data breach." *USA Today,* 19 December 2013.

Halbert, J. 2003. "Mining Back-Office Operations May Bolster the Bottom Line." *Los Angeles Business Journal,* April 14, www.findarticles.com (last visited November 4, 2004).

Hoffner, J., J. George, and J. Valacich. 1996. *Modern Systems Analysis and Design.* Reading, MA: Benjamin/Cummings.

Hollander, A. S., E. L. Denna, and J. O. Cherrington. 2000. *Accounting, Information Technology, and Business Solutions.* 2nd ed. New York: Irwin/McGraw-Hill.

Hurst, J. 2007. *The Capability Maturity Model and Its Applications.* www.giac.org/resources (last visited September 26, 2014).

Hurt, R. 1994. "Wholelife Counseling Center." *Journal of Accounting Case Research,* pp. 97–98.

IFRS Foundation, www.ifrs.org

Internet Encyclopedia of Philosophy. 2004. "Ethics." www.utm.edu/research/iep/e/ethics.htm (October 4).

Jaruzelski, B., F. Ribeiro, and R. Lake. "ASP 101: Understanding the Application Service Provider Model." Retrieved 9 February 2014 from www.boozallen.com/media/file/ASP_Whitepaper.pdf.

Johnston, R. 2003. "A Strategy for Finding the Right Accounting Software." *Journal of Accountancy,* September, pp. 39–46.

Jonietz, E. 2001. "Wireless Stockroom." *Technology Review,* July/August, p. 32.

Kishel, G., and P. Kishel. 1993. "Safeguarding Your Business." *Black Enterprise,* July, pp. 98–104.

Langenderfer, H., and J. Rockness. 1989. "Integrating Ethics into the Accounting Curriculum: Issues, Problems, and Solutions." *Journal of Accounting Education,* Spring, pp. 58–69.

Lemos, R. (2006, August). "Gangland Web Attacks; How Not to Get Whacked by the Botnet Mafia." *PC Magazine* 25(13), 116. ABI/INFORM Trade & Industry database (Document ID: 11070446111; February 1, 2009).

Louwers, T., R. Ramsay, D. Sinason, and J. Strawser. 2005. *Auditing and Assurance Services.* 1st ed. New York: McGraw-Hill/Irwin.

Mangalindan, J. P. 2012. "Amazon's core? Frugality." Retrieved 9 February 2014 from tech.fortune.cnn.com.

MarketingPlan.net. 2014. "Marketing Strategies of Amazon.com." www.marketingplan.net/amazon-com-marketing-strategies/ (February 9).

McCarthy, W. E. 1982. "The REA Accounting Model: A Generalized Framework for Accounting Systems in a Shared Data Environment." *Accounting Review,* July, pp. 554–77.

McDonald, C. 2001. "A Review of Continuing Professional Education." *Journal of Continuing Higher Education,* Winter, pp. 29–40.

Nesbitt, K. 2002, February 8. "Designing a Knowledge Management System." http://academic.edu.2081/products/faulknerlibrary/00018382.htm (May 2, 2005).

Porter, M. 1985. *Competitive Advantage: Creating and Sustaining Superior Performance.* New York: Free Press.

Porter, M. 1998. *Competitive Advantage: Creating and Sustaining Superior Performance.* New York: Free Press.

Ricciardi, S. 1994. "Database Design: Redundancy and Normalization." *PC Magazine,* January 25, pp. 285–89.

Rosenblum, P. "The Target data breach is becoming a nightmare." *Forbes,* 17 January 2014.

Rouse, M. (2010) "Cloud Computing Essential Guide." Retrieved 1 March 2014 from searchcloudcomputing.techtarget.com/definition/cloud-computing.

Rowley, J. 1999. "What Is Knowledge Management?" *Library Management,* pp. 416–19.

Santosus, M., and J. Surmacz. 2005. "The ABCs of Knowledge Management." www.cio.com (April 28).

Schein, E. 2010. *Organizational Culture and Leadership.* 4th ed. Jossey-Bass.

Simon, H. 1997. *Administrative Behavior.* 4th ed. New York: Free Press.

Skinner, R. 2012. "The New Clarity Standards and What You Should Know about Their Effect on Your Next Audit." Retrieved 3 March 2014 from www.dhgllp.com.

Soares, S. 2012. "A Framework that Focuses on the 'Data' in Big Data Governance." Retrieved 1 March 2014 from www.ibmdatamag.com.

Stapleton, G., and C. Rezak. 2004. "Change Management Underpins a Successful ERP Implementation at Marathon Oil." *Journal of Organizational Excellence,* Autumn, pp. 15–22.

Sylla, C., and H. J. Wen. 2002. "A Conceptual Framework for Evaluation of Information Technology Investments." *International Journal of Technology Management,* pp. 236–61.

Umble, E., and M. Umble. 2002. "Avoiding ERP Implementation Failure." *Industrial Management,* January/February, pp. 25–34. Reprinted with the permission of the Institute of Industrial Engineers. 3577 Parkway Lane, Suite 200, Norcross, GA 30092, 770-449-0461. Copyright © 2002.

Walker, K. B., and E. Denna. 1997. "Arriveder ci, Pacioli? A New Accounting System Is Emerging." *Management Accounting,* July, pp. 22–30.

Wells, J. 2004. *Principles of Fraud Examination.* 1st ed. New York: John Wiley & Sons.

Wolcott, S., and C. Lynch. 2005. "Steps for Better Thinking." www.wolcottlynch.com (April 29).

XBRL International, www.xbrl.org.

XBRL US, www.xbrl.us.

# Index

*Italic* page numbers indicate figures and tables. **Bold** page numbers indicate glossary definitions.

## A

AAA (American Accounting Association), accounting defined by, 21
access controls, in information security, 201
accounting
  *vs.* bookkeeping, 21–22
  definition of, 21, **338**
  ethics in, *303,* 303–305
accounting cycle, 22–28, **338**
accounting information systems (AIS)
  auditing and, 325–326
  definition of, 4, **338**
  importance of, 3, 4–6
  structure of, 7–8, **338**
  types of, 28, 141–143
accounting rules, interpreting, 30
accuracy, in evaluating information, 9, *10*
ACP (Audit Clarity Project), 319–320, *320,* **338**
acquisition/payment process
  about, 6
  in AIS structure, *241,* 241–245
  critical thinking about, 247–248
  description of, 239–241
  documents in, *241,* 241–244, *242, 243*
  file structures in, *244,* 244–245
  relationship to other processes, 248–249, 271
  risk in, *53,* 53–54
  steps in, 239–241, *240*
  systems documentation for, 247
adaptability, in information technology selection, *86,* 87
Adelphia Communications Corporation, 305–306, **338**
adjusted trial balance, in accounting cycle, 26–27
adjusting entries
  in accounting cycle, *25,* 25–26, *26*
  definition of, **338**

administrative security controls
  definition of, **338**
  in information security, 201–202
adverse reports, 317
agents
  definition of, **338**
  in REA modeling, 143, 150
AICPA (American Institute of Certified Public Accountants)
  core competencies of, 5–6, **338**
  on trust services, 180–181
AIS (accounting information systems)
  auditing and, 325–326
  definition of, 4, **338**
  importance of, 3, 4–6
  structure of, 7–8, **338**
  types of, 28, 141–143
Amazon
  e-business used by, 179–180
  enterprise resource planning system of, 178
  transaction processing at, 20
American Accounting Association (AAA), accounting defined by, 21
American Institute of Certified Public Accountants (AICPA)
  core competencies of, 5–6, **338**
  on trust services, 180–181
American National Standards Institute (ANSI), on flowchart symbols, 105
Andersen, Arthur, 306, **340**
annotation, in flowchart design, *106,* 107
ANSI (American National Standards Institute), on flowchart symbols, 105
applications, in CoBIT enablers, 204, *204*
application service providers (ASP), 187–188, **338**
assertions, in financial statements, 324
asset valuation, 303, *303*
associated computer crimes, 197
Association of Certified Fraud Examiners, 44

Audit Clarity Project (ACP), 319–320, *320*, **338**
auditing
  AIS and, 325–326
  critical thinking about, 326–328
  definition of, **338**
  standards for, 319–322, **338**
  steps in, *322*, 322–325
  types of, 317–319
authentication, in access control, 201
authority, in evaluating information, 9
authorization, in access control, 201
Autonomy, and HP, 300
autonomy of practice, in professionalism, 302
availability, in information security, 200


B

background checks
  in human resource process, 268
  in internal controls, 47
balance sheet, 27
Bank of America, internal controls at, 39
bank reconciliation
  in acquisition/payment process, 246
  in internal controls, 47
  in sales/collection process, 225
Bank Secrecy Act, 327
Barnes & Noble
  business process flowchart of, 102
  data flow diagram of, 119
  REA model of, 140
batch control totals, in internal controls, 48
behavior
  in AIS, 69–70
  in CoBIT enablers, 204, *204*
  in fraud, 327
Bell, Nancy, 301
Big Data, 291, **338**
big transaction data, 291
billing, in sales/collection process, 218, *219*,
    224–225, 249
bill of lading, in sales/collection process, 220, *220*, 249
biometric data, 291
Bitcoin, auditing of, 316
blind copies, of purchase orders, 243, 249

block coding, 29, *29*
Blue Security, 205–206
bonding
  in acquisition/payment process, 246
  in internal controls, 48
bookkeeping
  *vs.* accounting, 21–22
  definition of, **338**
bounded rationality, 286, **338**
BPM (business process management)
  basic principles of, 68–69, **338**
  critical thinking about, 71–72
  definition of, **339**
  generalized model of, 67, **340**
  nature of, 66–68
  in sales/collection process, 226
brick-and-mortar sales, 182, *183*
Brown's taxonomy of risk, 42–44, *43*, **338**
build, in systems development life cycle, *82*, 83, 90
business processes. *See also* acquisition/payment
    process; conversion process; financing process;
    human resource process; sales/collection process
  about, 6
  definition of, 217, **338–339**
  in ERP implementation, 185
  in REA modeling, 144, 150
  risk in, *53*, 53–54
  value chain for, 217, *217*, **343**
business process management (BPM)
  basic principles of, 68–69, **338**
  critical thinking about, 71–72
  definition of, **339**
  generalized model of, 67, **340**
  nature of, 66–68
  in sales/collection process, 226
business strategy risk, 43, *43*


C

California State University, Work Group on
    Information Competence, 9
capability maturity model (CMM)
  about, *84*, 84–86
  critical thinking about, 88–89
  definition of, **339**

cardinalities
    definition of, **339**
    in REA modeling, 145–146, *146,* 148,
        150–151, *151*
career planning, 306–307, **339**
Carter's taxonomy, 197, 205
cash
    in acquisition/payment process, 246, 249
    internal control over, 50–51
    in sales/collection process, 223–224, 225, 249
    theft of, 246, 266–267
cash disbursement, in acquisition/payment process,
        240, *240,* 249
cash discounts, on customer invoices, *220,*
        220–221
change
    behavioral responses to, 69
    in ERP implementation, 185
chaotic level, in capability maturity model, 84–85
characteristics of a professional, 301
charts of accounts, 28–29, *29,* 31–32
checks
    in acquisition/payment process, 246
    in sales/collection process, *220,* 222
closing entries, in accounting cycle, 27, *28*
cloud computing, 292, **339**
CMM (capability maturity model)
    about, *84,* 84–86
    critical thinking about, 88–89
    definition of, **339**
CoBIT (Control Objectives for Information and
        Related Technology) framework, 202–204, *203,*
        *204,* 206
    definition of, **339**
    in sales/collection process, 226
coconspirators, 318–319
coding systems, 28–29, *29*
collection, in sales/collection process, 218, *219*
column headings, in flowchart design, 107, 110
Committee of Sponsoring Organizations (COSO)
    definition of, **339**
    enterprise risk management framework of,
        64–66, **340**
    Internal Control Integrated Framework of, 44–47,
        *45,* 323, **341**
    internal controls defined by, 40

common files, 223, 244, **339**
communication
    business process management and, 69
    as core competency, 6
competencies, in CoBIT enablers,
        204, *204*
compliance audits, 318, 324
compound primary key, 129, **339**
computer crimes
    CoBIT framework and, 202–204
    critical thinking about, 205–206
    information security and, 200–202
    taxonomy for, 197–200, 205, **343**
computer file backups, in internal
        controls, 47
computer fraud, 198
computer networks
    definition of, **339**
    in e-business, 179
computers, role in AIS, 12
conceptual framework
    definition of, **339**
    relation to accounting information systems,
        4–5, *5*
confidential information, disclosure of, 198
confidentiality, in information security, 200
conflict-of-interest policy, 245
consistency, auditing standards on, 322
consultants, business process management
        and, 69
consumers, in e-business, 181
context diagram, 125, *126,* **339**
control activities
    in enterprise risk management, 65, *65,* 66
    in Internal Control Integrated Framework, *45,*
        45–46
control environment, in Internal Control Integrated
        Framework, *45,* 45–46
Control Objectives for Information and Related
        Technology (CoBIT) framework, 202–204,
        *203, 204,* 206
    definition of, **339**
    in sales/collection process, 226
conventions
    for data flow diagrams, 121–122, **342**
    for flowcharts, 104–105

conversion process
    about, 6, 261
    in AIS structure, 262–263, *264*
    definition of, **339**
    documents in, 262, *262*
    internal controls in, 263, *263*
    organization of, 261–262
    relationship to other processes, 271
    risk in, *53,* 53–54, 263, *263*
core competencies, for accounting professionals,
        5–6, **338**
corroborative witnesses, 318
COSO (Committee of Sponsoring Organizations)
    definition of, **339**
    enterprise risk management framework of,
        64–66, **340**
    Internal Control Integrated Framework of, 44–47,
        *45,* 323, **341**
    internal controls defined by, 40
cost
    of e-business, 179, 180
    in information technology selection, *86,* 87
cost-benefit analysis, **339**
cost-effectiveness, in conceptual framework, 4–5, *5*
countermeasures, for information overload, 285, **339**
coverage, in evaluating information, 10
credentials, of management, 323
credit approval, in sales/collection process, 218, *219,*
        223–224, 248
credit risk, 42, *43*
credits, in transaction analysis, 23, **342**
critical thinking
    about, 11
    about acquisition/payment process, 247–248
    about auditing, 326–328
    in auditing, 325–326
    about business process management, 71–72
    about capability maturity model, 88–89
    about computer crime, 205–206
    as core competency, 5
    about data flow diagrams, *131,* 131–133
    about enterprise resource planning, 188–189
    about enterprise risk management, 71
    about ethics, 307–308
    about expectancy theory, 72
    about financing process, 270
    about flowchart design, 110
    about information technology selection, 88–89
    about knowledge management, 291–292
    about REA models, 149–152, *150*
    about risk, *53,* 53–54
    about sales/collection process, 226
    in statement evaluation, 11–12
    about systems development life cycle, 88–89
    unstructured problems and, 3
    about XBRL, 171, *171*
cryptography, in information security, 201
culture, in CoBIT enablers, 204, *204*
currency, in evaluating information, 9–10
Currency Transaction Report, 327
customer check, in sales/collection process, *220,* 222
customer distrust, in e-business, 181
customer invoices, in sales/collection process, *220,*
        220–221, 249

D

data
    capturing for financial statements, 4, 23
    in ERP implementation, 186
data analytics, 291–292, **339**
databases. *See also* relational databases
    in auditing, 327
    critical thinking about, 131–133
    designing, 127–129, *130, 131,* 131–133
    in enterprise resource planning systems, 184, *184,*
        *188,* 188–189, *189*
    in event-driven systems, 141
    in flowchart design, *106,* 108
    from REA models, 147–149
database tables, *127,* 127–128
    definition of, **339**
    from REA models, 147–149, *149, 151,* 151–152
data encryption
    in e-business, 181
    in internal controls, 48
data entry screens, preformatted, in internal
        controls, 49
data flow
    in data flow diagrams, *120,* 121, *122,* 122–123
    definition of, **339**

data flow diagrams (DFDs)
    critical thinking about, *131,* 131–133
    flowcharts and, 123–125
    leveled sets of, *125,* 125–126, *126,* **341**
    rules for, 121–122, **342**
    symbols in, *120,* 120–121
data integrity, in information security, 200
data stores
    in data flow diagrams, *120,* 121, 122, *122*
    definition of, **339**
DDOS (distributed denial-of-service attacks), 199, 205
debits, in transaction analysis, 23, **342**
debt covenant, 267
debt financing, 265
decision, in flowchart design, *106,* 107
decision making
    barriers to, 283–286
    as core competency, 6
    ethics in, 308
decision/management events, in REA modeling, 143–145
decision models, 286. *See also* knowledge management
defined level, in capability maturity model, 85
delays, risk from, 198, 205
delivery
    with e-business, 180
    in sales/collection process, 224
denial-of-service attacks, 199, 205
deontology, 304, *304,* **340**
deposits
    in internal controls, 50
    in sales/collection process, *220,* 222
depreciation, definition of, 163, 301
descriptive analytics, 291
design, in systems development life cycle, *82,* 82–83, 90
DFDs (data flow diagrams)
    critical thinking about, *131,* 131–133
    flowcharts and, 123–125
    leveled sets of, *125,* 125–126, *126,* **341**
    rules for, 121–122, **342**
    symbols in, *120,* 120–121
directors' and officers' liability, 43, *43*
disclaimers, 317
disclosure, auditing standards on, 322

distributed denial-of-service attacks (DDOS), 199, 205
dividend payment process, 270, *270*
documentation, in internal controls, 47
document flowcharts, 103–104, **340**
document matching
    in internal controls, 48
    in sales/collection process, 249
documents
    in acquisition/payment process, *241,* 241–244, *242, 243*
    in conversion process, 262, *262*
    definition of, **340**
    in financing process, 265–267
    in flowchart design, *106,* 107
    in human resource process, 267, *269*
    in investigative audits, 318
    prenumbered, in internal controls, 49
    in sales/collection process, 219–222, *220, 221, 222*

E

earnings smoothing, 303, *303*
e-business (e-commerce)
    benefits and costs of, 179–180
    categories of, 181–182, **340**
    definition of, 179, **340**
    internal controls for, 180–181
    sales process in, 182–184, *183*
    trust services for, 180–181
echo checks, in internal controls, 48
e-commerce. *See* e-business
eight-step model for dilemmas, 305, **340**
elements, of financial statements, 4
embezzlement, 51
employee monitoring, in acquisition/payment process, 246
Enron, 306, **340**
enterprise resource planning (ERP) systems
    critical thinking about, 188–189
    databases in, 184, *184, 188,* 188–189, *189*
    definition of, 184, **340**
    implementation of, 185–186, **339**
    organization of, 184, *184*

enterprise risk management (ERM)
    application service providers in, 187
    critical thinking about, 71
    framework for, 64–66, **340**
envisioning, in Steps for Better Thinking, 290, *290*
equality, in transactions, 23
equity financing, 265
error, in information systems, 198
estimating, 30
ethical egoism, 304, *304, 307*, **340**
ethics
    cases in, 305–306
    in CoBIT enablers, 204, *204*
    critical thinking about, 307–308
    eight-step model for dilemmas, 305, **340**
    nature of, 303
    in professionalism, 302
event-driven systems, 28, 142–143
    REA modeling of, 143–145
    relational databases in, 141
event identification, in enterprise risk management, 65, *65*
events
    definition of, **340**
    in REA models, 144, 150
evidence, in auditing, 322
expectancy theory, 70, *70*
    critical thinking about, 72
    definition of, **340**
expectations, in ERP implementation, 185
exploring, in Steps for Better Thinking, 289–290, *290*
eXtensible Business Reporting Language (XBRL)
    benefits of, 169, **338**
    critical thinking about, 171, *171*
    definition of, 163, **343**
    global taxonomies for, 168
    in internal controls, 170
    structure of, 165–167, *168*
    tagging tools for, 169
    terminology for, 163–164, *164*
external agents, in REA modeling, 143
external entities
    in data flow diagrams, *120,* 121, 122, *122*
    definition of, **340**
external transactions, 22, **340**
extortion, risk from, 200

F

Facebook, IPO of, 266
fair value accounting, 303, *303*
FASB (Financial Accounting Standards Board), conceptual framework by, 4–5, *5,* **339**
FCPA (Foreign Corrupt Practices Act), 41, **340**
fiduciary duty, 322–323, **340**
field work, in auditing, *321,* 321–322
file, in flowchart design, *106,* 107
file backups, in internal controls, 47
Financial Accounting Standards Board (FASB), conceptual framework by, 4–5, *5,* **339**
financial audits, 317
financial risk, 42, *43*
financial statements
    in accounting cycle, 27
    assertions in, 324
    in auditing, 317, 325
    in e-business, 183–184
    elements of, capturing data on, 4, 23
    XBRL for, 165–166
financing, in information technology selection, *86,* 87
financing process
    about, 6
    in AIS structure, 265–267
    critical thinking about, 270
    definition of, **340**
    dividend payment process, 270, *270*
    documents in, 265–267
    internal controls in, 266–267, 270
    relationship to other processes, 271
    risk in, *53,* 53–54, 266–267
    transactions in, 266, **340**
    types of, 265
firewalls
    in information security, 201
    in internal controls, 48
First Normal Form (1NF), 128–129
flat files, 128, **340**
flowcharts
    accounting information systems and, 108–109
    conventions for, 104–105
    data flow diagrams and, 123–125
    designing, 106–108, 110–111, *111*
    of sales/collection process, *219*

symbols for, 105, *106,* 107, 110

tools for, 105

types of, 103–104

Foreign Corrupt Practices Act (FCPA), 41, **340**

foreign keys, 129, **340**

forms, in databases, 127, *127,* **340**

frameworks, in CoBIT enablers, 204, *204*

fraud

as behavioral issue, 69

as human risk, 268–269

as risk, 198, 205

fraud audits, *318,* 318–319, 326–328

freight terms, 220, **340**


**G**

generalized model of BPM, 67, **340**

generally accepted accounting principles (GAAP), in auditing, 317, 322

general-purpose financial statements

in accounting cycle, 27

definition of, **340**

general standards, for auditing, 321, *321*

generic process, in flowchart design, *106,* 107

globalization, of business, 70

Global Leger taxonomy (XBRL-GL), 168

goals

in ERP implementation, 186

in knowledge management, 288

Google, information systems concepts at, 80

governance, *vs.* management, 203

government, in e-business, 182

governmental and not-for-profit organizations (GNFPs), 318

graphical trend analysis, 326–327


**H**

hacktivism, 200

hardware flowcharts, 104, **340**

hazard risk, 43, *43*

hierarchical coding, 29, *29*

HP, and Autonomy, 300

human error risk, 43, *43*

human-generated data, 291

human judgment, 30, 183, **341**

human resource process

about, 6

in AIS structure, 267–270, *268*

definition of, **341**

documents in, 267, *269*

internal controls in, 268–270

purpose of, 267

relationship to other processes, 271

risk in, *53,* 53–54, 268–270

human risk, in human resource process, 268

Humphrey, Watts, 84, **343**

hybrid production systems, 262


**I**

IC (information competence)

criteria for, 9–11

definition of, **341**

identification, in access control, 201

identifying, in Steps for Better Thinking, 289, *290*

IFRS (International Financial Reporting Standards) Taxonomy, 168

implementation, in systems development life cycle, *82,* 83, 90

incidental computer crimes, 197

income statement, 27

independence, of auditors, 321

information

in CoBIT enablers, 204, *204*

manipulation of, 199

theft of, 199

information and communication

in enterprise risk management, 65, *65,* 66

in Internal Control Integrated Framework, *45,* 45–46

information characteristics, in information overload, 284

information competence (IC)

criteria for, 9–11

definition of, **341**

information events, in REA modeling, 143–145

information overload, 283–285, *284,* **339, 341**

information security, *200,* 200–202
   administrative controls in, 201–202
   availability in, 200
   basic principles of, 200, **338**
   CoBIT framework for, 202–204, *203, 204*
   confidentiality in, 200
   data integrity in, 200
   internal controls for, 201–202, 205–206
   physical controls in, 201
   technical controls in, 201
information systems, risks and threats to, 197–200, 205
information technology (IT)
   in acquisition/payment process, 246
   in auditing, 317–318, 326–327
   in billing, 225
   capability maturity model for, *84,* 84–86
   critical thinking about, 88–89
   definition of, **341**
   in ERP implementation, 186
   human judgment and, 30
   in information overload, 284
   in internal controls, 52
   in order fulfillment, 224
   selection of, 86–89
   systems development life cycle for, 81–83
   three-stage process for evaluating, 87, *88,* **343**
infrastructure, in CoBIT enablers, 204, *204*
initial public offering (IPO), steps in, 265–266
initiation, in systems development life cycle,
   81–82, *82,* 89
input manipulation, 199
inputs, in AIS structure, 7, *7*
inspection, in acquisition/payment process, 246
instance document
   definition of, **341**
   in XBRL, 164, *164,* 167
instrumentality, 70, *70*
instrumentality computer crimes, 197, 205
insurance
   in internal controls, 48
   in sales/collection process, 224, 249
integrity of management, 323–324
internal agents, in REA modeling, 143
internal audits, in internal controls, 48
Internal Control Integrated Framework (COSO),
   44–47, *45,* 323, **341**

internal controls
   in acquisition/payment process, 245–247
   in AIS structure, *7,* 8
   applications of, 50–52
   in auditing, 322, 324–325, 326
   for cash, 266–267
   in conversion process, 263, *263*
   definition of, 40, **341**
   for e-business, 180–181
   evaluating, in auditing, 323–324
   examples of, 47–50
   in financing process, 266–267, 270
   in flowcharts, 109
   in human resource process, 268–270
   importance of, 41–42
   for information security, 201–202, 205–206
   purpose of, 41, *41*
   in sales/collection process, 223–225, 226
   with XBRL, 170
internal environment, in enterprise risk management,
   64, 65, *65*
internal transactions, 22, **341**
international audit, 319
International Financial Reporting Standards (IFRS)
   Taxonomy, 168
interviews
   in investigative audits, 318
   practicing for, 307
intrusion, in information systems, 198–199
   detection systems for, 201
   prevention systems for, 201
inventory
   in acquisition/payment process, 245, 246
   internal controls for, 52
   in sales/collection process, 224
   theft of, 246
investigative audits, *318,* 318–319
invoices
   in acquisition/payment process, *241,* 244, 246
   in sales/collection process, *220,* 220–221, 249
IPO (initial public offering), steps in, 265–266
ISACA (Information Systems Audit and Control
   Association), 46
   Control Objectives for Information and Related
   Technology, 202–204
iterative, **341**

## J

job costing systems, 261, 262–263, **341**
journals, in accounting cycle, 23–25
junction tables, 148, *148,* **341**

## K

*kaizen,* 85
knowledge audit, 288
knowledge base, in professionalism, 302
knowledge management systems (KMS)
    critical thinking about, 291–292
    definition of, 287, **341**
    objectives of, 287
    steps in creating, 287–289, **342**
knowledge maps, 288, *288*
Krispy Kreme Doughnuts
    acquisition/payment process of, 238
    conversion process of, 260
    financing process of, 260
    human resource process of, 260
    sales/collection process of, 216

## L

language, XBRL as, 166–167
legal and regulatory risk, 43, *43*
leveled sets
    of data flow diagrams, *125,* 125–126, *126*
    definition of, **341**
Level Zero diagrams, 125, *125,* **341**
liability, directors' and officers', 43, *43*
limit checks, in internal controls, 48
lines, in flowchart design, *106,* 108
liquidity risk, 42, *43*
lockbox systems, in internal controls, 48
logic bombs, 199

## M

machine-to-machine data, 291
macro-level issues
    definition of, **341**
    in information technology selection, *86,* 86–87

Madoff, Bernie, 307–308, **338**
malicious software (malware), risk from,
    199, 205
managed level, in capability maturity model, 85
management
    *vs.* governance, 203
    integrity of, 323–324
management audits, 318
manual process, in flowchart design, *106,* 107
manufacturing, conversion process in, 261
many-to-many relationships, 148, *148*
market risk, 42, *43*
Markopolis, Harry, 307
McCarthy, W. E., 141, **341**
micro-level issues
    definition of, **341**
    in information technology selection, *86,*
        87–88
Microsoft Corporation, XBRL used in, 162
Microsoft Visio, 105, **341**
mission statement, in career planning, 306–307
mnemonic codes, 29, *29*
Monetary Instrument Log, 327
monitoring
    in acquisition/payment process, 245
    in enterprise risk management, 65, *65,* 66
    in Internal Control Integrated Framework, *45,*
        45–46
motivation, in expectancy theory, 70

## N

namespace
    definition of, **341**
    in XBRL, 164, *164,* 167
need
    in acquisition/payment process, 239, *240*
    in information technology selection, 86, *86*
Netflix
    knowledge management system of, 282
    pricing issues with, 289–290
neutral third-party witnesses, 318
normalization
    of database tables, 127–129, *128, 129,* 147–148
    definition of, **341**

## O

objectives
    in enterprise risk management, 64, 65, *65*
    in REA modeling, 144, 150
objectivity, in evaluating information, 9, *10*
off-page connector, in flowchart design, *106,* 107
on-page connector, in flowchart design, *106,* 107
operating costs, with e-business, 180
operating events, in REA modeling, 143–145, *144*
operational audits, 317
operational risks, 43, *43*
operations and maintenance, in systems development
    life cycle, *82,* 83, 90
opinions, auditing standards on, 322
optimized level, in capability maturity model, 85
order fulfillment, in sales/collection process,
    218, *219,* 224, 249
order placement, in sales/collection process,
    218, *219,* 220, *220,* 221, 248
organizational design, in information overload, 284
organizational environment
    in auditing, 326
    in REA modeling, 144, 150
organizational processes, in ERP implementation, 186
organizational strategy, business process management
    and, 68
organizational structure, in CoBIT enablers,
    204, *204*
outputs, in AIS structure, 7, *7*


## P

packing list, in sales/collection process, 220, *220*
Papa John's International, management concepts
    in, 63
payment
    in acquisition/payment process, 240, *240,*
    246–247
    in sales/collection process, 218, *219*
payroll forms
    definition of, **342**
    in human resource process, 267, *269*
penalties, for noncompliance, 325
PeopleSoft, 184

personal factors, in information overload, 283
personnel, in information technology selection, *86,*
    86–87
physical security
    definition of, **342**
    in information security, 201
    in internal controls, 48
picking list, in sales/collection process, 220, *220*
planning, in systems development life cycle, 81–82,
    *82,* 89
policies, in CoBIT enablers, 204, *204*
Ponzi, Charles, 305, **339**
Porter's value chain, for business processes,
    217, *217,* **343**
post-closing trial balance, 27, *28*
power supply backup, in internal controls, 47
predefined process, in flowchart design, *106,*
    107–108
predictive analytics, 291–292
preferred vendors, 245–246
preformatted data entry screens, in internal
    controls, 49
prenumbered documents, in internal
    controls, 49
prescriptive analytics, 292
primary keys
    in database tables, 127, 129, **339**
    definition of, **342**
primitive processes, 126, **342**
principles, in CoBIT enablers, 204, *204*
principles of debits and credits, 23, **342**
prioritizing, in Steps for Better Thinking, 290, *290*
problem solving, as core competency, 6
procedures manuals, development of, 109
process costing systems, 261, 263, **342**
processes. *See also* business processes
    in AIS structure, 7, *7*
    in CoBIT enablers, 204, *204*
    in data flow diagrams, *120,* 120–121, 122, *122*
    definition of, **342**
    in event-driven systems, 142
    primitive, 126
process parameters, in information overload, 284
product and service delivery
    with e-business, 180
    in sales/collection process, 224

production systems, types of, 261–262
professionalism, 301–302, 307, 321
professional judgment, 319, 325–326, **342**
professionals, characteristics of, 301, **339**
program flowcharts, 103, **342**
program manipulation, 199
project management, in ERP implementation, 185
Public Companies Accounting Oversight
    Board, 40
purchase authorization, in acquisition/payment
    process, 240, *240*, 248
purchase order, in acquisition/payment process, *241,*
    241–243, *243*, 246, 248
purchase requisition, in acquisition/payment process,
    241, *241, 242*, 248
purchasing, in acquisition/payment process,
    240, *240*

Q

qualified reports, 317
queries, in databases, 127, *127,* **342**

R

REA modeling
    about, 143–145
    cardinalities in, 145–146, *146,* 150–151, *151,* **339**
    critical thinking about, 149–152, *150, 151*
    databases created from, 147–149
receivables, in sales/collection process, 218, *219*
receiving, in acquisition/payment process, 240, *240,*
    *241,* 243–244, 246, *247,* 247–248, 249
relapse errors, 286, **342**
relational databases. *See also* databases
    definition of, **342**
    designing, *127,* 127–129, *130*
    in enterprise resource planning systems, 184, *184,*
        *188,* 188–189, *189*
    in event-driven systems, 141
remittance advice, in sales/collection process, *220,*
    *222, 222*
repeatable level, in capability maturity model, 85
reporting standards, in auditing, 322

reports
    in auditing, 317, 320, *320*
    in databases, 127
    in e-business, 183–184
    in financial auditing, 317
    XBRL for, 169
request for goods/services, in acquisition/payment
    process, 239, *240*
requirements analysis, in systems development life
    cycle, 82, *82,* 89
research
    in career planning, 307
    as core competency, 6
resource management, as core competency, 5
resources
    definition of, **342**
    in REA modeling, 143, 144, 150
restrictive endorsement
    in internal controls, 50
    in sales/collection process, 225
résumé building, 307
returns, in acquisition/payment process, 240, *240*
revenue recognition, 303, *303*
Rigas, Gus, 305–306
Rigas, John, 305–306
risk
    in acquisition/payment process, 245–247
    Brown's taxonomy of, 42–44, *43,* **338**
    in conversion process, 263, *263*
    critical thinking about, *53,* 53–54
    in financing process, 266–267
    in human resource process, 268–270
    to information systems, 197–200, 205
    in internal control design, 42–44, **342**
    in sales/collection process, 223–225
    with XBRL, 170
risk analysis, as core competency, 6
risk assessment
    in enterprise risk management, 65, *65,* 66
    in Internal Control Integrated Framework, *45,*
        45–46, 47
risk response, in enterprise risk management,
    65, *65,* 66
rules
    for accounting, interpreting, 30
    for data flow diagrams, 121–122, **342**

## S

salami technique, 199
sales/collection process
  about, 6
  in AIS structure, 219–223
  bricks-and-mortar, 182, *183*
  business process management in, 226
  CoBIT in, 226
  critical thinking about, 226
  description of, 218–219, *219*
  documents in, 219–222, *220, 221, 222*
  in e-business, 182–184, *183*
  file structures in, 223, *223*
  internal controls in, 223–225, 226
  relationship to other processes, 248–249, 271
  risk in, *53,* 53–54, 223–225
  steps in, 218–219, *219*
  systems documentation for, 225
  transactions in, 226
SAP, 184
Sarbanes-Oxley Act of 2002 (SOX)
  auditing and, 324–325
  definition of, **342**
  enterprise risk management and, 66
  fraud and, 198
  information on, 9, *10*
  internal controls and, 40, 41–42
satisficing, 286, **342**
SBT (Steps for Better Thinking), 288, *288,* **342**
SDLC (systems development life cycle), 81–83
  critical thinking about, 88–89
  definition of, **343**
Second Normal Form (2NF), 128–129, *130*
security, of source documents, 22
security awareness training, in information security, 202
security policies, in information security, 202
security reviews, in information security, 202
segregation of duties
  in acquisition/payment process, 246
  in e-business, 181
  in internal controls, 50, 51, 52
  in sales/collection process, 225
sequential coding, 29, *29*

sequential numbering
  in internal controls, 51
  in source documents, 22
service interruption, risk from, 198, 205
Service Organization Control (SOC) Reports, 188
services, in CoBIT enablers, 204, *204*
shipping, in sales/collection process, 218, *219,* 249
sinking fund, 267
six-step process, for REA models, 144, **342**
skills
  in CoBIT enablers, 204, *204*
  in professionalism, 302
SmartDraw, 105, **342**
social media data, 291
SOC (Service Organization Control) Reports, 188
source documents
  in accounting cycle, 22–23
  definition of, **342**
  designing, 30
SOX (Sarbanes-Oxley Act of 2002)
  auditing and, 324–325
  definition of, **342**
  enterprise risk management and, 66
  fraud and, 198
  information on, 9, *10*
  internal controls and, 40, 41–42
specification
  definition of, **342**
  in XBRL, 164, *164,* 167
stakeholders, in information security, 203
Starbucks, retail activities of, 2
statement evaluation, critical thinking in, 11–12
statement of cash flows, 27
statement of changes in shareholders' equity, 27
statistical tests, 327
Steps for Better Thinking (SBT), 288, *288,* **342**
storage, in AIS structure, 7, *7*
stove piping, 141
strategically significant operating activities
  definition of, **342**
  in REA models, 149
strategic fit, in information technology selection, 86, *86*
strategic risks, 43, *43*
streamlining, with e-business, 180

StrengthsFinder, 306
structure, of accounting information systems, *7, 7–8*
supervision, in auditing, 321–322
Suspicious Activity Report, 327
symbols
    in data flow diagrams, *120*
    in flowchart design, 105, *106,* 107, 110, **343**
system boundary, in flowchart design, 106–107, 110
systems audits, 316–317
systems development life cycle (SDLC), 81–83
    critical thinking about, 88–89
    definition of, **343**
systems documentation
    for acquisition/payment process, 247
    for sales/collection process, 225
systems flowcharts, 103, **343**
systems risk, 43, *43*
SysTrust, 180–181


T

tagging software, for XBRL, 169
target
    of computer crimes, 197, 205
    of fraud, 318–319
Target Stores, security breach at, 196
task parameters, in information overload, 284
taxonomy
    for computer crime, 197, 205, **343**
    definition of, **343**
    for e-business, 181–182
    global, 168–169
    in XBRL, 164, *164,* 167, *168*
technical security controls
    definition of, **343**
    in information security, 201
technology breakdowns, in e-business, 181
terminator, in flowchart design, *106,* 108
testing, in systems development life cycle, *82,* 83, 90
theft, of inventory, 246
Third Normal Form (3NF), 128–129
Thomas, Paula, 10
threats, to information systems, 197–200, 205, **342**

three-stage process, for evaluating information technology, 87, *88,* **343**
top management
    business process management and, 68
    in ERP implementation, 185
training
    of auditors, 321
    behavior and, 70
    in ERP implementation, 185
    in human resource process, 269
    in information security, 202
    in information technology selection, *86,* 87
    in internal controls, 50
transaction limits, in source documents, 22
transactions
    in accounting cycle, 22
    analysis of, 23
    in financing process, 266, **340**
    recognizing, 30–31
    recording of, 23–25, 30
    in sales/collection process, 226
trial balance, in accounting cycle, *25,* 25–26
    adjusted, 26–27
    post-closing, 27, *28*
Trojan horses, 199
trust services, for e-business, 180–181
*t*-tests, 327


U

University of Maryland, 9–11
unmodified reports, 317
unstructured problems
    critical thinking and, 3
    definition of, **343**
user training, in internal controls, 50
utilitarianism, 304, *304,* **343**


V

vacations, in human resource process, 268–269
valence, 70, *70*
validity, 8
value chain, for business processes, 217, *217,* **343**

vendor
    conflict-of-interest policy for, 245
    preferred, 245–246
    reliability of, *86,* 87, 245
vendor invoices, in acquisition/payment
        process, *241,* 244, 246
view-driven systems, 28, 141–142
virtue ethics, 304, *304,* **343**
viruses, 199
visual display, in flowchart design, *106,* 108
visual maps, in knowledge management,
        288, *288*


W

web data, 291
web sites, defacement of, 200
WebTrust, 180–181

weighted-rating technique, 88–89, **343**
worms, 199


X

XBRL (eXtensible Business Reporting Language)
    benefits of, 169, **338**
    critical thinking about, 171, *171*
    definition of, 163, **343**
    global taxonomies for, 168
    in internal controls, 170
    structure of, 165–167, *168*
    tagging tools for, 169
    terminology for, 163–164, *164*


Y

Yellow Book, 318, **343**